The Postulates of Quantum Mechanics for a System Consisting of Two Particles

I

The wave function, Ψ, belonging to a system composed of two particles, is a function of x_1, y_1, z_1, x_2, y_2, z_2, and t.

II

The wave equation for Ψ is obtained from the classical expression for the total energy of the system by replacing the dynamical variables by operators:

dynamical variable		operator	
x_1 (position)	$\rightarrow$	x_1	
p_{x_1} (momentum)	$\rightarrow$	$\dfrac{\hbar}{i}\dfrac{\partial}{\partial x_1}$	$\left.\right\}$ similarly for y_1, z_1, x_2, y_2, z_2
W (total energy)	$\rightarrow$	$-\dfrac{\hbar}{i}\dfrac{\partial}{\partial t}$	

and by the insertion of the wave function Ψ as the operand.

III

Ψ, and $\partial\Psi/\partial x_1$, $\partial\Psi/\partial y_1$, $\cdots$, $\partial\Psi/\partial z_2$, must be everywhere continuous, finite, and single valued, throughout "configuration space" (the full range of all six variables).

IV

Ψ is normalized, that is,

$$\int_{\substack{\text{all configu-}\\ \text{ration}\\ \text{space}}} \Psi^* \, \Psi \; dx_1 dy_1 dz_1 dx_2 dy_2 dz_2 = 1$$

V

The expectation value of the ob⎯⎯⎯⎯⎯⎯⎯⎯⎯⎯⎯⎯⎯⎯⎯he wave function by the formula

$$\bar{\alpha} = \int_{\substack{\text{all configu-}\\ \text{ration}\\ \text{space}}} \Psi^* \alpha_{\text{(operator)}} \Psi \; dx_1 dy_1 dz_1 dx_2 dy_2 dz_2$$

INTRODUCTION TO QUANTUM MECHANICS

INTRODUCTION TO

QUANTUM MECHANICS

CHALMERS W. SHERWIN
University of Illinois

HOLT, RINEHART AND WINSTON · NEW YORK

6 7 8 9

Printed in the United States of America

PREFACE

A generation has passed since the theory of wave mechanics, or quantum mechanics, was first formulated, and it has been almost two generations since it became apparent that the atomic world is characterized by a type of discontinuous behavior not known to the macroscopic world to which our senses have most direct access. During most of this time, the theory of the mechanics of atomic-sized systems has been the concern of the research scientist, usually in physics and chemistry, and it has been taught, quite appropriately, in graduate schools. As with all great theories, however, quantum mechanics has constantly increased its domain of application, and today, for those interested in understanding basic science—even on the advanced undergraduate level—the principles of the theory have become a vital necessity. Furthermore, with the explosive growth of atomic and nuclear technology, the need for a working knowledge of quantum mechanics has been extended to many areas in engineering and applied science.

A glance at any of the modern undergraduate textbooks on atomic and solid state physics will show that quantum mechanics has "infiltrated" them. For example, there was a time when courses in atomic spectra were basically descriptions, from the experimental point of view, of energy levels, spectral lines, and selection rules. Today it is almost impossible to talk of these matters without using the only theory that adequately organizes and interprets the experiments. No one is satisfied with the relatively simple models of a generation ago. Realizing this, many authors of textbooks in modern physics undertake the Herculean task of teaching the essentials of quantum theory, as well as of describing a wide range of experiments.

The situation is clear. Quantum Mechanics should take its place earlier in the physics curriculum and should be considered to be as basic to later study as classical mechanics and electricity. When this is done, modern physics—atomic, nuclear, and solid state—can be taught more effectively.

In classical mechanics, one does not worry about the precession of the perigee of a satellite or the nutation of a gyroscope until one has mastered Newton's Laws for the more simple cases. So in quantum mechanics, one must be concerned initially with the simple applications. Unfortunately, some of the most interesting applications involve the more advanced theory, and there is a strong temptation, for example, to wrestle in quantum mechanical terminology with "L–S coupling" when the student has only a vague idea of what a wave function is. In contrast, this textbook emphasizes simple problems, even at the expense of neglecting some favorite—and important—concepts. Since a large part of the complexity of quantum theory is due simply to geometry, we concentrate on one-dimensional systems, which clearly display a surprisingly large fraction of the key ideas and revolutionary concepts. In a first course, it is much more important to apply exact theory to simple cases than to apply approximate theory to complex cases.

The historical approach to a subject, although of great importance in demonstrating how theories are actually developed, can also be very confusing. Today, for example, one does not belabor the erroneous ideas of Newton's and Galileo's predecessors. One says rather: "Here is a theory that works. Its essential predictions can be tested fairly easily. Let us learn to use it." Later, the serious student will study the origin of the ideas in more detail.

Thus, in this book, except for a brief chapter on some of the key experimental findings that led to the quantum theory, we are content merely to postulate the theory in a page or two, and then to use it. In defense of this approach there is one excellent argument—it is efficient.

At points where our limited mastery of the theory permits comparison, we refer to the relevant experimental observations, which are, of course, the true foundation upon which the theory rests.

It must be remembered that this is a first course and in order to place it as early as possible in the student's career we have required minimum dependence on topics in advanced physics and mathematics. Thorough courses in elementary physics and in calculus are essential, however, as is some knowledge of differential equations, complex variables, and orthogonal functions. The use of numerical methods in solving the wave equation in both Cartesian and spherical coordinates gives a maximum of insight with a minimum of mathematical technique. We avoid philosophical discussion as much as possible and concentrate on the actual use of the theory. For the sake of simplicity, we consider only bound systems and the free particle. Collision theory and matrix mechanics are left for the more advanced textbooks.

Most of the book is concerned with particles without intrinsic "spin." The subject is quantitatively treated only in the last chapter, where it is shown to follow from the postulates as a consequence of relativity.

Quantum mechanics is a discipline with which one does not easily become familiar. It is not so much because the basic ideas are difficult as because they are strange. It takes time to appreciate them, and the student of physical science should be introduced to them as early in his career as possible.

C. W. S.

Urbana, Illinois
  May, 1959

CONTENTS

APPENDIXES

INTRODUCTION TO QUANTUM MECHANICS

INTRODUCTION TO QUANTUM MECHANICS

THE EXPERIMENTAL BASIS OF QUANTUM MECHANICS

Before a revolutionary theory is formulated, there is a profusion of experiments, which relate to the problem at hand and contribute to its solution but which do not, in general, get to the heart of the matter. Even in this early stage of confusion certain experiments often stand out as particularly important, but in retrospect one can always identify a small number of crucial experiments which firmly established the new interpretation of nature.

The discontinuous behavior that characterizes the atomic world was first discovered by Planck[1] in his analysis of the spectral shape (intensity of emitted light *vs.* frequency) of black body radiation. He could interpret the form of the experimentally observed curve only by assuming that the electromagnetic radiation was quantized in units of $h\nu$ where h is a constant and ν is the frequency of the radiation. The theoretical curve of Planck matched the experimental curve only when he assumed that $h = 6.55 \times 10^{-27}$ erg sec, a value which turned out to be within 2 percent of the presently accepted value of 6.625×10^{-27} erg sec.[2]

All the discontinuities in nature are meted out in units based directly upon h. The existence of this number and its particular size together form one of the great mysteries of nature. It appears explicitly or implicitly in every

---

[1] M. Planck, *Ann. Physik*, **4**: 553, 1901.
[2] For an excellent discussion of black body radiation, see F. K. Richtmeyer, E. H. Kennard, and T. Lauritsen, *Introduction to Modern Physics* (McGraw-Hill Book Co., Inc., New York, any edition): chapter on "The Origin of the Quantum Theory."

equation in quantum theory. It is the basic reason for the strangeness of the microscopic world which, with its ubiquitous discontinuities, constantly does violence to our common-sense understanding of the *apparent* continuity of the macroscopic world.

Unfortunately, the first observation (here, black body radiation) of a new aspect of nature is usually not of its most simple manifestation. The photo-electric effect, however, provides a striking and simpler demonstration of the quantum phenomena. The relationship between the frequency of light, ν, and the observed (maximum) energy of ejection, E_m, of photoelectrons,

$$E_m = h\nu - e\phi \qquad [1-1]$$

(the Einstein photoelectric equation[3]), shows, in a very clear way, the quantization of radiation and also permits an independent measurement of h. The binding energy or "work function" of the surface, $e\phi$ (e = coulomb, ϕ = ergs/coulomb = volts $\times$ 10^7), is the energy in ergs needed to remove, with no residual kinetic energy, one of the least tightly bound electrons. The maximum kinetic energy, E_m, is controlled only by the frequency, $\nu = c/\lambda$, of the light, and not by its intensity. The faintest star light produces electrons just as energetic as those from the strongest laboratory source; the only difference is that the former are fewer in number.[4]

Light of frequency ν, selected by a prism or grating, produces photoelectrons. Their maximum energy E_m is measured by the retarding potential, V, needed to turn back the fastest. Thus $E_m = eV$, and a plot of E_m vs. ν gives, by $[1-1]$, a straight line whose slope is h. This is plotted in Figure 1.1a.

These two experiments (black body radiation and the photoelectric effect) imply the quantization of light, but a third class of experiments shows that atomic systems also have a characteristic discreteness. This is most clearly shown in the spectrum of a gaseous light source, such as atomic hydrogen. The many sharp frequencies (spectral lines) that are observed can be explained by assuming that the atoms have discrete energy levels, and that the observed radiation is caused by the atom making a transition from a higher level to some lower level. The spectral frequencies are given by Δ Energy = $h\nu$ (h = erg sec, ν = cycles/sec), the Bohr frequency condition. The principal levels and several of the distinct series of spectral lines of the hydrogen atom are shown in Figure 1.1b.

In 1915 Bohr proposed an ingenious explanation based on the hypothesis that the angular momentum of the electron about the central massive particle, the proton, was quantized in units of $h/2\pi$. At first sight the theory seemed successful, and indeed the main features of the energy levels were accounted for. Sommerfeld's extension of the theory, to include relativity, provided a quantitative explanation of some of the finer details of the energy levels. None-

---

[3] A. Einstein, *Ann. Physik*, ser. 4, **17**: 132, 1905.
[4] For further discussion, see F. K. Richtmeyer, E. H. Kennard, and T. Lauritsen, *op. cit.*, chapter on "The Photo Electric Effect."

theless, the theory was found to be inadequate. The orbiting "point-electron" should radiate electromagnetically and quickly spiral into the nucleus rather than "jump" downward from one discrete energy level to another, finally settling into a perfectly stable lowest state. Also, there seemed to be no explana-

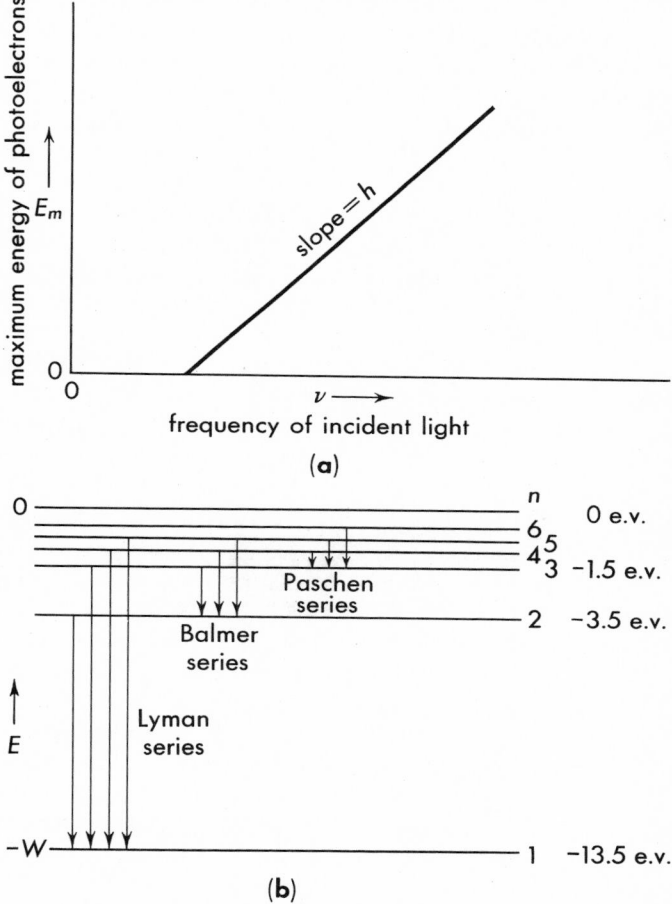

Fig. 1.1. **a.** The photoelectric effect. **b.** The energy levels and the radiative transitions of the hydrogen atom.

tion of why transitions occurred between certain levels and not between others. Finally, the theory made no headway in the explanation of more complex spectra such as those of He and Li. Since this theory is usually described in elementary textbooks, we shall not discuss it further here.[5] It is, however, a

---

[5] See, for example, F. K. Richtmeyer, E. H. Kennard, and T. Lauritsen, *op. cit.*, chapter on "The Nuclear Atom, and the Origin of Spectral Lines."

classic example of how a theory, although only partially true, will yet produce many quantitatively correct predictions.

The key experimental fact about the atomic spectra is, however, that they consist mainly of sharp, distinct frequencies, and this fact is adequately

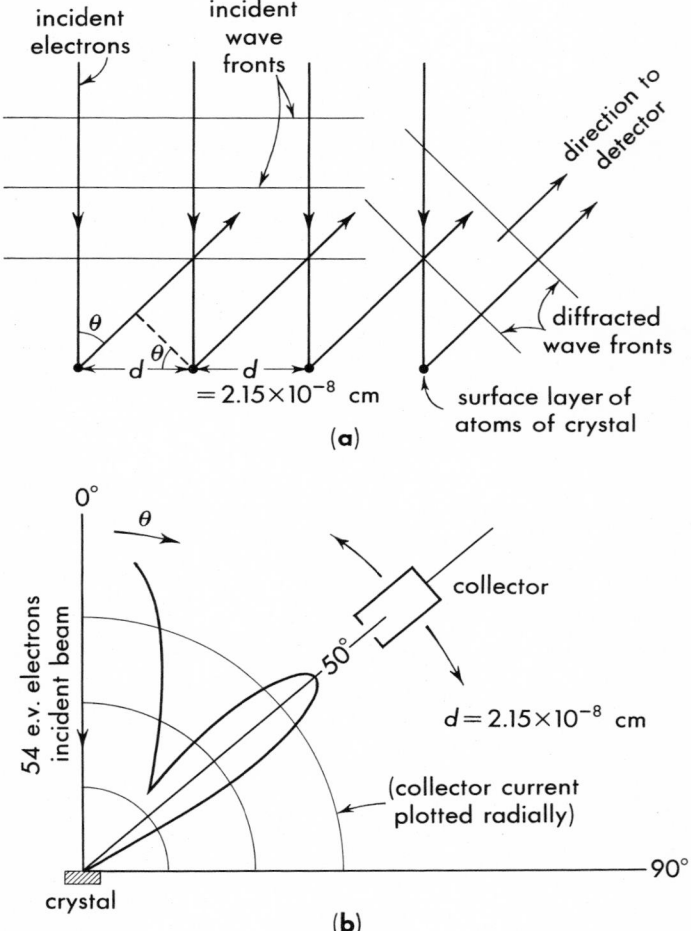

Fig. 1.2. **a.** Diffraction of electron waves from a surface grating. **b.** The Davisson-Germer experiment.

explained only when one does *not* consider electrons to be only particles, but to have a wave nature as well.

The most direct evidence that a new theory of matter is needed is found in the experiments of Davisson and Germer,[6] in which electrons, reflected

---

[6] Davisson and Germer, *Nature*, April 16, 1927; *Phys. Rev.*, **30**: 706, 1927.

from a (diagonal) cleavage surface of a nickel crystal, showed the characteristic interference patterns of waves. Shortly before these experiments, de Broglie[7] had proposed that with each particle of momentum $p = mv$ there was associated a wave of wavelength

$$\lambda = \frac{h}{p} \qquad\qquad [1\text{--}2$$

where h = erg sec

p = gm cm/sec

λ = cm

The experiments of Davisson and Germer, and G. P. Thompson quantitatively confirmed this relationship.

Since further confirmed by the wavelike behavior of many types of systems (atoms, molecules, neutrons, etc.), these first experiments of Davisson and Germer opened a new era in the history of experimental physics. Their importance cannot be overstated.

In one of the experiments[8] of Davisson and Germer, electrons of very nearly uniform energy 54 e.v. are normally incident on a nickel crystal whose atomic spacing (measured by x-rays) is 2.15×10^{-8} cm (Fig. 1.2a). A collector (Fig. 1.2b) can be moved through the angle θ, in the plane of the diagram. Near $\theta = 0°$, a strong, directly reflected electron current is detected, but at $\theta = 50°$ a rather sharp peak of intensity is observed. This shifts to a different angle if the electron energy is changed appreciably from 54 e.v., showing that the phenomenon depends upon the velocity of the electrons.

de Broglie's equation can be written, for low-energy electrons, as

$$\lambda = \frac{h}{mv} = h\sqrt{\frac{150}{meV}} = \frac{12.27}{\sqrt{V}} \times 10^{-8} \text{ cm} \qquad\qquad [1\text{--}2a$$

where $V =$ the accelerating potential, in volts, of the electrons of mass $m = 9.11 \times 10^{-28}$ gm and charge 4.80×10^{-10} esu. By the de Broglie relationship, the wavelength of 54 e.v. electrons is 1.67×10^{-8} cm. [In the equation above, v (cm/sec) is obtained from: $\frac{1}{2}mv^2 = eV/300$.][9]

For any plane waves incident on a grating of spacing d, the condition of reinforcement is

$$n\lambda = d \sin \theta \qquad\qquad [1\text{--}3$$

If the experimental value of $d = 2.15 \times 10^{-8}$ cm and $\theta = 50°$ (the center of the peak) is inserted (here $n = 1$) the waves have a measured λ of 1.65×10^{-8} cm.

Thus the measured wavelength based on known crystal constants and the

---

[7] L. de Broglie, Thesis, Paris, 1924; *Ann. de Phys.*, (10) **3**: 22, 1925.

[8] For a discussion of the reflection of matter waves from crystals, see H. T. Flint, *Wave Mechanics* (1953, Methuen & Co., London; John Wiley & Sons, New York): Chapter 5.

[9] In MKS units, $h = 6.625 \times 10^{-34}$ joule sec, $m = 9.11 \times 10^{-31}$ kg, $e = 1.60 \times 10^{-19}$ coulomb, V = volts. Using $\frac{1}{2}mv^2 = Ve$, we obtain $\lambda = (12.27/\sqrt{V}) \times 10^{-10}$ meters.

calculated wavelength using the de Broglie equation are within 1 percent of each other.

Many similar experiments show agreement. In all cases, if one thinks of electrons as being waves with the de Broglie wavelength, the observations are explained.

In Figure 1.2, only the scattering from the surface layer of atoms in the crystal was considered and, at these low electron energies, this plane of atoms is dominant. At slightly higher energies, Bragg type reflections (see Problem 1.3) are also observed from the deeper layers. The angle is different from that predicted by the free space wavelength, owing, as Bethe and Eckart[10] have shown, to a shift in the index of refraction of the electron waves as they enter the crystal lattice (see Problem 1.5).

At considerably higher energies (25,000 e.v.) the electrons completely penetrate small crystals and show the typical x-ray type of diffraction patterns due to the scattering from many layers. These experiments measure the lattice spacings in agreement with x-ray values to within experimental error (1 percent or so).

Electrons have been scattered (at grazing incidence) from optical gratings[11] and found to show the correct wave properties (see Problem 1.2).

Neutral particles, such as hydrogen, helium, mercury, cadmium, and arsenic atoms or molecules, on reflection from crystals show the same wave properties. The velocities are generally kept low so that the wavelength of these heavy particles will be reasonably long. The predicted maxima and the calculated maxima are consistently in agreement.

With the development of nuclear reactors providing intense beams of neutrons, very accurate confirmation of the matter-wave theory has been possible. Zinn[12] carefully measured the velocity of the neutrons, and since they penetrate crystals much as x-rays do, the typical x-ray patterns are observed. Again the theory is confirmed.

To the basic experiments (demonstrating the quantization of the energy of light and atomic systems, and the wave properties of matter) one must add an enormous number of other experiments which confirm and elaborate the conclusions. Even on the nuclear scale, a factor of 10^4 in smallness compared to the atomic scale, the same type of phenomena are observed.

Although the simple relationship $\lambda = h/p$ quantitatively explains the scattering experiments, and the Bohr model of the atom accounts for certain features of the hydrogen spectrum, these theories are completely inadequate to account for a host of observations. What is needed is a general theory—one which with a fairly small set of assumptions can be systematically applied to many different types of problems.

In the short period from 1925 to 1928, Heisenberg, Schrödinger, Born,

---

[10] Bethe and Eckart, *Naturwiss.*, **15**: 787, 1927.
[11] Rupp, *Zeit. f. Phys.*, **52**: 8; Worsnop, *Proc. Phys. Soc.*, **37**: 284.
[12] W. H. Zinn, *Phys. Rev.*, **71**: 752, 1947.

Dirac, and many others laid the foundations of what is one of the greatest theories of all time, the theory of quantum mechanics. In generality and in range of application, it is unsurpassed. It has been so successful that one cannot discuss atomic and nuclear matters without some understanding of this basic theory.

Because the predictions of quantum mechanics agree with so many different types of accurate, careful, repeated experiments—the last court of appeal for all theories—this theory is almost certain to become a permanent part of man's equipment for understanding and analyzing a large and very important part of nature. However its conceptual foundations or philosophy may change in the future, it has already, in a thousand ways, proved its utility and power. Thinking "classically" about atoms and nuclei is natural since we are macroscopic beings and we directly observe (and obey) the laws of classical mechanics. For much of modern physics, however, only mental images which are in conformity with the wave nature of matter will lead to the understanding of experiments.

PROBLEMS

Problem 1.1.

(a) In the Davisson-Germer experiment (Fig. 1.2), if the incident electron energy is changed to 64 e.v., where should the peak occur for the scattered electrons?

(b) At what energy of incident electrons should the second-order maximum ($n = 2$) occur at 50°?

(c) If some foreign gas atoms were to attach themselves at every other lattice site (Fig. 1.2), at what electron energy would the 50°, first-order, maximum occur? (This would have the effect of doubling the lattice spacing. It has been observed experimentally.)

Problem 1.2. Rupp scattered electrons at nearly grazing incidence from an optical grating of spacing, $d = 7.70 \times 10^{-4}$ cm, as measured with light of known wavelength (see Fig. 1.3a). Both α and θ are very small angles.

(a) With the aid of Figure 1.3b, show that for zero order ($n = 0$) all wavelengths are reflected.

(b) With the aid of Figure 1.3c, show that diffraction maxima occur when

$$\tfrac{1}{2} d\, \alpha(\alpha + 2\theta) = n\lambda$$

where d is the grating constant *and* α and θ are small. (For small angles, $\cos x \simeq 1 - \dfrac{x^2}{2}$).

(c) Suppose a very narrow beam of incident electrons is observed to have *reflection* at $\theta = 10^{-3}$ radian. For this angle of incidence, what incident electron energy will produce a first-order ($n = 1$) *diffraction* maximum at $\alpha = 10^{-3}$ radian?

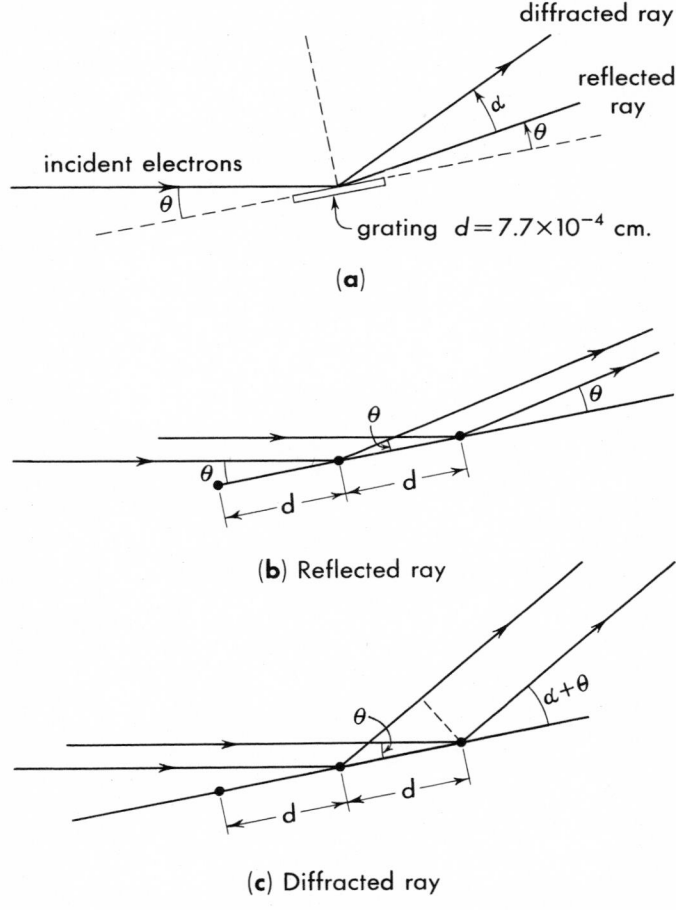

(a)

(b) Reflected ray

(c) Diffracted ray

Fig. 1.3. The diffraction of electrons from an optical grating.

Problem 1.3. For a rectangular crystal, Bragg reflections occur with the aid of two "gratings" of atoms—one aligned parallel to the surface and the other perpendicular to the surface (Fig. 1.4).

(a) Show that the Bragg formula satisfies the requirements for a maximum diffracted wave for a grating perpendicular to the surface

$$n\lambda = 2\, d_2 \sin \theta$$

where θ is the angle of incidence *and* reflection, measured from the surface, and d_2 is the grating (atom) spacing in the direction perpendicular to the surface, and also satisfies, in zero order, the grating equation of the array of atoms of arbitrary spacing (d_1) parallel to the surface. Thus both gratings scatter waves, each producing a maximum at the same angle, but only one of the gratings selects wavelengths.

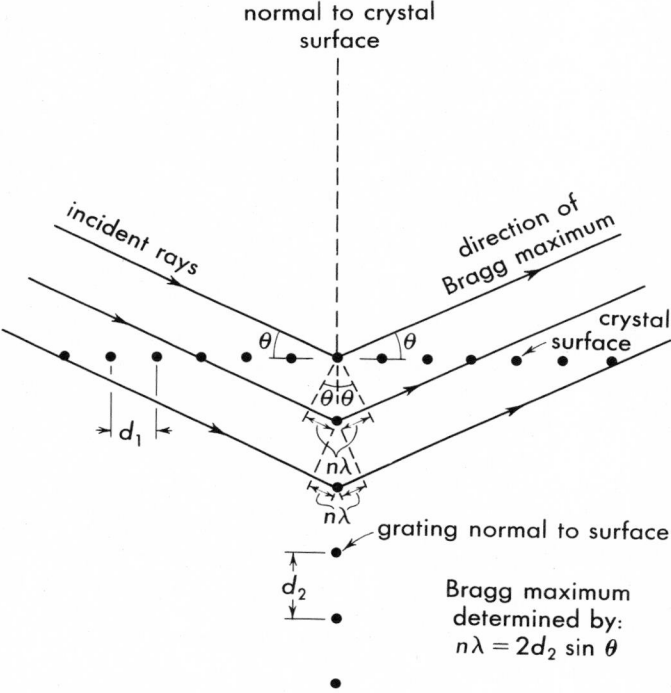

Fig. 1.4.　Bragg diffraction. The effective grating is normal to the surface.

(b)　For a crystal with $d_2 = 1.5 \times 10^{-8}$ cm, and for $\theta = 30°$, calculate the velocity of neutrons which will produce the first-order Bragg reflection. (Mass of neutron $= 1.66 \times 10^{-24}$ gm.)

(c)　To produce neutrons at this low velocity, one permits fast-moving reactor neutrons to come into thermal equilibrium with some cold material, such as carbon. Using the kinetic theory relationship

$$\left(\frac{1}{2} mv^2\right)_{\text{average}} = \frac{3}{2} kT$$

where k is Boltzmann's constant and T is degrees Kelvin, at what temperature will a carbon block produce an abundant supply of neutrons whose velocity is in the general range of that required in (b)?

(d) Two mechanical shutters, spaced 10^3 cm apart and opening, in sequence, for a very short interval, are used to select neutrons of a particular velocity out of the beam of the cold neutrons. What must be the spacing of their opening times to select the velocity in (b)?

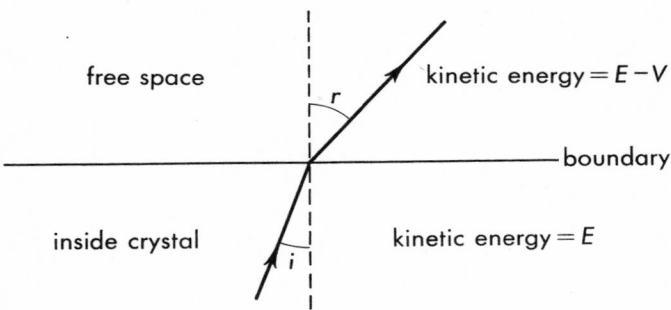

Fig. 1.5. The trajectory of electrons deflected at a potential boundary.

Problem 1.4. Show by classical mechanics that when electrons of initial kinetic energy E cross a potential boundary of height V so that their kinetic energy becomes $E - V$, the analogue of Snell's law holds—that is,

$$\frac{\sin i}{\sin r} = \sqrt{\frac{E - V}{E}}$$

(See Fig. 1.5.) (Note: The component of the electron velocity which is parallel to the boundary cannot change.)

Problem 1.5. When electrons enter a crystal they "drop into a potential well" of average depth 10 e.v. or so and shorten their wavelength compared to free space.

(a) Using de Broglie's relationship, show that when 54 e.v. electron waves outside the crystal become 64 e.v. electron waves inside the crystal their wavelength shortens by about 10 percent.

(b) Show that the angle of the maximum intensity of the electrons diffracted from the *second* layer of atoms (not shown) in Figure 1.2, is the same as for the first, or surface layer (the

d_1 grating of Figure 1.4). In analogy with light, the index of refraction, μ, of electron waves is

$$\mu = \lambda(\text{free space})/\lambda(\text{medium})$$

(Note that the shift in the angle of reinforcement inside the crystal is exactly cancelled by the refraction of the waves at the surface.)

(c) Show that for the Bragg reflections $n\lambda = 2d_2 \sqrt{\mu^2 - \cos^2 \theta}$, so that in this case the angle of reinforcement of the matter waves does depend upon μ (λ = the free-space wavelength).

(d) Let $n = 1$, $d_2 = 1.5 \times 10^{-8}$ cm. For free-space 54 e.v. electrons, find θ. What would θ have been if there were no change in the wavelength of the electron waves as they entered (and left) the crystal?

BASIC POSTULATES

2.1. Matter waves

In electricity, one is accustomed to the idea of a field surrounding a charged particle. The electric field of a charged pith ball is not completely localized, but spreads throughout space. We think of the field and the charged particle as being inseparable, that is, as two aspects of the same entity. The experiments of Chapter 1, particularly those on the scattering of electrons and atoms, show that matter cannot be completely localized on an atomic scale. We are more accustomed to the idea of incompletely localized charges than to un-localized matter, but both phenomena are equally mysterious.

The basic experiments can be explained quantitatively by assuming that with each bit of matter there is associated a new type of field represented by the symbol Ψ, and that this field has a wavelike character. The wavelength of these waves in free space is given by the de Broglie equation $\lambda = h/mv$, which, as we shall see, comes quite naturally out of the complete theory. These Ψ-waves are intimately associated with the particles to which they belong, and the behavior of the particles is found to be predictable only with the knowledge of what the Ψ-waves are doing at any instant. First, the basic postulates of quantum mechanics give rules for calculating, for any system, the complete wave function $\Psi(x, y, z, t)$. Second, they tell us how to calculate the expected value of observable quantities with the aid of the Ψ-function. The theory cannot predict the detailed behavior of individual systems but only the average behavior of a large number of systems. This ability to predict only the average behavior of many systems is strikingly shown in the Davisson-Germer experiment, where if we substitute a counter device, which detects *single* electrons, for the "Faraday cage" (a simple current collector), we find that individual electrons are observed at many different angles, and only the *total* of all the counts shows the characteristic interference pattern. (See the discussion in Section 2.3 referring to Fig. 2.2.) In any case, the theory of matter waves only concerns itself with predictions of the average behavior of many systems. There seems to be no more adequate way to interpret experimental observations.

Like the **E** and **B** fields of electricity, the Ψ-function is not itself directly observable. It is a tool for calculation. Since it gives results that are in agreement with experiment it has a certain degree of reality.

As we shall see, the Ψ (or rather Ψ* Ψ) function is the only contact the macroscopic world has with the microscopic world.[1] One might say that Ψ* Ψ is the "window to the world of the atom." What is not revealed by the wave function using the methods of the theory cannot be found out, and, as we shall see, calculations using the theory always involve both Ψ* and Ψ.

Quantum mechanics was first formulated in terms of matrix algebra by Heisenberg. An equivalent form, independently discovered by Schrödinger, is known as wave mechanics. The Ψ-function explicitly appears in Schrödinger's formulation and it is this form of the theory that is considered the easiest one to learn. The terms *quantum mechanics* and *wave mechanics* have gradually become nearly synonymous because the theories are basically the same. We shall use only the expression "quantum mechanics."

2.2.　The basic postulates of quantum mechanics

In classical mechanics one is accustomed to working with the distance x, the momentum p, the total energy W, etc. These are examples of quantities called dynamical variables. In the solution of practical problems one finds expressions involving these variables, which will give numerical values under any specified conditions.

In quantum mechanics the dynamical variables play a completely new role. They are converted by a set of rules into mathematical operators which then operate on the wave function Ψ. An example of an operator is d/dx. When placed in front of a function, say $f(x)$, this symbol has a definite meaning. $f(x)$ is called the operand. We shall proceed to the use of operators in Schrödinger's method of quantum mechanics.

In the statement of the postulates, we shall at first use only one coordinate, x, and the time, t. This makes the ideas easier to visualize. Other coordinates can be added later with little difficulty.

---

[1] Ψ* is the complex conjugate of Ψ, thus Ψ* Ψ = | Ψ |². See Appendix III for a short discussion of complex numbers.

Postulate I

To each system with one degree of freedom there belongs a wave function $\Psi(x, t)$.

Postulate II

The classical expression for the total energy W of the system ($p_x = mv_x$ is the x-component of the momentum, and $V(x)$ is the potential energy) is

$$\frac{1}{2m} p_x^2 + V(x) = W \qquad [2\text{-}1$$

which is converted into a wave equation by the following substitution of operators for dynamical variables:

dynamical variable		operator
x	$\rightarrow$	x
$f(x)$	$\rightarrow$	$f(x)$
p_x	$\rightarrow$	$\dfrac{\hbar}{i}\dfrac{\partial}{\partial x}$
W	$\rightarrow$	$-\dfrac{\hbar}{i}\dfrac{\partial}{\partial t}$

where

$$\hbar \equiv \frac{h}{2\pi}$$

and by the insertion of the operand $\Psi(x, t)$. Thus, equation [2–1] becomes

$$-\frac{\hbar^2}{2m}\frac{\partial^2\,\Psi(x,\,t)}{\partial x^2} + V(x)\,\Psi(x,\,t) = -\frac{\hbar}{i}\frac{\partial\Psi(x,\,t)}{\partial t} \qquad [2\text{-}2$$

This is the Schrödinger wave equation, including time, for a one-dimensional system whose potential energy depends only on x.

Postulate III

$$\Psi(x,\,t)$$

and

$$\frac{\partial\Psi(x,\,t)}{\partial x}$$

must be continuous, finite, and single valued, throughout "configuration space" (here, all values of x).

Postulate IV

$$\int_{-\infty}^{+\infty} \Psi^*\,\Psi dx = 1, \text{ i.e., } \Psi^*\,\Psi \text{ is normalized.} \qquad [2\text{-}3$$

We shall often refer to this equation as the requirement of the "integrable square."

Postulate V

The average value, $\bar{\alpha}$, of any dynamical variable α, which corresponds to the operator $\alpha_{(operator)}$, is calculated from the wave function by the formula

$$\bar{\alpha} = \int_{-\infty}^{+\infty} \Psi^* \, \alpha_{(operator)} \, \Psi \, dx \qquad\qquad [2\text{-}4$$

These five postulates contain the essentials of quantum mechanics, and the remainder of the book will be devoted to working out their implications.

The brief statement of the postulates is certainly not the only or even the most general formulation of the principles but, as we shall see, these principles are easy to apply to simple systems and quickly lead to quantitative results. There are other types of operators (particularly those concerning the electromagnetic field) which are not listed here. We have yet to extend the postulates to include more dimensions. Nonetheless, the consequences of this relatively simple set of postulates are very important and very diverse and will give a good picture of what quantum mechanics is and how it is used.

Compared to the postulates of quantum mechanics, Newton's Laws are more simple to state and use, and Maxwell's equations, with auxiliary requirements, are probably more elaborate.

We have discussed briefly the idea of the wave function, stated in Postulate I, but some comments about the other postulates will be helpful before we turn to direct application, which is the best exposition of their meaning.

The formation of the wave equation, and particularly the selection of the operator substitutions stated in Postulate II, seems very arbitrary. One should note, however, that it is reasonable to expect that there should be some connection with classical mechanics, since the smallest of systems visible in an ordinary microscope obeys the classical laws. Regarding the operator substitutions, one should remember that the wavelike nature of matter was already beginning to be appreciated when Schrödinger first stated his theory, and that the wave equation [2–2] is similar to some of the familiar wave equations in classical physics. These particular operator substitutions are of the type needed to convert the expression for the total energy of a particle into a differential equation which will have periodic, wavelike solutions.[2] Whatever the hints might have been, however, it is plain that there was a great deal of pure invention in the formulation of this set of rules.

Postulate III contains requirements which all physical waves meet, whether

---

[2] Appendix VIII outlines the relationship between the Schrödinger wave equation and the wave equation of classical physics, using the de Broglie wavelength.

they are water waves, sound waves, or electromagnetic waves. That is, no real waves have infinite amplitudes, and their amplitude and slope (variation of amplitude with distance) are continuous and at any point, x, unambiguous—that is, single valued. It has been shown that the requirement of finiteness is more rigorous than necessary, but this will not affect our considerations here.[3]

Thus, to require that matter waves should be "well behaved" functions of space is very reasonable if we are to regard them as having reality.

Again, those waves that are most directly observable meet the normalization requirement, Postulate IV, or its equivalent. The waves in a rope require a certain amount of energy to produce one cycle of any specified finite amplitude. With a finite amount of energy, therefore, only a certain number of cycles can be produced. This group of waves, often called a wave packet, will travel indefinitely down a rope (if we assume that there is no energy loss to the wave). The disturbance has zero amplitude out in front of the wave packet and zero amplitude behind the wave packet. Thus, if $y(x, t)$ is the wave on a rope (Fig. 2.1), the disturbance is always bounded in space—even though it may be moving. Also, at every time t the area under the curve $y^2(x, t)$ is finite. By multiplying y by an appropriate constant, the area can be made to be unity, i.e. normalized. Later in the book (Section 5.6) we shall quantitatively analyze wave packets such as those sketched in Figure 2.1.

Sound waves or electromagnetic waves echoing in a hollow cavity have an amplitude which is limited by the amount of energy supplied in their creation, and their spacial extent is limited by the walls of the cavity. Thus, at any time, the area under the curve (amplitude)^2 *vs.* x (we assume only one dimension), is finite. By selecting a scaling factor the area can be made to be unity.

There is particular significance in the requirement that matter waves have

$$\int_{-\infty}^{+\infty} \Psi^* \, \Psi \, dx = 1 \qquad\qquad [2\text{–}3$$

M. Born first pointed out that if $\Psi^* \Psi \, dx$ is interpreted as the *probability* that a particle is to be found in a particular interval x to $x + dx$ at the time t, then one can make an interpretation of experiments such as the ones on electron scattering.[4] Thus, the finiteness of energy limits the spacial extent of any packet of mechanical or electromagnetic waves, but it is the finite bound on *probability* that limits the spacial extent of matter waves, i.e., the probability is unity that a given particle can be located somewhere between $x = -\infty$ and $x = +\infty$.

As we shall see, the auxiliary conditions, that Ψ should be well behaved and normalized, are quite as important as the wave equation itself. The wave

---

[3] W. Pauli, *Handbuch der Physik* (2nd ed.), **24**, Part 1, 123, 1933.
[4] Born's interpretation of $\Psi^* \Psi$ as the probability density may be directly inferred from Postulate V.   See Problem 2.4.   Also, see discussion in Section 5.3.

equation permits many solutions. It is the auxiliary conditions which select certain solutions, that is, which cause "quantization." The size of the discontinuities resulting from quantization are regulated by Planck's constant *h*.

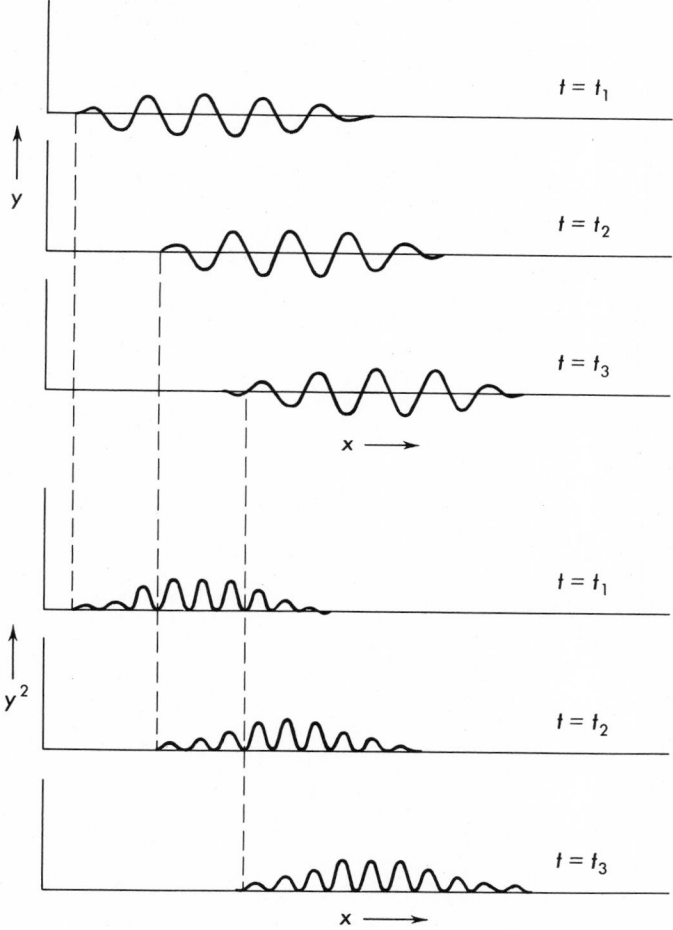

Fig. 2.1.　Packet of waves travelling in the positive *x*-direction.

As Schrödinger pointed out in the introduction to his first paper,[5] the appearance of the quantum rules (for the hydrogen atom) is just as natural as is the existence of the resonance rules for a vibrating string.

Postulate V is of key importance, for it is always through this formula that one calculates observable quantities which can be compared to experiment.

---

[5] E. Schrödinger, *Ann. der Physik*, **79**: 361, 1926.

Again the idea of probability comes in, since it is not *one* observation that is predicted, but the *average* of many. The symbol $\bar{a}$, with the bar above the a, is called the expectation value, and the formula [2–4] of Postulate V is called the expectation value formula. This postulate also highlights the intimate relationship between variables and the operators to which they correspond and furthermore it is the immediate cause for the dominating role played by $\Psi^* \Psi$ in the contact with the atomic world. Thus far, no one has devised a means for the prediction of observable quantities (the count in a geiger counter, the dark line on a photographic film, etc.) which gives any more information than that provided by Postulate V. This postulate is indeed the only "window" to the world of the atom and the nucleus.[6]

As presented, these basic postulates of quantum mechanics might be compared to Newton's Laws for classical mechanics. They do not include the phenomena of the electromagnetic field (or the meson field), and we have not yet included special relativity. However, these essential features can be added without changing the basic point of view. We shall see in Chapter 11 how Dirac inserted the requirements of relativity within the framework of these postulates. Dirac and Yukawa, respectively, are mainly responsible for the extension of the theory to electromagnetic radiation and to meson fields.

The five postulates (or one of the alternative, somewhat more general, formulations of basic quantum theory) have been so successful in predicting and correlating observable results that they, or their equivalents, are bound to be included in any possible theory which might, in the future, be found to be more general or more accurate than quantum mechanics as it is now known. For example, at low velocities the mechanics of special relativity reduce, with extreme precision, to Newton's Laws. Also, as we shall see, the laws of quantum theory smoothly change into Newton's Laws when applied to macroscopic systems. (See Bohr's correspondence principle, Section 3.6.)

Few theories in the history of science have been as successful as quantum mechanics. In its domain of application (*all* theories apply in some limited domain) it now reigns supreme, and is likely to continue to do so for the foreseeable future.

Just as one can write a textbook about the applications of Newton's Laws, the consequences of the postulates of thermodynamics (or statistical mechanics), the postulates of relativity, or of classical electricity and magnetism, so the basic postulates of quantum mechanics lead to many consequences. All great theories have this in common: They are reducible to a small number of postulates. They represent a codification of knowledge, a summarizing of experience.

As we have already mentioned, the five postulates are not really complete. There are many *implied* concepts and inferences which a complete statement

---

[6] In Chapter 10 we see that this *interpretation* of Postulate V is oversimple. There is no question, however, about its accuracy when used as a tool for calculating the results of experiment.

of the theory should define much more accurately than we have done here: the idea of probability is an example. Except for the concept of probability, we shall discuss these background implications only as the occasion arises. Few subjects are so conducive to philosophical discussion as is quantum mechanics and its unexpressed assumptions, but we shall direct almost all our efforts into seeing what quantum mechanics *is* (the postulates) and how it *works.*

The concept of probability needs further elaboration before we plunge into the task of applying the theory of quantum mechanics.

2.3. Probability

The theory of probability originally came from the practical problem of calculating the odds in games of chance. Its history is therefore essentially practical and involves constant interplay between theory and observation. For example, one makes the statement that the probability of observing any particular number, say a 2, when throwing a symmetrical six-sided die is 1/6. The operational meaning of this statement is this: If one casts the same die 6,000 times in the practical manner of casting, one expects that in very nearly 1,000 cases the die will come to rest with number 2 face up. That is, one predicts that in 1/6 of all of the basic operations—which are, as far as is known, identical—the specified result will occur. The result of any *individual* throw cannot be predicted (as the operation is performed in practice), but the total number of successes in a given large number of operations can be predicted with considerable accuracy.

Note that the statement that the probability of occurrence of a certain event is $1/k$ *always* implies a certain repetitive experiment, such as throwing the die. Alternatively, one could throw 6,000 (as far as is known, identical) dice once and obtain the same result.

The word probability *does not have an operational meaning in the practical sense unless the particular repetitive experiment to which it refers is specified.* In games of chance and in the prediction of experimental results, this practical definition works very well.

As an example, consider the electrons incident upon the crystal grating in the Davisson-Germer experiment. Suppose in Figure 1.2b, instead of the single collector, there is a set of electron multipliers[7] arranged in an arc at different angles, θ (Fig. 2.2a). The particular electron multiplier, or counter, located at the angle of maximum reinforcement of the Ψ-waves will record

---

[7] An electron of adequate velocity impinging upon certain materials will eject several other electrons. These in turn may be accelerated and can be caused to impinge upon a second surface, thus producing more electrons. A sequence of nine or ten such processes produces a current pulse large enough to observe with ordinary amplifiers. Thus a single electron can be detected. The whole set of surfaces operate in a vacuum, since the electrons can then move freely from one surface to the next (see Fig. 2.2c).

the greatest number of counts, but some counts will occur at other angles as well. Quantum mechanics will only predict the number of counts in each counter after a given time: it predicts that out of N electrons incident upon the crystal,

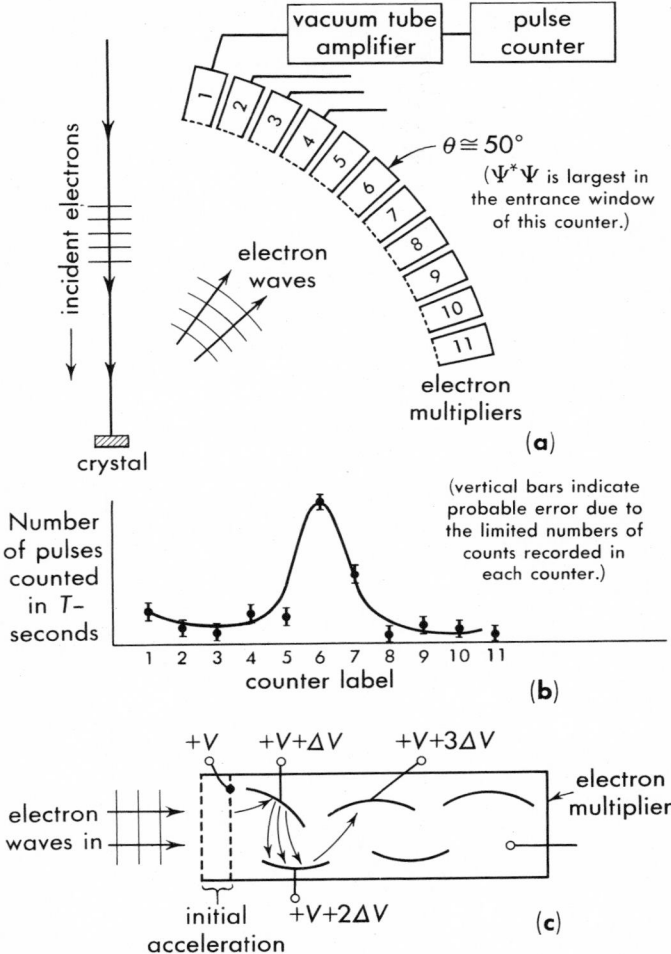

Fig. 2.2. A schematic description of a possible method of performing the Davisson-Germer experiment, in which individual electrons are detected.

a certain fraction p will be observed in any particular counter (Fig. 2.2b). If the product pN is very large compared to 1, the prediction is quite exact. The physical point of observation of any single electron cannot be predetermined. The repetitive experiment is this: Electrons whose direction and speed are defined (within some specified tolerance) are first incident upon a crystal of given size and physical structure and then detected in a counter of given geometrical aperture and location. Out of all such electrons, what fraction will cause a count in the counter? In principle, one proceeds as follows: The average value of $\Psi^* \Psi$ over some time interval T is calculated for the region of space occupied by the counter aperture. Suppose that (the average value of $\Psi^* \Psi$) × (some geometrical factor) $= 10^{-6}$. One then predicts that, out of 10^{10} incident electrons, very nearly 10^4 will be detected by the particular counter. One assumes that the Ψ-waves from all of the electrons arrive at any particular counter, but in only a certain fraction of the cases will the particle happen to "materialize" at that particular region of space, that is, cause one or more electrons to appear at the photo-cathode of the counter. Thus the Ψ-waves give only the probability of detecting a single whole electron.[8]

The calculation we have been discussing is, in practice, quite difficult to perform with accuracy. We refer to it here only to emphasize the importance of probability concepts in quantum mechanics, and the necessity of specifying the particular repetitive experiment whose results are being predicted.

There are several definitions in probability theory that will be needed. We shall list them and then work out an example, the "wheel of fortune," which will illustrate the application of each definition.

The probability density function $P(x)$ is defined by: The probability that x will be observed to have the value between x and $x + dx$ is

$$P(x) \, dx \qquad\qquad [2\text{--}5$$

Let x range from $-\infty$ to $+\infty$, then, as x is always observed to have *some* value,

$$\int_{-\infty}^{+\infty} P(x) \, dx = 1 \qquad\qquad [2\text{--}6$$

that is, it is certain that x will have some value in its full range.

The mean, or average value, of $f(x)$ is designated as $\bar{f}(x)$, and is defined to be

$$\bar{f}(x) \equiv \int_{-\infty}^{+\infty} f(x) \, P(x) \, dx \qquad\qquad [2\text{--}7$$

The average value of $[f(x)]^2$ is designated as $\overline{[f(x)]^2}$, and is

$$\overline{[f(x)]^2} = \int_{-\infty}^{+\infty} [f(x)]^2 \, P(x) \, dx \qquad\qquad [2\text{--}8$$

---

[8] This is the generally accepted interpretation. For further discussion, see references in Section 10.6.

The standard deviation in $f(x)$ is designated by σ and defined by

$$\sigma^2 = \overline{[f(x) - \bar{f}(x)]^2} = \int_{-\infty}^{+\infty} [f(x) - \bar{f}(x)]^2 \, P(x) \, dx \qquad [2\text{--}9$$

σ measures the "spread" or uncertainty in the predicted value of $f(x)$. There is a result of general validity which can be easily obtained from equation [2–9] and the earlier definitions:

$$\sigma^2 = \underbrace{\int_{-\infty}^{+\infty} [f(x)]^2 \, P(x) \, dx}_{= \overline{[f(x)]^2}} - 2\bar{f}(x) \underbrace{\int_{-\infty}^{+\infty} f(x) \, P(x) \, dx}_{= \bar{f}(x)} + [\bar{f}(x)]^2 \underbrace{\int_{-\infty}^{+\infty} P(x) \, dx}_{= 1}$$

Thus, the standard deviation in $f(x)$ is given by

$$\sigma^2 = \overline{[f(x)]^2} - [\bar{f}(x)]^2 \qquad [2\text{--}10$$

or in words, σ^2 is "the mean square, minus the square of the mean."

The importance of this result lies in its relation to Postulate V, the calculation of expectation value. Given the wave function, Ψ, one can calculate $\bar{a}$ and also $\overline{(a)^2}$. Now, if the square of the former is equal to the latter, we have σ^2 equal to zero. This in turn carries the implication that the expectation value $\bar{a}$ is an exact, certain number, that is, that all of the repetitive experiments will yield the same result. This particular type of result is of great importance in quantum mechanics.

To see how these definitions and concepts of probability work out, we shall apply them to a simple case.

Imagine a "wheel of fortune" which has 360 pins. It is carefully made and perfectly balanced, and we find that if it is spun 10^6 times, in very nearly $1/360$ of all trials it will stop in a particular one-degree interval. In Figure 2.3a we plot the experimental values of $P(\theta) \, d\theta$ where here $d\theta$ is 1 degree. Thus, $P(\theta)$ has the constant value of $1/360$ per degree from $\theta = 0$ to $\theta = 360$ degrees, the full range of θ. The area under the curve is unity, as it is certain that some value between 0 and 360 degrees will occur on every spin.

Next, in Figure 2.3b, we suppose that some magnet or other device is placed in such a manner that the wheel tends to stop in the neighborhood of $180°$. A large number of trials discloses the plotted points which outline the probability distribution function drawn in the figure. Since $P(\theta)$ is now larger near $180°$ it must be smaller elsewhere so that the area under the curve is still unity.

Finally, in Figure 2.3c, we suppose that a device is placed on the wheel which causes it to stop on the $180°$ pin on every spin. Many experiments show that this result is a certainty, and therefore for the interval of one degree which brackets the $180°$ point, $P(\theta)$ must be unity per degree, and zero elsewhere.

It is clear from symmetry that the average value of θ will be 180° in all cases in Figure 2.3, but there are varying degrees of certainty. In (a), although it is true that the average of all observations will be very near 180°, there is a large spread in the individual values. In (b), values near 180° occur relatively

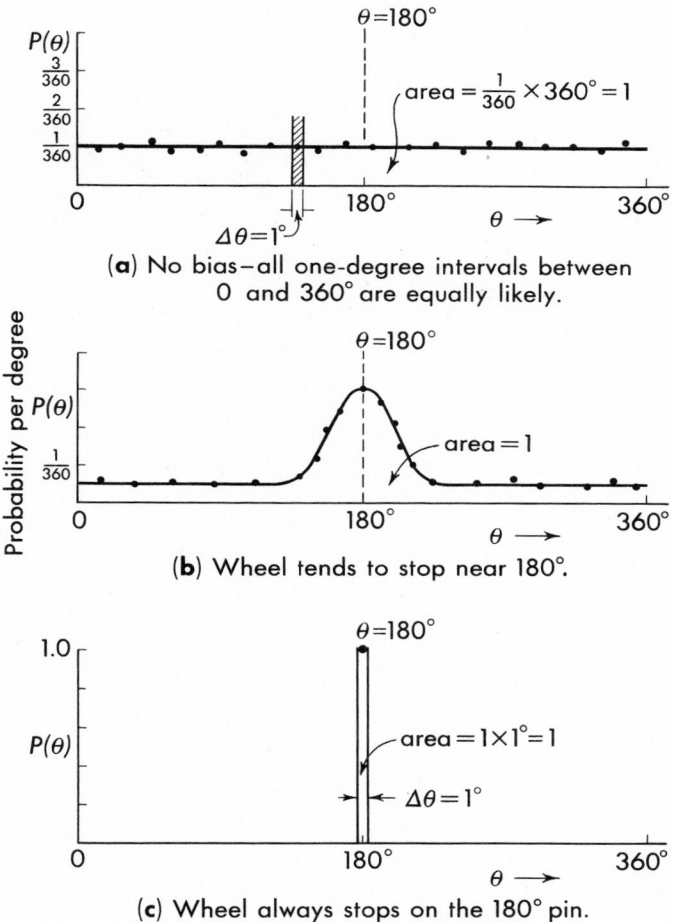

(a) No bias—all one-degree intervals between 0 and 360° are equally likely.

(b) Wheel tends to stop near 180°.

(c) Wheel always stops on the 180° pin.

Fig. 2.3. The wheel of fortune.

frequently, but still the individual values range over the whole interval. In (c) all of the individual values are exactly 180°, and there is no uncertainty in the prediction of the observed result.

In Figure 2.4a, a particular function $f_1(\theta) = \theta$ is plotted, and also $f_2(\theta) = \theta^2$. For the simple case, where $P(\theta) = 1/2\pi$ per radian, we calculate

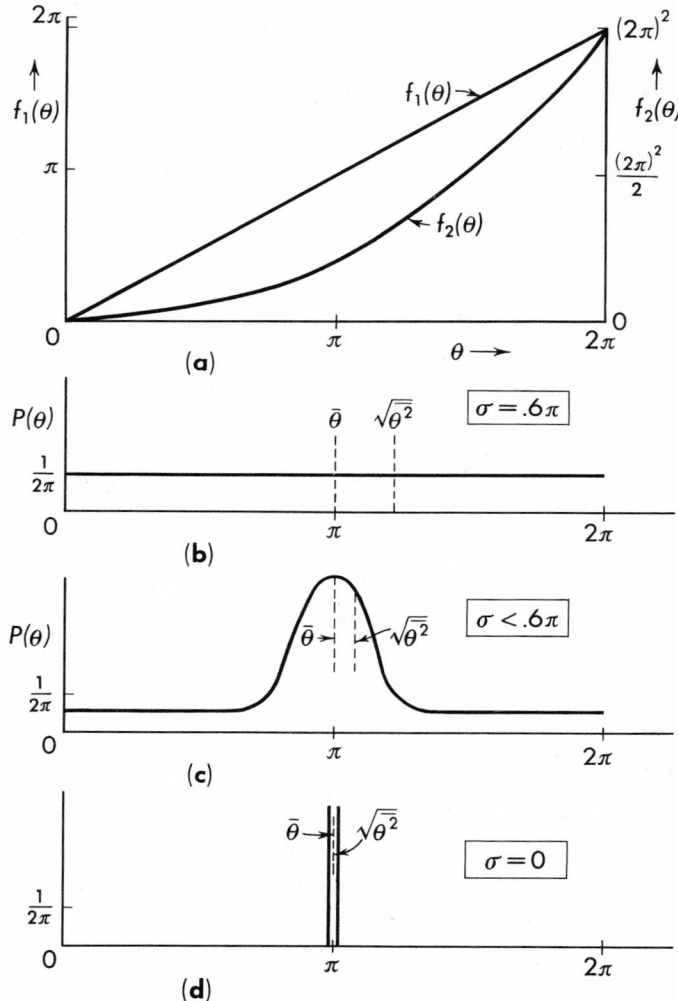

Fig. 2.4. The calculation of $\bar{\theta}$ and $\overline{\theta^2}$ for three different probability distributions.

$$\bar{\theta} = \int_0^{2\pi} \theta\left(\frac{1}{2\pi}\right) d\theta = \pi$$

$$\overline{\theta^2} = \int_0^{2\pi} \theta^2\left(\frac{1}{2\pi}\right) d\theta = (2\pi)^2/3$$

$$\sigma = \sqrt{\frac{(2\pi)^2}{3} - \pi^2} = \frac{\pi}{\sqrt{3}}$$

The values of $\bar{\theta}$ and $\sqrt{\overline{\theta^2}}$ are shown in Figure 2.4b. $\sqrt{\overline{\theta^2}}$ is considerably larger then $\bar{\theta}$. Therefore the standard deviation, σ, is quite large, 0.6π.

For the intermediate case (Fig. 2.4c), although from symmetry $\bar{\theta}$ is the same as before, $\sqrt{\overline{\theta^2}}$ is only slightly larger than $\bar{\theta}$, and σ is less than before.

Finally, for the last case (Fig. 2.4d), since the observed values are always 180°, both $\bar{\theta}$ and $\sqrt{\overline{\theta^2}}$ have this value.

It is clear that, for any symmetrical probability distribution function, the expectation value of some observed function $f(\theta)$ (here, $f(\theta) = \theta$) becomes more and more precisely defined as σ becomes smaller and smaller, that is, as $\overline{[f(\theta)]^2}$ becomes more nearly equal to $[\bar{f}(\theta)]^2$.

It can be shown[9] that if for all (integral) n

$$[\bar{f}(x)]^n = \overline{[f(x)]^n}$$

then the probability distribution function, $P(x)$, must be of the type shown in Figures 2.3c and 2.4d, or, in other words, that $P(x)$ must have a value of unity for one value of x and zero for all other values of x.

If, in the use of Postulate V, one finds that

$$(\bar{a})^2 = \overline{a^2}; \; (\bar{a})^3 = \overline{a^3}; \; (\bar{a})^4 = \overline{a^4}; \; \cdots$$

then this particular observable quantity, a, will have an exactly predictable result for all systems having the same wave function. If, on the other hand, this does *not* occur [in practice it is adequate to show that $(\bar{a})^2 \neq \overline{a^2}$], then one knows that all systems, even though they are known to have the same wave function, will *not*, if observed, give a unique, definite result for the particular observation belonging to the operator being used. In this case, the individual values of a will "cluster about the mean," $\bar{a}$. The "spread" in this cluster depends on σ.

Thus, even though it makes predictions on the basis of probability, quantum mechanics will under some conditions predict an exact, certain result. Whenever this happens there are further important consequences which will be discussed later.

2.4.   The wave equation for Ψ*

Unlike most wave equations in physics, the Schrödinger equation involves complex numbers. If, in equation [2–2], i is everywhere changed to $-i$, we have

$$-\frac{\hbar^2}{2m}\frac{\partial^2 \Psi^*(x,t)}{\partial x^2} + V(x)\,\Psi^*(x,t) = +\frac{\hbar}{i}\frac{\partial \Psi^*(x,t)}{\partial t} \qquad [2\text{--}11]$$

which is the wave equation for Ψ*. $V(x)$, the potential energy, is a real function. This equation is completely equivalent to [2–2]. It is merely an alternate

---

[9] J. V. Upensky, *Introduction to Mathematical Probability* (1937, McGraw-Hill Book Co., New York): Appendix II. We have just shown one case of the reverse of this theorem: Given $P(\theta)$ as in Figure 2.3c, then $(\bar{\theta})^2$ must equal $\bar{\theta}^2$. The extension to higher powers of θ is simple.

method of writing [2–2]. Let

$$\Psi = a + ib \qquad \text{in [2–2]}$$

and

$$\Psi^* = a - ib \qquad \text{in [2–11]}$$

Equating real and imaginary parts,[10] we have

$$-\frac{\hbar^2}{2m}\frac{\partial^2 a}{\partial x^2} + V(x)\, a = -\hbar\frac{\partial b}{\partial t}$$

$$-\frac{\hbar^2}{2m}\frac{\partial^2 b}{\partial x^2} + V(x)\, b = \hbar\frac{\partial a}{\partial t}$$

[2–12

which are coupled partial differential equations in the two real variables a and b.

One can work equally well with [2–2], [2–11], or [2–12], but the complex-number method of notation is much more convenient than the real-variable method.

In [2–12], observable results will always involve not a or b alone, but $a^2 + b^2$, since the product $\Psi^* \Psi$ appears in the calculations of expectation value.

A brief outline of some of the features of the complex number notation, as related to quantum mechanics, is found in Appendix III.

PROBLEMS

Problem 2.1. If $P(x)$ has the form shown in Figure 2.5a:

(a) Determine the scale of the ordinate.
(b) Calculate $\bar{x}$, $\bar{x^2}$, and $\bar{x^3}$.

Problem 2.2. For a wheel of chance, the probability of stopping between θ and $\theta + d\theta$ is $P(\theta)\, d\theta$ when $P(\theta) = 1/360$ per degree. The wheel has a radius, R, of 100 cm (see Fig. 2.5b). x is the projection, on the x-axis, of the stopping point.

(a) Calculate $P(x)$ per cm, given $P(\theta) = 1/360$ per degree. Plot.
(b) Calculate $\bar{x}$, $\bar{x^2}$, and σ.

Problem 2.3. Let

$$P(x) = k\left(\sin 2\pi\,\frac{x}{L}\right)^2$$

---

[10] If $A = a + ib$ and $B = c + id$ are complex numbers, the equation $A = B$ is shorthand notation for the *two* equations, $a = c$ and $b = d$.

defined in the interval from $x = 0$ to $x = L$, and where k is a constant
(see Fig. 2.5c).

   (a) Calculate k.
   (b) Calculate $\bar{x}$, $\overline{x^2}$, and σ.

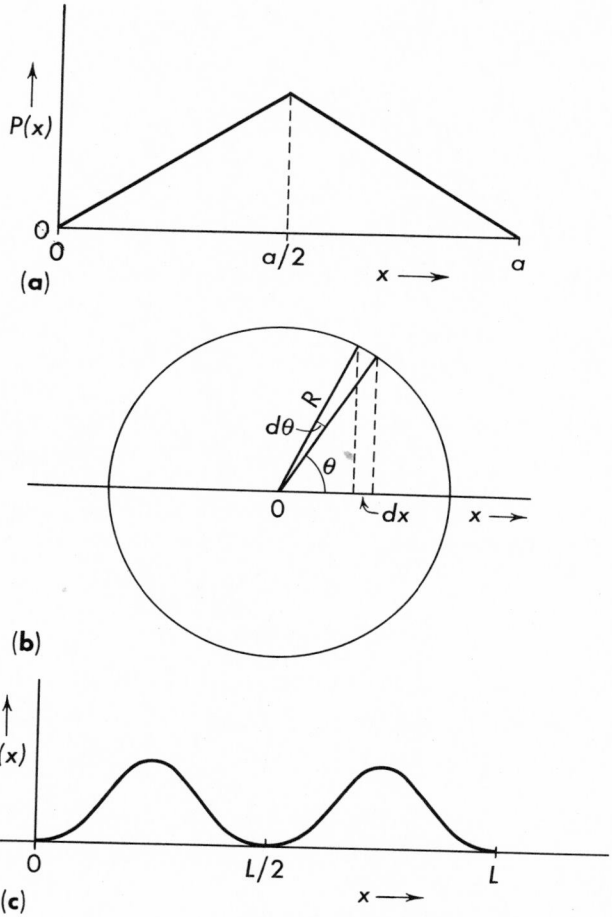

(a)

(b)

(c)

Fig. 2.5. a. The probability distribution for Problem 2.1. **b.** The
calculation of the x-component of the wheel of chance. **c.** The
probability distribution for Problem 2.3.

   Problem 2.4.   If, for $0 \leq x \leq a$, a normalized wave function
is

$$\Psi(x, t) = A \sin \frac{\pi x}{a} e^{-i\frac{E_0}{\hbar} t}$$

where E_0 and A are real constants,

(a) Find A.

(b) Calculate the expectation value of x. Discuss the significance of $\Psi^* \Psi$.

(c) Calculate the expectation value of x^2.

(d) Calculate the expectation value of W, the energy.

(e) Calculate the expectation value of W^2.

Problem 2.5. Calculate $\overline{f(x)}$, $\overline{f^2(x)}$, and σ where

$$f(x) = -b \text{ from } x = 0 \text{ to } x = a/2, \text{ and}$$

$$f(x) = +b \text{ from } x = a/2 \text{ to } x = a$$

for the two different probability distribution functions,

(a) $P(x) = $ constant from $x = 0$ to $x = a$, and

(b) $P(x)$ has the form given in Figure 2.5a.

In each case, normalize $P(x)$.

3

THE SOLUTION OF THE WAVE EQUATION

3.1. The separation of the time-dependent wave equation

Partial differential equations are usually difficult to solve in terms of simple functions except for one very important class of cases: that class for which the solution happens to be the *product* of functions of the variables. A linear partial differential equation then "separates" into *ordinary* differential equations. Consider the time-dependent Schrödinger equation [2–2],

$$-\frac{\hbar^2}{2m}\frac{\partial^2 \Psi(x, t)}{\partial x^2} + V(x)\,\Psi(\dot{x}, t) = -\frac{\hbar}{i}\frac{\partial \Psi(x, t)}{\partial t}$$

We assume that the solution, $\Psi(x, t)$, can be expressed as a *product* of the functions of two independent variables, x and t, that is,

$$\Psi(x, t) = \psi(x)\,\phi(t) \qquad\qquad [3–1$$

If, upon substitution of this assumed solution into the equation, there result two ordinary differential equations (each of which contains only *one* of the independent variables), the original equation is said to be "separated." A functional form of a solution can sometimes be found (and a numerical solution can always be found) for each of the equations separately.

To see that [3–1] results in the "separation" of [2–2], we substitute [3–1] into [2–2] and divide through by $\psi(x)\,\phi(t)$,

$$\frac{1}{\psi(x)}\left\{-\frac{\hbar^2}{2m}\frac{d^2\,\psi(x)}{dx^2} + V(x)\,\psi(x)\right\} = -\frac{\hbar}{i}\frac{1}{\phi(t)}\frac{d\,\phi(t)}{dt} \qquad [3–2$$

The right side is a function of time alone, and the left side is a function of x alone. Since x and t are *both* independent variables, [3-2] can be true only if each side is equal to some constant which we will call W.[1]

Thus

$$\frac{d\,\phi(t)}{dt} = -\frac{i}{\hbar}\,W\,\phi(t) \qquad\qquad [3\text{-}3$$

and

$$\frac{d^2\,\psi(x)}{dx^2} + \frac{2m}{\hbar^2}\,\{W - V(x)\}\,\psi(x) = 0 \qquad\qquad [3\text{-}4$$

Equation [3-3] can be integrated at once, setting the arbitrary multiplicative constant equal to unity,

$$\phi(t) = e^{-i\frac{W}{\hbar}t} \qquad\qquad [3\text{-}5$$

It is clear that $\psi(x)$ is the amplitude of Ψ, since now

$$\Psi(x, t) = \psi(x)\,e^{-i\frac{W}{\hbar}t} \qquad\qquad [3\text{-}6$$

Equation [3-4] is called the Schrödinger amplitude equation. We shall usually refer to it as the amplitude equation.

Neither the time equation [3-3] nor the amplitude equation [3-4] places any requirements on the value of the constant W, since for *any* W there can be found a Ψ which satisfies the two differential relationships [3-3] and [3-4]. We shall see that Postulates III (continuity, finiteness, and single valued-ness) and IV (integrable square) select, out of this infinity of particular solutions, only *certain* amplitude functions, $\psi(x)$, which belong to *particular* values of W. We shall identify these values of W by an integral subscript, n. Thus, when Postulates III and IV are included, only certain $\psi(x) = \psi_n(x)$ which "belong" to $W = W_n$ are, by basic hypothesis, acceptable wave functions for real systems.

The finding of the ψ_n's and W_n's for different systems and conditions will occupy a considerable portion of this book.

3.2. The solution of the amplitude equation for the harmonic oscillator, using numerical methods

For the simple harmonic oscillator of mass m, the potential energy is

$$V(x) = \tfrac{1}{2}\,kx^2$$

---

[1] If it is known that $f_1(x) = f_2(t)$ for any independently chosen values of x and t, it must be true that each function is a constant. Suppose that f_1 varied with x. If it were equal to f_2 for some particular x, then it would not be equal to f_2 for some other value of x. But x is an independent variable and can assume *any* value in the range where f_1 is defined.

where k is a constant characteristic of the oscillator,[2] and the amplitude equation [3–4] is

$$\frac{d^2\psi}{dx^2} + \frac{2m}{\hbar^2}\left\{W - \tfrac{1}{2}kx^2\right\}\psi = 0 \qquad\qquad [3\text{–}7$$

where ψ is well behaved, and [3] where $\int \psi^* \psi\, dx = 1$.

We shall first solve this equation using numerical methods and later find the analytical form of the solutions. There is nothing quite as illuminating regarding "what is going on" during the integration of a differential equation as the working out of a few sample solutions using a step-by-step integration process. Also, no other method shows so dramatically the dominating role of the boundary conditions.

In terms of finite differences [3–7] may be written

$$\frac{\Delta(\text{slope})}{\Delta x} = -\frac{2m}{\hbar^2}\left\{W - (1/2)\,kx^2\right\}\psi; \ \ \text{slope} = \frac{d\psi}{dx} \qquad [3\text{–}8$$

In words, after progressing from x to $x + \Delta x$ the slope of the curve changes from whatever it was at x by the amount

$$-\frac{2m}{\hbar^2}\left\{W - (1/2)\,kx^2\right\}\psi\,\Delta x$$

For these instructions to be applicable, one *must* know, or assume, the values of ψ and $d\psi/dx$ at some starting point.

Let $\psi = \psi_0$ and $d\psi/dx = (d\psi/dx)_0$ at $x = 0$.

Then

$$\psi_0 = \psi_0; \qquad\qquad\qquad\qquad\qquad\qquad \text{at } x = 0$$

$$\psi_1 = \psi_0 + \underbrace{\left(\frac{d\psi}{dx}\right)_0}_{\text{initial slope} \equiv s_0} \Delta x; \qquad\qquad\qquad \text{at } x_1 = \Delta x$$

$$\psi_2 = \psi_1 + \underbrace{\left[s_0 - \frac{2m}{\hbar^2}\left\{W - (1/2)\,kx_1^2\right\}\psi_1\,\Delta x\right]}_{\text{new slope} \equiv s_1}\Delta x; \ x_2 = 2^{\Delta}x \qquad [3\text{–}8a$$

$$\psi_3 = \psi_2 + \underbrace{\left[s_1 - \frac{2m}{\hbar^2}\left\{W - (1/2)\,kx_2^2\right\}\psi_2\,\Delta x\right]}_{\text{new slope} \equiv s_2}\Delta x; \ x_3 = 3^{\Delta}x$$

---

[2] A classical oscillator of mass m, whose spring constant is k, has a frequency

$$\nu_0 = \frac{1}{2\pi}\sqrt{\frac{k}{m}}$$

Thus the constant k can also be expressed as $4\pi^2\nu_0^2 m$.

[3] Postulate IV requires integration over the full range of variables, but, for brevity, we shall often not explicitly indicate the limits of integration.

$$\psi_4 = \psi_3 + \left[s_2 - \frac{2m}{\hbar^2} \{W - (1/2)\, kx_3^2\}\, \psi_3\, \Delta x \right] \Delta x; \quad x_4 = 4\Delta x$$

Figure 3.1 illustrates this process for the case where ψ_0 and $(d\psi/dx)_0$ are positive, and where $W - (1/2)\, kx^2$ is positive.

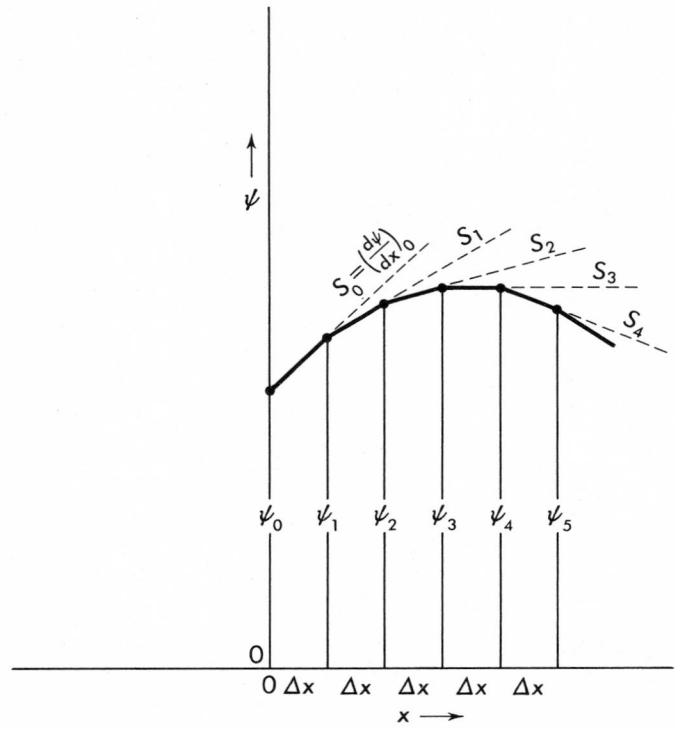

Fig. 3.1. The numerical integration of the wave equation for the harmonic oscillator, for arbitrary initial conditions at $x = 0$.

Whenever $(W - (1/2)\, kx^2)$ is positive, the graph of ψ vs. x will be constantly curving *toward* the x-axis, as in Figure 3.1. Whenever the term $(W - (1/2)\, kx^2)$ is negative, the graph of ψ vs. x will steadily curve *away* from the x-axis. Thus, the constant parameter W plays a key role in controlling the curvature of ψ vs. x. By selecting different values of W, curves of different *shape* result.

Starting with an arbitrary ψ_0 and $(d\psi/dx)_0$, as in Figure 3.1, one can plot the unique $\psi(x)$ which results. Figure 3.2 shows the shape of such a curve, where the initial conditions are those of Figure 3.1. For example, from $x = 0$ to $x = x_a$, the critical point where the term $(W - (1/2)\, kx^2)$ becomes negative, the graph curves toward the x-axis. Near x_a the graph is a straight line since here $\Delta(\text{slope}) = 0$ for a change of x to $x + \Delta x$. For $x > x_a$ the graph curves away from the x-axis, in this case never reaching it. It finally goes to infinity with an infinite slope. Working from $x = 0$ toward negative x, the graph continues to curve toward the x-axis, crosses it with a straight region [here, $\psi = 0$, so $\Delta(\text{slope}) = 0$] and continues to curve toward the x-axis until the critical value $x = -x_a$ is reached. Here there is a short straight section, and then it starts to curve *away* from the x-axis, rapidly going to $-\infty$.

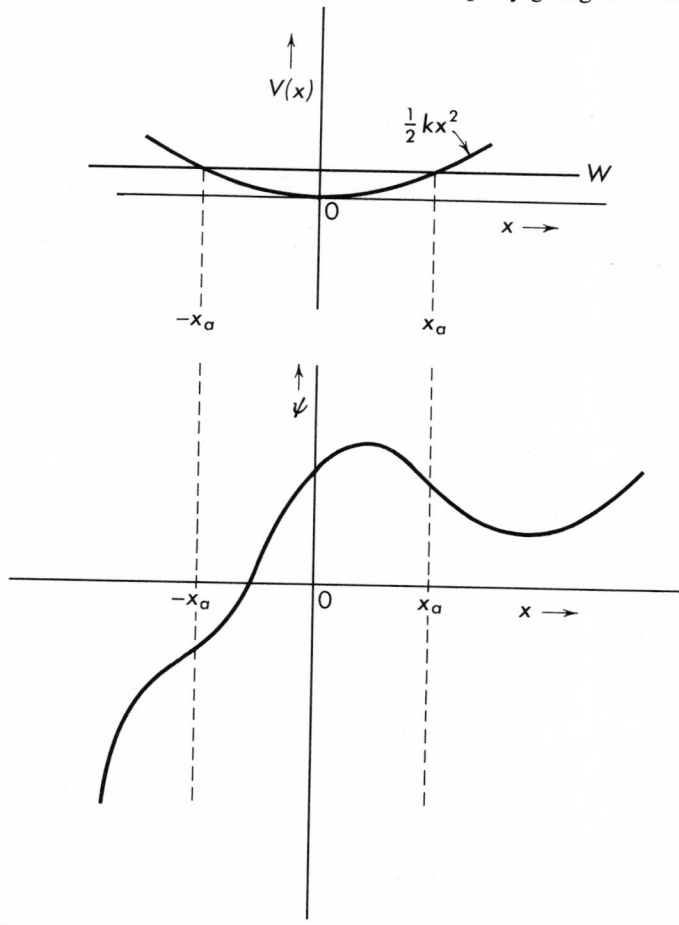

Fig. 3.2. An ill-behaved solution to the wave equation for the harmonic oscillator.

The curve in Figure 3.2, or rather the series of points (if the steps Δx are small enough and the arithmetic calculations are accurate), will be very close to a mathematically exact solution to the simple harmonic oscillator wave equation [3–7]. However, this curve clearly fails to meet the auxiliary requirements and it will therefore not correspond to any real system. ψ must approach zero as $x \to \pm\infty$ for it to be a well-behaved, normalized function.

We make use of the symmetry of the potential function $V(x)$ and note that, if the slope is zero at $x = 0$ (where $\psi = \psi_0$), then, whatever the shape of $\psi(x)$ for positive values of x, it will be mirrored for negative values of x. In Figure 3.3, a particular, numerical example is plotted. Here at $x = 0$, $\psi_0 = 100$, and $(d\psi/dx)_0 = 0$. Also $m = 1.11 \times 10^{-26}$ gm, $k = 10^{+4}$ erg/cm², and three values of W have been used,[4] $W = W_0 = (1/2) \times 10^{-12}$ erg, $W = 1.1\ W_0$

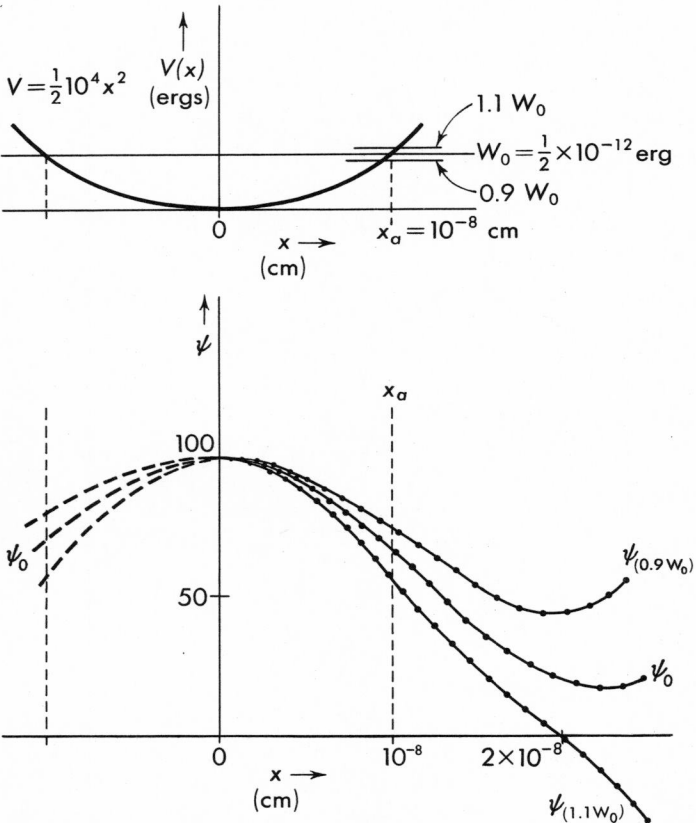

Fig. 3.3. The harmonic oscillator. The numerical calculation of the eigenfunction ψ_0, belonging to the lowest possible system energy, W_0. (Note: ψ_0 does not approach the x–axis only because of the unwanted numerical error.)

---

[4] To save time in numerical calculations we concentrate here on values of W near $(1/2)h\nu$, where ν is $(1/2\pi)\sqrt{k/m}$, the classical frequency of oscillation. That this value is particularly significant is known from the mathematical solution given in Appendix I. With an automatic computer, however, we could find this particular value of W very quickly with no foreknowledge. The method of numerical integration used here is known as Euler's method. See A. A. Bennett, W. E. Milne, and H. Bateman, *The Numerical Integration of Differential Equations* (1956, Dover Pub., Inc., New York): p. 60.

and $W = .9W_0$. The steps, Δx, used in these calculations were 10^{-9} cm. A curve based on twenty steps in the positive x-region is plotted in Figure 3.3.

We illustrate this calculation, using equations [3–8a].

$$\psi_0 = 100 \qquad\qquad\qquad\qquad\qquad\qquad \text{at } x = 0$$

$$\psi_1 = 100 + \underbrace{(0)}_{s_0}\ \underbrace{(10^{-9})}_{\Delta x} = 100 \qquad\qquad\qquad \text{at } x_1 = 10^{-9} \text{ cm}$$

$$\psi_2 = 100 + \left[s_0 - \frac{2m}{\hbar^2}\,(W - [1/2]\,kx_1^2)\,\psi_1\,\Delta x \right]\,\Delta x \qquad \text{at } x_2 = 2 \times 10^{-9} \text{ cm}$$

We insert $W = 1/2 \times 10^{-12}$ ergs

$$k = 10^{+4} \text{ ergs/cm}^2$$

$$\frac{h}{2\pi} = \hbar = 1.05 \times 10^{-27} \text{ erg sec}$$

$$\psi_2 = 100 + \left[(0) - \underbrace{10^{14}\left\{ 100 - \frac{(1 \times 10^{-9})^2}{10^{-18}} \right\}}_{\frac{2m}{\hbar^2}\,(W - [1/2]\,kx_1^2)}\,\underbrace{(100)}_{\psi_1}\,\underbrace{(10^{-9})}_{\Delta x} \right]\,\underbrace{(10^{-9})}_{\Delta x}$$

$$= 100 + \underbrace{[0 - .99 \times 10^9]}_{\text{new slope, } s_1}\,\underbrace{(10^{-9})}_{\Delta x} = 99$$

$$\psi_2 = 99 \qquad\quad s_1 = -.99 \times 10^9, \qquad\quad \text{at } x_2 = 2 \times 10^{-9}$$

$$\psi_3 = 99 + \underbrace{\left[\underbrace{-.99 \times 10^9}_{s_1} - 10^{14}\left\{ 100 - \frac{(2 \times 10^{-9})^2}{10^{-18}} \right\}\,\underbrace{(99)}_{\psi_2}\,\underbrace{(10^{-9})}_{\Delta x} \right]}_{\text{new slope, } s_2}\,\underbrace{10^{-9}}_{\Delta x}$$

which gives the following results:

$$\psi_3 = 97.1 \qquad\quad s_2 = -1.94 \times 10^9, \qquad\quad \text{at } x_3 = 3 \times 10^{-9}$$

If this process is continued for fifteen or twenty steps it will be clear, as Figure 3.3 shows, that the value of W chosen yields a wave function that obeys the wave equation, is everywhere continuous and finite, and possesses an integrable square, as required by the basic postulates.

An infinite number of very small steps would be needed to prove that ψ reaches the x-axis and stays there. In practice, one merely finds a value of W which gives a reasonably small ψ at a reasonably great distance x, and then shows that, on either side of this value of W, the wave function ψ is ill-behaved, but in opposite directions, as in Figure 3.3.

In Figure 3.3 it is clear that ψ_0, belonging to W_0, is heading toward the x-axis in the desired manner, whereas for $W = .9\,W_0$ the wave function ψ curves too gradually in the region $0 \leq x \leq x_a$, intercepting x_a at too high a value. For $x > x_a$ it curves away from the x-axis, but it never quite reaches it, and continuing to curve away from the x-axis, ψ goes to $+\infty$. The ψ belonging to $1.1 \, W_0$ curves too sharply in the region $0 \leq x \leq x_a$ and intercepts $x = x_a$ at too low a value. Even though it now starts curving away from the x-axis, it nonetheless intersects it with finite slope, crosses the axis, and then heads toward $-\infty$.

Thus, values of W slightly above W_0 and slightly below W_0 have wave functions which behave very differently. Both are unsatisfactory.

The satisfactory function, ψ_0, is called an *eigenfunction*, and the corresponding value of W, W_0 is called an *eigenvalue*. ψ_0 and W_0 could have been found by systematic search, using, for example, an automatic computer.

Thus $W_0 = 1/2 \times 10^{-12}$ erg is one possible value of the separation constant W. Indeed it is the lowest possible energy value for this constant since, as can be seen from Figure 3.3, all lower W's will behave similarly to $W = 0.9 \, W_0$.

Postulate V tells us how W_0 is related to the system energy. If many systems with wave function ψ_0 are examined, the average value of the energy will be,

$$\overline{W} = \int_{-\infty}^{+\infty} \Psi_0^* \left(-\frac{\hbar}{i} \frac{\partial}{\partial t} \right) \Psi_0 \, dx$$

and, since here

$$\Psi_0 = \psi_0 \, e^{-i \frac{W_0}{\hbar} t}$$

we have

$$\overline{W} = W_0 \int_{-\infty}^{\infty} \psi_0^2 \, dx$$

We have taken care to insure that $\psi_0^2 \to 0$ rapidly[5] as $x \to \pm\infty$, so that there is a finite area under the curve $\psi_0^2(x)$. We set the scale of the ordinate so as to make

$$\int_{-\infty}^{+\infty} \psi_0^2 \, dx = 1$$

(which is equivalent to multiplying the original $\psi_0(x)$ by some constant), with the result that Postulate IV is satisfied, and thus,

$$\overline{W} = W_0$$

Thus, the expectation value of the energy is just the eigenvalue, W_0.

The expectation value of W^2 for a system with wave function Ψ_0 is

---

[5] If ψ_0^2 (where ψ_0 is taken from Figure 3.3) is plotted against x, the curve will be down to only a few percent of its maximum value when $x = 2x_a$, and will continue to fall rapidly as x increases.

$$\overline{W^2} = \int_{-\infty}^{+\infty} \Psi_0^* \left(-\frac{\hbar}{i}\frac{\partial}{\partial t}\right)\left(-\frac{\hbar}{i}\frac{\partial}{\partial t}\right)\Psi\, dx = W_0^2$$

Thus, σ^2 is zero, and (since $\overline{W^3} = W_0^3$, etc.) W_0 is a certain result. That is, *all* systems with the wave function ψ_0 have the same energy, W_0.

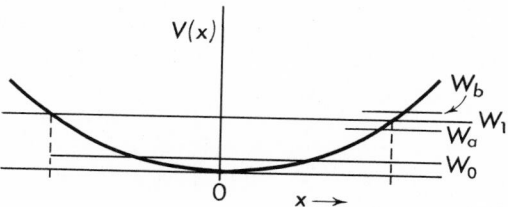

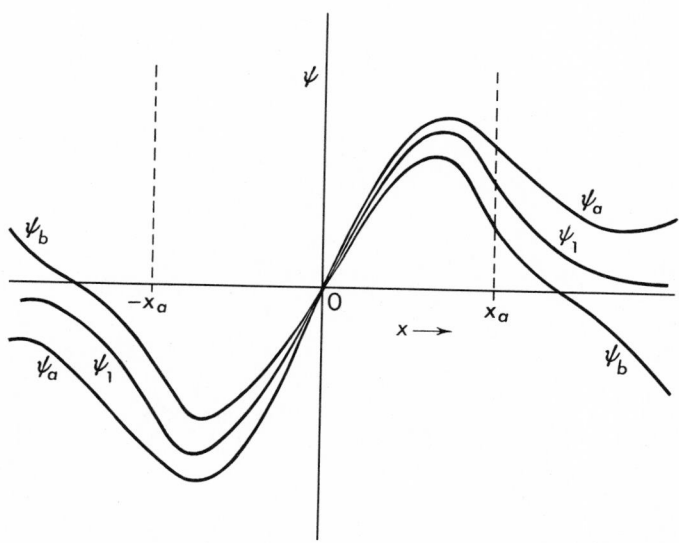

Fig. 3.4. The harmonic oscillator. The first excited state.

The lowest energy, W_0, of a system is called the *zero point energy*. There is no way for ψ-waves of smaller curvature to be associated with a mass m in the potential well of the size and shape specified. Thus, systems simply cannot exist with less energy than W_0.

In Figure 3.4 a different type of symmetry is used. Here, if one starts with $\psi_0 = 0$, and the initial slope is finite, one obtains for ψ, curves for $+x$ and $-x$ of the same shape but of different sign.

To produce this curve, it is clear that a higher total energy, W_1, is needed to provide the sharper curvature between $x = 0$ and $x = x_a$. Only if ψ is heading *toward* the x-axis at $x = x_a$ will it have the possibility of ultimately reaching the x-axis, while always curving away from it. In the figure, three cases are shown, but only one value, $W = W_1$, produces a satisfactory eigenfunction,

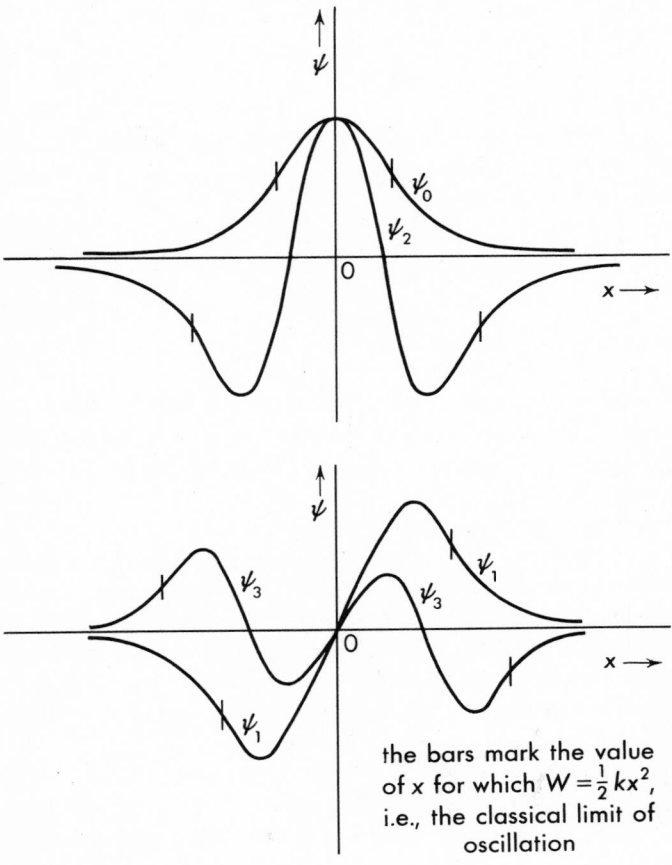

the bars mark the value of x for which $W = \frac{1}{2} kx^2$, i.e., the classical limit of oscillation

Fig. 3.5. The harmonic oscillator. The eigenfunctions belonging to the four lowest energy states.

ψ_1. If searched for by systematic calculation, one finds that the value of W which makes this occur is $W_1 = 3W_0$.

In Figure 3.5 are plotted ψ_0, ψ_1, and, in addition, ψ_2 and ψ_3, the two next higher energy eigenstates.[6] The ψ-functions in Figure 3.5 all have finite

---

[6] A system is said to be in an eigenstate when its characteristic energy has an exactly predictable value, an eigenvalue.

area between ψ^2 and the x-axis, but each will need to be multiplied by a numerical factor to cause the area (under ψ^2) to equal unity as required for a normalized function.

Note that $\psi(x)$ is *always* "heading toward" the x-axis at the classical turning points. Only thus can catastrophe be avoided as x increases without limit.

It is found that $W_2 = 5W_0$ and $W_3 = 7W_0$ and that, in general,

$$W_n = (2n + 1)\, W_0 \qquad\qquad [3\text{-}9$$

where to each W_n belongs a ψ_n. For $n =$ even the x's are all symmetrical about $x = 0$, and for $n =$ odd they are all antisymmetrical about $x = 0$. (If $f(-x) = f(x)$, f is symmetrical. If $f(-x) = -f(x)$, f is antisymmetrical.)

Also, it is always found that $W_0 = (1/2)\, h\nu_0$ where

$$\nu_0 = \frac{1}{2\pi} \sqrt{\frac{k}{m}}$$

the classical frequency of the oscillator. This was true, for example, in the case in Figure 3.3.

Thus—and this is typical—a given system will have a whole family of possible energies (eigenvalues) and possible wave functions (eigenfunctions). Often these families of functions are expressible as simple formulas, but this is not essential, only convenient.

The important point is this: *The quantization of energy of a bound system arises as a natural consequence of the wave equation and the indispensable auxiliary requirements on ψ.* As will be demonstrated, these quantized energy levels are in agreement with experiment. The basic postulates have been found to predict correctly the discrete energy levels in all systems for which the total energy expression (including potential energy, here $V(x)$) is known.

By way of illustrating the above ideas, we now consider light absorption in diatomic molecules.

It is found that the vibrating diatomic molecule has a potential function which is dependent on the separation of the two constituent atoms and which, in a good approximation, is $(1/2)\, k(r - r_0)^2$ where r_0 is their equilibrium separation.

Experimentally, one finds a set of energy levels such as those given by equation [3-9] where $\nu_0 = (1/2\pi)\sqrt{k/\mu}$, and $\mu = m_1 m_2/(m_1 + m_2)$. μ is called the "reduced mass" of the system consisting of two molecules of mass m_1 and m_2, respectively. As we shall see later when we apply the theory to two-body systems (Chapter 4 and Appendix IV), the reduced mass must enter into considerations involving the *relative* motion of two masses which have a mutual potential energy, and, of course, the vibration of two atoms, along the line joining them, is one type of relative motion. When one atom is much heavier than the other, then μ is very nearly equal to the mass of the lighter atom.

Classically, the light atom experiences almost all of the motion, so it is reasonable that its mass should dominate the determination of the set of angular frequencies of vibration $W_n/\hbar$ of the system wave function, $\psi\, e^{-i\frac{W_n t}{\hbar}}$.

If light, covering a continuous range of frequencies from the visible to the infrared, is transmitted through a diatomic gas (such as HCl), it is found

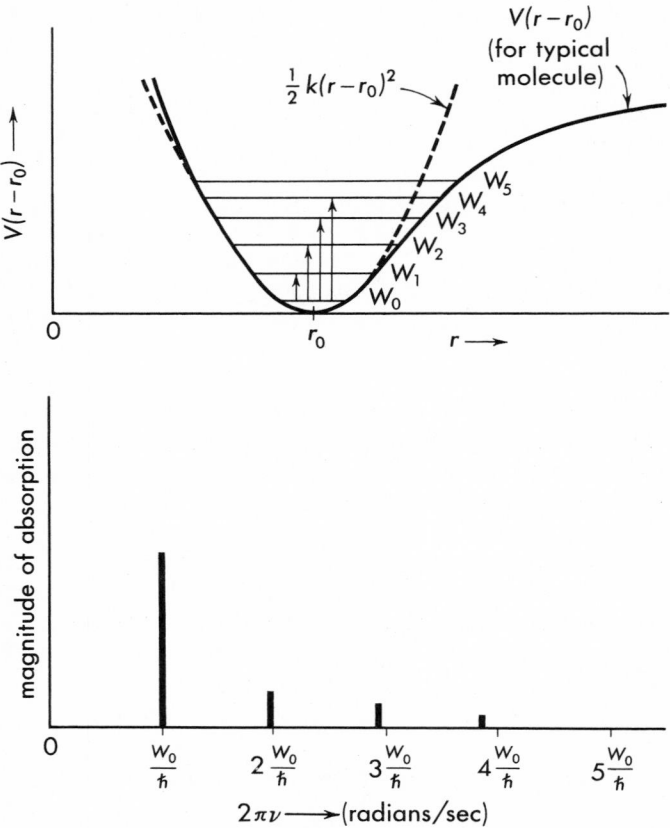

Fig. 3.6. The energy levels and the absorption spectrum of a diatomic molecule (vibration spectrum).

that certain frequencies of light are noticeably attenuated, or absorbed, by the gas. It is possible for the gas molecules to increase their energy of vibration at the expense of energy taken from the light. Classically, such molecules would absorb appreciably only at their resonant frequency, $\nu_0 = (1/2\pi)\sqrt{k/\mu}$, but as can be seen from Figure 3.6, the typical molecule, which is initially in a very low state of vibration (quantum-mechanically, the zero-point state), shows absorption not only at the classical frequency ν_0 (determined by the shape of the absorption curve near the equilibrium separation, $r = r_0$), which is the *difference* between the vibration frequency of ψ_0 and ψ_1, but also at frequencies at nearly twice this frequency, three times this frequency, etc. It is true that the absorption at these higher frequencies is not very great, but it is clearly observable and unmistakably shows the presence of the discrete higher energy states predicted by the quantum theory. (In Chapter 10, Section 10.5, we shall return to this problem, calculate the intensity of the absorption line near $2\nu_0$ relative to that of the strong absorption line at ν_0, and show that the higher frequency absorption line is only possible when the potential energy function $V(r - r_0)$ is not a true parabola.) At large separation distances, as Figure 3.6 shows, $V(r - r_0)$ becomes flat, corresponding to the disappearance of the attractive force. For values of r less than r_0, $V(r - r_0)$ rises somewhat more steeply than does the ideal harmonic oscillator. The net result of this deformation in $V(r - r_0)$ is that the higher values of the energy are depressed somewhat below the values they would have had if the parabolic form of the curve near $r = r_0$ continued to large values of $|r - r_0|$. (Problem 3.4 is concerned with the quantum explanation of this effect.) The nonuniform spacing of the energy levels is the reason for the not-exactly-integral relationship of the absorption frequencies given in Figure 3.6. These deviations permit the experimental determination of the shape of the potential energy curve. This, in turn, gives important information about the nature of the chemical bond. For example, under some conditions, the observation of the "vibration spectra," which we have been discussing here, permits an accurate determination of the binding energy of the molecule (i.e., the value of $V(r - r_0)$ as $r \to \infty$).

In the actual observation of vibration spectra, the effects of the rotation of the molecule are also noticeable, but in spite of this the unique consequences of molecular vibration can be clearly observed. A further discussion of the vibration spectra of diatomic molecules can be found in a book written by G. Herzberg.[7]

3.3. The particle in a one-dimensional box, finite walls

A second simple, one-dimensional system, somewhat divorced from reality but illustrative of the principles of the theory, is a particle in a box with finite walls. The meaning of this expression is best understood by referring to the potential energy curve $V(x)$ in the upper part of Figure 3.7. $V(x)$ is zero for $-x_a \leq x \leq x_a$, and has a constant, finite value, V_0, outside this range. A classical particle will be trapped in this "potential well" when its kinetic energy inside the well is less than V_0. Only when the kinetic energy is larger than V_0 can the particle escape. If $V(x) \to +\infty$ at $x = \pm x_a$, then the walls are infinitely high, and a trapped particle cannot escape no matter what its energy.

---

[7] G. Herzberg, *Molecular Spectra and Molecular Structure* (1939, Prentice-Hall, Inc., New York): pp. 57 and 104ff.

The eigenfunctions, two of which are shown in Figure 3.7, can be found by the same numerical methods we have just discussed. However, the mathematical form of the satisfactory solutions is quite simple here. They illustrate, again, the great importance and significance of the continuity conditions of Postulate III.

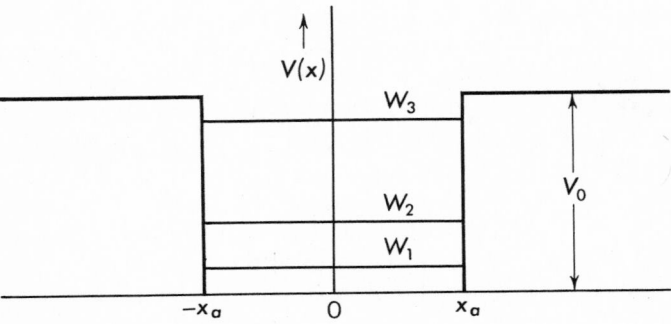

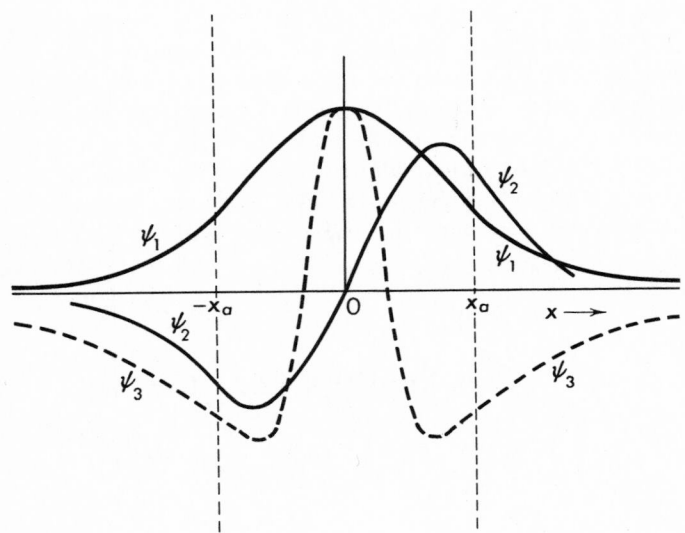

Fig. 3.7. The one-dimensional box with finite walls.

Inside the well $V = 0$, so the wave equation becomes

$$\frac{d^2\psi}{dx^2} + \frac{2m}{\hbar^2} W \psi = 0$$

[3–10

whose general solution, when W is a positive constant, is

$$\psi = A_1 \cos kx + A_2 \sin kx$$

$$k^2 = \frac{2mW}{\hbar^2}, \, k = \frac{2\pi}{\lambda} \qquad\qquad [3\text{--}11$$

where λ is the wavelength of the (standing) waves *inside* the box. The wavelength λ is the distance by which x must be changed in order that $\cos kx$ and $\sin kx$ return to their initial values: $\cos kx = \cos k(x + \lambda)$. We see that large values of W cause large k and small λ.

λ is merely the de Broglie wavelength for the particle inside the well. By [3–11] $\lambda = h/\sqrt{2mW}$, and since inside the well $V = 0$, the total energy, W, is $(1/2)\, mv^2$, so we have $\sqrt{2mW} = mv$, and

$$\lambda = \frac{h}{mv} \qquad\qquad [3\text{--}11a$$

This, of course, is not accidental. Schrödinger "built in " the de Broglie wavelength into the basic wave equation.[8] (Appendix VIII shows how the wave equation of classical physics can be converted into the Schrödinger equation with the aid of de Broglie's relationship.)

Returning to the general wave function [3–11], symmetry requires that either $\cos kx$, *or* $\sin kx$ must be used alone. This can be seen by reference to Figure 3.7 where $\cos kx$ is used for the central part of ψ_1, and for ψ_3, and $\sin kx$ is similarly used for ψ_2. (In Figure 3.7 the k's are different. The sine curve ψ_2 has a larger value of k, a higher characteristic energy W, and shorter wavelength than ψ_1.) The cosine curves are symmetrical about $x = 0$, and the sine curve is antisymmetrical about $x = 0$. If, for either case, the function is well behaved for $x \to +\infty$, then it must also be well behaved for $x \to -\infty$. This would not be true for any mixture of sine and cosine functions. (See Problem 3.17.)

We first consider ψ_1. Inside the well, it has the form

$$\psi_1 = A_1 \cos kx \qquad\qquad [3\text{--}12$$

For $x > x_a$ (and $x < -x_a$) the wave equation is

$$\frac{d^2\psi}{dx^2} + \frac{2m}{\hbar^2}\{W - V_0\}\,\psi = 0 \qquad\qquad [3\text{--}13$$

where $W - V_0$ is now a *negative* constant. This equation has the solution

$$\psi = B_1\, e^{k_1 x} + B_2\, e^{-k_1 x}$$

$$k_1^2 = \frac{-2m}{\hbar^2}(W - V_0) \qquad\qquad [3\text{--}14$$

---

[8] Figure 3.5 shows that the harmonic oscillator wave functions show a periodic tendency related to "wavelength." Since, in this case, the kinetic energy (and therefore mv) is not constant at all values of x, the wavelength is not constant with x.

This solution is not periodic and has no wavelength λ associated with k_1.

Note that [3–11] always curves *toward* the x-axis, and [3–14] always curves *away* from the x-axis. (The harmonic oscillator eigenfunctions show similar behavior in the corresponding regions, as can be seen from Figures 3.3, 3.4, and 3.5.)

For $x > x_a$, only the solution

$$\psi = B_2\, e^{-k_1 x} \qquad\qquad [3–15$$

can apply, since the other solution would make $\psi \to \pm\infty$ as $x \to \infty$, depending on the sign of B_1.

Similarly, for $x < -x_a$, the solution must be

$$\psi = B_1\, e^{+k_1 x} \qquad\qquad [3–16$$

The solution, symmetrical in x, made up of [3–12], [3–15], and [3–16], in the appropriate ranges of x, fully satisfies Postulate II (the wave equation) and partially satisfies Postulate IV (normalization) since the solution, ψ, has a finite area under the x-axis. We have yet, however, to meet the requirement that ψ and $d\psi/dx$ be continuous. This problem arises at $x = -x_a$ and also at $x = +x_a$, where the various sections of the solution join together.

At $x = x_a$ the continuity conditions are,

(amplitude continuous): $\quad A_1 \cos kx_a = B_2\, e^{-k_1 x_a}$ $\qquad\qquad [3–16a$

(slope continuous): $\quad A_1(-k) \sin kx_a = -k_1\, B_2\, e^{-k_1 x_a}$ $\qquad [3–16b$

and, at $x = -x_a$,

(amplitude continuous): $\quad A_1 \cos k(-x_a) = B_1\, e^{k_1(-x_a)}$ $\qquad\qquad [3–16c$

(slope continuous): $\quad A_1(-k) \sin k(-x_a) = k_1\, B_1\, e^{k_1(-x_a)}$ $\qquad [3–16d$

The requirement for normalization is (for the $x > 0$ region)

$$\int_0^{x_a} (A_1 \cos kx)^2\, dx + \int_{x_a}^{\infty} (B_2\, e^{-k_1 x})^2\, dx = 1/2 \qquad [3–16e$$

There are five relationships, and five undetermined constants, A_1, B_2, B_1, k, and k_1. (The unknown, W, appears in both k and k_1.)

Referring to the five equations [3–16] only by letter, we note that (a) and (c) together, and also (b) and (d) together, require that

$$B_1 = B_2 \qquad\qquad [3–17$$

Also, either (a) or (c) alone requires, with [3–17], that

$$\frac{A_1}{B_1} = \frac{e^{-k_1 x_a}}{\cos kx_a} = f_1(W) \qquad\qquad [3–18$$

whereas either (b) or (d) alone requires, with [3–17], that

$$\frac{A_1}{B_1} = \frac{k_1\, e^{-k_1 x_a}}{k \sin k x_a} = f_2(W) \qquad\qquad [3\text{--}19$$

equations [3–18] and [3–19] can *both* be true only if $f_1(W) = f_2(W)$, that is, if

$$\tan k x_a = \frac{k_1}{k}$$

that is,

$$\tan \frac{\sqrt{2mW}}{\hbar}\, x_a = \frac{\sqrt{-\,2m(W - V_0)}}{\sqrt{2mW}} \qquad\qquad [3\text{--}20$$

Since x_a is specified already, the transcendental equation [3–20] fixes the value of $W = W_1$, and thus determines *both* k and k_1. This equation may be solved by graphical means. Thus, the five equations determine the five unknowns, and so the wave function is completely specified for the given $V(x)$. As in the case of the numerical methods, a unique eigenvalue, W_1, is thus selected for the lowest state.

For the wave function of next shortest wavelength, inside the well (ψ_2 of Figure 3.7), one must match at x_a and $-x_a$ a pure sine wave, from equation [3–11], to exponential functions. One obtains the eigenvalue W_2, which belongs to the normalized eigenfunction ψ_2.

The next shortest wavelength eigenfunction, ψ_3 (a cosine wave), is shown as the dotted curve in Figure 3.7. It is matched to the appropriate exponentials in a similar manner to the above, thus locating the next higher eigenvalue, W_3.

It is apparent from Figure 3.7 that if one seeks a still higher eigenvalue, W_4, it is likely to be found above V_0, the height of the well.[9] If $W > V$, ψ must curve toward the x-axis for *all* x, although most sharply in the region $-x_a < x < x_a$. If the potential well stays at V_0 all the way to $+\infty$ and $-\infty$, then the area under the periodic curve $\psi^2(x)$ in the regions $x < -x_a$ and $x > x_a$ will be infinite if the curve $\psi(x)$ has a finite amplitude. If, however, we now assume that at $x = \pm x_b$, there is a further step of adequate size in $V(x)$ (see Fig. 3.8), then the wave function will have the needed exponential form at large positive and negative values of x, producing thereby a curve $\psi^2(x)$, of finite area. In Figure 3.8b the typical shape of such an eigenfunction ψ_n is shown for the potential function in Figure 3.8a, and for the case where $W_n > V_0$. Because of the large value of x_b, it can be shown (see Problem 3.8) that there are many closely spaced energy levels such as W_n, starting just above $W = V_0$.

The low amplitude of ψ_n inside the well indicates that the particle is unlikely to be found there. This agrees with the classical picture, in which the

---

[9] For different m, V_0, or x_a there could be a different number of bound states.

particle has a high velocity when inside the well and thus spends only a small fraction of its time there.

The principles employed in locating states such as ψ_n in Figure 3.8b are exactly the same as those we have used thus far. For $|x| > x_b$ exponential solutions must be used. From x_a to x_b sine or cosine functions with

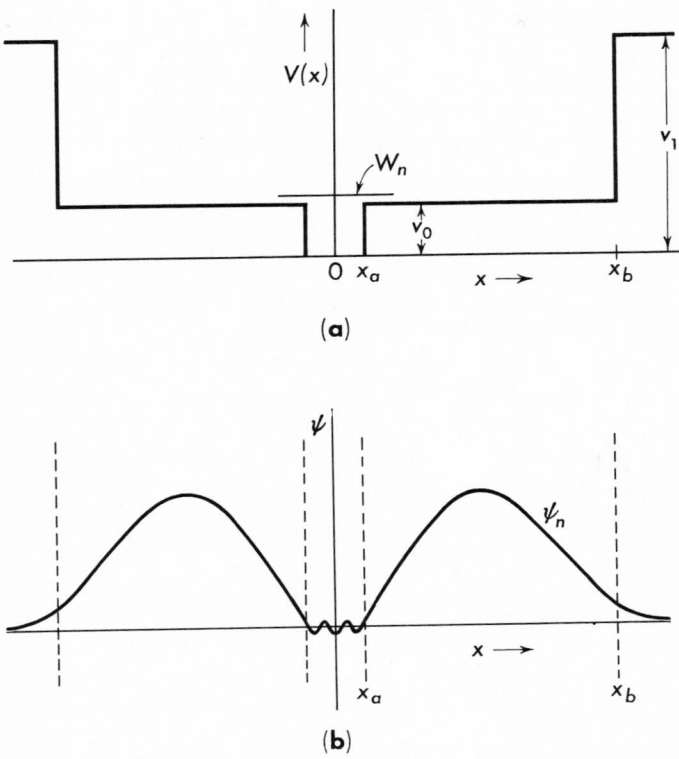

(a)

(b)

Fig. 3.8. The one-dimensional, finite, potential well V_0, with distant boundaries, V_1.

$k_1^2 = (2m/\hbar^2)(W - V_0)$ must be used, and from 0 to x_a sine or cosine functions with $k^2 = (2m/\hbar^2)W$ must be used. A similar solution may be found for the negative x regions.

At $x = -x_b$, $x = -x_a$, $x = x_a$, and $x = x_b$, ψ and $d\psi/dx$ must be continuous. Also, $\displaystyle\int_{-\infty}^{+\infty} \psi^2 \, dx = 1$. These conditions will specify each ψ_n and its associated W_n.

If x_b is very large ($\rightarrow\infty$), there are many closely spaced states, starting at $W = V_0$. These are called the states of the "continuum." We shall, however, never regard the "box" at $\pm x_b$ as being truly infinite, but only large compared to the dimensions, $\pm x_a$, of the small system inside the box. When this is true the energy levels of the system, although *very* closely spaced, are not truly continuous, and the "continuum" is not conceptually different from bound states.

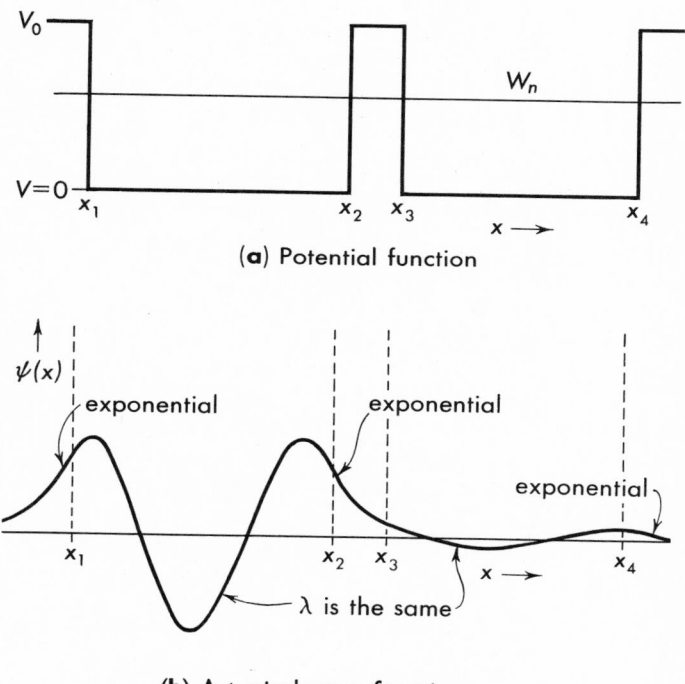

(a) Potential function

(b) A typical wave function

Fig. 3.9.   Two potential wells separated by a finite potential barrier. The wave function in **(b)** is not an eigenfunction, but has the time-varying properties described in Chapter 5.

For the harmonic oscillator (Fig. 3.5) and for the box with finite walls (Fig. 3.7), the wave function extends a considerable distance into the classically forbidden region (beyond the "limits of oscillation" or the "classical turning points"—where W, the total energy, is less than $V(x)$, and where, therefore, the kinetic energy is negative). If ψ^2 (where ψ is normalized) were plotted for each curve in Figures 3.5 and 3.7, the curves are the probability density functions. Thus, ψ^2 predicts that there is a chance of finding the particle in the classically forbidden region. This typically quantum mechanical effect is the basis of the phenomenon of "barrier penetration." In this effect, a particle, known to be trapped behind a barrier too high for it to surmount classically, can, after a sufficient time, have a high probability of being found outside the barrier.

There is much experimental evidence that this penetration phenomenon occurs.

As a qualitative example, consider the one-dimensional system of Figure 3.9. The bound particle has characteristic energy W_n, which is less than V_0. There are, however, *two* regions of positive kinetic energy ($W_n > V$). In Figure 3.9, we see sketched the wave function of one of the many possible eigenstates. As in the previous examples, $\psi(x)$ curves *toward* the x-axis (sinusoidal function) when the kinetic energy is positive, and away from the axis (an exponential function) when the kinetic energy is negative. It is clear from the drawing that both ψ and its slope can be made continuous at every boundary. The classically forbidden region, x_2 to x_3, *because of its limited spacial extent*, does not completely "attenuate" the wave function, ψ. Thus ψ has a finite amplitude on *both* sides of the barrier. For the system in the particular state of Figure 3.9, ψ^2 is much larger inside the left-hand potential well, and the probability is large that, upon examination, the particle will be found there. However, there is also a finite probability of finding the particle in the right-hand well. The particle must be regarded as existing, in the positive kinetic energy state, in *both* wells. Classically, it could only exist in one *or* the other.

The spontaneous emission of an alpha particle from a nucleus is an example of a particle tunneling through a radial potential barrier, of limited radial extension. The vibrating nitrogen atom in the ammonia molecule and "cold emission" electrons are other examples of barrier penetration. The quantitative treatment of these problems can be found in the more advanced textbooks. We wish to observe here that whenever a barrier is finite in height and finite in spacial extension the wave function belonging to a single particle can, and indeed must, penetrate the barrier, if the basic postulates are to be satisfied.

3.4. The box with infinite walls

If the height V_0 of the potential barrier in Figure 3.7 is very large compared to the energy W of the particle, the wave function becomes particularly simple. The exponential part of the wave function ($> x_a$ and $< -x_a$) has a very large attenuation. In the limit, as $V(x) \to \infty$ at $x = \pm x_a$, the exponential section becomes negligible in extent, and the wave function comes to zero at $x = \pm x_a$, having there a discontinuity in slope. This discontinuity produces an unacceptable wave function in the strict sense of the postulates, and indeed infinitely high potential barriers are not observed for real systems.[10] Nevertheless, this assumption is often a good approximation and results in simple

---

[10] A classical particle, upon colliding with an infinitely steep potential barrier, will experience an infinite force.

sine and cosine wave functions based on the wave equation [3–10] (see Fig. 3.10).

In the limit, with infinite walls, Postulate III is reduced to requiring that $\psi = 0$ at the wall. ψ_n now has the same form as the resonant or standing wave modes of the vibrating string with both ends fixed.

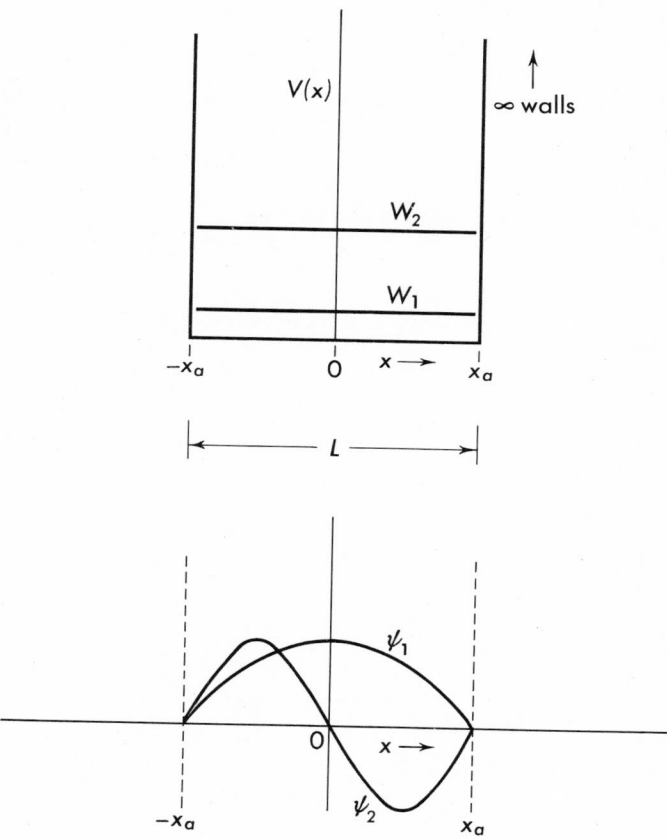

Fig. 3.10. The one-dimensional system with infinite potential barriers.

When analyzing the infinite wall box, it is usually convenient to place the origin at $-x_a$ in Figure 3.10 and consider the box to have a length L ($L = 2x_a$).

Thus the lowest energy state (longest wavelength, $\lambda = 2L$) has the eigenfunction

$$\psi_1 = A_1 \sin \frac{\pi x}{L} \qquad \left(k_1 = \frac{\pi}{L}; \; k_1^2 = \frac{2mW_1}{\hbar^2} \right)$$

The next eigenfunction is

$$\psi_2 = A_2 \sin \frac{2\pi x}{L} \qquad \left(k_2 = \frac{2\pi}{L}; \, k_2^2 = \frac{2mW_2}{\hbar^2} \right)$$

and, in general,

$$\psi_n = A_n \sin \frac{n\pi x}{L} \qquad \left(k_n = \frac{n\pi}{L}; \, k_n^2 = \frac{2mW_n}{\hbar^2} \right) \qquad [3\text{-}21$$

where A_n is given by the normalization requirement

$$\int_0^L A_n^2 \sin^2 \frac{n\pi x}{L} \, dx = 1, \text{ or } A_n = \sqrt{\frac{2}{L}} \qquad [3\text{-}22$$

Thus, the normalized eigenfunctions for the particle in a one-dimensional box with infinite walls at $x = 0$ and $x = L$ are,

$$\psi_n = \sqrt{\frac{2}{L}} \sin \frac{n\pi x}{L}, \; W_n = \frac{n^2 \pi^2 \hbar^2}{2mL^2}$$

and

$$[3\text{-}23$$

$$\Psi_n = \psi_n \, e^{-i\frac{W_n}{\hbar} t}$$

The characteristic energy increases as n^2, as is shown in Figure 3.10 for the first two levels.

3.5. Mathematical description of the eigenfunctions of the harmonic oscillator

We have seen, in Section 3.2, how the eigenfunctions of the amplitude equation for the simple harmonic oscillator can be found by numerical methods. These functions are also derivable by more conventional mathematical methods. A common technique for finding eigenfunctions and their characteristic values, or *eigenvalues*, is given in Appendix I. The results, for the harmonic oscillator, are

$$\psi_n(x) = N_n \, e^{-\xi^2/2} \, H_n(\xi); \; \xi = \sqrt{a} \, x$$

where

$$a = \frac{2\pi m \, \nu_0}{\hbar}$$

and

$$\nu_0 = \frac{1}{2\pi} \sqrt{\frac{k}{m}}; \; \hbar = \frac{h}{2\pi}$$

$$N_n = \left\{ \left(\frac{a}{\pi} \right)^{1/2} \frac{1}{2^n \, n!} \right\}^{1/2}$$

$$W_n = (n + 1/2) \, h\nu_0 \qquad n = 0, 1, 2, 3, \; \cdots$$

and where the $H_n(\xi)$ are the Hermite polynomials. The first five of these are

$$H_0(\xi) = 1$$
$$H_1(\xi) = 2\xi$$
$$H_2(\xi) = 4\xi^2 - 2$$
$$H_3(\xi) = 8\xi^3 - 12\xi$$
$$H_4(\xi) = 16\xi^4 - 48\xi^2 + 12$$

These ψ_n's are normalized to unity, that is,

$$\int_{-\infty}^{+\infty} \psi_n(x)\,\psi_m(x)\,dx = 1 \quad \text{when } n = m$$

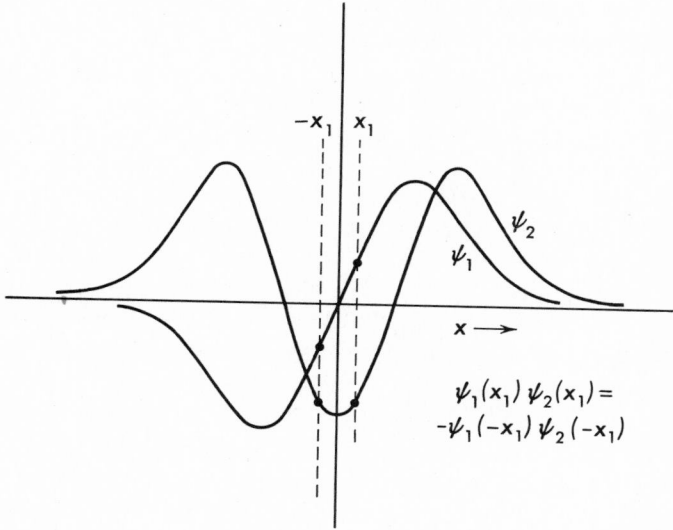

$$\psi_1(x_1)\,\psi_2(x_1) = -\psi_1(-x_1)\,\psi_2(-x_1)$$

Fig. 3.11. Graphical demonstration of the orthogonality of ψ_1 and ψ_2 for the harmonic oscillator.

but it is also true that

$$\int_{-\infty}^{+\infty} \psi_n(x)\,\psi_m(x)\,dx = 0 \quad \text{when } n \neq m$$

Thus, the family of functions $\psi_n(x)$ for the simple harmonic oscillator are normalized and orthogonal.

Families of eigenfunctions for *any* system have the orthogonality property (whenever $W_n \neq W_m$) due to the fundamental nature of the wave equation itself. For this particular system, the orthogonality can be proved for certain cases by simple arguments based on symmetry. In Figure 3.11, ψ_1 and ψ_2 are plotted. Due to the symmetry of ψ_2 about $x = 0$ and the antisymmetry of ψ_1 about $x = 0$, the contribution $\psi_1(x_1)\ \psi_2(x_1)\ \Delta x$, to the integral is exactly *equal and opposite in sign* to the contribution $\psi_1(-x_1)\ \psi_2(-x_2)\ \Delta x$. This is true for any ψ_n with even n multiplied by any ψ_n with odd n. It requires a more general argument to show that the same result holds for all other cases when $n \neq m$.

In Appendix II it is shown from the general form of the wave equation (Postulate II) and the auxiliary requirements upon the wave function (Postulates III and IV) that eigenfunctions belonging to different values of the characteristic energy must always be orthogonal, that is, that $\int \psi_n^* \psi_m\, dx = 0$.

The orthogonality properties of eigenfunctions are extremely important in both the development and the application of quantum theory.

3.6. The correspondence principle

To give a quantitative explanation of the microscopic world of the atom with all its complexity and variety should be triumph enough for quantum mechanics. Newton's mechanics is a very successful theory and is quite satisfactory for the macroscopic world, even though it fails when applied to atomic-sized systems. (For example, classically, there should be only *one* absorption line in the absorption spectrum in Figure 3.6.) Is it too much to expect that quantum mechanics should *also* apply in the macroscopic world?

In 1923, Bohr proposed that any really satisfactory quantum theory (then being sought) must "in the classical limit" gradually approach the results of classical mechanics and classical electricity. When physical systems are in a high degree of excitation, that is, when they are in states that have very large quantum numbers and therefore possess characteristic energies that are large compared to the energy of the lowest state, one should expect that the results of quantum calculations will approach closely the results of classical calculations for the same system. In other words, it was proposed by Bohr that the quantum calculations correspond to the classical calculations at the threshold of the classical domain, and indeed, that the results of quantum theory ought to be experimentally indistinguishable from the results of classical theory inside the established classical domain.

Such a wide range of application for a theory is certainly desirable, although there is no a priori reason why it should be attainable. Quantum mechanics has, remarkably enough, succeeded in including classical mechanics (and classical electricity, by the quantization of the electromagnetic field) within its ken, and the correspondence principle has proved very useful both in guiding the formation of the theory and in extending its boundaries.

In this book we shall consider, on several occasions, the extension of the quantum theory into the classical realm, and one of the most striking examples of the gradual transition from the unfamiliar quantum effects to the familiar classical effects is already within range of our analysis.

As we have seen, $\Psi^*\Psi$ is the probability density function which measures (by Postulate V) the probability that the particle composing the system will be found in any given region. In Figure 3.12, we plot $\Psi^*\Psi(=\psi^*\psi)$ for the four harmonic-oscillator eigenfunctions of Figure 3.5, and also the probability

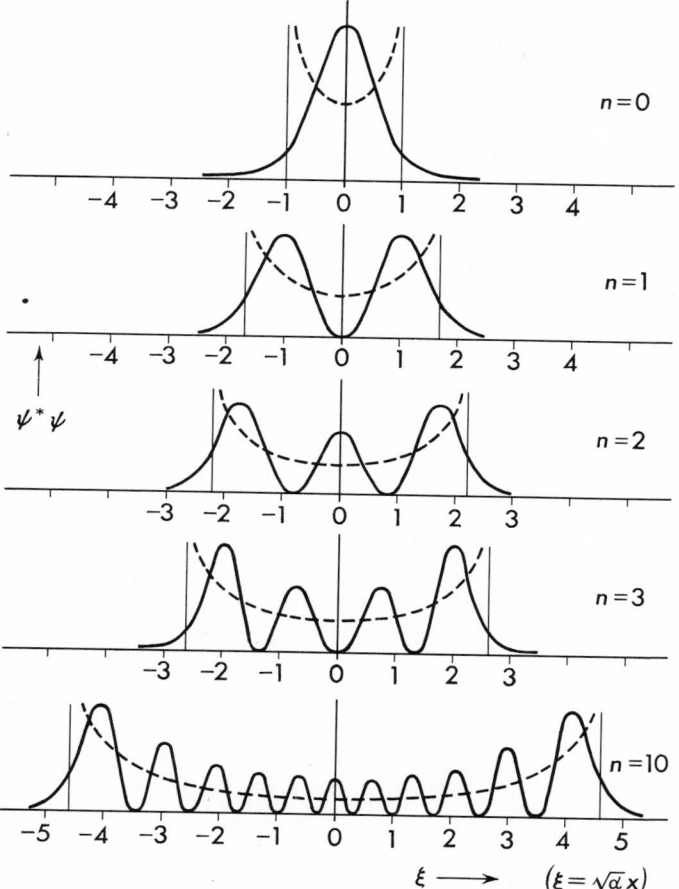

Fig. 3.12. Some sketches of the probability density functions for the harmonic oscillator. The dotted curve in each sketch is the probability density function for the classical oscillator with the same physical constants and the same energy.

density function for Ψ_{10}. Superimposed on these graphs by the dashed lines is the probability density function for the classical harmonic oscillator, obtained in Problem 3.12. The classical oscillator has the greatest probability of being found near one of its turning points. That is, if examined at random time intervals, it will most often be found in the region where its velocity is low.

The probability distribution, as calculated by quantum mechanics, is very unlike the classical distribution for the eigenstate, $n = 0$, but as the quantum number becomes higher and higher, the distribution becomes more and more similar to the classical one. For very large n, except for periodic fluctuations, the quantum mechanical distribution becomes, for all practical purposes, indistinguishable from the classical distribution. (When n is 10^3 or 10^6, these fluctuations would become very difficult to observe experimentally, and truly macroscopic oscillators have quantum numbers much higher than these. See Problem 3.13.)

Thus, when we also view the macroscopic world through the "window of $\Psi^* \Psi$," we find that the picture we see is the familiar one of experience.[11]

It is often (although by no means always) true that the quantum calculation for the macroscopic mechanical system is more difficult than the corresponding classical calculation using Newton's Laws, but it gives the correct result. From electrons to planets, there is only *one* system of mechanics, quantum mechanics.

PROBLEMS

Problem 3.1.   A wave on a string obeys the equation

$$\frac{\partial^2 y}{\partial x^2} = \frac{1}{v^2} \frac{\partial^2 y}{\partial t^2}$$

where v, the velocity of propagation, is $\sqrt{T/\rho}$ ($T =$ tension, and $\rho =$ mass/unit length).

(a) Let $y = f(x) \phi(t)$ and show how the equation separates into two. Let $A =$ the separation constant.

(b) Assume the ϕ equation to have the solution

$$\phi = B\, e^{-i2\pi\nu t}$$

and show that $A = -4\pi^2\, v^2/v^2$

(c) If it is required that $y = 0$ at $x = 0$, and also at $x = L$ (the resonant string), show that the only possible solutions to the original equation are

$$y_n = (\text{const.}) \sin \frac{n\pi x}{L}\, e^{-i2\pi\nu t}; \quad \nu = \frac{nv}{2L}$$

This problem is similar to that of the resonances of a matter wave, Ψ, in the infinite-wall, one-dimensional box, equation [3–23]. Discuss the similarities and differences.

---

[11] A more exact method of describing the macroscopic harmonic oscillator is discussed at the end of Section 5.1.

Problem 3.2. In Figure 3.3, it was shown from numerical calculations that an eigenstate for the harmonic oscillator exists near $W_0 = (1/2) \times 10^{-12}$ erg where $m = 1.11 \times 10^{-26}$ gm, and $k = 10^{+4}$ erg/cm^2.

(a) For the same oscillator, assume that $W = W_1 = (3/2) \times 10^{-12}$ erg, and show by numerical calculations that an eigenstate exists in the neighborhood of this energy. Let $\psi_0 = 0$ and let the initial slope $= 2.0 \times 10^9$. Take $\Delta x = 10^{-9}$ cm. Show the contrasting behavior of ψ for $W = (1.2) W_1$, and $W = (.8) W_1$. [Because $\psi^2 \Delta x =$ pure number, $\Delta\psi/\Delta x$ has units, cm$^{-3/2}$.]

(b) Identify, on the graph, the classical limits of oscillation.

(c) On a second graph, sketch the real part of $\Psi'_1(x, t)$ at several different times.

(d) On a third graph, plot $\Psi_1^* \Psi_1$, the probability density function. Estimate from the graph what fraction of the time one can consider the particle to be outside the classical limits of oscillation.

Problem 3.3. Classically, an elastic ball can bounce on a horizontal surface in a uniform gravitational field with any amount of total energy. Imagine a helium atom ($m = 4 \times 1$ amu., 1 amu. $= 1.66 \times 10^{-24}$ gm) bouncing against gravity, with perfect reflection, on an idealized, perfectly flat, horizontal surface (an infinite-wall barrier), $g = 980$ cm/sec^2.

(a) Draw the potential energy curve for this case, and beneath it sketch the *approximate* form that ψ must have for each of the two lowest energy levels. Indicate the classical turning points (maximum height) on the diagrams. (Remember that $\psi(x)$ must have a negative slope at the classical turning point if it is to avoid catastrophe as $x \rightarrow +\infty$.)

(b) Estimate the *order of magnitude* of W_1, the lowest energy state, and its corresponding classical turning point, $x_1 = W_1/mg$. (Hint: Note that curvature of $\psi(x)$ near $x = 0$ is approximately the same as for the $\psi_1(x)$ which occurs [with no gravitation] with an infinite barrier, both at $x = x_1$ and at $x = 0$, for which case, $W_1 = \pi^2\hbar^2/2 \, mx_1^2$. A numerical calculation, using $\Delta x = (1/5) x_1$, will show that the value of W found this way is slightly too small, but a W which is 20 percent larger than this is too large.)

(c) What will be the classical turning point for an electron ($m = 1/1823$ amu) under these conditions? Actually, the electric charge on the electron (compared to its mass) is so great that an observation of the behavior of an isolated electron in the gravitational field is quite impractical. Any stray electric field, so small as to be unobservable by ordinary means, could completely mask any gravitational effects on the electron.

(d) Using the de Broglie equation, find the wavelength associated with an electron after it has fallen from rest a distance x_1, which is your answer for part (c). Is this consistent with your answer?

(e) Estimate the classical turning point for the lowest energy state of a point mass of 100 gm, bouncing on a hard flat surface.

Problem 3.4. Draw a figure, such as Figure 3.4, and show W_0, W_1 and W_2 and also ψ_0, ψ_1, and ψ_2. Now deform $V(x)$ in the region between W_1 and W_2 so as to make the curve $V(x)$ somewhat more flat (for both $+x$ and $-x$) than the original potential function, $(1/2) kx^2$. Then show qualitatively, with the aid of the sketch and the wave equation, that W_1 and W_2 are closer together than are W_0 and W_1, and that this difference will increase as the magnitude of the deformation increases. (It is by this difference in spectral-line frequencies that the shape of the potential energy curve for a chemical bond is often determined. The $V(x)$'s do become flatter as the vibration amplitude increases, as we have assumed here, but not symmetrically about r_0.)

Problem 3.5. In Problem 3.3 we assumed that the surface upon which the helium atom bounces is flat and merely produces a reflection of the ψ-waves. Real surfaces consist of atoms that are never at rest. These vibrating atoms can collide, classically, with even the slowest incoming helium atoms and give them a considerable velocity. The average velocity of gas molecules coming from a surface is given, by kinetic theory, as $[(1/2) mv^2]_{av} = (3/2) kT$.

Suppose that the surface with which the helium atoms collide consists of many bound hydrogen atoms which, spectroscopic evidence shows, have a characteristic absorption (or emission) of light of frequency $\nu = 10^{14}$ cps. (We assume that the H atoms are bound to a heavy rigid structure, and also that they vibrate independently, perpendicular to the surface.)

(a) Calculate the zero-point energy of the vibrating H atoms. Compare this to the lowest energy state of the bouncing helium atom.

(b) Suppose the surface were so cold that only these zero-point vibrations occur (i.e., $kT \ll h\nu$ where k is Boltzmann's constant). Why must the bouncing helium atom be completely ignored by these relatively energetic H atoms?

Problem 3.6. A particle of nucleonic mass (1.66×10^{-24} gm) is trapped in an infinite-wall, one-dimensional potential well, of width 10^{-13} cm (the typical diameter of a small nucleus).

(a) Calculate the force that this particle must be exerting on the wall when the particle is in its lowest energy state. Convert this force into pounds to get an appreciation of its magnitude. Does this give body to the qualitative statement, "nuclear forces are very powerful"? (Hint: Assume the width of the well is slowly decreased by an amount Δx, and calculate the new characteristic energy. Force $= -\Delta W/\Delta x$.)

(b) Calculate the average force that a classical particle of the same mass and energy will exert on the walls of the box.

(c) Calculate W_1, W_2, and W_3 for this system. Convert your results into electron volts.

(d) Calculate W_1 when $m = 9.1 \times 10^{-28}$ gm, the electron mass, and discuss the possibility of binding electrons inside a nucleus.

Problem 3.7

(a) Show from semiqualitative arguments that the stationary state near 10 e.v. is the only one available for an electron in a one-dimensional square potential well, 20 e.v. deep and 10^{-8} cm wide.

(b) Find the normalized, time-dependent wave function.

(c) Find the energy of this state.

Problem 3.8. Assume the potential well of Problem 3.7 is centered at $x = 0$ and that $V = 0$ inside the well. At $+500 \times 10^{-8}$ and -500×10^{-8} cm, add, as in Figure 3.8, a new potential barrier, extending from 20 e.v. to $+\infty$. We examine the states just above 20 e.v.

(a) Show by means of a graph that a wave function whose wavelength is about 2000×10^{-8} cm in the region outside the small well, *cannot* be made to meet the continuity requirements on both ψ and $d\psi/dx$ at $x = \pm (1/2) \times 10^{-8}$ cm.

(b) Show that a wave function whose wavelength is very nearly 1000×10^{-8} cm exterior to the small well, can be made to fit smoothly to a cosine wave of much shorter wavelength centered at $x = 0$. (Hint: Use the fact that λ, outside the narrow well, is to very high accuracy a constant, no matter what amplitude the wave function has inside the narrow well.)

(c) Find the energy of this state.

(d) Find the ratio of interior maximum amplitude to exterior maximum amplitude of ψ.

(e) On examining this system at random, what is the probability that the electron will be found in the small well?

Problem 3.9. In Problem 1.2 the index of refraction of electrons was mentioned. Consider an energy level of the system of Problem 3.8 which is somewhere in the neighbourhood of $W = 120$ e.v., so that outside the small well the electron kinetic energy is *about* 100 e.v. and has a characteristic wavelength λ_0.

(a) Approximately, how much shorter is the wavelength λ_i, inside the small well? List the conditions that must be met if a satisfactory wave function exists. (It is not necessary to find the mathematical form of this wave function, but a sketch should be drawn, illustrating the general appearance of a wave function corresponding to a system energy of about 120 e.v.)

Problem 3.10. Equation [3–23] gives the complete wave function for the one-dimensional particle in a box with infinite walls. Calculate for the lowest state the expectation value of

(a) The total energy W and also W^2,

(b) The coordinate x and also x^2,

(c) The momentum p and also p^2. (Note: it is not usually true that $\overline{p^2} = 2m\overline{W}$.)

Note: A squared operator is applied twice in succession.

(d) Which of these expectation values represents a sharp, or certain, result?

(e) Repeat these calculations for the next state of higher energy.

(f) Plot the probability density function for each case and discuss the results of (b) and (c) in the light of this graph.

Problem 3.11. In Chapter 3, including the problems, we have analyzed five one-dimensional, bound systems: (1) The harmonic oscillator. (2) The particle in a box, infinite barrier. (3) The particle in a box, finite barrier. (4) The particle in a box with a central, short-range, finite potential well. (5) The bouncing mass in the earth's gravitational field. For each case, compare qualitatively, with the aid of graphs, the classical and quantum solutions (for the lowest n, and also for $n \gg 1$) with respect to (a) energy spectrum and (b) the probability of finding the particle, as a function of x.

Compare quantitatively, wherever possible, the classical frequency of each system with the frequency of vibration of the wave function ψ, in the lowest energy state. What happens as the system energy increases? Do these two frequencies appear to have any simple relationship?

Problem 3.12. Calculate the probability distribution function of the classical harmonic oscillator. Suggestion: Consider the projection, on the *x*-axis, of a point on the rim of a uniformly rotating wheel. The wheel is examined at random intervals, and the location of the point on the rim is noted. (The calculation is basically the same as that in Problem 2.2. One calculates the probability that *x* will lie in the range *x* to $x + dx$.)

Problem 3.13. Show that a harmonic oscillator, so small that it can only be observed with the aid of a microscope, does not demonstrate quantum phenomena. Assume that a small object, about 10^{-4} cm in diameter, with a mass estimated at 10^{-12} gm, is observed under a microscope to vibrate on the end of a very small fiber. It has a frequency of 100 cycles per second and a maximum aplitude of 10^{-3} cm.

(a) What is the approximate quantum number for the system in the state described?
(b) What would be its energy, in electron volts, if it were in its zero-point vibration? (Note: At room temperature, typical molecules have an average energy of about 1/40 e.v.)
(c) What would be its classical turning point if it were in its lowest possible state? Compare this distance with the wavelength of visible light (about 5000×10^{-8} cm).

Problem 3.14. The experimental infrared absorption spectrum of HCl^{35} has the following set of lines: 2886 cm^{-1}, 5668 cm^{-1}, 8347 cm^{-1}, and 10993 cm^{-1}, the first being very strong, and the others progressively weaker (see Herzberg, *op. cit.*, p. 57). [The unit cm^{-1} refers to "wave number," or $1/\lambda$, the number of waves per cm in the light. Wave number $= v/c$, and $E = h\nu$, so that wave number $= E(\text{ergs})/h(\text{erg sec}) c(\text{cm/sec})$ or wave number (cm^{-1}) $= (5.0 \times 10^{15}) \times E$ (in ergs).]

(a) Construct the energy level diagram for the lowest vibrational levels of HCl^{35}.
(b) Calculate the force constant, *k*, characteristic of this molecule near its equilibrium separation. $m_H = 1$ amu, and $m_{Cl} = 35$ amu, where 1 amu $= 1.66 \times 10^{-24}$ gm.
(c) From the line spacings in the rotational spectrum (see Herzberg, *op. cit.*, p. 86) r_0 has been measured to be 1.3×10^{-8}

cm. Using the value of k above (and assuming $k = $ constant), calculate the energy in e.v. needed to separate the atoms by an additional 10^{-8} cm. Compare your result with the fact that typical chemical bonds are a few electron volts.

(d) From the spectral data, set a lower limit to the binding energy of the molecule.

Problem 3.15.   *The Comparison of the Classical and Quantum Vibrators for the Nonparabolic Potential Energy Curve.*   Figure 3.6 shows that the potential energy curve of the typical diatomic molecule (such as HCl) is parabolic only near the equilibrium point, and flattens out at large values of r.

(a) Qualitatively, how will the frequency of vibration of the classical oscillator vary as its total energy increases?

(b) Assume that many such classical oscillators have their energy values distributed over a range large enough to extend into the nonparabolic region of the potential energy curve, and sketch the shape of the absorption (or emission) spectrum near ν_0.

(c) According to quantum mechanics (see Section 10.4 and 10.5) the (approximate) harmonic oscillator tends to shift only one level in energy when absorbing or emitting radiation. (It tends to obey the selection rule, $\Delta n = \pm 1$.) Sketch the quantum spectrum in the neighborhood of ν_0 for an assembly of oscillators whose characteristic energy values range over a number of quantum states, and compare it to the classical spectrum.

The comparison of the classical and quantum oscillators near $2\nu_0$, $3\nu_0$, etc., is considered in Section 10.5. We note here, however, that if the classical oscillator has a very low energy it moves in a nearly perfect parabolic potential and cannot absorb measurable energy at any frequency except ν_0.

Problem 3.16.   Show, using qualitative arguments based upon the curvature characteristics of $\psi(x)$ required by the wave equation, that as long as m, x_a, and V_0 are not zero for the system in Figure 3.7, there is always at least one bound state.

Problem 3.17.   Show, using graphical arguments, that if the wave function inside the finite-wall potential well of Figure 3.7 is the sum of both sine and cosine terms as in [3–11], it cannot meet the requirement of the integrable square.

Problem 3.18.   A particle of mass m slides without friction in the potential well formed by two inclined planes in the gravitational field of the earth ($g = 980$ cm/sec²), as shown in Figure 3.13. $\theta = 0.1$ radian.

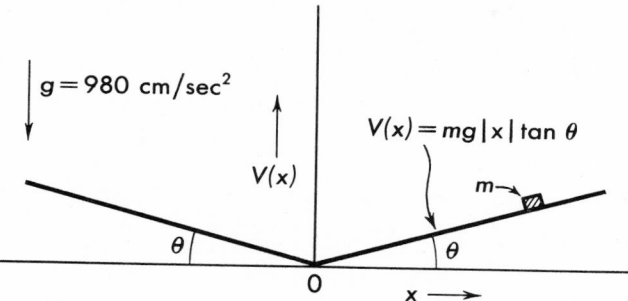

Fig. 3.13.   A particle of mass m oscillating between two inclined planes in the gravitational field.

(a)   Sketch the form of two eigenfunctions belonging to the two lowest energy states.

(b)   Estimate a value of W suitable for an initial trial value in the numerical search for W_0, the lowest energy. (Suggestion: Try a value of W which would give a free-space wavelength λ such that $\lambda/2 = 2x_a$ where $x_a =$ the classical turning point given by $W = mgx_a \tan \theta$.) Let $m = 1$gm.

(c)   Divide x_a into about four or five intervals, and try, using numerical calculations, the value of W selected in (b).

(d)   For $n \gg 1$, sketch $\psi_n^* \psi_n$. Using the correspondence principle, calculate, except for a constant factor, the shape of the envelope of the curve $\psi_n^* \psi_n$ for $n \gg 1$. (Note: Classically, the probability of finding a particle in a particular interval x to $x + dx$ is proportional to $(1/v)$, where v is the classical velocity in the interval.)

THE WAVE EQUATION IN
THREE DIMENSIONS

Thus far, we have considered only one-dimensional systems. Of these, only the harmonic oscillator (such as the vibrating molecule) is observed in nature. Although one-dimensional systems illustrate most of the quantum-mechanical features, there are some features—such as the quantization of angular momentum—which need two or more dimensions before they make their appearance.

Unfortunately, three-dimensional systems usually involve considerable geometrical complexity. However, such systems—for example, the hydrogen atom—are of great theoretical and practical importance. For an adequate appreciation of quantum mechanics, it is essential, therefore, to solve some of the more simple three-dimensional problems.

4.1. The basic postulates for three dimensions and two particles

Postulate I
    The wave function Ψ for a single particle moving in three dimensions is a function of x, y, z, and t.

Postulate II
    The additional substitutions of operators for the dynamical

variables p_y and p_z are:

$$p_y = mv_y \rightarrow \frac{\hbar}{i}\frac{\partial}{\partial y}$$

$$p_z = mv_z \rightarrow \frac{\hbar}{i}\frac{\partial}{\partial z}$$

[4–1]

and the Schrödinger wave equation becomes

$$-\frac{\hbar^2}{2m}\left(\frac{\partial^2 \Psi}{\partial x^2} + \frac{\partial^2 \Psi}{\partial y^2} + \frac{\partial^2 \Psi}{\partial z^2}\right) + V(x, y, z)\, \Psi = -\frac{\hbar}{i}\frac{\partial \Psi}{\partial t}$$

[4–2]

Postulate III

$\Psi\,(x, y, z, t)$ *and* $\dfrac{\partial \Psi}{\partial x}$, $\dfrac{\partial \Psi}{\partial y}$, *and* $\dfrac{\partial \Psi}{\partial z}$ *are finite, continuous, and single valued throughout "configuration space"[1] (here, all values of x, y, and z).*

Postulate IV

The requirement of the integrable square becomes

$$\iiint \Psi^* \,\Psi\, d\tau = 1$$

[4–3]

where $d\tau$ = volume element (for example, $d\tau = dx\,dy\,dz$).

Postulate V

The expectation value $\bar{\alpha}$ of the dynamical variable α is

$$\bar{\alpha} = \iiint \Psi^* \,\alpha_{(op)}\, \Psi\, d\tau$$

[4–4]

Water waves, sound waves, and electromagnetic waves—although having different wave equations—all meet the requirements of Postulates III and IV. In Chapter 2 (see Fig. 2.1) we discussed the behavior of a packet of waves propagating along a rope. We pointed out that there are neither infinite amplitudes nor infinite slopes for such waves. Also, for a fixed amount of energy used in forming the wave (each element of the rope contains energy when the wave is passing through it), the wave train must have a finite length.

---

[1] "Configuration space" is a term referring to the spatial coordinates of the wave function. To a single particle, located at x, y, and z in physical space there belongs a wave function Ψ, dependent upon x, y, and z, in "configuration space." For the single particle, both physical space and configuration space have the three ordinary dimensions. As we shall see below, however, when there are *two* particles located in the physical space x, y, and z, the wave function depends upon *six* spatial variables (the three coordinates of each particle). One then speaks of Ψ as being defined in a six-dimensional "configuration space," since the value of Ψ can be determined only after specifying all six spatial variables.

A two-dimensional example of a wave packet which shows these features in a very graphic manner is the spreading ring of wavelets that is formed by a stone dropped into a still pond. The spreading ring of wavelets can be seen to obey Postulates III and IV, for two dimensions. Let $\Psi(x, y, t)$ be the amplitude of the wave at any point x, y on the horizontal plane, at any time t. A study of the spreading ring due to the initial impact of the stone will show that Ψ, $\partial\Psi/\partial x$, and $\partial\Psi/\partial y$ are all finite and continuous everywhere. This seems obvious upon casual observation, but one could, if necessary, take stereoscopic photographs of the ring of wavelets at any instant and with suitable instruments measure the quantities listed, to demonstrate, experimentally, their finiteness and continuity.

One can see, qualitatively, that $\int\int_{-\infty}^{+\infty} \psi^2 \, dx \, dy$ is finite at any stage of expansion of the ring (that is, at any time t). The waves have zero amplitude inside the ring, and, of course, zero amplitude outside the ring in the region to which the disturbance has not yet reached. Such a ring of wavelets is observed to decrease steadily in amplitude as it spreads to larger and larger radii. It can be demonstrated both theoretically and experimentally that, for a loss-less medium, $\int\int_{-\infty}^{+\infty} \psi^2 \, dx \, dy$ is constant at all stages of the expansion.

Another feature of the spreading ring of water wavelets caused by a sudden disturbance is strikingly similar to matter waves. The individual waves travel faster than the main ring, or group, of waves. One can observe a given wave which seems to arise out of nothing on the inside edge of the spreading ring and watch it grow in size, moving ever outward, at a velocity greater than that of the ring itself. On reaching the middle of the main ring, the wave being followed by the eye gradually decreases in amplitude, finally sinking into nothing out in front of the main ring. For small-amplitude water waves, the velocity of propagation of an individual wave is twice that of the main ring or "group" of waves. The "group" consists of a whole succession of individual waves, each of which is going through the same process of growth and decay that we have just described. For (non-relativistic) matter waves, the velocity of the individual waves (or "phase velocity") is lower than the velocity of the group, the "group velocity."

The quantitative mathematical analysis of wave packets will be discussed briefly in Chapter 5. We mention the water-wave packets because they provide a graphic link between the qualities of the macroscopic observable waves and those of the matter waves[2] whose existence we must infer by more indirect means.

A system of water waves with fixed boundaries, such as the stationary

---

[2] An excellent discussion of wave packets and de Broglie waves is found in D. Bohm, *Quantum Theory* (1951, Prentice-Hall, Inc., N.Y.): p. 59.

pattern of ripples in a pan of water, also has everywhere a finite slope, a continuous amplitude, and an integrable square.

We now consider the extension of the basic postulates to two-particle systems.

If a system consists of two particles mass m_1 located at x_1, y_1, and z_1, at t, and mass m_2 located at x_2, y_2, and z_2, at t, then

$$\Psi = \Psi(x_1, y_1, z_1, x_2, y_2, z_2, t).$$

The wave equation now involves these seven variables, and the volume element $d\tau$ involves the products of the differentials of the six spatial variables,

$$d\tau = dx_1\, dy_1\, dz_1\, dx_2\, dy_2\, dz_2.$$

It is only reasonable to expect that when two particles compose a system the wave function must depend upon both. Each particle can be regarded as possessing kinetic and potential energy, and also as having a position in physical space. The systematic application of Postulate I, the substitution of operators for dynamical variables, automatically gives wave equations which, for two particles, have six spatial variables. At every time t, Ψ is regarded as having a definite value at every point in six-dimensional configuration space.

The probability interpretation of $\Psi^* \Psi\, d\tau$ can be readily extended to the two-particle system.

We have already noted that for the single particle,

$$\Psi^*(x, y, z, t)\, \Psi(x, y, z, t)\, d\tau$$

is the probability that at time t the particle will be found in the particular volume element $d\tau$, that is, that x will lie between x and $x + dx$, y will lie between y and $y + dy$, and z will lie between z and $z + dz$.

For two particles, $\Psi^* \Psi\, d\tau$ is the probability that at time t each of the six variables lies in the range specified by the volume element

$$d\tau = dx_1\, dy_1\, dz_1\, dx_2\, dy_2\, dz_2$$

in configuration space. This means that particle 1 will be found in $dx_1\, dy_1\, dz_1$ of physical space, and particle 2 will be found in $dx_2\, dy_2\, dz_2$ of physical space, at the same instant$_t$.

The complete set of Postulates for two particles and three dimensions is shown on the end-papers.

It is apparent that quantum-mechanical calculations become rapidly more difficult as the number of dimensions and the number of particles increase—but this is also true of classical mechanics. In practice, only certain simple cases involving a high degree of symmetry can be solved exactly. Two of these, the particle inside a rectangular box and the hydrogen atom, will be discussed in this chapter.

4.2. The particle in a rectangular box

We consider the potential function $V(x, y, z)$ to be zero inside a box bounded by $x = 0$ and $x = a$, $y = 0$ and $y = b$, and $z = 0$ and $z = c$. Outside of these bounds V is a positive constant, V_1, V_2, or V_3. This potential function can be expressed (approximately but with simplicity) as follows:

$$V(x, y, z) = V_x(x) + V_y(y) + V_z(z) \qquad [4\text{--}5$$

where

$$V_x(x) = 0 \text{ for } 0 \leq x \leq a, \text{ and } V_1 \text{ elsewhere}$$
$$V_y(y) = 0 \text{ for } 0 \leq y \leq b, \text{ and } V_2 \text{ elsewhere}$$
$$V_z(z) = 0 \text{ for } 0 \leq z \leq c, \text{ and } V_3 \text{ elsewhere}$$

The wave equation becomes

$$-\frac{\hbar^2}{2m} \left[\frac{\partial^2 \Psi}{\partial x^2} + \frac{\partial^2 \Psi}{\partial y^2} + \frac{\partial^2 \Psi}{\partial z^2} \right] + [V_x(x) + V_y(y) + V_z(z)] \Psi = -\frac{\hbar}{i} \frac{\partial \Psi}{\partial t} \quad [4\text{--}6$$

Let

$$\Psi = \psi(x, y, z) \, \phi(t) \qquad [4\text{--}6a$$

As before (see Section 3.1), the equation separates into two parts, one a function of x, y, and z and the other a function of t. Set each equal to a constant W. The time-dependent equation is identical to [3–3] and has the same solution, [3–5],

$$\phi(t) = e^{-i \frac{W}{\hbar} t} \qquad [4\text{--}6b$$

The amplitude equation is

$$\frac{\partial^2 \psi}{\partial x^2} + \frac{\partial^2 \psi}{\partial y^2} + \frac{\partial^2 \psi}{\partial z^2} + \frac{2m}{\hbar^2} \{W - V_x(x) - V_y(y) - V_z(z)\} \psi = 0 \qquad [4\text{--}7$$

We assume that ψ is the product of three functions, each dependent upon only one variable.

$$\psi(x, y, z) = X(x) \cdot Y(y) \cdot Z(z) \qquad [4\text{--}8$$

Substituting this expression into [4–7] and dividing by $X(x) \, Y(y) \, Z(z)$, we have

$$\underbrace{\frac{\hbar^2}{2m} \frac{1}{X(x)} \frac{d^2 X(x)}{dx^2} - V_x(x)}_{\text{function of } x \text{ only}} + \underbrace{\frac{\hbar^2}{2m} \frac{1}{Y(y)} \frac{d^2 Y(y)}{dy^2} - V_y(y)}_{\text{function of } y \text{ only}}$$

$$\underbrace{+ \frac{\hbar^2}{2m} \frac{1}{Z(z)} \frac{d^2 Z(z)}{dz^2} - V_z(z)}_{\text{function of } z \text{ only}} = -W \qquad [4\text{--}9$$

Since [4–9] must be true for all values of the three independent variables x, y, and z, it is necessary that *each* of the three parts equals a constant. Let the x-dependent part equal a constant $-W_x$, and let the other parts equal the constants $-W_y$ and $-W_z$, respectively. Thus

$$W_x + W_y + W_z = W \qquad\qquad [4\text{-}10$$

and [4–9] becomes three ordinary differential equations,

$$\frac{d^2\, X(x)}{dx^2} + \frac{2m}{\hbar^2}\{W_x - V_x(x)\}\, X(x) = 0$$

$$\frac{d^2\, Y(y)}{dy^2} + \frac{2m}{\hbar^2}\{W_y - V_y(y)\}\, Y(y) = 0 \qquad\qquad [4\text{-}11$$

$$\frac{d^2\, Z(z)}{dz^2} + \frac{2m}{\hbar^2}\{W_z - V_z(z)\}\, Z(z) = 0$$

Thus we start with the wave equation [4–6], which is of second order in x, y, and z and first order in t, and end up with four separated, ordinary differential equations. This is possible because of the form of the original equation, particularly the fact that $V(x, y, z)$ was a sum of terms each dependent upon only *one* of the three space variables and also independent of t.

Unless the wave equation can be "separated," as is done here, it is unlikely that a simple mathematical expression for the wave functions can be found. Here, however, each equation can be solved individually and a "formula" for $\Psi(x, y, z, t)$ can be formed from the product of the four individual solutions.

Even though only a few physical systems can be treated in a complete manner, these cases are of great importance since they form the foundation upon which rest the (approximate) solutions for more complex systems. In later chapters we shall use, on many occasions, the eigenfunctions of the particle in a box.

For ψ to be well behaved and to meet the integrable square requirement (Postulates III and IV), it is necessary that $X(x)$, $Y(y)$, and $Z(z)$ *each* meet these requirements. The problem in each coordinate becomes identical to the problem of the one-dimensional, finite, potential well discussed in Chapter 3. If the potential "walls" are infinite (an idealization), then $X(x) = 0$ at $x = 0$ and at $x = a$, $Y(y) = 0$ at $y = 0$ and $y = b$, and $Z(z) = 0$ at $z = 0$ and $z = c$. There is now a discontinuity in the slope at the boundaries due to the infinite walls (which, of course, are not realized in real physical systems).

Although either sine or cosine functions of x, y, or z are mathematically acceptable solutions to [4–11], for the infinite-wall box with the origin at one corner only the sine functions have the necessary zero amplitude at the boundaries. (See the discussion of the infinite-wall, one-dimensional box in Section 3.4.)

For the infinite-wall box, any integral number n_x of half wavelengths can be fitted into the x-dimension of the potential well. The normalized $X(x)$

eigenfunctions are

$$X_{n_x}(x) = \sqrt{\frac{2}{a}} \sin \frac{n_x \pi x}{a} \qquad 0 \le x \le a$$

$$W_{n_x} = \frac{n_x^2 \, \hbar^2 \, \pi^2}{2ma^2} \qquad n_x = 1, 2, 3, 4, \cdots$$

[4–12

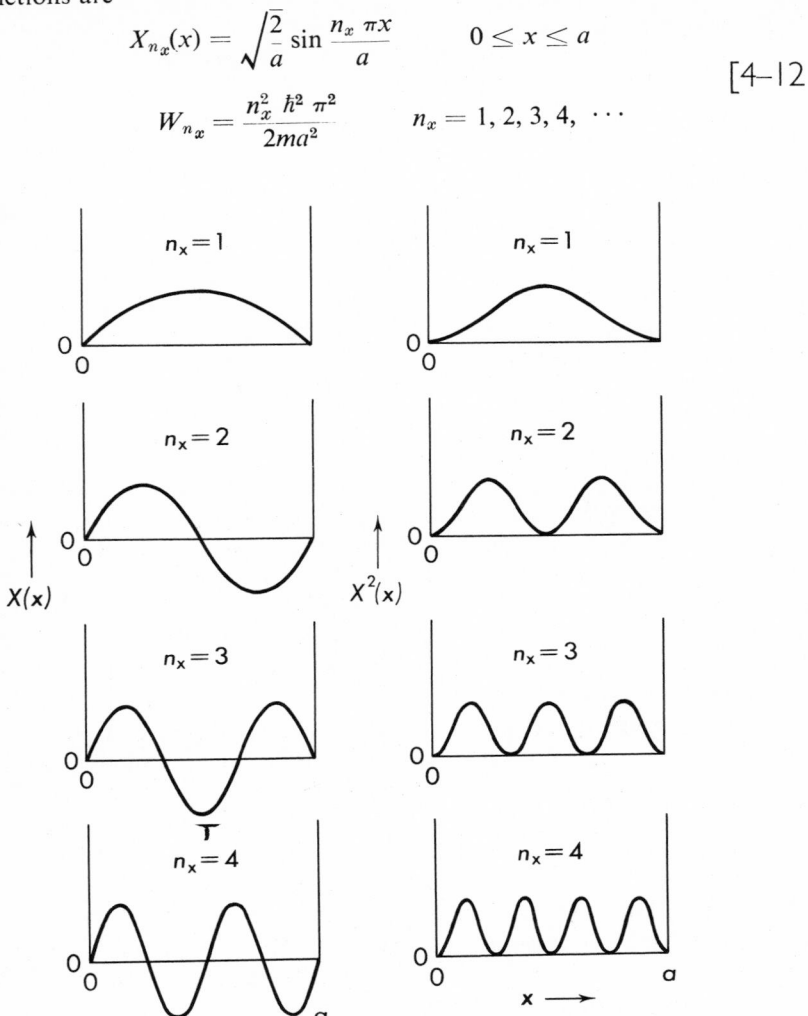

Fig. 4.1. The x-dependent eigenfunctions of a particle in an infinite-wall rectangular box of three dimensions.

The first four of the functions X are plotted in Figure 4.1, along with X^2, which measures the probability density along the x-axis. Similar eigenfunctions exist for Y and Z. Therefore, by [4–8],

$$\psi_{n_x \, n_y \, n_z}(x, y, z) = \sqrt{\frac{8}{abc}} \sin \frac{n_x \pi x}{a} \sin \frac{n_y \pi y}{b} \sin \frac{n_z \pi z}{c}$$

[4–13

where n_x, n_y, and n_z *independently* may have any of the values $1, 2, 3, 4, \cdots$, and where

$$W_{n_x\, n_y\, n_z} = W_{n_x} + W_{n_y} + W_{n_z} = \frac{\hbar^2\,\pi^2}{2m}\left(\frac{n_x^2}{a^2} + \frac{n_y^2}{b^2} + \frac{n_z^2}{c^2}\right) \qquad [4\text{-}14$$

$$\Psi_{n_x\, n_y\, n_z} = \psi_{n_x\, n_y\, n_z}(x, y, z)\, e^{-i\frac{W_{n_x\, n_y\, n_z}}{\hbar}t} \qquad [4\text{-}15$$

are the complete, time-dependent eigenfunctions of a particle of mass m inside a rectangular box of sides a, b, and c.

An exact solution such as this is not in general possible if anything should destroy the symmetry. For example, if any wall were not exactly perpendicular to an axis, the equation would not be separable, and although eigenstates would exist they would have different spatial forms and different eigenvalues which would not be expressible by simple "formulas" such as [4–13], [4–14], [4–15].

If the box were rectangular but the coordinate axes were not aligned along the edges, one would obtain a different and more complicated expression for ψ. If spherical coordinates are used, the wave equation is not separable. Thus the orientation of the axes and the selection of coordinate systems are both critical to the attainment of a useful solution of the wave equation. For many problems there is no known method of finding an exact solution.

In the solution [4–13], [4–14], [4–15] a new and important phenomenon appears. For some cases, two or more *different* eigenfunctions have the *same* eigenvalue. For example, if $a = b = c$ (cubical box), then

$$\psi_{211} = \sqrt{\frac{8}{a^3}}\,\sin\frac{2\pi x}{a}\,\sin\frac{\pi y}{a}\,\sin\frac{\pi z}{a}$$

and

$$\psi_{121} = \sqrt{\frac{8}{a^3}}\,\sin\frac{\pi x}{a}\,\sin\frac{2\pi y}{a}\,\sin\frac{\pi z}{a}$$

and also

$$\psi_{112} = \sqrt{\frac{8}{a^3}}\,\sin\frac{\pi x}{a}\,\sin\frac{\pi y}{a}\,\sin\frac{2\pi z}{a}$$

have different spacial distributions. However, they all have the same characteristic energy,

$$W_{211} = W_{121} = W_{112} = \frac{\hbar^2\,\pi^2}{2m}\left(\frac{1^2 + 1^2 + 2^2}{a^2}\right)$$

This energy level[3] W_{211} is said to be "degenerate"—specifically, threefold degener-

---

[3] The characteristic value of the total energy of the system is the expectation value of the energy operator $(-\hbar/i)\,(\partial/\partial t)$ calculated by Postulate V. Using the eigenfunction [4–15] we obtain, at once, $\overline{W} = W_{n_x n_y n_z}$. As we saw in Problem 2.4 (and as is also shown in Section 4.9), a system whose eigenfunction has the form of [4–15] will have no dispersion in the expectation value of its energy, $\overline{W}$. A system with discrete energy W is said to be in a state whose "energy level" is W.

ate—since there are three different eigenfunctions that belong to it. If, on the other hand, a, b, and c have no integral relationships, it is generally true that each eigenvalue has only a single, unique eigenfunction. Such energy levels are "nondegenerate."

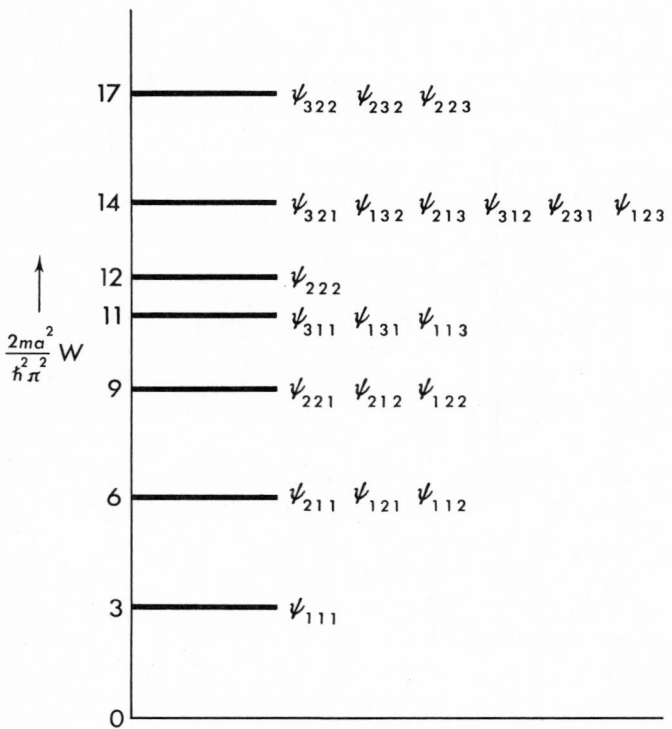

Fig. 4.2. The energy levels of the cubical, infinite-wall box, and a list of the eigenfunctions that belong to each level.

In Figure 4.2 the energy levels for the cubical box are plotted, along with a list of the distinct wave functions that belong to the energy level. For example, when W has a value such that

$$\frac{2ma^2}{\hbar^2 \pi^2} W = 14$$

there are six distinct wave functions. This energy level is sixfold degenerate.

If the walls of the box are not infinitely high but consist of only a finite potential "step," the wave functions for any eigenstate will have a longer wavelength and will not go to zero at each boundary. The eigenfunctions will have a finite value at the boundary and connect smoothly to the external, exponentially decreasing function, as in Section 3.3. The higher the potential "step," the smaller (and the less significant) is the external exponential section of the wave function. (For the analysis of this case, it is simpler to shift the origin to the center of the box.)

If one visualizes a cloud inside the box whose density or blackness at any point is given by[4] $\Psi_n^* \Psi_n$ which, by [4-15], is equal to $\psi_n^* \psi_n$ or here, ψ_n^2, one has a graphic picture of a typical three-dimensional wave function. (A pattern similar to this is the standing-wave pattern of sound waves in a room with reflecting walls.) The particle of mass m is most likely to be found in a volume element $d\tau = dx\, dy\, dz$, where the cloud is the most dense. For the infinite-wall box the particle will never be found on any of the boundaries, but is most likely to be found in regions where ψ^2 is large. For the box with finite walls, the cloud has low, but not zero, density at the walls and fades gradually to zero in regions of increasing distance outside the boundary surfaces.

In imagining the cloud whose density is $\Psi_n^* \Psi_n$ we must visualize a stationary pattern since $\Psi^* \Psi$ does not vary with time. Ψ_n itself [4-15] contains the time-dependent factor $e^{-i\frac{W_n}{\hbar}t}$, and therefore its real and imaginary parts are each time dependent, but in such a way that the *amplitude* of Ψ_n is constant. In the complex plane, Ψ_n is represented by a vector of constant amplitude, rotating with a frequency $W_n/\hbar$ radians/sec, and as Fig. 1, Appendix III, shows, the real and imaginary parts can vary in time but $\Psi^* \Psi = |\psi|^2$ is constant in time.

A system for which the wave function is an *eigenfunction* Ψ_n has a time-independent probability density function, $\Psi^* \Psi = \psi^* \psi$. Whenever the probability density is time independent the system is said to be in a "stationary state," or an "eigenstate." In Section 4.9 we see in addition that when the wave function belonging to a system is an *eigenfunction*, the system *energy* is exactly predicable. Thus we have the threefold association:

system wave function is an eigenfunction	$\longleftrightarrow$	time-independent probability density function	$\longleftrightarrow$	no uncertainty in the expectation value of the system energy

Whenever the potential energy of the system $V(x, y, z)$ is constant in time it will be possible for a stationary state to exist, since then the wave equation can be separated into two equations, one dependent on space alone and one dependent upon time alone, as in [4-6a]. (We shall see later in Chapter 5 that even when the potential energy is constant it is possible for a system to be in a nonstationary state. This occurs when the system wave function is the sum of two or more eigenfunctions.)

---

[4] Here n symbolizes a particular set of numbers, $n_x n_y n_z$. If all eigenfunctions, $\Psi\, n_x n_y n_z$, are listed in some order, then n identifies a particular function in the list.

4.3. The particle in a central field

Although the particle in the rectangular box has particularly simple wave functions, and the boundary conditions that cause the eigenstates to occur are easy to visualize, the pure form of this type of system is not observed in nature. However, an electrically charged particle, such as an electron, attracted by a massive, oppositely charged particle is a system that *is* observed, namely the hydrogen atom. The eigenstates for this problem were calculated by Schrödinger in his first paper on wave mechanics. The calculated characteristic energy values of the states of this system correspond, with high accuracy, to the measured energy levels of the hydrogen atom.

Fundamentally, the problem of the particle in a central, attractive field is the same as the problem of the particle in a rectangular box. The box is now spherical in shape and does not have perfectly sharp boundaries, but the matter waves still form resonant, standing-wave patterns inside it. There is, however, considerable mathematical complexity caused by the spherical geometry. Also there are some new features because of the spherical symmetry of the walls of the box.

The basic problem is simply stated: When $V(x, y, z)$ is a spherically symmetrical function of space, $V(r)$, find the functions $\psi(x, y, z)$, or rather $\psi(r, \theta, \phi)$, which are solutions to the wave equation, are well behaved, and have integrable squares (i.e., are bounded in space).

We will eventually use the electrostatic potential, $V(r) = -e^2/r$ ergs, in the actual calculations, since this is the potential energy of particle of charge $-e$ (esu) at a distance of r cm from another charge, $+e$ (esu).[5] In the initial part of the calculation, however, it is not necessary to assume any more about the potential energy of the system than that it depends only on r.

In the hydrogen atom the nuclear mass is 1836 times that of the electron, and, classically, the system rotates about its center of mass near, but not exactly at, the nucleus. Appendix IV shows how the wave equation for nucleus-plus-electron can be separated into two parts, one dependent on the translational motion of the center of mass of the system and the other upon the relative motion of the two parts with respect to the center of mass. As Appendix IV shows, the translational motion equation is the same as one which we have considered already (single particle in a rectangular box). The relative motion equation is identical in form to that of a single particle moving in a central field, fixed at the origin.

The analysis in Appendix IV is included only for completeness. It shows that the complete wave function for a two-particle system does depend upon six spatial variables, as was stated earlier. Also, it shows that one must, for full accuracy, make allowance for the rotational motion of the system about its center of mass, and for the translation of the center of mass. For the purpose

---

[5] If e is in coulombs and r is in meters, then $V(r) = -(1/4 \pi \varepsilon_0)(e^2/r)$ joules. Here, $(1/4 \pi \varepsilon_0) = 9 \times 10^9$ newtons m^2/coulomb.

of understanding the nature of the states of the hydrogen atom, however, we could assume that the heavy nucleus remains fixed at the origin, and the light electron moves in the fixed, central field. As is pointed out below, the exact equation differs from that which would result from using the approximation just outlined only by a small fractional correction to the electron mass.

A single particle of mass μ moving in a fixed potential field $V(r)$, has the amplitude equation

$$\frac{\partial^2 \, \psi(x, y, z)}{\partial x^2} + \frac{\partial^2 \, \psi(x, y, z)}{dy^2} + \frac{\partial^2 \, \psi(x, y, z)}{\partial z^2} + \frac{2\mu}{\hbar^2} \{W - V(r)\} \, \psi(x, y, z) = 0$$

where   [4–16⁶

$$r = \sqrt{x^2 + y^2 + z^2}$$

This is identical to [4–7] (a particle in a rectangular box) *except for the form of V*. The time-separation has been performed in the usual manner.

Unfortunately [4–16] cannot be separated in x, y, and z coordinates, that is, there is no way to cause [4–16] to break up into three ordinary differential equations, each dependent only on one of the variables x, y, and z. This is because x, y, and z appear inside the radical, in r, in the potential V. If, however, one uses a spherical coordinate system (Fig. 4.3) as a reference frame in which to describe the location of the particle and also to describe the wave function $[\psi = \psi(r, \theta, \phi)]$, then [4–16] *can* be separated into three ordinary equations.

A question arises at once regarding the expression in the wave equation (originating from the classical formula for kinetic energy),

$$\left(\frac{\partial^2}{\partial x^2} + \frac{\partial^2}{\partial y^2} + \frac{\partial^2}{\partial z^2} \right) \psi(r, \theta, \phi)$$ [4–17

since we now have two different coordinate systems involved in the same equation. From Figure 4.3 the relationship between these two systems is

$$x = r \sin \theta \cos \phi$$
$$y = r \sin \theta \sin \phi$$ [4–18
$$z = r \cos \theta$$

If the wave equation is to be written completely in spherical coordinates,

---

⁶ Appendix IV shows that the equation describing relative motion of two masses m_1 and m_2 is identical to [4–16]. For two particles, the reduced mass, μ, is

$$\frac{m_1 \, m_2}{m_1 + m_2}$$

If $m_1 =$ the electron mass, and m_2 the proton mass, then

$$\mu = \left(\frac{1836}{1837}\right) m_1$$

The consequences of this factor, though small, are clearly observable in the spectra of hydrogen. If one assumes that the nucleus is fixed, then one would use m_1 in [4–16] rather than μ.

all expressions involving x, y, and z must be converted into ones involving only r, θ, and ϕ.

It can be shown, using the coordinate conversion relationship [4–18], that [4–17] becomes

$$\frac{1}{r^2}\frac{\partial}{\partial r}\left(r^2\frac{\partial \psi}{\partial r}\right) + \frac{1}{r^2 \sin \theta}\frac{\partial}{\partial \theta}\left(\sin \theta \frac{\partial \psi}{\partial \theta}\right) + \frac{1}{r^2 \sin^2 \theta}\frac{\partial^2 \psi}{\partial \phi^2} \qquad [4\text{--}19$$

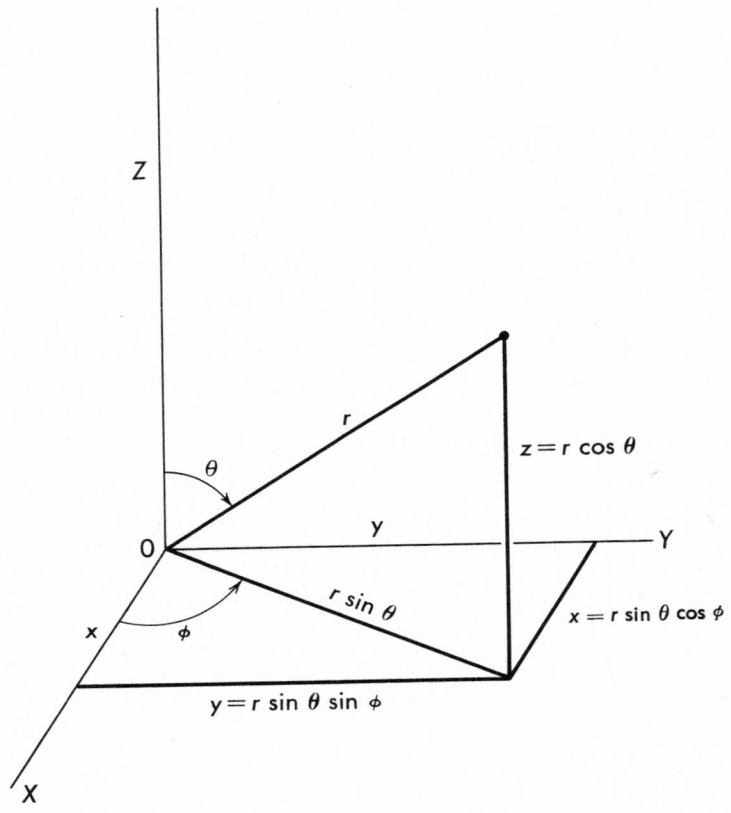

Fig. 4.3. The spherical coordinate system.

where ψ is $\psi(r, \theta, \phi)$. Appendix V outlines the simpler problem of showing the converse—namely, that [4–19] reduces to [4–17] when x, y, and z are related to r, θ, and ϕ by [4–18]. Thus, [4–19] is just the quantum-mechanical operator, arising from the classical expression for the kinetic energy, applied to ψ. *The only difference from the cases previously discussed is that the coordinate system is spherical instead of Cartesian.*

The amplitude equation [4–16] becomes

$$\frac{1}{r^2} \frac{\partial}{\partial r} \left(r^2 \frac{\partial \psi}{\partial r} \right) + \frac{1}{r^2 \sin \theta} \frac{\partial}{\partial \theta} \left(\sin \theta \frac{\partial \psi}{\partial \theta} \right) + \frac{1}{r^2 \sin^2 \theta} \frac{\partial^2 \psi}{\partial \phi^2}$$

$$+ \frac{2\mu}{\hbar^2} \{W - V(r)\} \psi = 0 \qquad [4\text{--}20$$

This equation can be separated into three equations by the substitution

$$\psi(r, \theta, \phi) = R(r) \, \Theta(\theta) \, \Phi(\phi) \qquad [4\text{--}21$$

Making this substitution in [4–20], and dividing through by ψ, [4–20] becomes

$$\frac{1}{r^2} \frac{1}{R} \frac{d}{dr} \left(r^2 \frac{dR}{dr} \right) + \frac{1}{r^2 \sin \theta} \frac{1}{\Theta} \frac{d}{d\theta} \left(\sin \theta \frac{d\Theta}{d\theta} \right)$$

$$+ \frac{1}{r^2 \sin^2 \theta} \frac{1}{\Phi} \frac{d^2\Phi}{d\phi^2} + \frac{2\mu}{\hbar^2} \{W - V(r)\} = 0 \qquad [4\text{--}22$$

If we multiply through by $r^2 \sin^2 \theta$, the term in Φ is dependent on only one of the independent variables, ϕ. This can be true only if this term is equal to a constant—which we shall designate by $-m^2$. Thus,

$$\frac{1}{\Phi} \frac{d^2\Phi}{d\phi^2} = -m^2 \qquad [4\text{--}23^7$$

After making this substitution in [4–22] and dividing through by $\sin^2 \theta$, we have

$$\frac{1}{R} \frac{d}{dr} \left(r^2 \frac{dR}{dr} \right) + \frac{1}{\sin \theta} \frac{1}{\Theta} \frac{d}{d\theta} \left(\sin \theta \frac{d\Theta}{d\theta} \right) - \frac{m^2}{\sin^2 \theta} + \frac{2\mu r^2}{\hbar^2} \{W - V(r)\} = 0 \quad [4\text{--}24$$

The two middle terms are dependent only on θ and must therefore together equal a constant, which we designate $-\beta$. Thus the θ-equation becomes,

$$\frac{1}{\sin \theta} \frac{d}{d\theta} \left(\sin \theta \frac{d\Theta}{d\theta} \right) - \frac{m^2}{\sin^2 \theta} \Theta + \beta\Theta = 0 \qquad [4\text{--}25$$

Since in [4–24] we set the θ-dependent terms equal to the constant $-\beta$, the r-dependent terms must equal $+\beta$. Thus,

$$\frac{1}{r^2} \frac{d}{dr} \left(r^2 \frac{dR}{dr} \right) - \frac{\beta}{r^2} R + \frac{2\mu}{\hbar^2} \{W - V(r)\} R = 0 \qquad [4\text{--}26$$

The equations [4–23], [4–25], and [4–26] are the three separated equations. Each is an ordinary differential equation dependent upon only one variable. These correspond to the three equations [4–11] for the particle in a box. The differences are due only to the different coordinate system—forced upon us by the spherically symmetrical potential function.

---

[7] If one assumes $+ m^2$ in [4–23], then the solution $\Phi = e^{\pm m\phi}$ is not periodic in ϕ.

There are three undetermined constants, m, β, and W. We shall see that these constants are selected by the basic requirements of the wave function—finiteness, continuity, single-valuedness, and the integrable square.

For the particle in the box there were also three constants, W_x, W_y, and W_z, which were determined by these same basic requirements. Each constant was separately determined. We shall see, however, that in the case of the r, θ, and ϕ equations, only m is uninfluenced by the selection of the other constants. The value of β will involve m, and the value of W will involve β (and therefore m).

4.4. The φ-dependent equation

We begin, therefore, with the selection of m. The ϕ-equation [4–23] has a solution

$$\Phi(\phi) = Ae^{im\phi} \qquad [4\text{--}27$$

which by direct substitution produces an identity.[8] In Figure 4.3 we see that as ϕ increases (assume θ and r constant, for the present) the point r, θ, ϕ moves in a circle about the z-axis, returning when $\phi = 2\pi$ to its original position. If $\psi(r, \theta, \phi)$ is to be single-valued, as the postulates require, then whatever the value of $\Phi(\phi)$ at $\phi = \phi_0$, it must be identical to the value of $\Phi(\phi)$ at

$$\phi = \phi_0 + 2\pi, \ \phi + 4\pi, \ \phi + 6\pi, \text{ etc.}$$

This single-valuedness is guaranteed if $m = $ any integer,[9] including zero,

$$m = \ \cdots \ -3, -2, -1, 0, +1, +2, +3 \ \cdots \qquad [4\text{--}28$$

Thus, the eigenfunctions $\Phi_m(\phi)$ are given by [4–27], where m has any integral value.

If each of the factors R, Θ, and Φ are separately normalized, then the total wave function will be normalized.

We thus require that

$$\int_0^{2\pi} \Phi_m^*(\phi) \ \Phi_m(\phi) \ d\phi = 1$$

We set $A = A_0 e^{i\delta}$, where δ is a constant. $e^{i\delta}$ is a constant "phase factor." The volume element, $d\tau = r^2 \sin \theta \ d\phi \ d\theta \ dr$ (Fig. 4.4) contains only the differential

---

[8] The same expression, using $-m$, is equally satisfactory.

[9] Suppose $m = 1$; $\Phi(0) = A(1 + 0)$; $\Phi(2\pi) = A(1 + 0) = \Phi(0)$, using $e^{im\phi} = \cos m\phi + i \sin m\phi$.

Suppose $m = 1.1$; $\Phi(0) = A(1 + 0)$; $\Phi(2\pi) = Ae^{i(1.1)2\pi}$
$$= A\left(\cos \frac{2\pi}{10} + i \sin \frac{2\pi}{10}\right) \neq \Phi(0)$$

of ϕ, and since the full range of ϕ is from 0 to 2π,

$$A_0^2 \int_0^{2\pi} d\phi = 2\pi A_0^2$$

[4-29

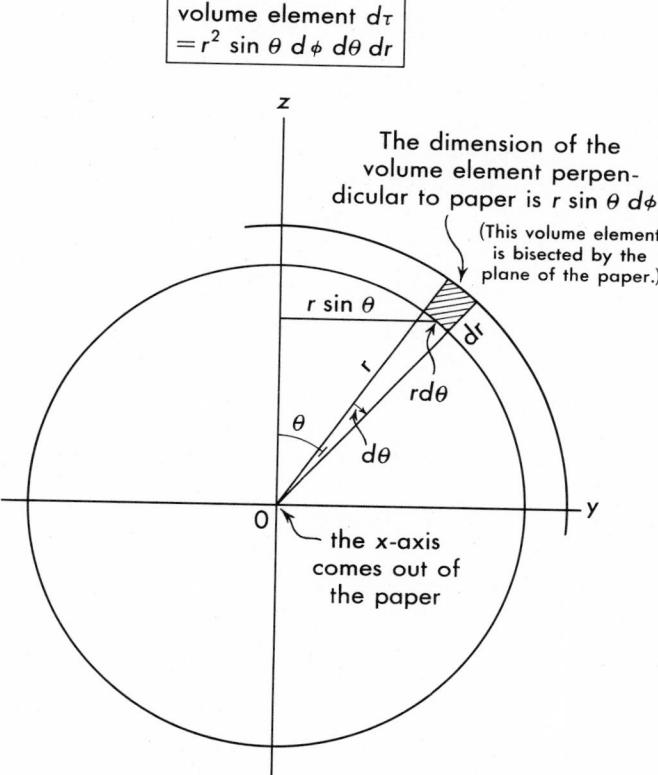

Fig. 4.4.   The volume element, $d\tau$, for the spherical coordinate system.

Therefore the normalized ϕ-dependent factor in the wave function ψ is

$$\Phi_m(\phi) = \frac{1}{\sqrt{2\pi}} e^{i\,m\phi}$$

[4-30[10]

$$m = \cdots -3, -2, -1, 0, 1, 2, 3, \cdots$$

---

[10] We ignore the constant phase factor $e^{i\delta}$, since it vanishes in all calculations involving $\psi^*\psi$.

4.5. The θ-dependent equation

The ϕ-dependent equation is simple in form, its solutions are well known, and its eigenfunctions are easy to find. A glance at the θ-dependent equation [4–25] shows that it is much more complex. However, its eigenfunctions are known from earlier physical and mathematical work as the Legendre functions. The θ-eigenfunctions can be found by methods similar to those used in Appendix I for the harmonic oscillator, and are so derived in many quantum mechanics textbooks.[11] We shall later use the results of these derivations. However, we shall first show, using numerical methods, how the eigenvalues of the parameter β are determined—for any given integral value of m. This process demonstrates the wide range of applicability of the method of numerical solution. Although this equation is quite different from any thus far considered, the method of numerical analysis is the same.

The θ-equation [4–25] becomes, after expansion of the first term,

$$\frac{d^2\Theta}{d\theta^2} + \frac{1}{\tan\theta}\frac{d\Theta}{d\theta} + \left(-\frac{m^2}{\sin^2\theta} + \beta\right)\Theta = 0 \qquad [4\text{--}31$$

$d\Theta/d\theta = $ slope, and writing $\Delta\theta$ for $d\theta$,

$$\Delta(\text{slope}) = -\left\{\frac{\text{slope}}{\tan\theta} + \left(\beta - \frac{m^2}{\sin^2\theta}\right)\Theta\right\}\Delta\theta \qquad [4\text{--}32$$

Thus, given an initial slope $= (\text{slope})_0$ and some initial value of Θ, Θ_0 at $\theta = \theta_0$, the instructions [4–32] specify that, after a step $\Delta\theta$, the new value of Θ will be $\Theta_0 + (\text{slope})_0\,\Delta\theta$, and the new slope will be $(\text{slope})_0 + \Delta(\text{slope})$, where [4–32] gives the instructions for finding $\Delta(\text{slope})$. Thus,

$$\Theta_0 = \Theta_0 \qquad\qquad\qquad\qquad\qquad\qquad \theta = \theta_0$$

$$\Theta_1 = \Theta_0 + (\text{slope})_0\,\Delta\theta \qquad\qquad\qquad \theta_1 = \theta_0 + \Delta\theta$$

$$\Theta_2 = \Theta_1 + \underbrace{\left[\underbrace{(\text{slope})_0}_{\text{initial slope}} - \underbrace{\left\{\frac{(\text{slope})_0}{\tan\theta_1} + \left(\beta - \frac{m^2}{\sin^2\theta_1}\right)\Theta_1\right\}\Delta\theta}_{\text{change in slope}}\right]}_{\text{new slope}\,=\,(\text{slope})_1}\Delta\theta$$

$$\theta_2 = \theta_1 + \Delta\theta$$

$$\Theta_3 = \Theta_2 + \underbrace{\left[(\text{slope})_1 - \left\{\frac{(\text{slope})_1}{\tan\theta_2} + \left(\beta - \frac{m^2}{\sin^2\theta_2}\right)\Theta_2\right\}\Delta\theta\right]}_{\text{new slope}\,=\,(\text{slope})_2}\Delta\theta$$

$$\theta_3 = \theta_2 + \Delta\theta$$

etc. $\qquad\qquad\qquad\qquad\qquad\qquad\qquad\qquad\qquad\qquad [4\text{--}33$

---

[11] For example, L. Pauling and E. B. Wilson, *Introduction to Quantum Mechanics* (1935, McGraw-Hill Book Co., Inc., New York): pp. 118 and 125.

The eigenvalue problem is to find well-behaved $\Theta(\theta)$ functions, with an integrable square, in the range

$$0 \leq \theta \leq \pi$$

The key equation in the above calculation is [4–32], since it is used in a repetitive manner in [4–33]. We note that in [4–32], Δ(slope) could become infinite when $\theta = 0$ or $\theta = \pi$, since $\tan \theta = 0$ and also $\sin \theta = 0$ at these points. How this infinite change in slope can be avoided (as it must be) depends upon the value of m. We shall begin by studying the case $m = 0$.

When $m = 0$, one can see at once that, *providing* $\beta = 0$, a solution to [4–31] is $\Theta = $ constant. When this is true, then $d\Theta/d\theta$ is zero at all points, including $\theta = 0$ and $\theta = \pi$, and [4–31] is everywhere satisfied. Thus, for $\beta = 0$, $\Theta = $ constant is an acceptable wave function, and we have found, for $m = 0$, one of the discrete values of the separation constant β.

Since the θ-dependent factor in the volume element $d\tau$ (Fig. 4.4) is $\sin \theta d\theta$, then for $\beta = 0$ and $m = 0$ the normalized θ-dependent eigenfunction is

$$\Theta(\beta = 0, m = 0) = \sqrt{2}/2 \qquad\qquad [4\text{--}34$$

since then,

$$\int_0^\pi \Theta^* \Theta \sin \theta \, d\theta = 1$$

This is the one of the θ-eigenfunctions, since it is a solution to the wave equation, is well behaved in its domain of definition, and is normalized.

We pause here to discuss the types of symmetry which we will expect to find in the solutions of the Θ-wave equation. As in Section 3.2, where we analyzed the harmonic oscillator, we will find that the hunt for the eigenfunctions can be greatly narrowed by noting, directly from the wave equation itself, that the solutions must have certain symmetry properties.[12]

As in the case of the harmonic oscillator, we can most easily start the step-by-step calculations at the point where the instructions show symmetry—here, $\theta = \pi/2$. If we find a well-behaved solution in going, say, from $\theta = \pi/2$ to $\theta = 0$ (here, the steps $\Delta\theta$ are negative), and if the initial conditions chosen at $\theta = \pi/2$ are suitable, we can immediately construct, by symmetry, the solution in the range from $\theta = \pi/2$ to $\theta = \pi$ ($\Delta\theta = +$).

What are the initial conditions at $\theta = \pi/2$ which permit symmetry about this point? As in the case of the harmonic oscillator, we must require either $\Theta = 0$ and slope $\neq 0$, or $\Theta \neq 0$, and slope $= 0$. A set of curves which meet this requirement are sketched in Figure 4.5. Except for the curve $\theta = $ constant in Figure 4.5a, which we have already seen is an eigenfunction, we do not, at the moment, have any evidence that these sketches will be similar to any of the

---

[12] For a discussion of symmetry and antisymmetry see Section 3.2, particularly Figures 3.4 and 3.5.

Θ-eigenfunctions which we are seeking. If, however, the basic instructions [4–32] are applied to either of the two types of initial conditions shown in the sketches, we will quickly discover that the calculated values of Θ will show

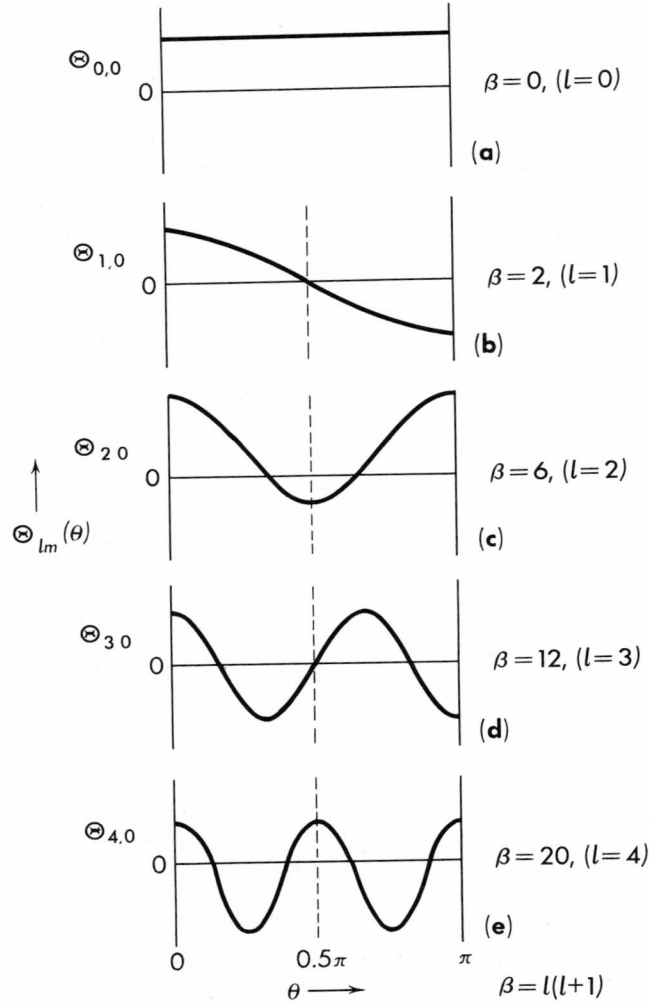

Fig. 4.5. Possible forms for the θ-eigenfunctions of the hydrogen atom, for $m = 0$.

either symmetry or antisymmetry, about $\theta = \pi/2$, in the manner of the curves in Figure 4.5.

Although we have been discussing a particular case of the Θ-equation, $m = 0$, the requirement that Θ have symmetry or antisymmetry about $\theta = \pi/2$

does not depend upon our selection of any of the possible integral values of m. We shall see later, for example, that when $m = 1$ the eigenfunctions will still be either symmetrical or antisymmetrical about $\theta = \pi/2$.

Returning to the case $m = 0$, we note from [4–32] that it is not *essential* that the slope, $d\Theta/d\theta$, be zero *everywhere*, as for the first eigenfunction $\Theta = \sqrt{2}/2$ [4–34]. It is sufficient that the slope be zero only at $\theta = 0$ and at $\theta = \pi$, the two points where $(1/\tan \theta)$ becomes infinite. A curve such as that in Figure 4.5b and also all of the other curves in the figure have the necessary zero slope at the two required points. We expect, therefore, to find a class of eigenfunctions of the general form as the curves sketched in Figure 4.5.

As an example, we will calculate the curve whose form is similar to Figure 4.5b.

We start, therefore, at $\theta = \pi/2$ with $\Theta = 0$ and $(\text{slope})_0 = -1$, and seek a value of β which will cause a well-behaved curve $\Theta(\theta)$ over the full range $0 \leq \theta \leq \pi$.

Negative values of β always cause Θ to be ill behaved, since, as [4–32] shows, once Θ is headed away from the abscissa it continues thus. However, near the value $\beta = 2$, the numerical calculation[13] of the function $\Theta(\theta)$ shows the behavior shown in Figure 4.6. In the figure, β is written as $l(l + 1)$. The reason for this is that, as we shall see later, the sequence of eigenvalues for the θ-equation turns out to be

$$\beta = 0, 2, 6, 12, 20, 30, \cdots$$

This is more simply expressed as

$$\beta = l(l + 1)$$

where

$$l = 0, 1, 2, 3, 4, 5, \cdots$$

l is called the azimuthal quantum number.

As Figure 4.6 shows, a variation of 20 per cent in l from the value 1.0 makes Θ ill behaved at $\theta = 0$ (and also at $\theta = \pi$). Thus with only sixteen steps used in calculating Θ between $\theta = \pi/2$ and $\theta = 0$, and with only slide rule accuracy, it is possible to locate an eigenvalue of Θ with only a few percent inaccuracy. However, if a digital computer is used and many more steps are calculated, the eigenvalue can be located with very small—though never zero—error.

The eigenfunction found numerically in Figure 4.6 for $m = 0$ and $l = 1$ is very nearly of the form $\cos \theta$, and indeed, as substitution will show, this is a solution to the wave equation [4–31]. If we require, as in [4–34], that the

---

[13] In the calculations for Figure 4.6, following the instructions [4–33], $\Delta\theta = -0.1$ radians. The computations were performed with the use of a table of tangents (tabulated by radians) and a slide rule.

θ-dependent part of the normalization integral be unity, i.e.,

$$\int_{0}^{\pi} \Theta_{lm}^{*}(\theta)\,\Theta_{lm}(\theta)\,\sin\theta\,d\theta = 1$$

then $\Theta_{lm}(\theta)$ is, for $l = 1$ and $m = 0$,

$$\Theta_{10}(\theta) = \frac{\sqrt{6}}{2}\cos\theta \qquad\qquad [4\text{--}35$$

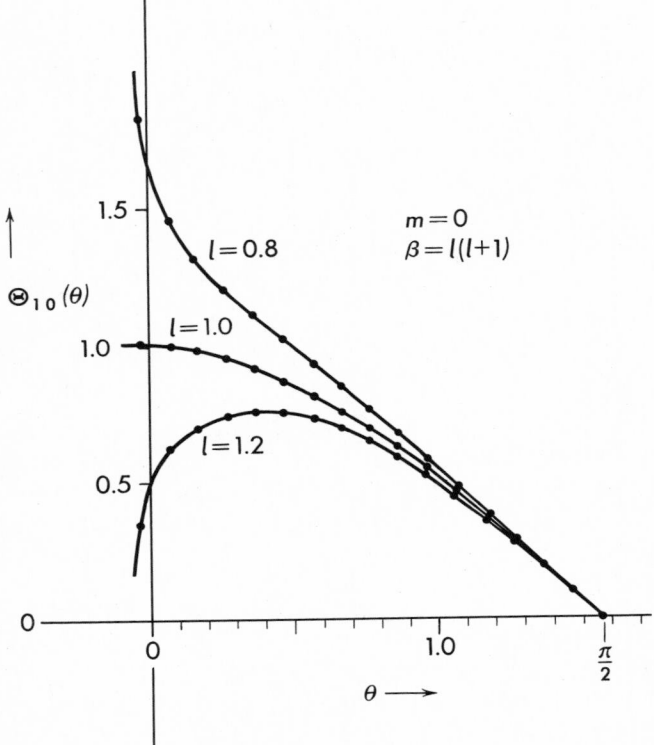

Fig. 4.6. The numerical integration of the θ-dependent equation for $m = 0$ and $\beta = 2$.

Continuing the search for eigenfunctions for the case $m = 0$ *and* when $\Theta = 0$ at $\theta = \pi/2$, we expect to find a solution of the general form of the curve in Figure 4.5d. One finds that when $\beta = 12$ (or $l = 3$), a curve of the same general form as Figure 4.5d results from the numerical calculations. Its mathematical expression is not as obvious as for the above case ($l = 1$, $m = 0$). Standard mathematical methods show that this eigenfunction has the form

$$\frac{5}{3}\cos^3\theta - \cos\theta$$

and this equation fits the calculated points. This function can be normalized and yields (for $\beta = 12$ or $l = 3$, and $m = 0$)

$$\Theta_{30}(\theta) = \frac{3\sqrt{14}}{4}\left(\frac{5}{3}\cos{}^3\theta - \cos\theta\right) \qquad [4\text{–}36$$

The next eigenfunction (for $m = 0$ and $\Theta = 0$ at $\theta = \pi/2$) is found at $\beta = 30$, i.e., $l = 5$.

It must be kept in mind that the numerical analysis we are outlining does not furnish the exact mathematical form of the eigenfunction which we are graphically developing. We are including the exact mathematical forms only for convenience in later calculation, although all quantum mechanical calculations *can* be made using only the numerical solutions for the eigenfunctions, without any reference to the explicit functional forms. We are here using a sort of hybrid system. On one hand, we solve the differential equations numerically to avoid mathematical complexity and, at the same time, to make the exact mathematical forms of the eigenfunctions look reasonable. On the other hand, we use the exact mathematical expressions for calculations, thereby avoiding the laborious arithmetical work involved in calculating with the numerical solutions themselves. Thus, we compromise and blend the two methods in an effort to maximize clarity and minimize dependence upon formal mathematical theory.

Let us now return to the details of the calculation of the other eigenfunctions which exist for the case where $m = 0$.

If we continue to assume $m = 0$ but change the initial conditions at $\theta = \pi/2$ to the other alternative ($\Theta \neq 0$ and slope $= 0$ as in Figure 4.5c, e), we obtain eigenfunctions at $\beta = 6$ (or $l = 2$) and $\beta = 20$ (or $l = 4$), which when normalized are

$$\Theta_{20}(\theta) = \frac{\sqrt{10}}{4}(3\cos^2\theta - 1); \quad \Theta_{40}(\theta)$$

$$= \frac{9\sqrt{2}}{16}\left(\frac{35}{3}\cos^4\theta - 10\cos^2\theta + 1\right) \qquad [4\text{–}37$$

When $m = 0$, eigenfunctions are found for
$\beta = 0, 2, 6, 12, 20, 30, \cdots$
$l = 0, 1, 2, 3, 4, 5, \cdots$ all positive integers.

As far as the ϕ-equation is concerned, m can have any one of the values, $m = 0, \pm 1, \pm 2, \cdots$. We have only found those eigenfunctions of θ which occur for $m = 0$. We must next look for θ-eigenfunctions for the case $m = +1$ or -1.

The basic equation [4–32] for calculation of the θ-functions is, as before,

$$\Delta(\text{slope}) = -\left[\frac{\text{slope}}{\tan\theta} + \left(\beta - \frac{m^2}{\sin^2\theta}\right)\Theta\right]\Delta\theta \qquad [4\text{–}32$$

but now we cannot set $m = 0$, so that an infinite change in slope (which characterizes an ill-behaved eigenfunction) can occur due to *both* $\tan \theta \to 0$ and $\sin^2 \theta \to 0$.

Let the slope k at $\theta = 0$ be finite, and (this is very important) we require in addition that near $\theta = 0$, $\Theta \simeq k\theta$. Also, for small θ, $\tan \theta \simeq \theta$ and $\sin^2 \theta \simeq \theta^2$. The two terms causing the infinity as $\theta \to 0$,

$$\left[\frac{\text{slope}}{\tan \theta} - \frac{m^2}{\sin^2 \theta} \Theta \right] \qquad [4\text{-}37a$$

now become, when $m = +1$ or -1, and using the above approximations for θ,

$$\left[\left(\frac{k}{\theta} \right) - \left(\frac{1}{\theta^2} \right) k\theta \right] = 0 \qquad [4\text{-}37b$$

Thus if at $\theta = 0$, Θ has the form $\Theta = k\theta$, and[14] $m = \pm 1$, there will be no infinities in the calculation of $\Delta(\text{slope})$. A similar situation exists at the point $\theta = \pi$.

As before, we must have either symmetry or antisymmetry about $\theta = \pi/2$ (due to the antisymmetry of $\tan \theta$ and the symmetry of $\sin^2 \theta$ about this point) so that we look for eigenfunctions of the general form shown in Figure 4.7a, b, c.

It can be shown that neither the function $\Theta = \text{constant}$ nor any of the other $m = 0$ functions whose forms are sketched in Figure 4.5 is a satisfactory eigenfunction when $m = \pm 1$ (see Problem 4.8).

Starting at $\theta = \pi/2$, as in Figure 4.7a, c, with zero slope and nonzero amplitude, we find that eigenfunctions occur for $\beta = 2(l = 1)$, and for $\beta = 12(l = 3)$. Starting at $\theta = \pi/2$ (Fig. 4.7b) with zero amplitude and finite slope, we find an eigenfunction for $\beta = 6(l = 2)$ and also for $\beta = 20(l = 4)$, although this is not sketched in Figure 4.7. These eigenvalues of β also occur, as we have seen, when $m = 0$.

Now, however, when $m = \pm 1$, there is *no* eigenfunction when $\beta = 0(l = 0)$ as there was when $m = 0$. The presence of the term $1/\sin^2 \theta$ causes an ill-behaved eigenfunction when $\beta = 0$, as sketched in Figure 4.7a (see Problem 4.9).

The normalized eigenfunction Θ_{lm} for $l = 1$ and $m = +1$ or -1, has the mathematical form

$$\Theta_{1, \pm 1} = \frac{\sqrt{3}}{2} \sin \theta \qquad [4\text{-}38$$

---

[14] We asserted earlier, with respect to the single-valuedness requirement of the ϕ-dependent equation [4–27], that the quantum number m must have integral values. We can see here that the θ-dependent equation also requires integral values for m. For example, the condition [4–37b], which avoids the infinite change in slope at $\theta = 0$ and at $\theta = \pi$, could not be met if m deviated from unity by even a small amount. Similarly, solutions of the form sketched in Figure 4.5, for $m = 0$ are possible only if m is exactly zero (see Problem 4.8).

This has the form and symmetry sketched in Figure 4.7a. The mathematical forms of the solutions $\Theta_{2,\pm 1}$ and $\Theta_{3,\pm 1}$ sketched in Figure 4.7b, c, are listed in Appendix VI.

We now consider the case $m = \pm 2$. For this, and for all larger magnitudes of m, there is no way to avoid infinite values at $\theta = 0$ and $\theta = \pi$ unless *both*

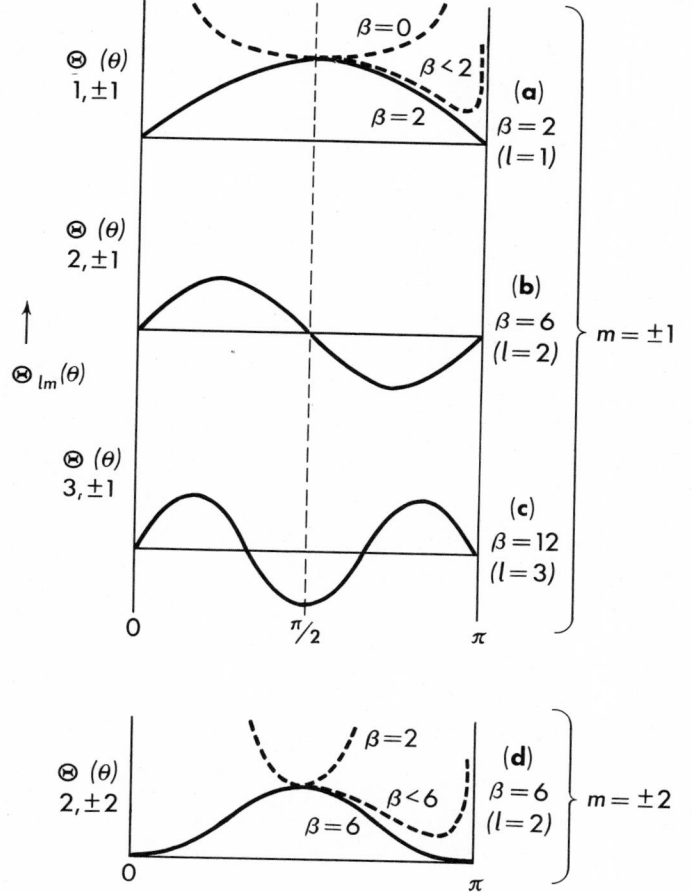

Fig. 4.7. Some θ-eigenfunctions for the hydrogen atom. The dotted curves indicate the behavior of $\Theta(\theta)$ for several unacceptable values of β.

$$\beta = l(l+1).$$

the slope and the amplitude of $\Theta(\theta)$ are equal to zero at these points. Such a curve is shown in Figure 4.7d. Its mathematical form turns out to be $\sin^2 \theta$.

When $m = \pm 2$, the only values of β which produce eigenfunctions are

$$\beta = 6, 12, 20, 30, \cdots$$
$$l = 2, 3, 4, 5, \cdots$$

One might describe this situation in the following manner, referring to the basic instructions [4–32]. When $m^2 = 4$, and when β is anything less than 6, $\Theta(\theta)$ simply cannot curve sharply enough to attain the required zero slope and zero amplitude at $\theta = 0$ and $\theta = \pi$. For example, Figure 4.7d shows what happens if $\beta = 2$. It is even worse if $\beta = 0$ (see Problem 4.9).

In summary, eigenfunctions of the ϕ-equation are found for any integral value of m

$$\cdots -3, -2, -1, 0, +1, 2, 3, \cdots$$

but eigenfunctions of the θ-equation, $\Theta_{lm}(\theta)$, exist *only* for the following cases

$$\text{for } m = 0, l = 0, 1, 2, 3, 4, \cdots$$
$$\text{for } m = 1, l = \quad 1, 2, 3, 4, \cdots$$
$$\text{for } m = 2 \; l = \qquad 2, 3, 4, \cdots$$

Since the complete amplitude function is,

$$\psi = \Phi_m(\phi) \, \Theta_{lm}(\theta) \, R(r)$$

the ill behavior of any factor will cause the ill behavior of ψ. Thus, there are *no eigenfunctions* ψ except for those combinations of l and m listed above.

The mathematical solution of the θ-equation is discussed in many textbooks.[15] The eigenfunctions are known as the associated Legendre functions.

One should note that, as in the case of the harmonic oscillator, the search for eigenfunctions by numerical methods is greatly aided—indeed in many cases made feasible—only by understanding and exploiting the general nature, and particularly the symmetries, of the differential equation that is being solved.

It is important to note that *any* radially symmetrical potential gives the above Φ_m and Θ_{lm}, so that until now we have not needed to specify the form of $V(r)$.

Although the numerical methods used here (particularly if manual computation is employed) seem rather clumsy, they have the great advantage of demonstrating in a graphic manner how eigenvalues arise in a system with spherical symmetry. Even more important, perhaps, is the graphic way in which this method demonstrates why certain combinations of the two quantum numbers, m and l, are forbidden. Conventional mathematical analysis yields, of course, the same results, but it is not so easy to see the reasons for them.

We shall see in the next section, by a similar analysis, that the r-dependent equation has well-behaved solutions only for definite values of a new quantum number n, which is related to the total energy W of the system. The r-dependent equation will have well-behaved solutions for only certain *combinations* of l and n.

Thus, the θ-dependent equation permits only certain combinations of m and l, and we shall see that the r-dependent equation will permit only certain

---

[15] See, for example, L. Pauling and E. B. Wilson, *loc. cit.*

combinations of l and n (where n measures the system energy, and where m, l, and n are all integers).

Although this analysis may seem detailed and painstaking, it is indispensable for a quantitative understanding of atomic structure. The end result is a family of eigenfunctions, each member of which is uniquely identified by a set of three integers, n, l, and m. Each eigenfunction represents a possible state of the hydrogen atom, just as each of the family of functions, $\sin (n\pi x/L)$, represents a possible pure state of vibration of a string, with ends fixed. It is only the geometry of the spherical case which complicates the form of the final result.

The analysis we are performing here is closely related to other problems in physics which involve spherical symmetry. Here we are finding the natural modes of vibration of matter waves in a spherical potential well, but the principles involved are basically the same as those used, for example, in finding the resonant modes of electromagnetic waves in a spherical cavity.

4.6. The *r*-dependent equation

In the *r*-dependent equation [4–26] for the amplitude function for the hydrogen atom,

$$\frac{1}{r^2} \frac{d}{dr} \left(r^2 \frac{d\,R(r)}{dr} \right) - \frac{l(l+1)\,R(r)}{r^2} + \frac{2\mu}{\hbar^2} \{W - V(r)\}\,R(r) = 0 \qquad [4\text{–}26$$

$$0 \leq r \leq \infty$$

the constant l appears. Since the ϕ and θ equations permit l (for $m = 0$) to range from 0 through all positive integers, it is necessary to find the eigenfunctions, if any, of [4–26] for *each* value, $l = 0, 1, 2, 3, \cdots$.

We now let $V(r) = - e^2/r$, the coulomb potential, since in [4–26] we must have an explicit form for $V(r)$.

Before analyzing this equation further, it can be put into a more convenient form by a change of variable

$$\rho = 2\alpha\,r \qquad [4\text{–}39$$

where the constant α, and a new, very important constant n, are defined to be

$$\alpha^2 \equiv - \frac{2\mu W}{\hbar^2}\,;\; n \equiv \frac{\mu e^2}{\hbar^2 \alpha} \qquad [4\text{–}40$$

Using [4–39] and [4–40] we see that

$$\rho = \frac{2}{n} \left(\frac{\mu\,e^2}{\hbar^2} \right) r, \text{ and } W_n = - \frac{\mu\,e^4}{2n^2\,\hbar^2} \qquad [4\text{–}41$$

Thus, as was mentioned above, n is a measure of system energy. The quantity

$$a_0 \equiv \frac{\hbar^2}{\mu\,e^2} = \frac{(1.05 \times 10^{-27} \text{ erg sec})^2}{\left(\dfrac{1836}{1837}\right)(9.1 \times 10^{-28} \text{ gm})(4.80 \times 10^{-10} \text{ esu})^2} = 0.528 \times 10^{-8} \text{ cm}$$

appearing in the expression for ρ is the "natural unit" of distance for the hydrogen atom.[16] (It is identical to the radius of the first Bohr orbit in the old quantum theory.)

W is the total energy of the system. It is now negative, since all terms on the right of [4–41], including the mass μ, are positive. This is because we define the mutual potential energy of two charges separated by an infinite distance to be zero. Classically, for a system of two particles to be bound, the total energy must be negative, i.e., K.E. $< |V(r)|$. In quantum mechanics, we find that $\Psi \to 0$ for large r only when W has certain discrete, negative values. Thus the particle "hovers" or the matter waves "resonate" about the attractive point (i.e., ψ is bounded in a region centered at the attractive point) only when the system energy, W, is negative.

Setting $R(r) = S(\rho)$ and using the above substitutions, [4–26] becomes[17]

$$\frac{1}{\rho^2}\frac{d}{d\rho}\left(\rho^2\,\frac{d\,S(\rho)}{d\rho}\right) + \left\{-\frac{1}{4} - \frac{l(l+1)}{\rho^2} + \frac{n}{\rho}\right\} S(\rho) = 0 \qquad \text{[4–42}$$

$$0 \le \rho \le \infty$$

where *only* the parameter n (related by [4–41] to the total system energy W) is free to be adjusted until an eigenstate i.e., a well-behaved $S(\rho)$ occurs.

In terms of finite increments, [4–42] becomes, after expansion of the first term, (slope $= dS/d\rho$)

$$\Delta(\text{slope}) = \left[-\frac{2(\text{slope})}{\rho} + \left\{\frac{1}{4} + \frac{l(l+1)}{\rho^2} - \frac{n}{\rho}\right\} S\right]\Delta\rho \qquad \text{[4–43}$$

By choosing an initial slope, and also an initial value of S, these instructions will generate, for any value of n, a function $S(\rho)$. Since ρ goes to infinitely large values, it is essential that, as $\rho \to \infty$, S approaches zero rapidly enough so that $\int S^*S\,\rho^2\,d\rho$ will not be infinite. (The volume element $d\tau$ is $r^2 \sin\theta\,d\phi\,d\theta\,dr$, and $r^2\,dr$ is proportional to $\rho^2\,d\rho$.) Also, it is apparent from [4–43] that some special conditions for S must be met at $\rho = 0$, since terms in $1/\rho$ and $1/\rho^2$ are present.

---

[16] In MKS, $a_0 = (\hbar \text{ joule sec})^2/\mu$ (Kg) $(1/4\pi\,\varepsilon_0)$ $(e$ coulomb$)^2 = 0.528 \times 10^{-10}$ m.
[17] In making the conversion from [4–26], note that:

$$\frac{d}{dr}\,S(\rho) = \frac{dS}{d\rho}\frac{d\rho}{dr},$$

etc.

We first consider the lowest possible value of l, $l = 0$. This simplifies the instructions [4–43] by removing the term $l(l + 1)/\rho^2$ but still an infinite value of $\Delta(\text{slope})$ will occur at $\rho = 0$, unless the *sum* of the two terms

$$\frac{-2(\text{slope})}{\rho} - \frac{nS}{\rho} \qquad\qquad [4\text{–}44$$

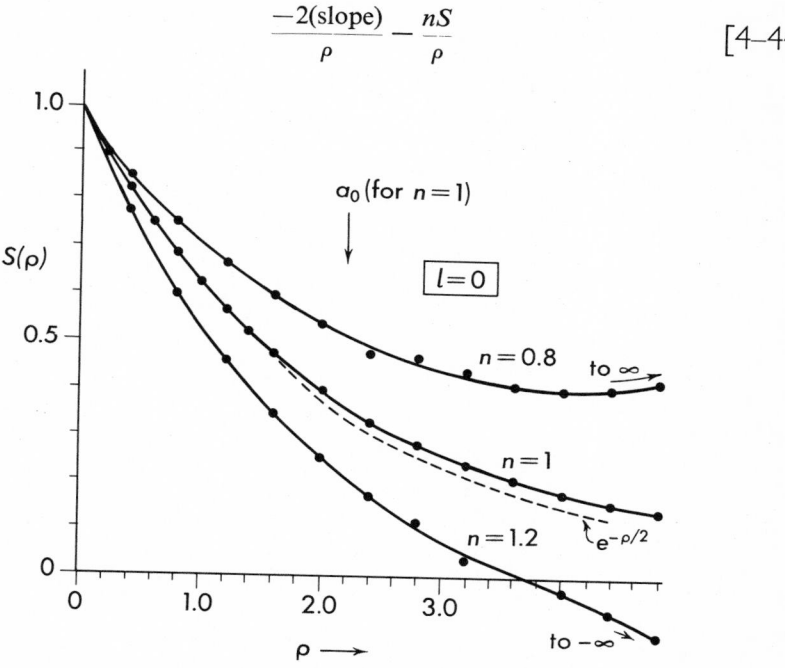

Fig. 4.8. The numerical calculation of the eigenfunction of the *r*-dependent equation for the hydrogen atom, for $n = l$ and $l = 0$.

is prevented from approaching ∞ as $\rho \to 0$. The sum [4–44] can be made zero by requiring that

$$(\text{slope})_{\rho=0} = -\frac{nS(0)}{2} \qquad\qquad [4\text{–}45$$

In other words, though we pick $\rho = 0$ as a starting point and are free to try any value n and also to choose any value of S at $\rho = 0$, we have subsequently no choice for the initial value of the *slope*, except that dictated by [4–45].

If we select $S(0) = +1$, and $n = 1$ then we must use $(\text{slope})_0 = -\frac{1}{2}$, and as Figure 4.8 shows, an eigenfunction exists. In Figure 4.8 we used $\Delta\rho = 0.2$ for small values of ρ, and $\Delta\rho = 0.4$ for larger values of ρ. (The initial slope *must* be $-1/2$, by [4–45].) The curve, connecting the numerically calculated points and labeled $n = 1$ in Figure 4.8, lies close to the dotted curve

$$S_{nl}(\rho) = S_{10}(\rho) = e^{-\rho/2}; \quad \rho = \frac{2r}{a_0} \qquad\qquad [4\text{–}46$$

which is the mathematically exact form for this (un-normalized) eigenfunction. Smaller steps, or improved methods of computation, will make the numerical points indistinguishable, on the scale of the figure, from the mathematical curve.

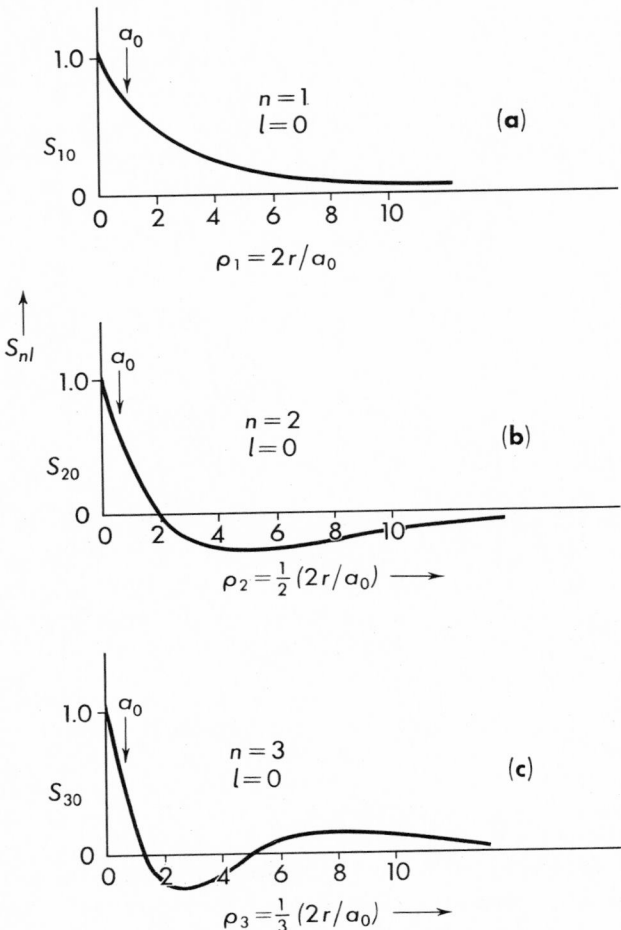

Fig. 4.9. The r-dependent eigenfunction of the hydrogen atom, for $l = 0$ and $n = 1$, 2, and 3.

If $n = .8$ or $n = 1.2$, as Figure 4.8 shows, $S(\rho)$ is ill behaved, approaching either $+$ or $-\infty$ for large ρ. We can see why there can be no eigenfunction for $n < 1$. Already, at $n = .8$, the curve for $S(\rho)$ never reaches the $S = 0$ axis, and, as n becomes smaller, this behavior becomes even more pronounced.

[Since $\rho = (1/n)\,(2r/a_0)$, the unit of ρ, as used on the graph, is different for each value of n in Figure 4.8. This contraction or expansion of the abscissa does not, however, alter the *shape* of the curves—and this is what determines the existence of the eigenfunction.]

For $l = 0$, eigenfunctions are found to exist for $n = 1, 2, 3, 4, \cdots$. Figure 4.9 shows the form of these functions for $n = 1, 2,$ and 3. For $n = 2, l = 0,$

$$S_{20}(\rho) = (2 - \rho)\, e^{-\rho/2} \qquad\qquad [4\text{–}47$$

The mathematical equations for the other functions are found in Appendix VI.

We turn next to the case where $l = 1$. To prevent an infinite value of $\Delta(\text{slope})$ at $\rho = 0$ (see [4–43]), it is necessary that

$$\frac{-2(\text{slope})}{\rho} + \left[\frac{l(l+1)}{\rho^2} - \frac{n}{\rho} \right] S$$

be finite as $\rho \to 0$. If $S = k\rho$ for small values of ρ, then (for $l = 1$) the above expression becomes

$$-\frac{2k}{\rho} + \frac{2}{\rho^2}\, k\rho - \frac{n}{\rho}\, k\rho = -n\,k$$

which is finite, as required. Thus, when $l = 1$, S must have zero magnitude and *any* finite slope, k, at $\rho = 0$.

It is remarkable that, although l is now unity instead of zero, an eigenfunction is again found for the case that $n = 2$ (Fig. 4.10). (There is, as we have already seen in Figure 4.9b, an eigenfunction for the case $l = 0$, $n = 2$.)

In Figure 4.10 $S(\rho)$ is plotted, by numerical calculation, for the case $l = 1$, $n = 2$. The initial slope was chosen as $+1$, and $\Delta\rho = 0.2$. This curve has the mathematical form

$$S_{nl}(\rho) = S_{21}(\rho) = \rho\, e^{-\rho/2} \qquad\qquad [4\text{–}48$$

When $l = 1$, $S(\rho)$ is not a suitable wave function for $n < 2$, as can be inferred from the dashed curve in Figure 4.10. The curve gets started away from the $S = 0$ axis and never returns. This is due to the presence of the term $l(l+1)/\rho^2 = 2/\rho^2$ which was not present when $l = 0$. Thus, there is *no* r-dependent eigenfunction for the combination $l = 1$, $n = 1$, since $S(\rho)$ will have a form similar to that sketched in Figure 4.10 for $n = 1$.

For $n = 3, 4, 5, 6, \cdots$, however, eigenfunctions exist. The form of $S(\rho)$ for $n = 3$ is sketched in Figure 4.10. Its mathematical form is

$$S_{31}(\rho) = (4 - \rho)\, \rho\, e^{-\rho/2} \qquad\qquad [4\text{–}49$$

Thus, when $l = 1$ an eigenfunction exists only when $n = 2, 3, 4, 5, \cdots$.

An examination of [4–43] for the case $l = 2$ shows that *both* the slope and $S(\rho)$ must be zero at $\rho = 0$. It now turns out that there is no value of n

less than $n = 3$ for which an eigenfunction exists. The term $l(l + 1)/\rho^2 = 6/\rho^2$ is now so influential[18] that only for $n \geq 3$ can the curve $S(\rho)$ be brought back to the $S = 0$ axis (see Problem 4.11). Thus, when $l = 2$, n can have only the values 3, 4, 5, 6, $\cdots$.

Similarly, when $l = 3$, $S(\rho)$, eigenfunctions exist only when $n = 4, 5, 6, \cdots$.

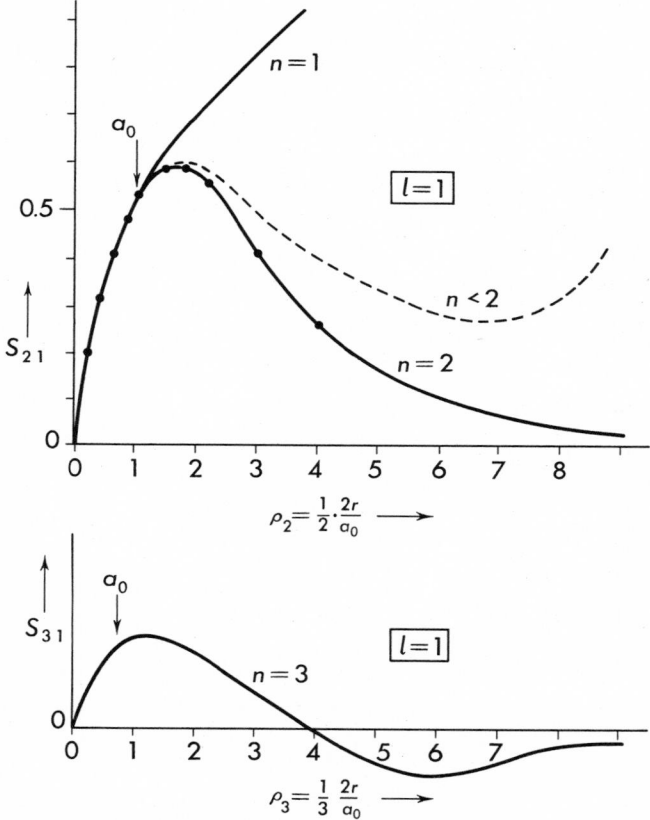

Fig. 4.10. The r-dependent eigenfunctions for the hydrogen atom for $l = 1$ and $n = 2$ and 3. It is clear from the upper figure that there is no eigenfunction for $n < 2$.

Appendix VI lists the normalized eigenfunctions $R(r)$ for the hydrogen atom. These functions are known as the associated Laguerre functions. They

---

[18] We shall find in Section 6.3 that $\sqrt{\hbar^2\, l(l + 1)}$ is the expectation value of the *magnitude of the angular momentum* of the system. It is reasonable that states with angular momentum ($l \geq 1$) must have an energy above that of the lowest state ($n = 1$, $l = 0$), since large angular momentum is associated with large kinetic energy of rotation.

can be found by methods similar to those used in Appendix I. They are discussed in many quantum mechanics textbooks.[19]

Summarizing the possible eigenfunctions of $R(r)$ [or $S(\rho)$], we find that when $l = 0$, eigenfunctions of the r-dependent equation exist for

$$n = 1, 2, 3, 4, 5, \cdots .$$

when $l = 1$, eigenfunctions of the r-dependent equation exist for

$$n = \quad 2, 3, 4, 5, \cdots .$$

when $l = 2$, eigenfunctions of the r-dependent equation exist for

$$n = \quad\quad 3, 4, 5, \cdots .$$

Also, from Section 4.5,

when $m = 0$, eigenfunctions of the θ-dependent equation exist for

$$l = 0, 1, 2, 3, 4, \cdots .$$

when $m = \pm 1$, eigenfunctions of the θ-dependent equation exist for

$$l = \quad 1, 2, 3, 4, \cdots .$$

when $m = \pm 2$, eigenfunctions of the θ-dependent equation exist for

$$l = \quad\quad 2, 3, 4, \cdots .$$

Finally, from Section 4.4, eigenfunctions of the ϕ-dependent equation exist for $m = 0, \pm 1, \pm 2, \pm 3, \cdots .$

Since *all three* factors, R, Θ, and Φ, which form ψ must *each* be well behaved and of integrable square in order for ψ itself to be an eigenfunction, we see from the summary above that only certain combinations of n, l, and m can occur:

$$n = 1: \quad l = 0, \text{ and } m = 0$$

$$n = 2: \begin{cases} l = 0, \text{ and } m = 0 \\ \quad \text{or} \\ l = 1, \text{ and } m = -1, 0, 1 \end{cases}$$

$$n = 3: \begin{cases} l = 0, \text{ and } m = 0 \\ \quad \text{or} \\ l = 1, \text{ and } m = -1, 0, 1 \\ \quad \text{or} \\ l = 2, \text{ and } m = -2, -1, 0, 1, 2 \end{cases}$$

---

[19] For example, see L. Pauling and E. B. Wilson, *op. cit.*, pp. 121 and 129.

4.7. The energy levels of the hydrogen atom

The *r*-equation has eigenfunctions only for certain definite values of the total energy W_n. By [4–41]

$$W_n = -\frac{\mu \, e^4}{2n^2 \, \hbar^2} \qquad [4\text{–}50$$

Since the proton : electron mass ratio is 1836, then

$$\mu = \left(\frac{1836}{1836 + 1}\right) \times (9.1 \times 10^{-28}) \text{ gm}$$

Using $e = 4.8 \times 10^{-10}$ esu and $\hbar = 1.05 \times 10^{-27}$ erg sec, we have[20]

$$W_1 = -2.15 \times 10^{-11} \text{ ergs} = 13.53 \text{ e.v.}$$
$$W_2 = W_1/4$$
$$W_3 = W_1/9$$
$$W_4 = W_1/16, \text{ etc.}$$

W_1 is the lowest possible, or "ground state," energy. In Figure 1.1 the Lyman series of the hydrogen spectrum consists of transitions from the higher levels, $n = 2, 3, 4, \cdots$, to the level at $n = 1$. The first line, between $n = 2$ and $n = 1$, should have an energy

$$E = h \, \nu = (2.15 \times 10^{-11}) \left(\frac{1}{1^2} - \frac{1}{2^2}\right)$$

and a frequency and wavelength

$$\nu = 2.43 \times 10^{15} \text{ cps and } \lambda = \frac{c}{\nu} = 1230 \times 10^{-8} \text{ cm}$$

This, and all of the other spectral lines in Figure 1.1, are in excellent agreement with experiment.[21] (These results were also obtained by the old quantum theory based upon the Bohr model of the atom.)

4.8. The complete hydrogen atom eigenfunctions

The complete wave function Ψ_T of a hydrogen atom in a large rectangular box whose walls act only on the center of mass of the atom (that is, upon the

---

[20] MKS: $W_1 \text{ (joules)} = \dfrac{-\mu(\text{Kg}) \, (1/4\pi \, \varepsilon_0)^2 \, e^4 (\text{coulomb})^4}{2 \cdot 1 \cdot \hbar^2 (\text{joule sec})^2} = -2.15 \times 10^{-18} \text{ joules.}$

[21] In Chapter 11 we shall see that the matter waves belonging to the electron have features usually described by the term "spin," which is related to the intrinsic magnetic moment of the electron. The energy levels listed here are not quite correct due to the neglect of these and other small effects.

atom as a whole) (see Appendix IV), is

$$\Psi_T = X_{n_x}(x)\, Y_{n_y}(y)\, Z_{n_z}(z)\, e^{-i\frac{W_{tr}}{\hbar}t} \cdot \underbrace{R_{nl}(r)\, \Theta_{lm}(\theta)\, \Phi_m(\phi)\, e^{-i\frac{W_n}{\hbar}t}}_{\Psi_{nlm}} \qquad [4\text{--}51$$

where x, y, and z are the coordinates of the center of mass and r, θ, and ϕ locate one particle with respect to the other in spherical coordinates. W_{tr} is the energy of translation, and W_n is the internal energy of the atomic system.

In [4–51] we have written out the complete wave function for a pair of particles (bound together into an atomic system, but also bound, as a system, inside a much larger potential well) in order to give an example of how quantum mechanics provides a complete and consistent description of assemblies of particles. In Chapter 1 we mentioned that experiments on the diffraction from a crystal grating of atoms, and even of molecules, show that these systems have the same type of wave properties as electrons. The waves are associated with the translational motion of the complete system. We see, with the aid of [4–51], how this can occur. If the diffraction grating reflects the atom as a whole (just as, in [4–51], we assume that the walls of the box reflect the atom as a whole) then due to its dependence upon x, y, and z, ψ_T will demonstrate the same interference effects as for a single point particle whose mass is $(m_1 + m_2)$, and whose translational kinetic energy is W_{tr} (see Appendix IV).

Referring to Appendix IV, we list for purposes of discussion the amplitude wave functions ψ_{nlm} belonging to the two lowest energy levels.

$$(a_0 = \hbar^2/\mu e^2 = 0.528 \times 10^{-8} \text{ cm})$$

For the lowest energy level, $n = 1$, so

$$W_1 = -\frac{\mu e^4}{2\hbar^2} = -2.15 \times 10^{-11} \text{ ergs}$$

$$\Psi_{100} = \frac{1}{\sqrt{\pi}}\left(\frac{1}{a_0}\right)^{3/2} e^{-r/a_0}\, e^{-i\frac{W_1}{\hbar}t} \qquad [4\text{--}52$$

For the next higher energy level, $n = 2$ and $W_2 = W_1/4$, there are four wave functions,

$$\Psi_{200} = \frac{1}{4\sqrt{2\pi}}\left(\frac{1}{a_0}\right)^{3/2}\left(2 - \frac{r}{a_0}\right) e^{-r/2a_0}\, e^{-i\frac{W_2}{\hbar}t}$$

$$\Psi_{210} = \frac{1}{4\sqrt{2\pi}}\left(\frac{1}{a_0}\right)^{3/2}(\cos\theta)\frac{r}{a_0} e^{-r/2a_0}\, e^{-i\frac{W_2}{\hbar}t}$$

$$\Psi_{211} = \frac{1}{4\sqrt{2\pi}}\left(\frac{1}{a_0}\right)^{3/2}\frac{e^{i\phi}}{\sqrt{2}}(\sin\theta)\frac{r}{a_0} e^{-r/2a_0}\, e^{-i\frac{W_2}{\hbar}t} \qquad [4\text{--}53$$

$$\Psi_{21-1} = \frac{1}{4\sqrt{2\pi}}\left(\frac{1}{a_0}\right)^{3/2}\frac{e^{-i\phi}}{\sqrt{2}}(\sin\theta)\frac{r}{a_0} e^{-r/2a_0}\, e^{-i\frac{W_2}{\hbar}t}$$

All the functions in [4–52] and [4–53] have the feature

$$\int_0^{2\pi} \int_0^{\pi} \int_0^{\infty} \Psi^*_{nlm} \, \Psi_{nlm} \, \underbrace{r^2 \sin\theta \, d\phi \, d\theta \, dr}_{d\tau} = 1 \qquad [4\text{–}54$$

that is, they are normalized.[22]

$\Psi^* \Psi$ is the probability that the particle will be found in the volume element $d\tau$. If one imagines three-dimensional forms whose density, or blackness, is proportional to $\Psi^* \Psi$, then $\Psi^*_{100} \, \Psi_{100}$ is a spherical form, most dense at the origin, and decreasing exponentially with radius. $\Psi^*_{200} \Psi^*_{200}$ forms two concentric spheres, with a null at $r = 2a_0$. For $\Psi^*_{211} \Psi_{211}$, the term $r^2 e^{-r/a_0}$ forms a radially "smeared" spherical shell which, by the term $\sin^2 \theta$, is then turned into a toroidal (doughnut-shaped) ring—since $\Psi = 0$ at $\theta = 0$ and at $\theta = \pi$. In a similar manner, one can visualize the wave functions for each of the stationary states of the hydrogen atom.[23]

The spatial form of the probability density permits a certain amount of physical interpretation. The spherically symmetrical pattern $\Psi^*_{100} \, \Psi_{100}$ is the standing-wave pattern of ingoing and outgoing spherical waves. A spherical cavity with reflecting walls, at R_0, containing at its center a small, concentric spherical sound wave generator, will produce a similar resonance. (The matter waves, however, are reflected from a *diffuse* barrier, the potential well, $-e^2/r$.) For the sound waves, the longest wavelength (lowest frequency) that will resonate will be $\lambda/2 = R_0$—i.e., the reflected wave from the walls is a shrinking sphere, and arrives back at the small central spherical generator just in time to be in phase, after reflection, with the next outgoing wave. The next resonance will occur at half this wavelength, and a null will occur at a radius midway between the generator and the walls. For matter waves, for $n = 2$, we also have a shorter wavelength and the null at one value of the radius, but again there are differences in detail due to the mathematical form of the wave equation including the diffuse reflecting barrier, $-e^2/r$ (see Problem 4.5).

Thus, the lowest energy state of the hydrogen atom, and also the states identified by Ψ_{200}, Ψ_{300}, may be regarded as a resonance due to radially symmetrical outgoing and incoming matter waves.

The states whose eigenfunctions are Ψ_{211} and Ψ_{21-1} have a torroidal-shaped probability density function and can be conceived as a resonance of

---

[22] As Appendix II points out, the postulates demand that whenever two eigenfunctions Ψ_1 and Ψ_2 have different characteristic energies (here, $n_1 \neq n_2$) then $\int \psi_1^* \psi_2 \, d\tau = 0$. Thus, for example, $\int \Psi^*_{100} \, \Psi_{200} \, d\tau$ is, by these general considerations, guaranteed to be zero. It happens to be true, however, that the four wave functions [4–53], even though they have the same characteristic energy, are orthogonal. If this did not happen to be true, four mutually orthogonal functions *could be* constructed from linear combinations of the original, non-orthogonal eigenfunctions (see end of Appendix II).

[23] For an excellent visual representation of the hydrogen eigenfunctions, see Harvey E. White, *Introduction to Atomic Spectra* (1934, McGraw-Hill Book Co. Inc., New York).

matter waves which are propagating around a circular path. Their curvature is caused by the radially varying index of refraction. (Potential energy—and therefore the wave length—vary with radius.) It is reasonable to expect, and we shall show later, that these states correspond to electrons with definite angular momentum about the *z*-axis.

Again, as in the case of the harmonic oscillator for low quantum numbers, the form of the wave function and the motion of the equivalent classical particle do not have much correlation. The too-liberal use of classical concepts for micro-systems can often be misleading, except, as the correspondence principle states, as one approaches the classical limit—i.e., for large quantum numbers.

4.9. The energy levels of a physical system

In this chapter we have often used the expression "energy levels" as referring to the physical system, whereas in the mathematical analysis we were merely finding those eigenvalues W_n of the parameter W that are needed to make the Ψ's well behaved and of integrable square.

However, as in the one-dimensional case of Chapter 3, it is easy to show that for both the box and for the hydrogen atom the eigenvalues of the parameter W_n are related to the expectation value of the energy of the system.

Postulate V states that

$$\overline{W} = \int \Psi^* \left(-\frac{\hbar}{i} \frac{\partial}{\partial t} \right) \Psi \, d\tau \qquad [4\text{-}55$$

and

$$\overline{W^2} = \int \Psi^* \left(-\frac{\hbar}{i} \frac{\partial}{\partial t} \right) \left(-\frac{\hbar}{i} \frac{\partial}{\partial t} \right) \Psi \, d\tau \qquad [4\text{-}56$$

For either the box or the hydrogen atom, we assume that Ψ is any one of the eigenfunctions, Ψ_k. (For the box, k stands for a particular set of values n_x, n_y, n_z. For the atom, k stands for a particular set of values n, l, m. In other words, k identifies *one* of the eigenfunctions out of the complete list of all eigenfunctions.)
Then,

$$\overline{W} = W_k \quad \text{and} \quad \overline{W^2} = W_k^2 \qquad [4\text{-}57$$

since for both cases

$$\Psi = \psi_k \text{ (space coord.) } e^{-i\frac{W_k}{\hbar}t} \qquad [4\text{-}58$$

and the integrals $\int \psi_k^* \psi_k \, d\tau$ are unity for all k. (For the box, $d\tau = dx \, dy \, dz$; for the atom, $d\tau = r^2 \sin \theta \, d\phi \, d\theta \, dr$.)

Thus, if a system has as its wave function an eigenfunction Ψ_k, it has a unique, exactly predictable, energy W_k. In the next chapter we will discuss systems with wave functions other than the particular type [4–58] and we will see that the energy of a system is not always an exactly predictable quantity.

Systems whose wave function Ψ is a single eigenfunction Ψ_k as in [4–58] also have a *probability density function* $\Psi^* \Psi$, independent of time. These states are called stationary states. Thus we see that stationary states and predictable energy are intimately associated.

4.10. Conclusion

We have seen that matter waves belonging to particles with three-dimensional motion are similar to those for one-dimensional motion, and three-dimensional bound systems have basically the same resonance effects as one-dimensional bound systems.

In this chapter we have found, with relative ease, the eigenfunctions of a particle in a rectangular box with infinitely high walls. We found, however, that the eigenfunctions for a particle, bound by a spherically symmetrical potential "wall," were mathematically much more complex—even though the basic principles used in finding the solution were the same. Unfortunately, without these eigenfunctions the quantitative understanding of atomic structure is impossible.

Once obtained, the Legendre and Laguerre functions can be used as tools for calculation in problems involving spherical symmetry much as one uses the sinusoidal functions in problems involving rectangular symmetry. In both cases, an understanding of the origin of the functions is essential for their proper use.

Electrons which happen to have positive total energy as $r \to \infty$ (they have K.E. at $r \to \infty$) will, upon approaching a nucleus, be deflected but will leave it again without being bound permanently. The characteristic energy values for these states are positive. We shall not discuss this type of system here except to note that the situation is quite similar to that in Figure 3.6, where we assumed the presence of a small potential well which influences the electron's motion but does not bind the electron. There we assumed the existence of reflecting walls at a great distance. For the three-dimensional case, eigenfunctions can be found for the new complete system, including, now, perfectly reflecting walls located at great distances. These new eigenfunctions will have the general appearance of those in Figure 3.6. They have a long wavelength (gradual curvature) at large distances from the central potential well. The waves *inside* the well (which must smoothly join the long waves) have sharp curvature but generally a low amplitude since, classically, the particle has high velocity inside the well and therefore spends little time as it whisks past the attractive charge. This problem—the scattering of particles—will be left to more advanced courses in quantum theory.[24] We merely point out here that the systematic application of the postulates will again produce distinct

---

[24] There is a qualitative discussion of scattering in Section 5.6.

eigenfunctions, now very numerous and closely spaced. As in the one-dimensional case in Chapter 3, these states are called the "continuum," for as the box becomes very large the eigenfunctions become infinitely numerous and the characteristic system energies W_k become very closely spaced.

4.11. Summary of Chapters 3 and 4

A single particle of mass m, moving in three dimensions, having a (classical) total energy W equal to

$$\frac{1}{2m}(p_x^2 + p_y^2 + p_z^2) + V(x, y, z) \qquad [4\text{--}59$$

has the wave equation

$$\left[-\frac{\hbar^2}{2m}\nabla^2 + V(x, y, z)\right]\Psi = -\frac{\hbar}{i}\frac{\partial}{\partial t}\Psi \qquad [4\text{--}60$$

where

$$\nabla^2 = \frac{\partial^2}{\partial x^2} + \frac{\partial^2}{\partial y^2} + \frac{\partial^2}{\partial z^2} \qquad [4\text{--}61$$

Let

$$\Psi = \psi(x, y, z)\, e^{-i\frac{W}{\hbar}t} \qquad [4\text{--}62$$

Then the wave equation [4–60] becomes

$$H\Psi = -\frac{\hbar}{i}\frac{\partial}{\partial t}\Psi, \quad \text{or} \quad H\Psi = W\Psi \qquad [4\text{--}63$$

and, since H is independent of t,

$$H\psi = W\psi \qquad [4\text{--}64$$

where

$$H = -(\hbar^2/2m)\,\nabla^2 + V(x, y, z) \qquad [4\text{--}65^{25}$$

H is called the Hamiltonian operator for the system. It is called by this name because it is derived by operator substitution from the expression for the total system energy [4–59], which, in classical mechanics, is the Hamiltonian function. The operator H can also be expressed in spherical or other appropriate coordinates.

There is always some ψ-function which, for *any* value of W, will produce an identity in [4–63], but (as we have seen) only for certain discrete, real values of W, W_k will the ψ-functions be well behaved and have an integrable square.

---

[25] Since i does not appear in H (the operator $H^* = H$), and since W is real, the complex conjugate of [4–63] is

$$H\Psi^* = +\frac{\hbar}{i}\frac{\partial}{\partial t}\Psi^* \text{ or } H\Psi^* = W\Psi^*$$

These are called eigenfunctions, and are usually designated by ψ_n or ψ_k where the index n or k is not necessarily a quantum number as we have been using them, but rather identifies a particular eigenfunction in a systematic list of all the eigenfunctions of a given system. For example, the amplitude eigenfunctions of the hydrogen atom are ψ_{100}, ψ_{200}, ψ_{210}, ψ_{211}, etc. The general symbol for an eigenfunction, ψ_n, merely identifies one of these unique functions by its order in the list. Thus, ψ_4 might refer to ψ_{211}.

By hypothesis, the eigenfunctions ψ_n can correspond to possible states of real systems. For these functions [4–63] becomes

$$H\Psi_n = W_n \Psi_n \quad \text{or} \quad H\psi_n = W_n \psi_n \qquad [\text{4–66}$$

W_n is an eigenvalue (a real constant) of the operator H, belonging to the eigenfunction ψ_n.

We have considered, in one dimension, the particle in a box, and the harmonic oscillator. In three dimensions, we have considered the particle in a box and also the particle moving in a fixed radially symmetrical potential, of the form $1/r$. We found a family of eigenfunctions, ψ_n, which belongs to each system. We also found, for each eigenfunction, an energy parameter W_n, which is, in each case, a real number, expressible in ergs. Sometimes different eigenfunctions have the same W_n, a situation described by the word *degeneracy*.

Since each of the eigenfunctions has an integrable square, it can always be multiplied by some constant so that it is normalized, that is,

$$\int \Psi_n^* \Psi_n \, d\tau = 1 \qquad [\text{4–67}$$

where $d\tau$ is the volume element. The integration is performed over all space variables throughout the region where Ψ is different from zero ("over all configuration space").

Also, we have seen that in general, when $W_n \neq W_k$,

$$\int \Psi_k^* \Psi_n \, d\tau = 0$$

That is, eigenfunctions belonging to different W_n's are orthogonal. The wave equation and boundary conditions alone do not guarantee the orthogonality of the Ψ_n's which have the *same* eigenvalue, W_n, for the operator H. However, it is always possible to construct linear combinations of the degenerate Ψ_n's which *are* mutually orthogonal.

Thus, for any bound system there is a set of discrete functions, Ψ_n, which are ortho-normal. Sometimes this set is finite in number, as in the case of the box with finite walls, and sometimes infinite in number, as in the case of the hydrogen atom.

The existence of a set of ortho-normal functions of space which belong to each particular form of the operator H (and therefore to each particular mechanical system) is of great practical importance. Unfortunately, in only a small fraction of systems of physical interest can the wave equation be solved

in closed form. Consequently, the greater part of quantum mechanical calculations consists of manipulating these sets of ortho-normal functions in the
manner that Fourier series are used to find solutions to otherwise intractable
differential equations.

PROBLEMS

Problem 4.1.   A rectangular box with perfectly reflecting walls
has the dimensions $a = b = 1 \times 10^{-8}$ cm, and $c = 3 \times 10^{-8}$ cm.
A particle of electronic mass ($m = 9.1 \times 10^{-28}$ gm) is trapped in
this box.

   (a) What energy W belongs to the lowest possible state?
   (b) Draw a chart, as in Figure 4.2, showing the first half-dozen
        characteristic energy levels, and then list the different wave
        functions that belong to each level.

Problem 4.2.   Calculate the pressure on the walls of the box of
Problem 4.1 due to the trapped electron, when in its lowest state. (Hint:
Use (force)$_x = -\partial W/\partial x$. Assume that the work done in a slow compression of the volume of the box appears in the stored energy of the
system.) Is the pressure the same on each wall? Consider a classical
particle with the same energy, and find the pressure it produces, using
the classical expression $F \Delta t = m \Delta v$ for the case that the particle is
moving parallel to one axis. (Note: The pressure on the walls of this
small imaginary box is not an observable quantity. However, gas
atoms inside a real box produce directly observable pressure, which
can be calculated, using the wave functions, by the same basic method
used here.)

Problem 4.3.   A box with dimensions the same as in Problem
4.1, containing an electron, has walls which are 20 e.v. high. (1 e.v.
$= 1.60 \times 10^{-12}$ erg).

   (a) What is the lowest energy level of this system? (Use results
        and methods of Problem 3.7.)
   (b) Is there a higher, bound eigenstate?

Problem 4.4.   A helium atom at 1 degree Kelvin is trapped in
a cubical box, 1 cm on a side.

   (a) Assume the eigenfunction of this system to be of the form
        ψ_{n11}. Estimate n. [$(1/2)(mv^2)_{av} = 3/2\,kT$. ($k$ = Boltzmann's
        constant.)]
   (b) What is the approximate spacing between energy levels for
        this system, in this energy range?

(c) Sketch or otherwise describe the probability density function for this system.

Problem 4.5. Calculate, by the steps outlined below, the approximate value of the lowest energy level for an $l = 0$ electron in a perfectly reflecting, spherical cavity of radius r_0 ($r_0 = 1 \times 10^{-8}$ cm). Let $V(r) = 0$ from $r = 0$ to $r = r_0$, and $V(r) = +\infty$, for $r > r_0$.

(a) Starting with [4–26], show that, for $l = 0$,

$$\Delta(\text{slope}) = \left\{ -\frac{2}{r}(\text{slope}) - \frac{2\mu W}{\hbar^2} R(r) \right\} \Delta r; \quad 0 \leq r \leq r_0$$

where $(\text{slope}) = dR(r)/dr$, $R(r)$ is the radial factor in the wave function, W (a positive number) is the system energy in ergs, and μ is the reduced mass in grams.

(b) What must be the value of the slope at $r = 0$?

(c) What must be the value of R at $r = r_0$?

(d) On a graph of R vs. r, and using (c) and (b), sketch the approximate form of $R(r)$ for the two lowest energy states. Also sketch on the same graph, in dotted lines, the general form of these two wave functions if, for $r > r_0$, V is very large but not infinite.

(e) The value of W which will cause $R(r)$ to meet the boundary conditions can be found, by systematic search, using the above differential instructions. The steps, Δr, may be as large as $r_0/5$ for purposes of approximate calculation. This problem has been solved by standard mathematical methods[26] which give the result that when

$$l = 0, \ W_n = n^2 \pi^2 \hbar^2/2\mu\, r_0{}^2, \quad n = 1, 2, 3, \cdots .$$

One can quickly show, by numerical calculations, that $R(r)$ meets the necessary requirements (for the lowest energy state) when $W = W_1$ where $W_1 = \pi^2 \hbar^2/2\mu\, r_0{}^2$.

(f) The mathematical form of the wave functions for $l = 0$ is $R(r) = (A \sin \alpha r)/r$, where $\alpha = \sqrt{2mW/\hbar^2}$. Mathematically, the energy levels are derived from the requirement $\alpha r_0 = n\pi$, where $n = 1, 2, 3, \cdots$. Why is this done? Sketch the $n = 2$ function. Does it meet the boundary conditions at $r = 0$?

(g) Given, $R_1(r)$ is proportional to $(\sin \alpha r)/r$, find the normalized Ψ_1.

(h) How would you start the process of searching, numerically, for an eigenfunction, when $l = 1$?

---

[26] See, for example, L. I. Schiff, *Quantum Mechanics* (1949, McGraw-Hill Book Co., Inc., New York): p. 76.

Problem 4.6.   A hydrogen atom has the wave function, Ψ_{100}.

(a) Plot $\Psi^{*}_{100}\,\Psi_{100}$. $(4\,\pi r^2\,dr)$ vs. r. Interpret.
(b) Consider the proton to be a sphere, of radius $= 10^{-13}$ cm. Assuming that Ψ_{100} is the correct wave function for the hydrogen atom at these short distances, calculate the chance that the electron will be inside the proton.
(c) Calculate the chance that the electron would be found outside the sphere, $r = a_0$.

Problem 4.7.   Find the Bohr radius a_0 and the energy W_1 of the lowest bound state for:

(a) Singly ionized helium, He $(Z = 2)$ and one electron.
(b) Positronium, a positive and negative electron each of mass m_e.
(c) Mesonium, a proton and a negative μ meson of mass $207\ (m_e)$.
(d) Two neutrons, bound by their gravitational field. (See Appendix VI for some of the necessary data.)

Problem 4.8.   Explain why the Θ-eigenfunctions for $m = 0$ (Fig. 4.5) are not suitable for $m = \pm 1$. (Hint: Note that all the eigenfunctions in Fig. 4.5 have zero slope and *non-zero* magnitude at both $\theta = 0$ and $\theta = \pi$. The basic instructions [4–32] permit this to occur if $m = 0$. Let $m \neq 0$, however, and find the value of Δ(slope) in [4–32] as $\theta \to 0$, and $\theta \to \pi$.)

Problem 4.9

(a) Using [4–32], show when $\beta = 0$, that $\Theta(\theta)$ must have the form sketched in Figure 4.7a.
(b) Explain the reason for the shape of the $\beta = 2$ curve in Figure 4.7d.
(c) Sketch a $\beta = 0$ curve for Figure 4.7d.

Problem 4.10.   Equations [4–52] and [4–53] give the five eigenfunctions corresponding to the two lowest energy states of the hydrogen atom. Ψ_{100} *must* be orthogonal to all the others since $W_1 \neq W_2$, but we have no guarantee that the other four [4–53] are mutually orthogonal.

Show that Ψ_{200} is orthogonal to Ψ_{210}, Ψ_{211}, and Ψ_{21-1}
and that Ψ_{210} is orthogonal to Ψ_{211} and Ψ_{21-1}
and that Ψ_{211} is orthogonal to Ψ_{21-1}

(Hint: Look first at the results of either the θ or the ϕ integration.)

Problem 4.11.   Show, with a few steps of numerical calculation, that when $l = 2$ there is no eigenfunction for $n = 2$. For this case, $S(\rho)$ and $dS/d\rho$ must both be zero at $\rho = 0$. Why? (Note: To make possible the first step in a calculation, it is sometimes necessary to assume the initial form of the function. Here, assume $S = $ (const) ρ^2, for ρ near zero.)

Problem 4.12.   Test the orthogonality of the two eigenfunctions belonging to the lowest degenerate level of the particle in the cubical box, Figure 4.2.

Problem 4.13.   Calculate the possible standing-wave patterns which can occur in a rectangular "ripple tank"—a flat pan containing water. Let the two dimensions be a and b. Identify a standing wave pattern by the fact that the wave amplitude is zero everywhere on the boundary. For two dimensions, the classical wave equation is (see Appendix VIII, [4])

$$\frac{\partial^2 u_0}{\partial x^2} + \frac{\partial^2 u_0}{\partial y^2} + A\, u_0 = 0$$

where $u_0 = $ amplitude and where

$$A = \frac{4\pi^2}{\lambda^2}$$

an undetermined constant.

(a) Using the same method as for matter waves, separate the equation, and find formulas for the eigenfunctions and for the eigenvalues (unique values for the constant A).
(b) Let $a = 2b$. On the x–y plane sketch a few contours (lines of equal amplitude) showing the mode of vibration characteristic of the lowest value of A. Label "hills" and "valleys."
(c) Sketch a contour diagram of the mode of vibration for the next highest value of A.

Problem 4.14.   Find expressions for the eigenfunctions and eigenvalues of matter waves of a particle of mass m in an infinite-wall, two-dimensional box where the x-dimension is a and the y-dimension is b.

(a) If $a = 2b$, sketch the wave functions on an x–y contour diagram, for the three lowest energy states of the system, and show the energy eigenvalues on an energy diagram such as Figure 4.2.
(b) Repeat the calculation for two more cases, $a = 1.1b$ and $a = b$, and discuss the statement, "degeneracy is a conse-

quence of spatial symmetry." Would degeneracy occur if a differed from b by one part in 10^6?

Problem 4.15. The two-dimensional symmetrical harmonic oscillator of mass m has the potential function

$$V(x, y) = (1/2) k(x^2 + y^2)$$

where $k = $ a constant.

(a) Find the eigenfunctions belonging to the two lowest energy levels of the system. (Hint: Separate the variables in x, y coordinates.) Since the potential function is symmetrical in x and y, one should expect degeneracy to occur.

(b) Sketch, in contours, on an x–y diagram, each of the eigenfunctions found in (a). On the graph, label areas by "hill" or "valley."

(c) Sketch, in contours, on an x–y diagram, the probability densities of each of the eigenfunctions found in (a).

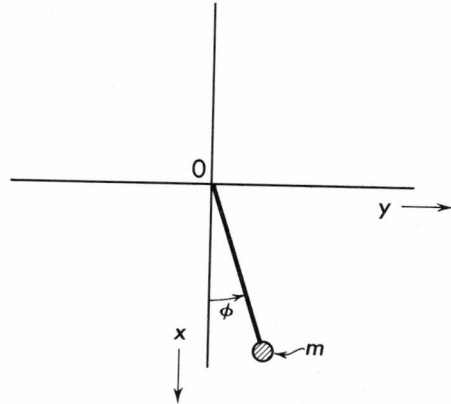

Fig. 4.11. The rigid rotator on a fixed axis.

Problem 4.16. *The Rigid Rotator on a Fixed Axis.* The mass m in Figure 4.11 rotates freely in the x-y plane ($\theta = \pi/2$) at a constant radius ($r = r_0$) from the fixed axis at 0.

(a) Show that the amplitude equation for this system is

$$\frac{d^2 \psi}{d \phi^2} + \frac{2m \, r_0^2}{\hbar^2} W \psi = 0$$

[Hint: This system differs from the hydrogen-like atom with an infinite mass nucleus in that $r = r_0$ and $\theta = \pi/2$. Thus, $\psi = \psi(\phi)$.]

(b) Show that the eigenfunctions and eigenvalues are

$$\psi_M = (1/\sqrt{2\pi})\, e^{iM\phi}, \quad W_M = M^2\, \hbar^2/2m\, r_0^2,$$

where

$$M = 0, \pm 1, \pm 2, \cdots$$

Note that, like the free particle, this system has no potential energy function and may have zero characteristic energy but, unlike the free particle, its energy states are quantized.

Problem 4.17. The Quantum States of the Pendulum. If, in Figure 4.11, a gravitational field g is directed along the $+x$-axis (downward on the diagram), the system becomes a pendulum with a mass m on the end of a weightless, rigid rod of length r_0. Its potential energy is

$$V(\phi) = mgr_0(1 - \cos\phi)$$

if V is defined to be zero when ϕ is zero.

(a) Show that for characteristic energies, $W_n \ll mgr_0$, ψ_n must be similar in form to the eigenfunctions of the harmonic oscillator.

(b) Sketch the potential function and, in correspondence with it, sketch the general form of ψ_0 and ψ_1 (assuming that there are at least two states for which W_n is less than mgr_0). Note: Eigenfunctions which have zero slope and non-zero amplitude at $\phi = 0$ must have zero slope, but may have any amplitude at the point $\phi = \pm\pi$. Also, eigenfunctions which have non-zero slope but zero amplitude at $\phi = 0$ must have zero amplitude, but may have any slope at the point $\phi = \pm\pi$. Explain.

(c) Sketch the form of an eigenfunction for a state which has a characteristic energy greater than $2\, mgr_0$. This function too must have one of the two types of symmetry discussed in (b).

(d) With the aid of the correspondence principle, sketch the form of ψ_n for a system in a state whose energy W_n is *slightly less* than $2\, mgr_0$. (It is necessary, of course, that $n \gg 1$ for the correspondence principle to be an accurate guide.)

Problem 4.18. The eigenfunctions of the pendulum discussed in Problem 4.17 are of assistance in giving some insight into the nature of the quantum states of a particle in a periodic potential well $V(x)$, shown in Figure 4.12.

(a) Assume that W_0 and W_1 have such values that ψ_0 and ψ_1 repeat (exactly) in one period of the potential—just as ψ_0 and ψ_1 were found to do in Problem 4.17. W_0 and W_1 are the two lowest energy states of the system. Sketch these two wave functions, showing the correspondence to the energy graph of Figure 4.12.

(b) Similarly, plot a typical ψ_n which belongs to $W_n > V_0$. Note that there are again only two possible types of symmetry for ψ_n. (Assume that some distant, high potential barriers exist which bind the W_n state.) W_0 and W_1 are typical "bound" states in a periodic lattice, and W_n is a "free"

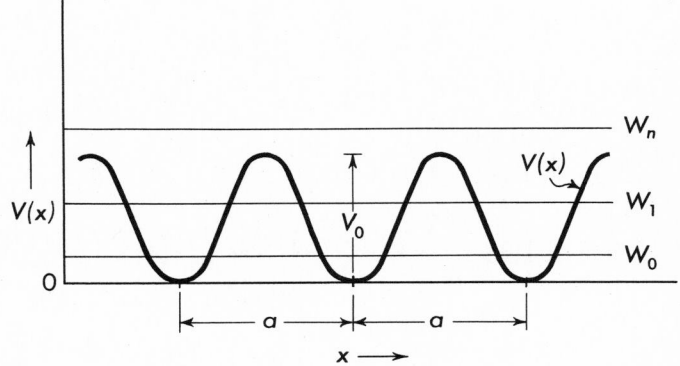

Fig. 4.12.   Bound and free states in a periodic, one-dimensional potential well.

particle (as in the "conduction band" of a crystal). ψ's which repeat in exactly *one* period of the lattice are not the only possible well-behaved wave functions. There are others (with slightly different energies) which repeat in 2, 3, 4, $\cdots$ periods of the lattice with the result that there are "bands" of states (over a continuous energy range) which are sometimes isolated by gaps containing no states. See Rojansky[27] for a discussion of the states of one-dimensional periodic functions.

[27] V. Rojansky, *Introductory Quantum Mechanics* (1942, Prentice-Hall, Inc., New York): pp. 269–76.

5

THE SUPERPOSITION OF STATES, AND SOME CALCULATIONS USING THE WAVE FUNCTION

Up to this point, we have been mainly concerned with Postulates I through IV. The use of these postulates has been essentially a mathematical exercise, whose end result is the identification of certain functions of space and time, $\Psi_n(x, y, z, t)$ or $\Psi_n(r, \theta, \phi, t)$, called eigenfunctions, which belong to each particular system. The one link to the world of experiment, however, is Postulate V, which is the calculation of the expectation value, or average value of an observable. So far, no one has devised a method of predicting any *more* than is predicted by Postulate V. This limitation has all the earmarks of being permanently imposed and forever preventing us from attaining the detailed knowledge of microscopic motion that we have become accustomed to with macroscopic motion. However, we must remember that the observation of a single electron or a single photon always involves some process using very great magnification. For example, a single electron, entering an electron multiplier, must ultimately cause 10^8 electrons to appear on the deflection plate of a cathode ray tube before an appreciable deflection can be observed with the unaided eye. The world dominated by quantum effects is very remote from that of direct experience. For the present, and in all likelihood permanently, we must be content with only those predictions about experiment that are given by Postulate V.

5.1. The superposition of states

Before performing calculations using Postulate V, we point out the important fact that the wave function of a system does not have to be merely *one* of the eigenfunctions which, as we have seen, satisfy the basic postulates. Any linear combination of eigenfunctions *also* satisfies Postulates I through IV, which determine the wave functions.[1] This result follows from the fact that the wave equation is linear (for example, Ψ^2 does not appear) and, since each of the eigenfunctions Ψ_n is itself well behaved and possesses an integrable square (i.e., is bounded in space), the sum of such functions will also be a solution to the wave equation, be well behaved, and be bounded in space. The postulates are as remarkable for what they do not say as for what they do say, and they certainly do not rule out Ψ-functions which are a superposition of the eigenfunctions, Ψ_n, of the Schrödinger wave equation.

Before showing mathematically that the above statements are true, we point out that equations of motion of macroscopic physical systems, such as vibrating strings or echoing rooms, show the same behavior. A string with its ends fixed has eigenfunctions of the same mathematical form as the wave functions of a particle in a box. It is a well-known fact that a string will vibrate in many modes or harmonics at the same time. Although the vibrating string obeys a different wave equation than does the particle in a box, the equation is linear and therefore any linear combination of eigenfunctions must satisfy the equation and also the boundary conditions. (Here, since the ends are fixed, the requirement is simply that the amplitude be zero at each end at all times.)

If one thinks of the *wave* nature of matter, it is easy to imagine an atom to consist of standing waves of many different frequencies, all simultaneously resonant. An echoing room or a resonating cavity, as used in radar, is often resonant at many frequencies *at the same time*.

In the notation used in Section 4.11 the wave equation including time is

$$H\Psi = -(\hbar/i)\,(\partial/\partial t)\,\Psi \qquad\qquad [5\text{--}1$$

Let

$$\Psi = a_n\,\psi_n\,e^{-i\frac{W_n}{\hbar}t} + a_k\,\psi_k\,e^{-i\frac{W_k}{\hbar}t} \qquad\qquad [5\text{--}2$$

that is, we assume that Ψ is a superposition (a linear combination) of two of the eigenstates (a_n and a_k are constants).

The complex conjugate of Ψ is

$$\Psi^* = a_n^*\,\psi_n^*\,e^{+i\frac{W_n}{\hbar}t} + a_k^*\,\psi_k^*\,e^{+i\frac{W_k}{\hbar}t} \qquad\qquad [5\text{--}3$$

Since, as was pointed out in Section 4.11, the operator H does not involve i

---

[1] The term "wave function" is applied to *any* Ψ-function which satisfies the basic postulates. The term "eigenfunction" always refers to one of the set of functions Ψ_n which are associated with stationary states.

(and also it does not involve t), we have

$$H\Psi_n = W_n\Psi_n \text{ and } H\Psi_k = W_k\Psi_k$$
$$H\Psi_n^* = W_n\Psi_n^* \text{ and } H\Psi_k^* = W_k\Psi_k^*$$

so that [5–2] is a solution of [5–1]—that is, it produces an identity, upon substitution. Also [5–3] is a solution to the complex conjugate of [5–1]. Thus Postulate II is satisfied.

It can be shown mathematically that the sum of well-behaved functions is usually a well-behaved function,[2] a result that is almost intuitively obvious. It is certainly true that the sum of any of the related eigenfunctions which we obtained in Chapters 3 and 4 is well behaved. Thus Postulate III is satisfied.

To see that Ψ satisfies Postulate IV, we calculate

$$\int \Psi^*\Psi\, d\tau = a_n^* a_n \int \Psi_n^*\Psi_n\, d\tau + a_k^* a_k \int \Psi_k^*\Psi_k\, d\tau$$
$$+ a_n^* a_k \int \Psi_n^*\Psi_k\, d\tau + a_k^* a_n \int \Psi_k^*\Psi_n\, d\tau \quad [5\text{–}4$$

The first two integrals on the right are unity and the second two are zero—due to the ortho-normality[3] of the ψ_n's. Therefore, to satisfy IV, we require that

$$a_n^* a_n + a_k^* a_k = 1 \qquad [5\text{–}5$$

and the new Ψ—the superposition of the two eigenstates—*is a fully satisfactory wave function, and does, therefore, correspond to a possible state of a real system.*

We can superimpose *all* of the eigenstates,

$$\Psi = \sum_n a_n\Psi_n \qquad [5\text{–}6$$

if only we require that

$$\sum_n a_n^* a_n = 1 \qquad [5\text{–}7$$

The property of being able to form a new solution to the wave equation by merely forming a linear combination [5–6] of the eigenfunctions (subject only to the condition [5–7]) has consequences of great importance. The surprising thing that happens is this: Any function $\Psi(x, t)$ that is well behaved and bounded in space at all times, as in Postulates III and IV, can be synthesized from the proper collection of the basic Ψ_n's.[4] The orthogonality of

---

[2] Using a complete, infinite set, it is possible to form a superposition which has finite discontinuities.

[3] The orthogonality and the normalization properties of eigenfunctions will be used again and again. These very properties are what make the eigenfunctions so valuable. The student should understand the mathematical basis of these properties. Appendix II discusses the orthogonality property.

[4] The "basic Ψ_n's," i.e., the family of eigenfunctions chosen to synthesize $\Psi(x, t)$, must be defined in the same domain as Ψ, and satisfy the same boundary conditions.

the basic Ψ_n's is the key to this remarkable result. We leave the more exact discussion of this theory (of orthogonal functions) to the textbooks of mathematics, but it is important to point out that *all* of the eigenfunctions belonging to a given family are needed to attain the maximum flexibility in synthesizing arbitrary functions.

We now show how to find the correct linear combination of orthogonal functions needed to synthesize a given function. For simplicity, we will consider a one-dimensional system. Let us suppose that at $t = t_0$, a system is known to have a *wave* function

$$\Psi(x, t_0) \qquad\qquad [5\text{-}8$$

which meets all the requirements of the postulates—that is, it is a solution to the wave equation, is well behaved, and is bounded in space by the requirement of the integrable square. The problem is to synthesize this *wave function* from the *eigenfunctions* of the system.

At the time $t = t_0$ we set the known function equal to a series of eigenfunctions, with undetermined coefficients, a_n:

$$\Psi(x, t_0) = a_1 \Psi_1 + a_2 \Psi_2 + a_3 \Psi_3 + \cdots \text{ all eigenfunctions}$$
$$= \sum_n a_n \Psi_n(x, t_0) \qquad\qquad [5\text{-}9$$

What are the values of the a_n's which make this true?

We can find each of the a_n's in turn, by the following method: To find the value of a_1, multiply both sides of [5-9] by Ψ_1^* and integrate both sides of the equation over the full range of the coordinate which was used in the determination of the eigenfunctions. Thus,

$$\int \Psi_1^* \Psi(x, t_0)\, dx = a_1 \int \Psi_1^* \Psi_1\, dx + a_2 \int \Psi_1^* \Psi_2\, dx$$
$$+ a_3 \int \Psi_1^* \Psi_3\, dx + \cdots \qquad\qquad [5\text{-}10$$

with the result that

$$a_1(t_0) = \int \Psi_1^* \Psi(x, t_0)\, dx \qquad\qquad [5\text{-}11$$

since all the other integrals on the right side of [5-10] are zero due to the orthogonality of the ψ_n's. In [5-11] we indicate that a_1 is determined at a particular time $t = t_0$.

In general,

$$a_n(t_0) = \int \Psi_n^*(x, t_0)\, \Psi(x, t_0)\, dx \qquad\qquad [5\text{-}12$$

We have assumed that $\Psi(x, t_0)$ is known, and each of the Ψ_n^*'s is known, so that each of the a_n's can be calculated at once. These values of a_n make [5-9] an identity.[5]

---

[5] For an introduction to the uses of orthogonal functions, see L. Pauling and E. B. Wilson, *Introduction to Quantum Mechanics* (1935, McGraw-Hill Book Co., Inc., New York): p. 151.

Since we originally required that $\Psi(x, t_0)$ be a normalized wave function, the calculation

$$\int \Psi^* \Psi \, dx = 1 \qquad [5\text{--}13$$

in which we substitute the expansion [5–9] for Ψ, will yield the result,

$$\sum_n a_n^* a_n = 1 \qquad [5\text{--}14$$

Thus, if the original wave function is normalized to unity, then the amplitudes of the "components" will automatically obey the condition [5–7] or [5–14].

By using the a_n's determined by [5–12] in the series [5–9], we have synthesized the wave function $\Psi(x, t_0)$.

As an example of the application of this theory, we will synthesize a function using the set of eigenfunctions for the one-dimensional, infinite-wall box of Section 3.4. By [3–23] the eigenfunctions are

$$\Psi_n = (\sqrt{2/L}) \sin (n\pi x/L) \, e^{-i\frac{W}{h}nt} \qquad [5\text{--}14a$$

where the box extends from $x = 0$ to $x = L$, and where $n = 1, 2, 3, \cdots$

We assume that at some instant, which we will define to be $t = 0$, the wave function of the system has the following form:

$$\Psi(x, t_0) = kx, \ 0 \leq x < L; \ \text{and} \ \Psi(x) = 0 \ \text{at} \ x = L; \ (t_0 = 0)$$

This wave function is plotted in Figure 5.1. It is, of course, discontinuous at $x = L$, and the slope is discontinuous at both $x = 0$ and $x = L$, so that this function cannot be a true wave function. However, by merely "rounding the corners" a *very* slight amount, it could be made well behaved and still be substantially unchanged in appearance—certainly on the scale of the diagram. Note that the function to be synthesized has the same domain of definition (and, after "rounding the corners," the same limits) as the complete set of orthogonal functions that are to be used.

In Figure 5.1 are plotted the first four terms of the series expansion [5–9]. The values of the expansion coefficients a were calculated, using [5–12] and the functions [5–14a]. It is apparent that with only four terms, the series expansion already provides a fair approximation to the specified function. As more terms are added, the series becomes closer to the function being synthesized.[6]

The details of the calculation are the subject of Problem 5.7.

At first sight it may seem surprising that a function such as $\Psi = kx$ could, under any conditions, be a solution to the wave equation, and yet it is clear enough that each of the eigenfunctions used in the synthesis is itself a solution,

---

[6] For the *discontinuous* function, as defined above, it is found that as the number of terms becomes very large, a tiny, sharp spike appears at $x = L$. As the number of terms is increased the height of the spike remains constant, although its width approaches zero. This is an example of the "Gibbs phenomenon." See Stanford Goldman, *Frequency Analysis, Modulation and Noise* (1948, McGraw-Hill Book Co., Inc., New York): p. 30.

and therefore the sum *must* be a solution. We shall see shortly (and also in Problem 5.10) that any particular function, such as $\Psi = kx$, has only a momentary existence. We chose $t = 0$ as the instant to make the synthesis, since at that instant all of the eigenfunctions were real and this simplified the

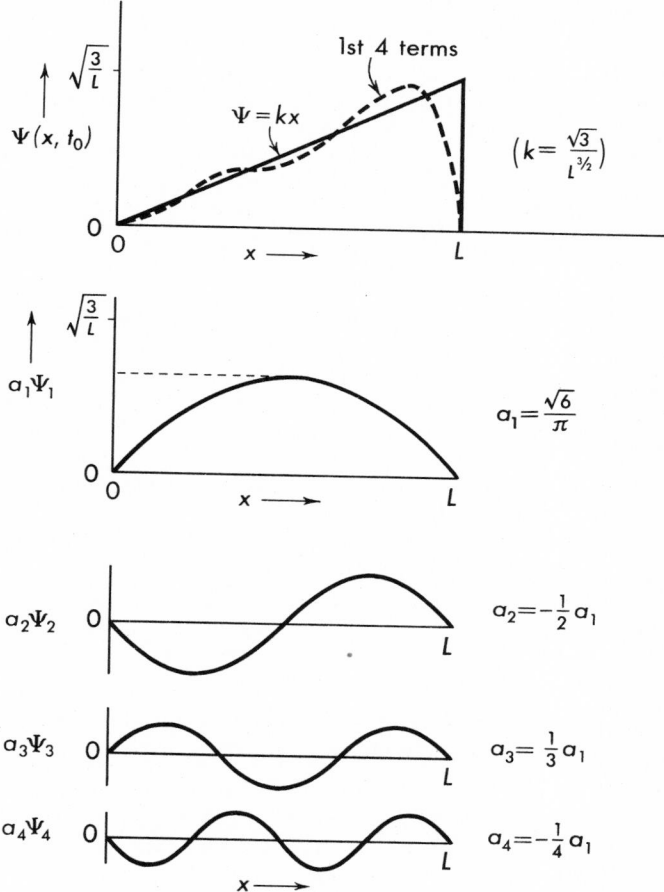

Fig. 5.1. An example of the synthesis of the wave function $\Psi = kx$ by a series of eigenfunctions.

calculations. At any later (or earlier) time the superposition of eigenfunctions will produce both a real and an imaginary part for Ψ, and both parts will, in general, have a form different from kx. The important point here is this: *At any instant t any well-behaved function can be synthesized by a particular superposition of eigenfunctions constructed, using* [5–12], *from the complete set of eigenfunctions.*

Having found the set of a_n's which will synthesize any particular $\Psi(x, t_0)$, we ask the question: Will these same a_n's, which we now designate as $a_n(t_0)$, calculated from [5–12] at $t = t_0$, continue to define a solution at some *other* arbitrary time t? This is equivalent to asking: Is

$$\Psi(x, t) = \sum_n a_n(t_0) \, \Psi_n(x, t) \qquad\qquad [5\text{–}15$$

also a well-behaved, normalized solution to wave equation [5–1]? Substituting [5–15] into [5–1] we obtain

$$\sum_n a_n(t_0) \, H\Psi_n(x, t) = -(\hbar/i) \sum_n a_n(t_0) \, (-i/\hbar) \, W_n \Psi_n(x, t)$$

which, using the important fact that H is independent of t (so that $H\Psi_n = W_n \Psi_n$), reduces to an identity, term by term.[7]

Thus, when the Hamiltonian operator H does not involve the time, a set of amplitudes of the component eigenstates can be found at any time, for which the system wave function is known, and each a_n will remain constant. Also, since $\Psi(x, t_0)$ was required to be normalized, the a_n's meet the requirement [5–7].

Although the a_n's are constant in time, this does not mean that $\Psi(x, t)$ is itself constant. Since $\Psi(x, t)$ is the sum of many terms, each with a time-dependent factor $e^{-i\frac{W_n}{\hbar}t}$, it will constantly vary in its spatial form as the components "beat" with each other.

Consider a simple case

$$\Psi(x, t) = a_1 \, \psi_1 \, e^{-i\frac{W_1}{\hbar}t} + a_2 \, \psi_2 \, e^{-i\frac{W_2}{\hbar}t} \qquad\qquad [5\text{–}16$$

where the wave function is a superposition of only two eigenstates. Clearly, $\Psi(x, t)$, and also the probability density,

$$\Psi^* \Psi = a_1^* a_1 \, \psi_1^* \, \psi_1 + a_2^* a_2 \, \psi_2^* \, \psi_2 + a_1 a_2^* \, \psi_1 \, \psi_2^* \, e^{-i\frac{W_1 - W_2}{\hbar}t}$$

$$+ \; a_1^* a_2 \, \psi_1^* \, \psi_2 \, e^{+i\frac{W_1 - W_2}{\hbar}t} \qquad\qquad [5\text{–}17$$

depend upon the time.

In the special case where the a's and the ψ_n's are real,

$$\Psi^* \Psi = a_1^2 \, \psi_1^2 + a_2^2 \, \psi_2^2 + a_1 a_2 \, \psi_1 \, \psi_2 \, [2 \cos (W_1 - W_2) \, t/\hbar] \qquad [5\text{–}18$$

The third term is called the interference term, and is due to the "beating" of the time-varying components, which make up the wave function. When many

---

[7] Summation signs provide great condensation of notation, but it is often easier to appreciate the significance of the mathematical expression if the summations are written out, in part.

component states are present, there will be an interference term for each pair of states.[8]

A system whose wave function is a single eigenstate will have a probability density function $\Psi^* \Psi = \psi^* \psi$, independent of time. However, we have seen that the addition of even one other state, whose amplitude a_2 is not zero, causes

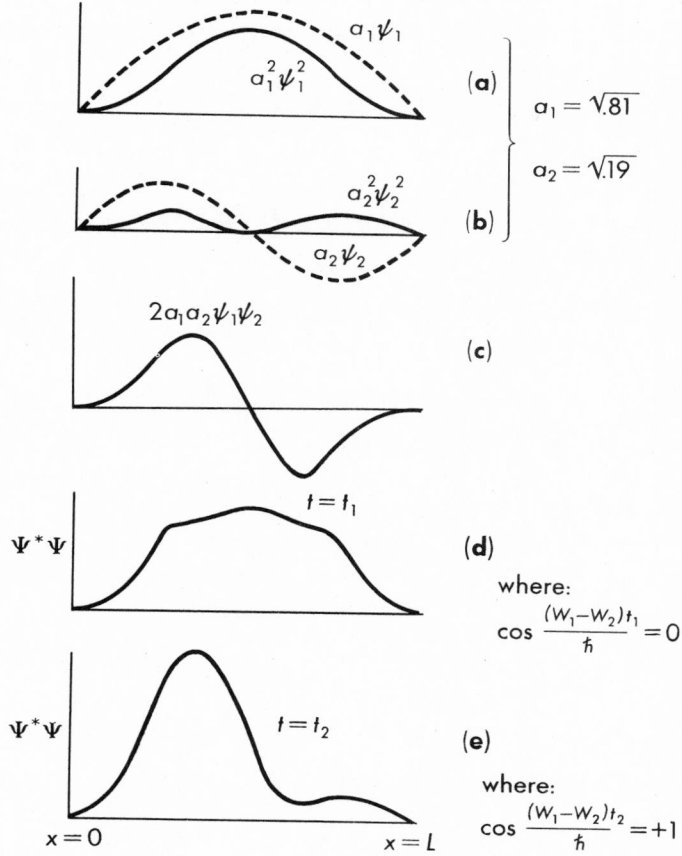

Fig. 5.2.   The superposition of two eigenfunctions of the infinite-wall box.

---

[8] For example, let $\Psi = a_1 \Psi_1 + a_2 \Psi_2 + a_3 \Psi_3$. For the case that the a_n's and the ψ_n's are real, using $\cos x = (1/2)(e^{ix} + e^{-ix})$,

$$\Psi^* \Psi(x, t) = a_1^2 \psi_1^2(x) + a_2^2 \psi_2^2(x) + a_3^2 \psi_3^2(x)$$

$$+ 2a_1 a_2 \psi_1 \psi_2 \cos (W_1 - W_2) t/\hbar + 2a_2 a_3 \psi_2 \psi_3 \cos (W_2 - W_3) t/\hbar$$

$$+ 2a_3 a_1 \psi_3 \psi_1 \cos (W_3 - W_1) t/\hbar$$

the probability density function to vary with time. The former state is called a stationary state. The latter state corresponds to the case where a particle can be loosely regarded as moving about in some periodic manner—since, as time progresses, the likelihood of finding the particle in any given interval dx (or, in three dimensions, in any volume interval $d\tau$) is systematically changing.

As an example of a system whose probability density varies with time, we consider a particle in an infinite-wall, one-dimensional box of length L, whose wave function is a superposition of the two lowest energy eigenstates (see Section 3.4),

$$\Psi_1 = \underbrace{\sqrt{2/L} \sin{(\pi x/L)}}_{\psi_1} e^{-iW_1 t/\hbar}, \text{ and } \Psi_2 = \underbrace{\sqrt{2/L} \sin{(2\pi x/L)}}_{\psi_2} e^{-iW_2 t/\hbar}$$

That is,

$$\Psi = a_1 \Psi_1 + a_2 \Psi_2$$

We choose a special case, so that we can plot our results quantitatively. Let $a_1 = \sqrt{.81}$ and $a_2 = \sqrt{.19}$. Thus, the a_n's and the ψ_n's are real, and Ψ is normalized. For this case [5–18] gives the variation of the probability density with time and distance.

Figure 5.2a, b, and c shows the x-dependence of each of the three terms in [5–18]. When t has such a value that $\cos{(W_1 - W_2)} t/\hbar = 0$, then Figure 5.2d gives the variation of probability density with space. When t has such a value that $\cos{(W_1 - W_2)} t/\hbar = + 1$, then as Figure 5.2e shows, the particle is most likely to be found to the left of center. When the cosine term is -1, then the particle is most likely to be found to be the right of center. The probability density is changing with time in a complicated manner, and at no time is the location of the particle sharply defined.

In this section, we have shown two very important things about wave functions of systems for which the Hamiltonian operator H is independent of time.

1. *Any* linear combination of system eigenfunctions, $\sum\limits_n a_n \Psi_n$, is a possible wave function—providing only that $\sum\limits_n a_n^* a_n = 1$.

2. If the normalized wave function of a system, $\Psi(x, t)$, is known at any particular time t_0, then it can be synthesized for all times t, by the linear combination $\Psi(x, t) = \sum\limits_n a_n(t_0) \Psi_n(x, t)$, where

$$a_n(t_0) = \int \Psi_n^*(x, t_0) \Psi(x, t_0) dx$$

To synthesize a well-behaved and bounded, but otherwise arbitrary wave function the complete set of eigenfunctions is needed in the expansion.

As an illustration of this type of calculation, we suppose that at $t = t_0$ a one-dimensional system with infinite potential walls at $x = 0$ and at $x = L$

has a real wave function which has the form $f(x)$ in Figure 5.3a. Since the eigenfunctions of this system are given by [3–23], and using [5–12] to determine the a_n's at $t = t_0$,

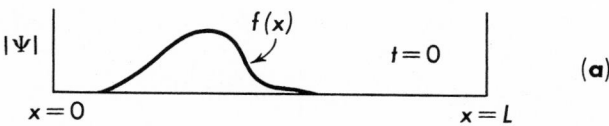

(a)

(b)

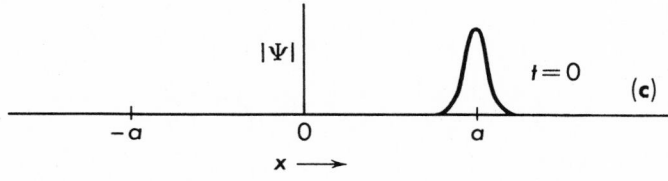

(c)

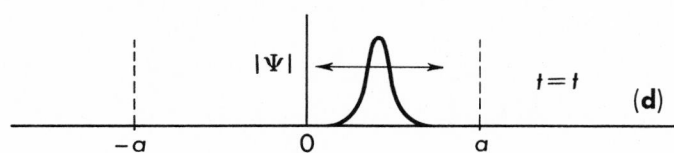

(d)

Fig. 5.3. Two examples of time-varying wave functions.

then, at arbitrary time t,

$$\Psi(x, t) = \sum_n \underbrace{\left[\int_0^L \sqrt{2/L} \, \sin(n\pi x/L) \, e^{+i\frac{W_n}{\hbar}t_0} f(x) \, dx \right]}_{= \, a_n(t_0)} \sqrt{2/L} \, \sin(n\pi x/L) \, e^{-i\frac{W_n}{\hbar}t}$$

$$\Psi(x, t) = \sum_n \left[(2/L) \int_0^L \sin(n\pi x/L) f(x) \, dx \right] \sin(n\pi x/L) \, e^{-i\frac{W_n}{\hbar}(t-t_0)} \qquad [5-19$$

At $t = t_0$ the series [5–19] will reproduce $f(x)$. At some later time it will produce some new curve—generally of a very different shape—such as that in Figure 5.3b. In any case, once Ψ is known, at any time t_0 its past and its future form is determined by [5–19] (see Problem 5.10).

In the case of the one-dimensional harmonic oscillator, it happens that the wave function, if initially of the form shown in Figure 5.3c (a Gaussian curve, located at $x = a$ at $t = 0$), will thereafter have the same *shape*. The center of the Gaussian curve oscillates sinusoidally back and forth about $x = 0$ with the classical frequency $\nu_0 = (1/2\,\pi)\,\sqrt{k/m}$ (see Section 3.2).[9] Figure 5.3d shows the wave function at some later time. All of the eigenstates are "excited" (i.e. their a_n's are not zero) in order to form this particular shape of wave function.

Schiff[10] shows that the states whose characteristic energies are in the neighborhood of $(1/2)\,ka^2$ (the total classical energy) are the biggest contributors, as the correspondence principle (Section 3.6) would lead one to expect.

For the first time we see a wave function that begins to "act like a particle." That is, it seems to be moving as an entity, with characteristic form. It is significant, however, that this situation occurs when the system is a linear superposition of eigenstates—excited with certain specified amplitudes. Each of these eigenstates has a characteristic curvature of its eigenfunction—that is, each has its own wavelength. A wave function whose appearance at successive instants resembles our macroscopic concept of a particle can only be formed by the superposition of many different waves spread over a finite range of wavelengths. In Section 5.6, on wave packets and scattering, we shall return to a more quantitative treatment of this subject.

In the next few sections we shall use some of these superimposed states (often called "mixed" states) as well as the single eigenstates (often called "pure" states) in calculations based on Postulate V.

5.2.   The calculation of system energy

In Chapters 3 and 4 we calculated the expectation value $\overline{W}$ of the total energy W of a system whose wave function is a single eigenfunction. The operator corresponding to the energy is $-(\hbar/i)\,\partial/\partial t$, which, by the wave equation [5–1] is equivalent to the operator H. When H is independent of time, any eigenfunction has the form,

$$\Psi_n = \psi_n\, e^{-i\frac{W_n}{\hbar}t} \qquad\qquad [5\text{--}20$$

---

[9] For the analysis of this problem, see L. I. Schiff, *Quantum Mechanics* (1949, McGraw-Hill Book Co., Inc., New York): p. 67.

[10] *Ibid.*

so that Postulate V yields, very simply,

$$\overline{W} = W_n$$
$$(\overline{W^2}) = W_n^2 \quad \text{and} \quad \sigma_W^2 = (\overline{W^2}) - (\overline{W})^2 = 0 \qquad [5\text{--}2]$$
$$(\overline{W^3}) = W_n^3 \quad \text{etc.}$$

Any experiment which measures the energy will, therefore, give the certain result W_n.

We cannot actually plot a probability distribution *function* $p(W)$ which describes an exactly predictable result W_n, since the function $p(W)$, as defined in Section 2.3, is continuous. If ΔW is zero, then $p(W)$ has to be infinitely large at $W = W_n$, be zero elsewhere, and have unit area.[11] When dealing with discrete measured values we shall use the term *probability distribution* instead of *probability distribution function*. Let $P(W_n)$ be the probability of observing the discrete result W_n, where n is an index which identifies each discrete value of W. Here, only *one* value of W, namely W_n, is observed in all cases. Thus, in Figure 5.4a, the graph of P *vs.* W has one bar, of unit height, located at $W = W_n$.

How can the system energy be observed? One way is to infer it from the radiation. Suppose hydrogen atoms which were initially in their lowest energy state, at -13.5 e.v. (see Fig. 1.1), were bombarded for a very short time by electrons of a little over 10 e.v. Some of the atoms would be excited into an $n = 2$ state (see Fig. 1.1), and would subsequently radiate light of frequency $\nu = (W_2 - W_1)/h$ (cycles/sec), the first line of the Lyman series. If this were the only frequency of light received from the atoms, one infers that, just after bombardment, all of the excited atoms were certainly in a state with energy W_2, since energy in amount $W_2 - W_1$ is delivered in each case in the form of light quanta. An important feature emerges here which is characteristic of the application of Postulate V. *The measurement operation always changes the system.* For example, in this experiment, to know that the atoms were in an $n = 2$ state, one has to receive their energy in the form of light. The atoms end up in their ground state. Thus the observation of the excited atoms necessitated a change in their state (that is, a change in the wave function which describes them). We have not yet discussed the quantum theory for systems that are changing from one state to another and our *interpretation* here of the results of calculations using Postulate V is too simple. (See Chapter 10, particularly the discussion at the end of the chapter.)

It should be pointed out here that the frequency *spread* of the emitted light, although very small, is not exactly zero as it would have to be for the transition between two infinitely sharp energy levels. If a typical excited atom is not interfered with by collisions, it will radiate a wave train for a duration of about 10^{-8} seconds at some definite frequency in the range of 10^{14} to 10^{15}

---

[11] A function with these properties is known as the "Dirac delta function."

cycles per second. The train of electromagnetic waves is thus the order of 3 meters in extent and contains 10^6 to 10^7 cycles. Because of the finite average length of the wave trains coming from atoms, a grating or other wavelength-

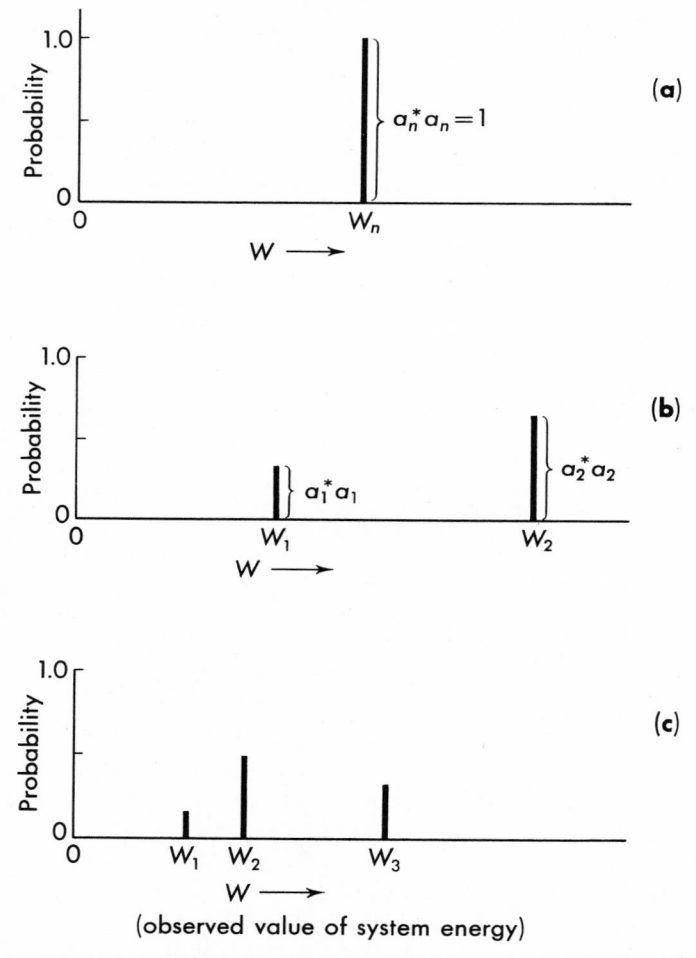

Fig. 5.4. The probability of observing different values of the energy of a system when the system wave function consists **(a)** of a single eigenfunction, **(b)** of a superposition of two eigenfunctions, and **(c)** of the superposition of three eigenfunctions.

measuring device will never—even under ideal conditions—measure an absolutely sharp frequency.[12] The lifetime of the excited state and the accuracy with

---

[12] See D. Bohm, *Quantum Theory* (1951, Prentice-Hall, Inc., New York): pp. 49f.

which its energy can be measured are intimately related—the longer the life, the longer the wave train, and the smaller will be the uncertainty in the measurement of the wavelength (and therefore of the energy). Problems of this sort are better discussed after one has a more quantitative method of describing atoms which are in the process of changing their state (see Chapter 10). For the moment, we are concerned only with the fact that the characteristic frequencies radiated by atoms are extremely sharp.

We next calculate the expectation value of the system energy for a system in a "mixed" state.

Let Ψ be the superposition of two eigenfunctions,

$$\Psi = a_1 \Psi_1 + a_2 \Psi_2, \text{ where } a_1^* a_1 + a_2^* a_2 = 1 \qquad [5\text{--}22$$

where $W_1 \neq W_2$,

then

$$\overline{W} = \int \Psi^* \, (-\hbar/i) \, (\partial/\partial t) \, \Psi \, d\tau$$

$$= \int (a_1^* \Psi_1^* + a_2^* \Psi_2^*) \, (a_1 W_1 \Psi_1 + a_2 W_2 \Psi_2) \, d\tau \qquad [5\text{--}23$$

Thus,

$$\overline{W} = a_1^* a_1 W_1 + a_2^* a_2 W_2$$

Similarly,

$$\overline{W^2} = a_1^* a_1 W_1^2 + a_2^* a_2 W_2^2 \qquad \left.\begin{array}{c} \sigma_W^2 = \overline{W^2} - (\overline{W})^2 \\ \sigma_W^2 \neq 0 \end{array}\right\} \qquad [5\text{--}24$$

$$\overline{W^3} = a_1^* a_1 W_1^3 + a_2^* a_2 W_2^3$$

Since σ_W^2 is *not* zero, there must be some "scatter" of the measured, individual values of W about the mean value $\overline{W}$.

If a probability distribution is known to be bounded, it is a result of statistical theory that, from a knowledge of *all* of the moments,[13] one can uniquely determine the probability distribution.[14] In the case at hand, the moments $\overline{W}$, $\overline{W^2}$, $\overline{W^3}$, etc., are expressed in such a way that it is easy to infer the probability P of observing a particular value of W. We see at once that the probability $P(W_n)$, plotted in Figure 5.4b, consists of just two "lines," one at W_1 with magnitude $a_1^* a_1$, and the other at W_2 with magnitude $a_2^* a_2$. We required that the original Ψ-function, [5–22], be normalized so that, of course,

$$a_1^* a_1 + a_2^* a_2 = 1$$

---

[13] If the probability of observing the discrete result W_n is $P(W_n)$, then the first moment is $\sum_n W_n P(W_n)$, the second moment is $\sum_n W_n^2 P(W_n)$, etc., where n identifies each of the discrete values observed.

[14] See Harald Cramér, *Mathematical Methods of Statistics* (1946, Princeton Univeristy Press, Princeton, N.J.) p. 174; also, J. V. Uspensky, *Introduction to Mathematical Probability* (1937, McGraw-Hill Book Co., Inc., New York): Appendix II.

If the original wave function is a superposition of *three* (nondegenerate) eigenfunctions, then the probability of observing different values of W has the form of Figure 5.4c. An observation of system energy will yield one of three values. The average value is

$$\overline{W} = a_1^* \, a_1 \, W_1 + a_2^* \, a_2 \, W_2 + a_3^* \, a_3 \, W_3$$

Where the W's are the characteristic energies of the three component states.

To be consistent with the postulates, we must grant each atomic system the possibility of having, as its wave function, any or all of the eigenfunctions, just as a room can resonate in one or all of its natural frequencies at the same time. Let many systems be given the *same* superposition of eigenfunctions. The unique, quantum phenomenon is that the act of the individual observation of system energy will yield only one of a set of discrete energy values (one for each eigenfunction, as above). The theory only attempts to predict—but it does it correctly—certain numbers, $\overline{W}$, $\overline{W^2}$, $\overline{W^3}$, etc., which can be experimentally determined only after many, many systems (with identical wave functions) have been observed. Furthermore, before observation occurs, each system must be regarded as possessing *all* component states constituting the common superposition. That is, before "being interfered with," the systems are, *as far as is known*, identical, and Postulate V predicts *only* the average behavior of the group. Unsatisfactory as this is to our intuitive feelings (based upon macroscopic experience), we again point out that there is no known way to predict results in any more detail than that provided by the wave function, using Postulate V.

We can see why, in Section 4.11, it was required that an eigenvalue of the energy operator be a *real* constant. Only when this is so will $\overline{W}$ be a real number. Since energy is an ordinary scalar quantity, it must be representable by a single number, *not* a pair of numbers as is required by a complex quantity. If the W_n's were complex, then $\overline{W}$ would be complex.

The specific forms of the quantum-mechanical operators associated with certain variables were merely listed as part of the postulates (II). One of the requirements which guided the original selection of these operators was that when they are used in Postulate V to predict experimental results they must make predictions in terms of actual, experimentally observable quantities. We see that, for all of the specific systems analyzed in Chapters 3 and 4, every one of the energy eigenvalues is a real constant. In particular, $\overline{W}$ is always a real number. We shall see in the remainder of this chapter, and in Chapter 6, that when other operators are used in Postulate V to make a prediction about some experimentally observable quantity, the results of the calculation are always in terms appropriate to actual laboratory measurement.

Problem 5.15 is concerned with the calculation of the energy of a system when the wave function is a linear combination of degenerate eigenfunctions.

5.3. The calculation of position

Postulate V tells us that the expectation value of x is

$$\bar{x} = \int \Psi^* \, x \, \Psi \, d\tau \qquad\qquad [5\text{--}25$$

where, if there is only one dimension, $d\tau = dx$. Since the operator belonging to the coordinate x is just x itself, there is no mathematical operation involved in forming the expression for $\bar{x}$ other than inserting a factor x in the integrand. In contrast to the case where the inserted operator involves differentiation, the order of appearance of x in the integrand is of no consequence.

The interpretation of $\Psi^* \Psi$ as the probability density follows directly from Postulate V. If $P(x) \, dx$ is the probability that an observed value of x lies in the interval x to $x + dx$, then by the definition based upon probability (Section 2.3)

$$\bar{x} = \int x P(x) \, dx$$

whereas, from Postulate V (for one dimension)

$$\bar{x} = \int x \Psi^* \, \Psi \, dx$$

For any time t, the expression $\Psi^* \Psi$ is a specific function of x and plays the role of the probability density. If Ψ happens to be an eigenfunction, then the probability density is constant in time.

Suppose that Ψ is an eigenfunction, Ψ_n, of the system. Then, for one dimension,

$$\bar{x} = \int \Psi_n^* \, x \, \Psi_n \, dx \text{ and } \overline{x^2} = \int \Psi_n^* \, x^2 \, \Psi_n \, dx$$

We see that there is a great difference between this calculation and that for the system energy W. Now, a variable, x, rather than the constant W, appears in the integrand. Before, we had the result

$$(\overline{W_n})^2 = \overline{W_n^2}, \text{ and } \sigma_W = 0$$

but now we may find, for a single state Ψ_n, that

$$(\bar{x})^2 \neq \overline{x^2}, \text{ and } \sigma_x \neq 0$$

Whereas W_n was the certain result of measuring the system energy when the wave function was known to be a single eigenfunction Ψ_n, it is now possible that there will *not* be a certain result of the measurement of x. There must be a spread in the measured values of x, should it turn out (as it usually does) that $\sigma_x \neq 0$.

Suppose Ψ is a superposition of two eigenfunctions. Then, for one dimension,

$$\bar{x} = \int (a_1^* \Psi_1^* + a_2^* \Psi_2^*) \, x(a_1 \Psi_1 + a_2 \Psi_2) \, dx \qquad [5\text{--}26$$

which becomes, on expansion,

$$\bar{x} = a_1^* a_1 \int \Psi_1^* \Psi_1 \, x dx + a_2^* a_2 \int \Psi_2^* \Psi_2 \, x dx + a_1^* a_2 \int \Psi_1^* \Psi_2 \, x dx$$

$$+ a_2^* a_1 \int \Psi_2^* \Psi_1 \, x dx \qquad\qquad [5\text{--}27]$$

The first two integrals are just the value of x averaged over the individual eigenstates. They are weighted by the factor $a_n^* a_n$. In the last section we have seen that this factor may be regarded as the probability that the system will, upon observation of its total energy, yield a result W_n (one of the eigenvalues of the energy). We might be tempted to regard the system as being *either* in state Ψ_1 with probability $a_1^* a_1$, *or* in state Ψ_2 with probability $a_2^* a_2$. This interpretation cannot be correct, however, since there are two other terms in [5–27]. These terms are *not* in general zero, in spite of the orthogonality of the Ψ's, due to the presence of the extra factor x in the integrand. If the system really were in either one state or the other, there would be no "interference terms" such as the last two in [5–27]. These *require* the simultaneous presence of both Ψ's, in the wave function of *each* individual atomic system.

The first two terms are time independent, but the last two terms "beat together" with the difference of the two characteristic frequencies belonging to the eigenstate functions. If at some time t many systems are observed, which at $t = t_0$ all had the *same* wave function $\Psi(x, t_0)$, a particular mean value of x will be found.

If another large number of systems [also having at $t = t_0$ the identical wave function $\psi(x, t_0)$] are observed at a different time t' we will in general find a different value of $\bar{x}$ (due to the time-dependent terms in [5–27]). Thus, when states are superimposed, the probability of finding the particle in a given region is constantly shifting with time, and this is only possible when the system is regarded as being simultaneously in all of the component states (of any specified superposition).

As an example of the calculation of the expectation values of x and x^2, we assume that a harmonic oscillator of mass m and spring constant k is in its lowest eigenstate Ψ_0. The normalized amplitude wave function (Appendix I) is

$$\psi_0 = \left(\frac{a}{\pi}\right)^{(1/4)} e^{-(\alpha x^2/2)} \qquad\qquad [5\text{--}28]$$

where

$$\alpha = 2\pi \, \nu_0 \, m/\hbar \quad \text{and} \quad \nu_0 = (1/2 \, \pi) \sqrt{k/m}$$

Thus,

$$\bar{x} = \left(\frac{a}{\pi}\right)^{\frac{1}{2}} \int\limits_{-\infty}^{+\infty} x \, e^{-\alpha x^2} \, dx$$

$$= 0, \text{ by symmetry} \qquad\qquad [5\text{--}29$$

And,

$$\overline{x^2} = \left(\frac{a}{\pi}\right)^{\frac{1}{2}} \int\limits_{-\infty}^{+\infty} x^2 \, e^{-\alpha x^2} \, dx$$

$$= \frac{1}{2a} \qquad\qquad [5\text{-}30$$

Since the standard deviation in x, σ_x, is defined by the relationship

$$\sigma_x = \sqrt{\overline{x^2} - (\bar{x})^2}$$

we have

$$\sigma_x = \sqrt{\left(\frac{1}{2a}\right) - 0} = 1/\sqrt{2a} \qquad\qquad [5\text{-}31$$

or,

$$\sigma_x = \left[\frac{1}{2\sqrt{\pi\, v_0\, m}}\right]\sqrt{\hbar}$$

The standard deviation σ_x is a measure of the spread, or scatter, of the many observed values of x.

If $P(x)$ is a Gaussian probability distribution function[15] (that is, of the form e^{-x^2}), then the majority of observations (specifically, 68 percent) will be found within the limits $\pm\sigma_x$, centered about the mean $\bar{x} = 0$. The fraction of the total number of observations that fall inside the limits $\pm\sigma_x$ depends upon the exact form of the probability distribution $P(x)$, but, for the distributions usually encountered, somewhat more than half of the observations will lie between these limits about the mean.

In quantum mechanics the expression Δx is often called "the uncertainty in x." It is sometimes regarded as measuring, in some not exactly specified way, the spread in the observed values of individual observations of the x-co-ordinate of the particle. Here, we shall specifically identify,

$$\sigma_x \equiv \Delta x \qquad\qquad [5\text{-}32$$

Thus, if we had 1,000 harmonic oscillators all with the same wave function Ψ_0, and we could insert into each oscillator, in turn, at some instant a set of adjacent particle detectors covering the whole range of x, we would always observe that only *one* detector registers the location of the particle. Each time we do this, of course, we interfere with the system. After having observed (interfered with) all 1,000 systems, we plot the frequency of occurrence of the different measurements. We will find a very nearly Gaussian distribution, that is, we will find that the average of all x-measurements is very nearly 0, and

---

[15] In contrast to the discrete values of W, in Section 5.2, the observed values of x can have a continuous range. Thus $P(x)$ can be a continuous function.

that approximately 680 of the 1,000 measurements are within the range $\pm 1/\sqrt{2a}$.

The electron diffraction experiment outlined in Figure 2.2a provides a good example of the uncertainty in the position measurement of an electron. Let x be the distance, measured along the arc where the electron multipliers are located. We can define Δx as half the width of the peak in Figure 2.2b. Δx is, in principle, calculable. We need only know the wave function $\Psi(x, y, z, t)$ of the wave "packets" approaching the array of detectors, and we can calculate $\bar{x}, \bar{x^2}, \bar{x^3}$, etc., which are characteristic of the observed distribution curve.

In contrast to the imaginary experiment described above where an array of particle detectors was supposed to be suddenly introduced into the physical space occupied by a harmonic oscillator, in a real experiment, such as the one in Figure 2.2, a moving wave packet actually collides with a fixed array of detectors. Both the harmonic-oscillator wave system and the moving wave packet are bounded in space (the detectors themselves measure the spread of the packet in the x-direction). In both cases the relative motion of the system of waves and the detectors bring them into spatial coincidence, and *one* of the detectors registers an event. This detection event is interpreted as "the arrival of a single particle at the entrance window of the detector recording the event." In both cases, the wave packet is greatly altered by the collision with the array of detectors.

5.4. The calculation of momentum

By Postulate V, the expectation value $\bar{p}_x$ of the x-component of the momentum, p_x or mv_x, is

$$\bar{p}_x = \int \Psi^* (\hbar/i) (\partial/\partial x) \Psi \, d\tau \qquad [5\text{--}33$$

and the expectation value of p_x^2 is,

$$\bar{p_x^2} = \int \Psi^* (-\hbar^2) (\partial/\partial x)^2 \Psi \, d\tau \qquad [5\text{--}34$$

For a one-dimensional system, $d\tau = dx$.

Since the inserted operators involve differentiation, their location in the integrand is important. Only after the operation on the right-hand Ψ is completed can the actual integration be performed.

Even if Ψ is a single eigenfunction Ψ_n of the system, we will often find,[16]

---

[16] Sometimes

$$\left(\frac{\hbar}{i}\right) \left(\frac{\partial}{\partial x}\right) \Psi_n = \text{(a real constant)} \cdot \Psi_n$$

with the result that $\sigma_{p_x} = 0$ (the free particle). See V. Rojansky, *Introductory Quantum Mechanics* (1942, Prentice-Hall, Inc., New York): p. 235. When this occurs, Ψ_n is said to be an eigenfunction of the momentum operator just as, when $H\Psi_n =$ (real const.) Ψ_n [4–66], Ψ_n is said to be an eigenfunction of the energy operator. It sometimes happens that a set of eigenfunctions Ψ_n belongs to more than one operator (see Problem 5.8).

as in the case of the calculation of x in the previous section, that

$$\overline{p_x}^2 \neq \overline{p_x^2} \text{ and } \sigma_{p_x} \neq 0$$

so that there must be some spread in the measured values of p_x.

When Ψ is a linear combination of eigenstates, we obtain results similar to those for the calculations of x in the previous section. We again find interference terms, implying that both states must be regarded as being present at the same time.

As an example of the calculation of the expectation values of p_x and p_x^2, we will use, once more, the ground state of the harmonic oscillator.

Thus,

$$\bar{p}_x = \left(\frac{a}{\pi}\right)^{\frac{1}{2}} \int_{-\infty}^{+\infty} e^{-\alpha x^2/2} \left(\frac{\hbar}{i}\frac{\partial}{\partial x}\right) e^{-\alpha x^2/2} \, dx$$

$$= (a/\pi)^{\frac{1}{2}} (-\hbar a/i) \int_{-\infty}^{+\infty} x \, e^{-\alpha x^2} \, dx$$

$$= 0$$

(since x is antisymmetrical, and $e^{-\alpha x^2}$ is symmetrical, about $x = 0$)

and,

$$\overline{p_x^2} = (a/\pi)^{\frac{1}{2}} \int_{-\infty}^{+\infty} e^{-\alpha x^2/2} \left(\frac{\hbar}{i}\right)^2 \frac{\partial^2}{\partial x^2} e^{-\alpha x^2/2} \, dx$$

which, upon differentiation, becomes

$$\overline{p_x^2} = (a/\pi)^{\frac{1}{2}} \hbar^2 \int_{-\infty}^{+\infty} (-a^2 x^2 + a) \, e^{-\alpha x^2} \, dx$$

In [5–30] we already have the result of the integration involving x^2 and, adding the integral of the other term, we have

$$\overline{p_x^2} = \hbar^2 a/2$$

So that

$$\sigma_{p_x} = \sqrt{\overline{p_x^2} - \overline{p_x}^2}$$

$$\sigma_{p_x} = \hbar\sqrt{a/2} \text{ or } \sigma_{p_x} = \sqrt{\hbar}\sqrt{\pi \nu_0 m} \qquad [5\text{–}35$$

The standard deviation of the p-measurements is once more dependent upon Planck's constant h. We identify Δp_x, "the uncertainty in p_x" with the standard deviation, thus,

$$\sigma_{p_x} \equiv \Delta p_x \qquad [5\text{–}36$$

How can the momentum of the vibrating particle be measured? We can measure v_x (the velocity) as follows. Let us imagine that at $t = 0$ we suddenly cut the spring ("turn off" the potential energy). The particle is now free. One of two particle detectors (each located a known distance along the $+x$- and $-x$-axis) will, at a later time, observe the arrival of the particle. If the detectors are located a large distance from the original system, i.e., at a distance $\gg \sigma_x$, then the value of each individual measurement of v_x is quite accurate. From the measured velocity, we calculate $p_x = mv_x$. Again, we must interfere with the system in order to make a measurement. (The subject of measurement is discussed further at the end of Chapter 10.)

The probability distribution of the observed values of p_x can, in principle, be inferred from the knowledge of the moments $\overline{p_x}$, $\overline{p_x^2}$, $\overline{p_x^3}$, etc., all of which can be calculated from the wave function. It can be shown that a Gaussian-shaped probability distribution $P(p)$ has the same moments that we calculate, using Postulate V, for the ground state of the harmonic oscillator.[17] In other words, this state has a Gaussian-shaped probability distribution for the momentum and the velocity. This is a very different shape from that which would be obtained by tabulating the measured, instantaneous velocity of identical *classical* harmonic oscillators examined at random times.

5.5. Limitations on measurement in quantum mechanics

In the foregoing sections we calculated the energy, the position (coordinate), and the momentum of a particle bound in a potential well and constituting a system. The theory only attempts to predict the results of many experiments performed upon identical systems. Sometimes, as in the case where the wave function is an eigenfunction, all experiments on energy measurement will yield the same result. That is, one can make a prediction that is completely certain. For the harmonic oscillator we found that even when the energy is exactly predictable, the other quantities—both position and momentum—have a dispersion in their individual measured values.

Let us summarize the results of these calculations for the case of the harmonic oscillator whose wave function is Ψ_0, the ground state of the system.

a. The system energy is certainly $W_0 = (1/2)\, h\nu_0$.
b. The average value of x is 0.
    The standard deviation, σ_x or Δx, of all the measurements on the x-coordinate is

$$\Delta x = \left[\frac{1}{2\sqrt{\pi \, \nu_0 \, m}} \right] (\hbar)^{\frac{1}{2}}$$

c. The average value of p_x is 0.

---

[17] See V. Rojansky, *op. cit.*, p. 99.

The standard deviation in the measurements of $p_x = mv_x$,

$$\Delta p_x = \sqrt{\pi \nu_0 m}\,(\hbar)^{\frac{1}{2}}$$

d.   The product of Δx and Δp_x is

$$\Delta x\,\Delta p_x = \hbar/2 \qquad\qquad\qquad [5\text{--}37$$

which is a constant, independent of both the mass of the particle and the classical frequency of vibration, ν_0. This product is dependent only upon the fundamental constant $\hbar$.

We have been analyzing only a particular, bound system—the harmonic oscillator, in the ground state—but we see that [5–37], which relates Δp to Δx, involves only the universal constant $\hbar$ and a numerical factor. *It is independent of the system parameters*, such as m, and k or ν_0.

An analysis of each quantum-mechanical system will always uncover a relationship, of the form of [5–37], between the uncertainty in a coordinate measurement and the uncertainty in the measurement of the corresponding momentum. The numerical constant will vary, but it is always found that ·

$$\Delta x\,\Delta p_x \geq (\sim\hbar) \qquad\qquad\qquad [5\text{--}38$$

In the particular case analyzed above, we assumed that we knew the wave function of a system, and then predicted the spread in the observed values of x and p when many identical systems were examined. If one analyzes different types of systems, such as free-traveling electrons being scattered by gratings or going through slits, the relationship [5–38] keeps appearing—for *all* wave functions. Note that [5–38] implies that if the apparatus is designed to give an accurate value of x for a particular electron (i.e., small Δx) then, by [5–38], Δp_x for the same electron *must* be large. Conversely, if the apparatus is designed to give an accurate measurement of p_x (i.e., Δp_x is very small), then Δx for the same electron must be very large. Thus, an accurate measurement of x will, for the same particle at the same time, exclude an accurate measurement of p_x and vice versa. *This is called the uncertainty principle. It follows from the basic postulates* and is intimately associated with the quantum theory of measurement. For a more complete discussion, the reader is referred to other textbooks.[18]

It should be pointed out that the experiments on the measurement of position and the velocity of a particle in a vibrating system are hypothetical, or *gedanken*, experiments. *Gedanken* experiments, or "thought experiments," are imaginary experiments used to prove, or illustrate, points. The experiments are not always practical, but they are always consistent with all known physical principles. These idealized cases illustrate the *techniques* of the quantum-mechanical method of predicting the location of dark lines on photographic film, the number of counts in a Geiger counter located behind a given slit, etc.

---

[18] See, for example, D. Bohm, *op. cit.*, Chapter 5.

Whatever scientists may think in the distant future about our present concepts of the wave-particle duality, it is certain that, as a method of predicting the average behavior of laboratory instruments, quantum theory has permanently established its utility.

5.6. Wave packets and the scattering of particles

Although this book is primarily concerned with bound systems, there is one system of great practical and conceptual interest, the free particle, which may be described quantitatively with only a small extension of the techniques of analysis used thus far. The analysis of the free particle demonstrates the utility of the principle of superposition of eigenfunctions, provides another system for the calculation of energy, momentum, and position, and illustrates (and illuminates) the uncertainty principle.

Having seen how the free particle is represented in wave mechanics, it is possible to describe in simple, qualitative terms how a particle, initially free, collides with a scattering center (its waves are diffracted by a localized potential), and thereafter is redirected in its motion. The exact, quantitative analysis of scattering is complex mathematically (one is forced, almost from the start, to use approximate methods), and it will not be attempted here.

We shall first demonstrate, by means of a numerical example, that a particular type of superposition of the eigenfunctions of a one-dimensional box of length L will form a moving, bounded, identifiable group of waves called a "wave packet." Instead of assuming, as before, that some particular potential function serves to define the edges of the box (at $x = -L/2$, and at $x = L/2$), we shall now require that the eigenfunctions obey "periodic boundary conditions," namely:

$$\psi(-L/2) = \psi(L/2), \text{ and } (d\psi/dx)_{x=-L/2} = (d\psi/dx)_{x=L/2} \qquad [5\text{–}39$$

In other words, we require that the eigenfunctions have the same amplitude and slope at the two ends of the domain of definition of the eigenfunctions.[19] Inside the box the eigenfunctions are

$$\Psi_k(x, t) = (1/\sqrt{L}) e^{ikx} e^{-i(W_k/\hbar)t} \qquad [5\text{–}40$$

where $k = 2\pi n/L = 2\pi/\lambda$ (since n = the number of λ's in the box)

$$W_k = \hbar^2 k^2/2m$$

$$n = 0, \pm 1, \pm 2, \pm 3, \cdots$$

since they are solutions to the wave equation [2–2] [for $V(x) = 0$]

$$-\frac{\hbar^2}{2m}\frac{\partial^2\Psi}{\partial x^2} = -\frac{\hbar}{i}\frac{\partial\Psi}{\partial t} \qquad [5\text{–}41$$

and Ψ_k satisfies the periodic boundary conditions [5–39].

---

[19] We have already used these boundary conditions in one case, Problem 4.18.

The Ψ'_k's of [5–40] are normalized (they possess an integrable square in their domain of definition), are orthogonal,[20] and are well behaved. Schiff points out that the above Ψ'_k's may be used to represent wave packets running either in the positive or negative x-direction, and conveniently allow a description of the process of reflection at the boundaries.[21]

If k is positive, the waves represented by [5–40] run in the positive x-direction, and if k is negative, the waves run in the negative x-direction, as can be seen by rewriting [5–40]

$$\Psi'_k = (1/\sqrt{L})\, e^{ik(x - \frac{\hbar k}{2m} t)} \qquad\qquad [5\text{–}42$$

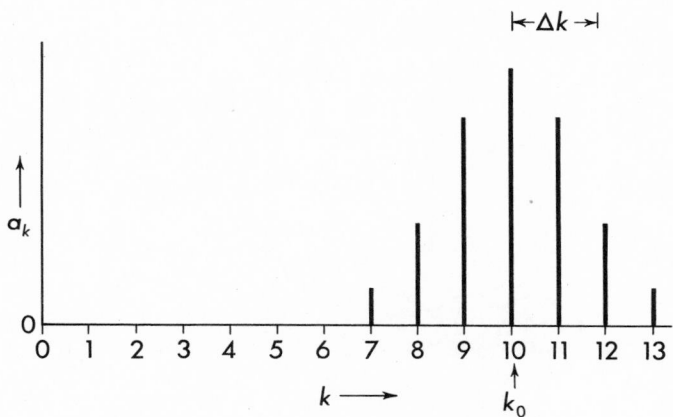

Fig. 5.5. The superposition of states which produce the wave packet of Figure 5.6.

The exponent (the "phase") is zero when $x = 0$ and $t = 0$. It is also zero at a later time t, at the position

$$x = \frac{\hbar k}{2m} t$$

Thus a point of specified phase—here, zero—moves in the x-direction with the velocity (the "phase velocity") ($\hbar k/2m$). The phase velocity of free-traveling matter waves Ψ'_k is proportional to k, that is, to the quantum number n.

Also, at any instant Ψ'_k repeats its value whenever the distance changes by an amount $\lambda = 2\pi/k$, the wavelength of the wave.

Now, any *single* eigenfunction Ψ'_k extends all the way across the box from $-L/2$ to $+L/2$. If, however, we excite *several* eigenfunctions in a narrow range of k-values, the sum (superposition) of such eigenfunctions will be a localized,

---

[20] See Appendix II.
[21] L. I. Schiff, *op. cit.*, p. 49.

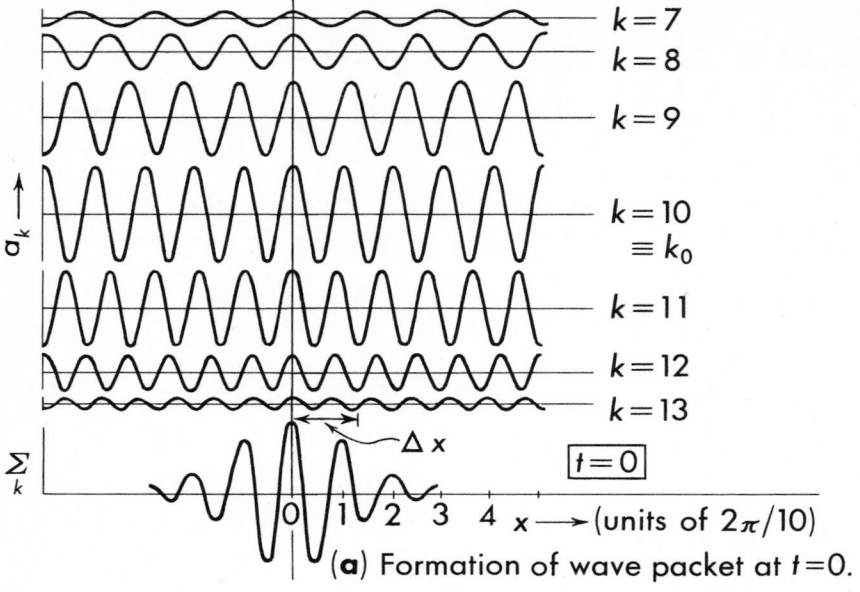

(a) Formation of wave packet at $t=0$.

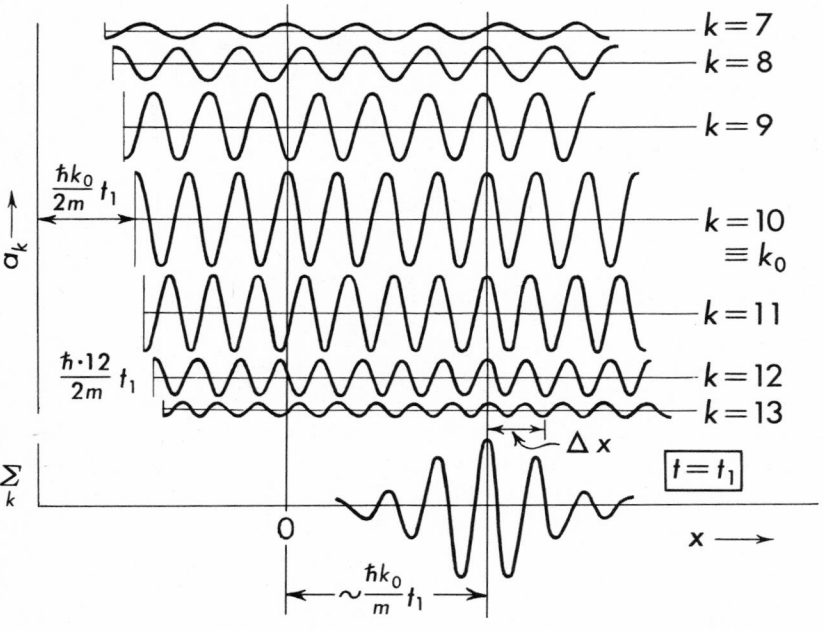

(b) Formation of wave packet at $t=t_1$

Fig. 5.6. Wave packet (real part) belonging to the superposition in Figure 5.5.

moving wave packet. To see how this occurs, we consider a numerical example whose spectrum of states (there are only seven excited states, all told) is given in Figure 5.5, that is

$$\Psi = a_7 \Psi_7 + a_8 \Psi_8 + a_9 \Psi_9 + a_{10} \Psi_{10} + a_{11} \Psi_{11} + a_{12} \Psi_{12} + a_{13} \Psi_{13}$$

The a_k's are all real, and their relative magnitudes are plotted in Figure 5.5. To normalize Ψ one requires that the sum $a_7^2 + a_8^2 + \cdots + a_{13}^2 = 1$. The center value of k is conventionally identified as k_0. Here it is the value $k = 10$.

In Figure 5.6a, the real part (cosine terms) of the seven eigenfunctions are plotted *at the particular time $t = 0$*. Each of the seven plotted curves has a wavelength equal, in each case, to $2\pi/k$, and has an amplitude specified in Figure 5.5. (The amplitude distribution was chosen to be approximately Gaussian in form since this function is used later in the mathematical analysis.) The sum of the seven wave forms (which may readily be obtained with the aid of a pair of dividers for a number of different values of x), yields the wave packet centered at $x = 0$. It is clear that, at $x = 0$, all of the waves add together, since they are all in phase at $t = 0$. The sum shows a second (lower) peak at $x = 2\pi/10$ and a third at $4\pi/10$, separated by negative peaks. Beyond $4\pi/10$, the sum-curve becomes small, oscillating about zero with a slightly irregular wavelength. The distinguishable group of waves—whose wavelength is very close to the wavelength of the wave identified by $k = 10$—has an approximately Gaussian amplitude distribution. From Figure 5.5 we estimate the standard deviation[22] in the spectrum of amplitudes Δk to be about 1.3 k-units (distance^{-1}), and from Figure 5.6a we estimate Δx at about

$$1.2 \left(\frac{2\pi}{10}\right) = 0.75 \text{ (distance)}$$

so

$$\Delta k \cong \frac{1}{\Delta x}$$

It is generally true (see below) that a narrow spectrum of the a_k's produces a long wave train in the packet, and a broad spectrum of the a_k's produces a short wave train in the packet.

We now ask, what happens after a short time delay? Each of the seven waves is traveling with its own phase velocity, $\hbar k/2m$, so that the small-k–waves (longer wavelengths) travel slowest, and the large-k–waves (shorter wavelengths) travel most rapidly. Figure 5.6 shows that, at $t = t_1$, all the pure k-waves have shifted to the right, each by a slightly different amount, proportional, in each case, to k. The *sum* of the shifted waves, plotted in Figure 5.6b, shows almost the same shape wave packet as at $t = 0$, *except that the packet has moved slightly more than twice as far as the average shift of the k-waves* (repre-

---

[22] For a Gaussian curve, $e^{-y^2/2\sigma^2}$, the amplitude is down to $1/\sqrt{e} = 0.6$ of the maximum, when $y = \sigma$. σ is the standard deviation.

sented by the wave $k = 10$). The vertical line, identifying the peak of the packet at $t = t_1$ in Figure 5.6, shows that the seven waves nearly, but not quite, add when each is at its maximum. Thus the packet at $t = t_1$ is actually slightly smaller in amplitude than the original packet at $t = 0$. (It is also slightly broader, although this is not too apparent in the figure.)

It is clear that the wave packet has a velocity (the group velocity) which, in this case, is very nearly twice the average phase velocity of the waves whose superposition forms the packet. If, however, all of the k-waves had the *same* phase velocity, then the whole set of waves in Figure 5.6a would move to the right *together*, and the group, or packet, would accompany them without changing form. In this case (as for light propagating in a vacuum) the phase velocity and the group velocity are equal. Clearly, then, it is the rate of change of phase velocity with wavelength which determines how much difference exists between the average phase velocity and the group velocity. (For the spreading circular wave packet observed on a still pond, although there is again a factor of two between the phase and group velocities, the dependence of phase velocity on wavelength is such that the *phase* velocity is the greater. The wavelets continually appear out of nothing on the inside of the spreading ring and, moving through the packet, sink to nothing just ahead of the packet.)

It should be noted that, for the correct relativistic wave functions, the phase velocity is much larger—actually greater than the velocity of light (see Chapter 11). The average group velocity (which is the only one which is observable) is the same (for $v \ll c$) for both the relativistic and the non-relativistic analysis.

Having seen from the above numerical example how a group of stationary state eigenfunctions closely grouped in momentum form a wave packet, we now show briefly how to obtain the same result in a more general way. Let the superposition be,

$$\Psi(x, t) = \sum_k a_k \Psi_k(x, t) \qquad [5\text{–}43$$

where the a_k's are real, and have an appreciable magnitude only in the neighborhood of $k = k_0$. Let σ_k be the standard deviation in k which is assumed to be given initially. Then $\bar{p}$ and the standard deviation in the momentum σ_p for the superposition are[23]

$$\bar{p} = \hbar \bar{k}, \qquad \sigma_p = \hbar \sigma_k \qquad [5\text{–}43a$$

Because the form is mathematically tractable, we assume for convenience of calculation that the a_k's have a Gaussian amplitude distribution whose stan-

---

[23] For the superposition [5–43], using Postulate V, where Ψ_k is given by [5–40] $\bar{p} = \sum_k a_k^2 \hbar k$, but $\sum_k a_k^2 k = \bar{k}$, so $\bar{p} = \hbar \bar{k}$. Similarly, $\overline{p^2} = \hbar^2 \overline{k^2}$. Thus $\sigma_p = \overline{p^2} - \bar{p}^2 = \hbar^2 (\overline{k^2} - \bar{k}^2)$ $= \hbar^2 \sigma_k^2$, so that $\sigma_p = \hbar \sigma_k$. NOTE: In the calculation of p or k, the "weighting factor" is a_k^2, *not* a_k.

dard deviation is Δk, that is, we form the superposition

$$\Psi(x, t) = \frac{1}{\sqrt{L}} \sum_k e^{-(k-k_0)^2/2(\Delta k)^2} \, e^{i\left[kx - \frac{W_k}{\hbar}t\right]}, \text{ where } W_k = \hbar^2 k^2/2m \qquad [5\text{--}44$$

This Gaussian distribution is analogous to the numerical one of Fig. 5.5. If L is permitted to become very large so that we may use the operation $\int dk$ instead of the discrete sum, and if $\Delta k \ll k_0$, it may be shown[24] that, after integration over all values of k from $-\infty$ to $+\infty$, [5--44] becomes

$$\Psi(x, t) = \sqrt{\frac{2\pi(\Delta k)^2}{1 + it(\hbar/m)\,(\Delta k)^2}} \exp\left[-\frac{\left(x - \frac{\hbar k_0}{m}t\right)^2}{2\left(\frac{1}{\Delta k}\right)^2 [1 + t^2(\hbar/m)^2\,(\Delta k)^4]}\right]$$

$$\exp\left[i\left(k_0 x - \frac{\hbar k_0^2}{2m}t\right)\right] \qquad [5\text{--}45$$

$$\exp\left[\frac{it(\hbar/m)\,(\Delta k)^2\left(x - \frac{\hbar k_0}{m}t\right)^2}{2\left(\frac{1}{\Delta k}\right)^2 [1 + t^2(\hbar/m)^2\,(\Delta k)^4]}\right]$$

This wave function, originally described by the superposition [5--44], is now expressed explicitly in terms of x and t. It represents a wave packet similar to the one obtained by numerical calculation in the example in Figure 5.6.

The first factor in [5--45] is an amplitude factor whose magnitude decreases with time.

The second factor is an x-dependent Gaussian amplitude function whose standard deviation Δx at $t = 0$ is $(1/\Delta k)$, but which increases with time. The region of maximum amplitude is moving in the positive x-direction with the velocity $\hbar k_0/m$—just *twice* the phase velocity, $\hbar k_0/2m$, of the waves at the center of the spectrum [5--44]—a phenomenon which was clearly revealed by the preceding numerical example.

The third factor in [5--45] is a periodic term which has the form of the eigenfunction belonging to the center value of k.

The fourth factor is also a time-varying quantity which repeats its value every time the exponent becomes a multiple of 2π. This event, however, does not depend linearly on the time t. For small enough values of t, this factor is shown below to be essentially constant, and therefore without influence, in the region of interest—that is, in the region where the packet is located.

---

[24] See, for example, D. Bohm, *op. cit.*, pp. 60–69. The shift from the discrete sum to the integral is the shift from the Fourier series to the Fourier integral.

From [5–45] we calculate the probability density

$$\Psi^* \Psi = \frac{2\pi(\Delta k)^2}{\sqrt{1 + t^2(\hbar/m)^2 \, (\Delta k)^4}} \exp\left[- \frac{\left(x - \frac{\hbar k_0}{m} t\right)^2}{\left(\frac{1}{\Delta k}\right)^2 [1 + t^2(\hbar/m)^2 \, (\Delta k)^4]} \right]$$

[5–46

which shows once again that the region of maximum probability is moving in the $+x$-direction with the constant group velocity,

$$V_g = \hbar k_0/m$$

[5–47

which must be the particle velocity, since the probability of observing the particle between x and $x + dx$, at any time t is $\Psi^* \Psi(x, t) \, dx$. We note, furthermore, that V_g is equal to the expectation value of the momentum $\bar{p}$ divided by the mass m. ([5–43 a] shows that $\bar{p} = \hbar \bar{k}$, and from the symmetry of the a_k distribution, $\bar{k} = k_0$.) This result also follows from classical mechanics, showing again that V_g corresponds to particle velocity.

As another example of the uncertainty principle, we calculate the product $\sigma_x \, \sigma_p$.

By Postulate V, the expectation value of x is $\bar{x} = \int \Psi^* \, x \Psi \, dx$. If we use $\Psi^* \Psi$ as given in [5–46], which is a Gaussian probability distribution in x whose center is moving in the $+x$-direction with the velocity V_g, we see by inspection (see Footnote 22) that at $t = 0$

$$\sigma_x = (1/\sqrt{2}) \, (1/\Delta k)$$

The expectation value of the momentum $\bar{p} = \int \Psi^*(\hbar/i) \, (\partial/\partial x) \, \Psi \, dx$ can be most simply found using the Ψ of the original superposition [5–44]. After using the operator on Ψ, multiplying the two series, and integrating term by term,

$$\bar{p} = \sum_k \{\exp[-(k - k_0)^2/(\Delta k)^2]\} \, \hbar k$$

The observed values of the momentum will center at $\hbar \bar{k} = \hbar k_0$, with the standard deviation,

$$\sigma_p = \hbar(1/\sqrt{2}) \, (\Delta k)$$

which is apparent from the form of the Gaussian function.

Thus, at $t = 0$,

$$\sigma_x \, \sigma_p = \hbar/2$$

However, as t increases, σ_x becomes larger, without limit, so that $\hbar/2$ is merely the *minimum* value of the product. Thus, the uncertainty principle is more accurately written

$$\sigma_x \, \sigma_p \gtrsim \hbar$$

[5–48

Returning to consideration of the wave function [5–45], we ask how long the wave packet will "hold together," that is, will not change its form appreciably. From the fourth factor of [5–45] we note that if we require that

$$\left| x - \hbar k_0 t/m \right|/(1/\Delta k)$$

be the order of unity—that is, if we restrict our attention to the region of the wave packet where the waves are most intense—then the nonperiodic time term is essentially constant if

$$t(\hbar/m)\,(\Delta k)^2 \gtrsim 1, \text{ or } t \gtrsim \frac{m}{\hbar\, k_0^2}\left(\frac{k_0}{\Delta k}\right)^2 \qquad [5\text{--}49$$

Using $V_g = \hbar k_0/m$, and $k_0 = 2\pi/\lambda_0$

$$t \gtrsim \frac{1}{2\pi}\,(\lambda_0/V_g)\,(k_0/\Delta k)^2 \qquad [5\text{--}50$$

The same condition keeps the maximum amplitude and also spatial spread of the packet essentially constant, as is apparent from the form of [5–46].

Defining $2\Delta x/\lambda_0$ to be the number of waves in a packet, and using $\Delta x \cong 1/\Delta k$, the number of waves in a packet becomes $(k_0/\pi\Delta k)$, and [5–50] becomes

$$\underbrace{t}_{\substack{\text{time that a packet}\\\text{will maintain un-}\\\text{distorted form}}} \gtrsim \underbrace{(\lambda_0/V_g)\,(k_0/\pi\Delta k)}_{\substack{\text{time for the particle to}\\\text{travel a distance equal}\\\text{to the length of the}\\\text{packet}}} \times \underbrace{(k_0/\pi\Delta k)}_{\substack{\text{number of}\\\text{wavelengths}\\\text{in a packet}}} \qquad [5\text{--}51$$

For example, if there are three waves in a packet, as in the numerical case worked out in Figure 5.6, the packet should move as a whole for a distance of about three times its own length before becoming smaller in amplitude and spreading out in space. In Figure 5.6 the packet actually moved about twice its own length, and the distortion is beginning to be apparent. If, on the other hand, a packet is formed from states with a very narrow momentum spread, the packet will contain many wavelengths and will travel many times its own length without changing shape.

As an example of the structure of a real wave packet, we consider the electron waves used in the Davisson-Germer experiment. In Figure 5.7 a hot filament "boils off "low-energy electrons (emits electron waves) with an energy uncertainty of about 1/15 e.v., due to the thermal perturbations of the electron energy levels in the crystal from which the electrons come. The electrons are accelerated by the constant 150-volt potential (the electron waves enter a 150-e.v. potential well—a region with a high index of refraction—and shorten their wave-length). From [5–40], given $W = 150$ e.v., $k = \sqrt{2mW}/\hbar$, we have

$$k = 6.3 \times 10^8 \text{ cm}^{-1}$$

so $\lambda = 10^{-8}$ cm. The energy of the electrons coming from the electron gun is known to an accuracy of about 1 part in 2,000, so that the momentum is known to an accuracy of about 1 part in 4,000 (since $W \sim p^2$, then $\Delta W/W \sim 2\Delta p/p$). The exact spatial shape of the wave packets formed by the initial mom-

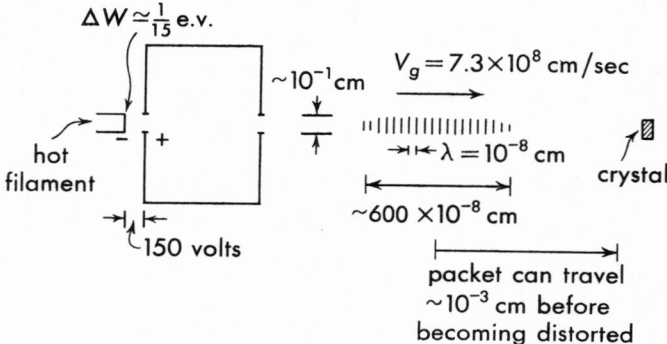

(a) Electron wave packet for Davisson-Germer experiment. 150 e.v. electrons (not to uniform scale).

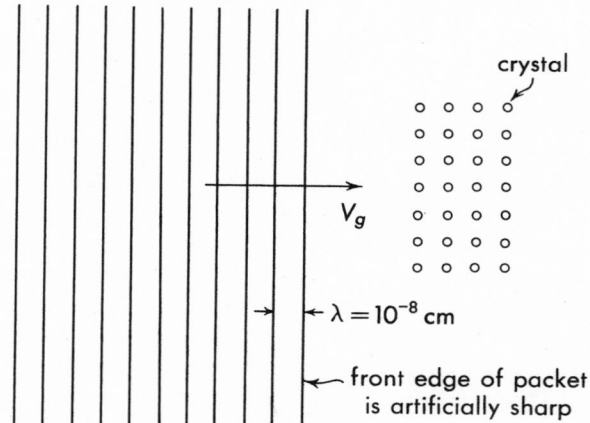

(b) Expanded view of wave packet approaching the scattering crystal. Each atomic scattering center will soon begin to diffract the electron waves.

Fig. 5.7. Sketches of electron wave packets.

entum spectrum depends upon the shape of the momentum distribution, but we assume that the latter is Gaussian.

The group velocity of the $\lambda = 10^{-8}$ cm waves is

$$\hbar k_0/m = (1.05 \times 10^{-27} \times 2\pi \times 10^8)/0.91 \times 10^{-27} = 7.3 \times 10^8 \text{ cm/sec}$$

Classically, the particle velocity is $\sqrt{2W/m} = 7.3 \times 10^8$ cm/sec

The wave packet contains about 600 waves and can travel about 600 times its own length—that is, of the order of 10^{-3} cm—before it loses its initially specified (at $t = 0$, $x = 0$) coherence and form. Thus, it can be scattered by a structure of considerable size—of the order of 10^{-3} cm—and each region of the scattering structure, such as the crystal drawn in Figure 5.6b will experience essentially the same waveform, except, of course, for the time delays that are appropriate to the path differences. (In actual practice, 150-e.v. electron waves are so strongly diffracted by the first few layers of a crystal that they do not penetrate very deeply into the crystal.)

The dimensions of the wave packet, in the two directions transverse to its motion, are determined by the defining slits. (Three-dimensional packets can be readily formed from the eigenfunctions of a large cubical box of length L which obey periodic boundary conditions on the walls.)

Although it is true that the wave packet in the above experiment only "holds together" for a distance of 10^{-3} cm, and the dimensions of the apparatus are of the order of 10 cm, to explain the experimental results the waves must maintain their coherent form only near the crystal. We define $t = 0$ to occur at a point in space ($x = 0$) where the wave packet is just approaching the crystal, as in Figure 5.7b and, if the packet holds together long enough to get into and out of the crystal, its subsequent directional behavior will be uniquely and permanently determined. It is the interplay of the diffracted wavelets from the orderly array of scattering centers which causes the characteristic reinforcement of the scattered waves in specific directions.

The question at once arises regarding the quantitative description of "scattered" or refracted waves from a localized region where the index of refraction is very different from the surrounding space. The system no longer represents a free particle in a box, since there now exists in the wave equation a new potential term, $V(x)$ (for the one-dimensional case). Thus all of the eigenfunctions are different.

A "narrow" superposition $[(\Delta k/k_0) \ll 1]$ of the new eigenfunctions will produce not *one* wave packet but, at certain times, *three or even four* wave packets, a situation which can be visualized with the aid of Figure 5.8. In Figure 5.8a we see a one-dimensional potential barrier of height V_0, and the average energy of the incident particle (the expectation value of W for the given superposition) is $\overline{W}_{k0}$.

The eigenfunctions of the new system are determined by the boundary conditions at the ends of the large box, plus continuity everywhere inside. There are many discrete, closely spaced states if L is large. A superposition of the new eigenfunctions (of a narrow range of energy values) will form, at $x = 0$ and $t = 0$, *at some distance from the barrier*, a wave packet that is quite indistinguishable from the ones we have been considering. An incident wave packet is shown in Figures 5.8b and c before it encounters the barrier. When, however, the packet begins to penetrate the potential barrier, as in Figure 5.8d, the superposition automatically gives a new shape to the packet, which then behaves as if it had four distinct parts: (1) the still-incoming packet; (2) a reflected packet, which is superimposed on the incoming packet, but which is

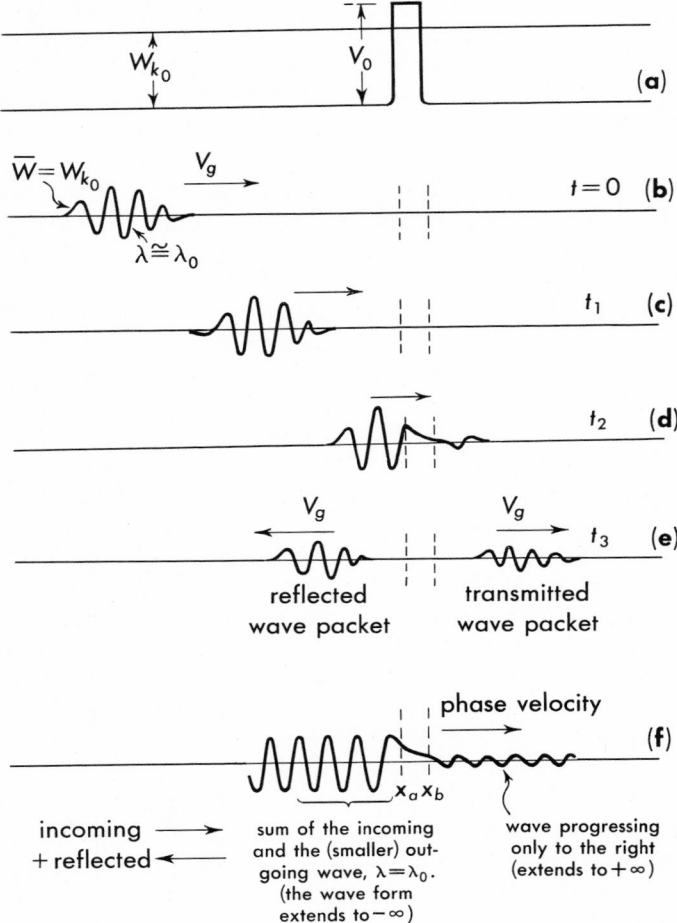

Fig. 5.8. *a–e.* The collision of a wave packet with a potential barrier. *f.* The corresponding steady state approximation with a single eigenfunction.

smaller in amplitude and which is composed of wavelets that have *negative* values of k; (3) an exponentially attenuated wave form inside the barrier (if $\overline{W}_{k_0}$ were higher than the barrier, then this wave form would be a packet formed of wavelets of longer wavelength than λ_0); (4) a transmitted packet still traveling in the $+x$-direction and smaller in amplitude than the incident packet. After the Ψ-waves have died down in the neighborhood of the barrier, we are left with only the (reduced-amplitude) reflected and the transmitted packets, each unchanged in spatial extent—except for the continual spreading, as shown in Figure 5.8e. The process in Fgure 5.8 is a striking example of barrier penetration.

It is apparent that an exact mathematical description of the process above is quite elaborate, and it has often been found necessary to use approximate methods to accomplish this task. One such approximate method—the analysis of only *one* of the pure components of the true wave packet—is sketched in Figure 5.8f. It is based upon the requirement that the wave packet be large compared to the scattering structure. When this is true, the extended wave packet completely envelopes the region of the scattering potential and appears at that stage (outside the potential barrier) to be simply a pure wave, of wavelength λ_0, infinite in extent. One forgets about the distant ends of the packet and merely connects the following four waves smoothly together, using the standard continuity conditions of the postulates. The waves are: (1) the incoming wave, $Ae^{i[k_0 x-(Wk_0/\hbar)t]}$, which extends from $-\infty$ up to x_a, the front edge of the barrier; (2) the reflected wave, $Be^{i[k_0 x+(Wk_0/\hbar)t]}$, which is traveling to the left and extends from x_a to $-\infty$; (3) a wave function, $De^{cx} + Ee^{-cx}$, where $c = $ a constant, and which is the most general solution to the wave equation in the region where V_0 is greater than W_{k_0}; (4) the transmitted wave, $Ce^{i[k_0 x-(Wk_0/\hbar)t]}$, which is traveling to the right. The continuity conditions at x_a and x_b suffice to give the relative amplitudes, B/A and C/A, of the reflected and transmitted waves to the incoming wave.[25] Since the wavelength λ_0 is the most representative of the waves composing the packet, it is reasonable that B/A and C/A should give the relative amplitudes of the reflected and transmitted packets.

In conclusion, we describe qualitatively the three-dimensional scattering of matter waves incident on a small (compared to λ_0), radially symmetric, fixed scattering potential. Figure 5.9a–e shows a two-dimensional view of the various stages of this process. Incident waves from a distant source with a specified spread in momentum are defined by the opening. Thus, in Figure 5.9a, we regard the wave packet as being completely defined. It now propagates toward the scattering center, and there, to maintain the continuity of Ψ at all times and points in space, it is necessary that an outgoing wave packet appear. This wave packet can be represented at large distances from the scattering center by superpositions of functions of the form $f(\theta, \phi) (1/r) e^{i[k_0 r-(Wk_0/\hbar)t]}$, since functions of this type are asymptotic solutions, to the order $(1/r)$, to the three-dimensional wave equation[26] [4–20] for $V(r) = 0$.

[25] See, for example, L. I. Schiff, *op. cit.*, p. 92.
[26] See *ibid.*, p. 100.

Also (because of the $1/r$ factor) these functions possess an integrable square. For $r \gg$ diameter of scatterer, the functions produce spherically spreading wave packets—whose amplitude depends upon θ and ϕ. (The z-axis points to the right in Figure 5.9.)

If we neglect the complicated region behind the scatterer where the original, but now receding, plane wave is superimposed on the outgoing spherical wave,

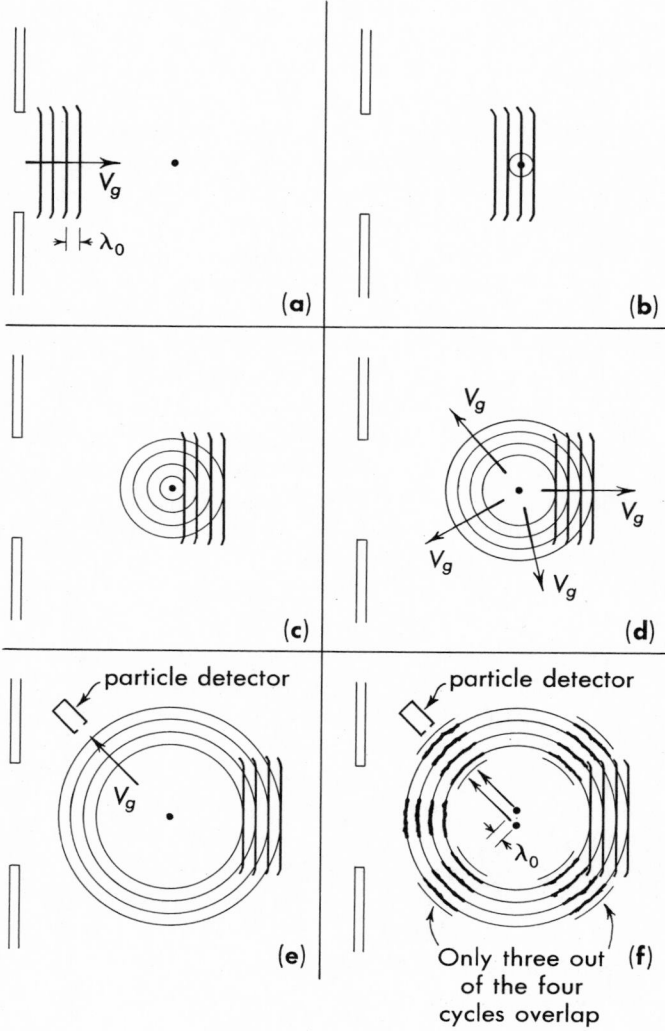

Fig. 5.9. a–e. Stages in the scattering of a plane wave from a scattering center which is small compared to λ_0. f. The scattering from two small centers separated by $1.4\,\lambda_0$.

we have a simple picture of spherically symmetric scattering. The outgoing wave travels with the same group velocity as the original wave. A particle detector has equal chance of observing scattered particles in all directions—except, of course, in the region of interference. An almost perfect two-dimensional model of this process is provided by a water-wave packet from a distant, sharp disturbance, being scattered from a small vertical rod protruding through the surface.

When two scattering centers are present, *each* emits a spherical, outgoing wave packet and, in the case shown in Figure 5.9f the two spherical wave packets overlap for about three of their four wavelets. Since there is a path difference of only one wavelength from the distant source to the detector, via the two routes, and since by [5–51] each packet will travel about four times its own length and remain coherent, there is no question about the existence of some *exact* time relationship between the probability waves at the entrance window to the detector. At the position shown, the probability of observing a particle is large. In between, where the two wave packets have—over the three wavelets, at least—opposed phases, the probability is much lower, but not actually zero. In the Davisson-Germer experiment, but more particularly in the similar G. P. Thompson experiment with deeply penetrating electrons, wave packets are generated at each of many scattering centers and the directions of reinforcement may be very sharply defined.

It is now apparent—even though our analysis has been limited, and, in good part, qualitative—that with the concept of the wave packet, wave mechanics can provide a consistent description of phenomena normally associated with the particle-like nature of matter. If, in the Davisson-Germer experiment, it were not for the fact that Geiger counters and electron multipliers produce output signals in the form of discontinuous bursts, we would in no way suspect that electrons had any particle-like qualities. Whenever these qualities *are* encountered, however, as in particle–particle scattering, they are successfully described in all *observable* aspects by wave packets, formed from a superposition of eigenfunctions, plus the predictions of Postulate V.

PROBLEMS

Problem 5.1. A particle of mass m is in an infinite-wall box of length L. Assume that at $t = 0$, $\Psi(x, 0)$ is a real constant A, for all values of x, $0 < x < c$, and 0 elsewhere ($c < L$).

(a) Show that $A = \sqrt{1/c}$.

(b) If $\Psi(x, t) = \sum_n a_n \Psi_n$, show that

$$a_n = \frac{1}{n\pi} \sqrt{\frac{2L}{c}} (1 - \cos n\pi c/L)$$

(c) Let $c = L/2$, and calculate the amplitude of excitation, a_n, of the six lowest eigenstates.

(d) What is the probability of finding the system energy to be either of the two lowest values?

Problem 5.2. For the system in Figure 5.2, calculate the expectation value of x at the two different times shown in Figure 5.2d and e. If a classical particle, *possessing an electric charge*, had its mean position changing in this manner, what would it be doing? (See Section 10.4.)

Problem 5.3. With the aid of some qualitative sketches, such as those in Figure 5.2, show that if the wave function is

$$\Psi = a_1\,\Psi_1 + a_3\,\Psi_3 \text{ where } a_1^2 = 0.81, \text{ and } a_3^2 = 0.19$$

the expectation value of x is $L/2$ at all times. Thus, a system in this particular "mixed" state will behave differently to the one in Problem 5.2 (and Figure 5.2).

Problem 5.4. Calculate the expectation value of p_x and p_x^2 for the particle in Problem 5.2 where the system is in the pure state Ψ_1.

Problem 5.5. A particle of mass 1 gm is supported by a spring. The system has a natural frequency of 10 cycles per second. When this system is in its lowest energy state, what is the uncertainty in the measurement of its x-coordinate?

Problem 5.6. Consider the hydrogen atom in its lowest energy state, Ψ_{100} (see [4–52] or Appendix VI). Calculate the expectation value of x and of x^2. Use the identity $x = r \sin \theta \cos \phi$. (Hint: for the calculation for $\bar{x}$, do the ϕ-integration first.)

Problem 5.7. Perform the calculations which are the basis for Figure 5.1.

(a) Show that k must equal $\sqrt{3}/L^{3/2}$ if Ψ is normalized.

(b) Calculate the amplitude factors a_n for the first four eigenfunctions in the expansion.

Problem 5.8. Show that the (energy) eigenfunctions of a particle in a one-dimensional, infinite-wall box are *also* eigenfunctions of the operator p_x^2, but not of the operator p_x. Show that ψ_0, for the harmonic oscillator, is not an eigenfunction of *either* p_x^2 or p_x.

Problem 5.9. For the classical harmonic oscillator, sketch the probability that the momentum p will, upon examination at random times, lie between p and $p + dp$. Compare this curve with the Gaussian probability function which Rojansky shows must be the correct one for the quantum harmonic oscillator in its lowest state. (See end of Section 5.4.)

Problem 5.10. In Figure 5.1 and Problem 5.7 we assumed that $t_0 = 0$. It was asserted in the discussion of Figure 5.1 that the particular function being synthesized, $\Psi = kx$, had a momentary existence (at $t = 0$) and that at a later or earlier time Ψ would have a different x-dependence. As an example of what Ψ would be at another time, let $t = h/W_4$ and calculate the new form of the *magnitude* $|\Psi|$ of the wave function. Consider only four terms, as in Figure 5.1. Discussion: Each of the terms in the series [5–9] is now complex due to the fact that the time-dependent terms are no longer unity. The a_n's are the same. Using the identity $e^{iy} = \cos y + i \sin y$, draw, free-hand but with appropriate amplitudes as in Figure 5.1, the *two* sets of sinusoidal curves—one for the real parts of the series and one for the imaginary parts of the series. At eight or ten equally spaced points along the x-axis, sum the four terms. (A pair of dividers such as is used in drafting can be very useful in making this summation.) At each point, the value of $|\Psi|$ is equal to [(real part)^2 + (imag. part)^2]$^{1/2}$. Plot $|\Psi|$ for the eight or ten points calculated.

Problem 5.11. Let electrons be emitted from a heated source with a spread in energy of about $\pm 1/15$ e.v. and let them all be accelerated in the x-direction by 15,000 volts. Assuming that the thermal energy spread at emission is the only source of uncertainty, calculate Δk, k_0, and λ_0. Calculate the length of the matter-wave packet which represents these electrons, and discuss the maximum size of the crystal which can contribute significantly to any *one* scattered wave packet. Show that the packets will travel a distance of the order of 10 cm before becoming distorted. Compare Δx at $t = 0$ to the so-called electron radius, 10^{-13} cm.

Problem 5.12. At $t = 0$, let $\Psi(x, 0) = A$ for $0 \le x < \dfrac{L}{2}$;

$\Psi = -A$ for $\dfrac{L}{2} < x \le L$.

    (a) Calculate the value of A.

    (b) Calculate the first eight of the a's in the expansion

$$\Psi(x, 0) = \sum_n a_n \Psi_n$$

when the Ψ_n are the eigenfunctions of the infinite-wall, one-dimensional box.

    (c) Sketch the eight components, as calculated in (b), add graphically, and compare with the original $\Psi(x, 0)$.

Problem 5.13. A harmonic oscillator of mass m and spring-constant k is in a state which is a superposition (with equal amplitudes) of Ψ_0 and Ψ_1.

    (a) Calculate $\bar{W}$.

    (b) Calculate $\bar{x}$, and plot $\bar{x}(t)$.

    (c) Compare $\bar{x}(t)$ with the $x(t)$ of the classical harmonic oscillator with the same mass and spring-constant, and with the same energy $\bar{W}$.

    (d) Qualitatively, what would happen if the oscillator were in a state which is the superposition of equal amounts of Ψ_0, Ψ_1, and Ψ_2?

Problem 5.14. A particle of mass m is in a two-dimensional, infinite-wall rectangular box whose x-dimension is a and whose y-dimension is b. Let $a = 2b$.

    (a) Suppose that the waves representing the particle are vibrating with equal amplitude in the two lowest states of the system ($n_x = 1$, $n_y = 1$; $n_x = 2$, $n_y = 1$). Calculate $\bar{x}(t)$ and $\bar{y}(t)$. What is the "particle" doing?

    (b) Suppose the wave function contains (in equal amounts) only the eigenstates $n_x = 1$, $n_y = 1$ and $n_x = 2$, $n_y = 2$. Describe the motion of the "particle."

    (c) What would happen, in both (a) and (b), if the higher state was weakly excited compared to the lower state?

    (d) What happens to the "particle" motion when there is no excitation of the higher state?

Problem 5.15. The Energy and Probability Density of a System whose Wavefunction is a Linear Combination of Degenerate States. Let $\psi = a_1 \psi_1 + a_2 \psi_2$, where $W_1 = W_2$, and $a_1^* a_1 + a_2^* a_2 = 1$.

    (a) Show that $\bar{W} = W_1$, a sharp value.

    (b) Show that $\Psi^* \Psi$ is time independent, and that there is an infinite number of possible, stationary probability distributions (one for each choice of the *relative* amplitudes of the two degenerate eigenfunctions).

Problem 5.16. Demonstrate how "periodic boundary conditions" will describe a free particle reflecting from the wall at −*L*/2 or +*L*/2. Suggestion: Along the *x*-axis, construct several identical boxes of length *L*. At the center of each box, at the time *t* = 0, form two wave packets with identical momentum distributions, except that for one, all of the *k*'s are negative. By means of sketches, describe the wave packets at later times. Concentrating on the events in the + half of one box, describe how one packet, formed at *t* = 0, moves toward the +*L*/2 boundary, changing form as it proceeds, and then reflects, *continuing* to change form as it comes back toward the center.

6

ANGULAR MOMENTUM

In Chapter 5 we calculated the average, or the expectation value, of total energy, position, and linear momentum. Given the wave function and the operator which belongs to the quantity being measured, Postulate V permits a direct calculation of the mean value, the standard deviation, etc., of any quantity which is, at least in principle, observable. In this chapter we shall use this method to calculate the expectation value of angular momentum.

The student will recall from classical mechanics that angular momentum was one of the very useful dynamical variables in describing physical systems. In the quantum-mechanical analysis of atomic and nuclear systems, angular momentum plays an even more dominant role. We thus devote this chapter to the description of angular momentum, not only because it illustrates the principles we have discussed thus far, but also because of its great importance in many of the applications of quantum mechanics.

Since angular momentum in classical mechanics involves the rotation of a mass about an axis, it therefore appears only when there is motion in at least two dimensions. We have considered two systems—the hydrogen atom and the rectangular box—which involve more than one dimension. Because of their great physical importance, we shall use the hydrogen wave functions as the basis of most of our calculations.

6.1. The angular momentum operators

The basic definition of the linear momentum, $\mathbf{p}$, of a particle of mass m and velocity $\mathbf{v}$ is

$$\mathbf{p} = m\,\mathbf{v} \qquad [6\text{--}1$$

As in Figure 6.1a, we first consider a mass m located by the vector **r** in the x–y–plane. The velocity vector of the particle also lies in the x–y–plane. In

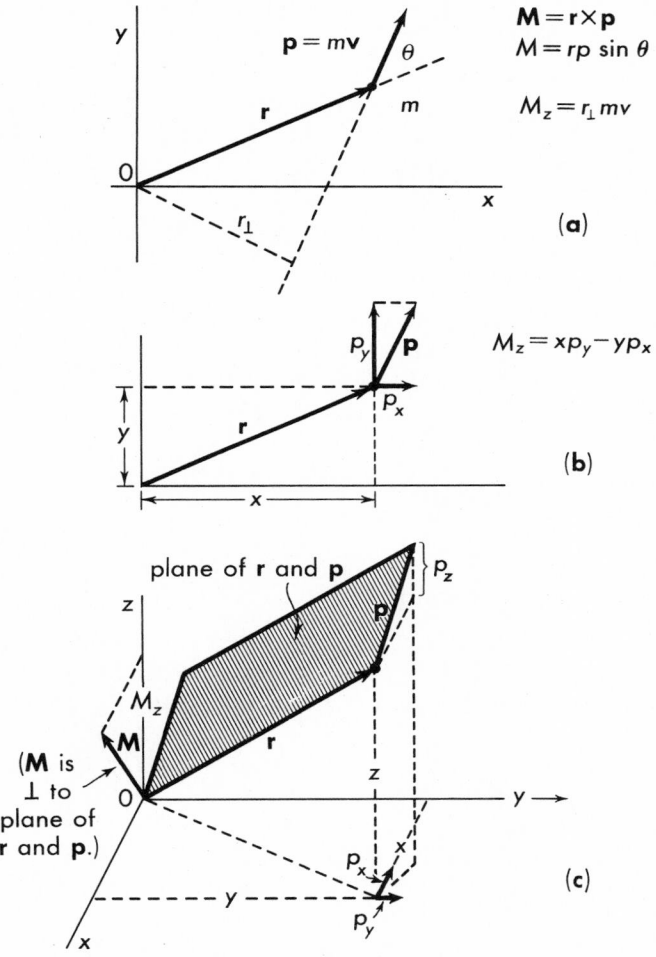

Fig. 6.1. The angular momentum, about 0, of a particle of mass m and velocity v, which is located by the vector r.

elementary mechanics, the angular momentum of the particle about an axis through 0, normal to the plane of x and y, is defined to have a magnitude

$$M_z = r_\perp \, mv, \text{ where } r_\perp = r \sin \theta$$

Thus,

$$M_z = (r \sin \theta) \, mv \qquad\qquad [6\text{--}2a$$

where M_z is represented by a vector normal to the plane defined by **r** and **p**, whose direction, in Figure 6.1a, points out of the paper, since this direction, by convention, indicates rotational motion in the counterclockwise sense.

Equation [6–2a] and Figure 6.1a are a special case of the more general definition

$$\mathbf{M} = \mathbf{r} \times \mathbf{p} \qquad \text{[6–2b}$$

where the $\times$ symbolizes the "cross product" or "vector product" of the two vectors **r** and **p**. **M** is perpendicular to the plane defined by **r** and **p**, and has the magnitude $(r \sin \theta)\, p$. If the fingers of the right hand are first pointed along the direction of the first term of the cross product, here **r**, and then the hand is rotated in the sense of the natural curl of the fingers, through an angle θ, *less* than 180°, toward the second vector, here **p**, then the right hand thumb points in the direction **M**.

Returning to the definition of M_z in equation [6–2a], we note, with the aid of Figure 6.1b, that M_z can be simply expressed in terms of the Cartesian coordinates of **r** and **p**. We first resolve **p** into its two components, p_x and p_y, and then apply the definition [6–2a] to each component separately. Thus, xp_y is the angular momentum about 0 due to p_y alone, and its direction is *out* of the paper. xp_y corresponds to counterclockwise rotation about 0. (Regarding **x** and $\mathbf{p}_y$ as vectors, the right hand rule described above, applied to $\mathbf{x} \times \mathbf{p}_y$, gives the same result.) Similarly, the angular momentum due to the x-component of momentum, p_x, is equal to $-yp_x$. The negative sign arises from the fact that p_x corresponds, in Figure 6.1b, to rotation in the negative, or clockwise, sense. Thus,

$$M_z = xp_y - yp_x \qquad \text{[6–3}$$

The same result can be obtained by applying the rules for the cross product to the right side of

$$\mathbf{r} \times \mathbf{p} = (\mathbf{x} + \mathbf{y}) \times (\mathbf{p}_x + \mathbf{p}_y)$$

and using the fact that the terms consisting of the cross product of **x** and $\mathbf{p}_x$, and of **y** and $\mathbf{p}_y$ are each zero since the vectors composing each of these two products are parallel. [In expanding the equation, it is essential, in each case, to keep **x** (or **y**) to the *left* of $\mathbf{p}_x$ (or $\mathbf{p}_y$).]

If, as in Figure 6.1c, **r** and **p** are *not* lying in any one of the coordinate planes, such as the x–y–plane, we can still calculate the components of **M** using the above principles. For example, as can be seen in Figure 6.1c, the projection of **p** into the x–y–plane yields the two components p_x and p_y. As before, xp_y points along the positive z-axis, and $-yp_x$ (note that in the figure p_x is a negative quantity) also points along the positive z-axis, and we once more obtain [6–3],

$$M_z = xp_y - yp_x$$

and a similar analysis yields,

$$M_y = zp_x - xp_z \qquad \text{[6–4}$$

and

$$M_x = yp_z - zp_y \qquad \text{[6–5}$$

These are the classical expressions for the x-, y-, and z-components of the angular momentum of a point mass about the origin of coordinates.

These classical expressions are converted into quantum-mechanical operators using the substitutions of Postulate II,

$$x \to x; \quad p_x \to (\hbar/i)\, \partial/\partial x; \quad p_y \to (\hbar/i)\, \partial/\partial y; \quad p_z \to (\hbar/i)\, \partial/\partial z$$

with the results,

$$\begin{aligned}
M_x &\to (\hbar/i)\,(y\,\partial/\partial z - z\,\partial/\partial y) \\
M_y &\to (\hbar/i)\,(z\,\partial/\partial x - x\,\partial/\partial z) \\
M_z &\to (\hbar/i)\,(x\,\partial/\partial y - y\,\partial/\partial x)
\end{aligned} \qquad \text{[6–6}$$

$$\underbrace{}_{\substack{\text{classical} \\ \text{variable}}} \quad \underbrace{}_{\substack{\text{quantum-mechanical} \\ \text{operator}}}$$

We shall also wish to know the operator belonging to the square of the angular momentum vector which classically, is

$$M^2 = M_x\,M_x + M_y\,M_y + M_z\,M_z \qquad \text{[6–7}$$

The transformation of this expression into an operator requires that the operator for M_x, M_y, and M_z each appears twice, due consideration being given to the rules for partial differentiation.

The "natural" coordinates for rotational motion in three dimensions are spherical coordinates, and the hydrogen atom wave functions, which we will use in the calculation of expectation value, are expressed in terms of r, θ, and ϕ. Appendix VII outlines the method by which the operators [6–6] and [6–7] corresponding to M_x, M_y, M_z, and M^2, may be shown to be represented by:

$$\begin{aligned}
M_x &\to (\hbar/i)\,(-\sin\phi\,\partial/\partial\theta - \cot\theta\cos\phi\,\partial/\partial\phi) \\
M_y &\to (\hbar/i)\,(\cos\phi\,\partial/\partial\theta - \cot\theta\sin\phi\,\partial/\partial\phi) \\
M_z &\to (\hbar/i)\,(\partial/\partial\phi)
\end{aligned} \qquad \text{[6–8}$$

$$M^2 \to -\hbar^2\left[\frac{1}{\sin\theta}\frac{\partial}{\partial\theta}\left(\sin\theta\,\frac{\partial}{\partial\theta}\right) + \frac{1}{\sin^2\theta}\frac{\partial^2}{\partial\phi^2}\right]$$

These results follow directly from the application of the rules of partial differentiation.

The definition of spherical coordinates is given by Figure 4.3. The particularly simple operator belonging to M_z is basically due to the fact that the angle ϕ measures directly the angular position of the particle about the z-axis. Rotation of the particle about either the x- or the y-axis can be accomplished only by varying *both* ϕ and θ, as can be seen by examination of Figure 4.3.

6.2. The expectation value of the z-component of the angular momentum

In Chapter 4 we found that the eigenfunctions of the hydrogen atom (due to the relative motion of the electron and nucleus) are

$$\Psi_{nlm} = R(r)_{nl}\,\Theta(\theta)_{lm}\,\Phi(\phi)_m\,[e^{-iW_n t/\hbar}] \qquad [6\text{--}9$$

where $\Phi_m(\phi)$ has the particularly simple form, $e^{im\phi}$, where $m = 0, \pm 1, \pm 2, \cdots$.

By Postulate V, the average value of the z-component M_z of the angular momentum is

$$\overline{M}_z = \int\int\int R^*(r)\,\Theta^*(\theta)\,\Phi^*(\phi)\,\underbrace{\left(\frac{\hbar}{i}\frac{\partial}{\partial\phi}\right)}_{\text{operator}}\,R(r)\,\Theta(\theta)\,\Phi(\phi)\,\underbrace{r^2\sin\theta\,dr\,d\theta\,d\phi}_{\substack{\text{volume}\\\text{element, }d\tau}} \quad [6\text{--}10$$

Since

$$\frac{\hbar}{i}\frac{\partial}{\partial\phi}\,e^{im\phi} = m\hbar\,e^{im\phi} \qquad [6\text{--}11$$

and since $\int \psi_{nlm}^*\,\psi_{nlm}\,d\tau = 1$, we have

$$\overline{M}_z = m\,\hbar \qquad [6\text{--}12$$

Similarly,

$$\overline{M_z^2} = (m\,\hbar)^2, \quad \text{so } \sigma = 0$$

$$\overline{M_z^3} = (m\,\hbar)^3,\ \text{etc.}$$

Thus, there will be no dispersion or spread in the observed values of the z-component of the angular momentum as one system after the other is examined —providing, of course, that the wave function for every system is known to be an eigenfunction with the quantum number m in its ϕ-dependent part.

Suppose that the wave function for the hydrogen atom is a superposition of three different (hydrogen) eigenfunctions. For example, let

$$\Psi = a_1\,\Psi_{211} + a_0\,\Psi_{210} + a_{-1}\,\Psi_{21-1}$$

The three constituent eigenfunctions have the same "principal quantum number," n, and therefore the same total energy, W_n. Also, they have the same azimuthal quantum number, $l = 1$. Their exact form is given in [4–53].

For this "mixed" state, the expectation value of M_z is

$$\overline{M}_z = \int\int\int \Psi^*\left(\frac{\hbar}{i}\frac{\partial}{\partial\phi}\right)\Psi\,d\tau$$

$$\overline{M}_z = a_1^*\,a_1(\hbar) + a_0^*\,a_0(0) + a_{-1}^*\,a_{-1}(-\hbar)$$

Similarly,

$$\overline{M_z^2} = a_1^*\,a_1(\hbar)^2 + a_0^*\,a_0(0) + a_{-1}^*\,a_{-1}(-\hbar)^2$$

$$\overline{M_z^3} = a_1^*\,a_1(\hbar)^3 + a_0^*\,a_0(0) + a_{-1}^*\,a_{-1}(-\hbar)^3$$

$$[6\text{--}13$$

It is clear that the probability distribution shown in Figure 6.2a will have the moments calculated in [6–13], and therefore it must be the actual distribution of the observed values. In other words, if we know that a large number of systems are in the state for which $n = 2$ and $l = 1$, but we have no further knowledge about the systems, then an experiment which measures M_z will have just *one* of three results, $M_z = -\hbar$, 0, or $+\hbar$. Without some further information, we can only state that the sum of the probabilities of the three possible results will be unity.

These calculations regarding the expectation value of M_z, M_z^2, etc., are very similar to those for the expectation value of the energy, W. The reason is not far to seek. *Both of the operators involved, upon being applied to the wave function, produce a real number, an eigenvalue.* This was not true for the calculations of the expectation value of x and of p_x, which were performed in Chapter 5. In these latter cases the employment of the operator did not produce a real number, i.e., an eigenvalue, with the result, for example, that $\bar{x}$, $\overline{x^2}$, $\overline{x^3}$, etc., implied some *continuous* probability distribution rather than a small group of discrete values.

We see then that it is a general rule, when the operator a, corresponding to some observable quantity a, produces the result

$$a \, \Psi_n = c \, \Psi_n$$

where c is a real constant (i.e., c is an eigenvalue of the operator a for the eigenfunction Ψ_n), that the observed values of c will always be one of a certain discrete set. If Ψ_n is a single eigenstate, then c will have only one observable value. If Ψ is a mixed state, made up on n component eigenstates, then c will have one of n distinct values.

Conversely, when the operator a does *not* result in a real constant times the original eigenfunction, then the observed values of the corresponding dynamical variable are found to be continuously distributed.

The question arises as to how M_z can be observed. As in every case so far considered, we find once again that to observe the state of an atom we must interfere with it in some manner (see Chapter 10).

Let us imagine hydrogen atoms to be in a "pure state" where $n = 2$ and $l = 1$. This is actually the first excited state of hydrogen, and the atom will quickly radiate to the ground state, $n = 1$, $l = 0$. We suppose, however, that we can make an observation of the atom in a time short compared to the lifetime of the state. In Figure 6.2b we see a narrow, collimated beam of hydrogen atoms, known to be in the state $n = 2$, $l = 1$, passing through a magnetic field perpendicular to the direction of the magnetic field. The field **B** is so designed that, although its direction is along the z-axis, its intensity varies strongly with z (increasing with increasing z). For more detail, see Appendix X.

It can be shown both experimentally and theoretically that the hydrogen atom, in the state $n = 2$, $l = 1$, possesses a magnetic moment, **μ**, directed opposite from **M**, since the charge is negative (see Problem 6.8). It is this

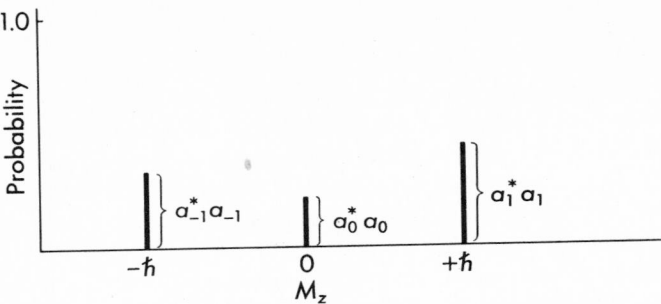

(**a**) Observed values of the z-component of the angular
momentum for the hydrogen atom in the state,
$n = 2$, $l = 1$ (spin neglected).

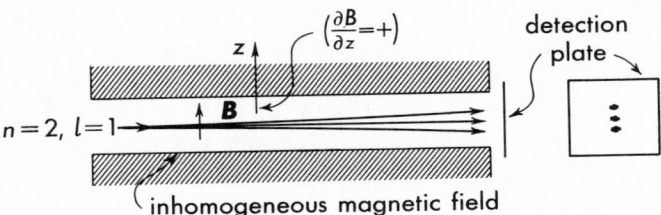

(**b**) The Stern-Gerlach experiment (spin neglected).

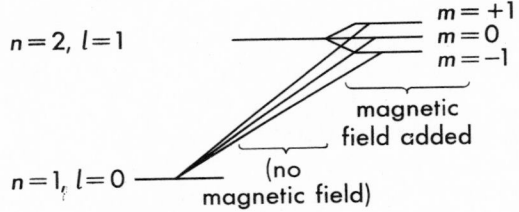

(**c**) The hydrogen spectrum — the Zeeman Effect
(spin neglected).

Fig. 6.2. The observation of the z-component of the angular
momentum, neglecting electron spin.

magnetic moment, associated with the z-component of the angular momentum,
which allows us to observe M_z. In a magnetic field directed along the z-axis,
as in Figure 6.2b, with a gradient $\partial B / \partial z$, an object with a component μ_z of
magnetic moment along the z-axis will experience a force, in the z-direction, of
magnitude[1]

$$F_z = \mu_z (\partial B / \partial z) \qquad [6\text{--}14$$

Thus, in Figure 6.2b the atoms will be deflected either up or down, or not at

---

[1] This equation is derived in Appendix X, "The Force on a Current Loop in an Inhomogeneous Magnetic Field."

all, depending upon the direction of orientation of their magnetic moments (and the angular momentum vector) with respect to the Z-axis.

The deflection of the atoms is thus a measure of the component of their magnetic moment in the z-direction—and therefore a measure of the component of the angular momentum M_z. As we have seen, quantum theory predicts that only three distinct values of M_z should be observed for the case of hydrogen atoms with $n = 2$ and $l = 1$. On the right side of Figure 6·2b is a sketch of a detection plate which would record the three distinct beams of atoms. Actually this particular experiment is impractical because of the short life of the state $n = 2$, $l = 1$. In addition, the electrons have an intrinsic magnetic moment and associated intrinsic angular momentum (or "spin") which would cause each of the three lines shown to split into two, since M_z for the electron "spin" alone turns out to have two possible values. Thus, Figure 6.2b is idealized, but systems very similar to this, when deflected by an inhomogeneous magnetic field, do show behavior of this type. In an experiment proposed by O. Stern in 1921, and performed by Stern and Gerlach in 1922, a beam of neutral Ag atoms was observed to split into two distinct beams due, in this case, to the intrinsic electron-spin angular momentum and the associated magnetic moment. In Chapter 11 we will discuss the origin of the intrinsic electron spin. The Stern-Gerlach experiment demonstrates that electron spin behaves in a manner similar to orbital angular momentum. Molecular beam experiments of the Stern-Gerlach type, and also related experiments employing the same principle, do in fact show that atoms with "orbital" wave functions of the same form as the $l = 1$ functions of the hydrogen atom, split into three distinct beams as the magnetic field in some specified direction (the z-direction) "forces the atoms to reveal their orientation."

Problems 6.5 and 6.8 are concerned with calculations for a simple case of the Stern-Gerlach experiment.

Another experimental means of exposing the three distinct observable values of M_z is to examine the optical spectrum of a hydrogen atom in a magnetic field. In Figure 6.2c, the energy level of the atom at $n = 2$, $l = 1$ splits into three distinct levels due to the three possible values of M_z along the direction of the magnetic field. The associated magnetic moment μ, belonging to the state where $l = 1$, causes the total energy of the atom to depend upon the component of magnetic moment μ_z along the direction of the field.[2] Again,

---

[2] With the aid of Figure 1, Appendix X, one can see that the potential energy of a current loop (the classical analogue of an electron in an $l = 1$ state) depends upon its orientation in the magnetic field. Consider the magnetic field in Figure 1c and d, Appendix X, to be uniform, and let α be the angle between μ and $\mathbf{B}$, and define $V(\alpha)$ to be zero when μ is perpendicular to $\mathbf{B}$ ($\alpha = \pi/2$). Then $V(\alpha) = \int_{\pi/2}^{\alpha} 2F \sin \alpha (d/2)\, d\alpha$, where $F = idB$ ($i =$ coulomb/sec). Integrating, $V(\alpha) = -ibd\,\mathbf{B}\cos\alpha$. Since $\mu \equiv ibd$, P.E. $= -\mu \cdot \mathbf{B}$. For a negative charge, the magnetic moment μ is directed opposite to the angular momentum $\mathbf{M}$, so the high-energy state of Figure 6.2c ($m = +1$, or $\overline{M}_z = \hbar$) must have its angular momentum vector pointing in the same general direction as the external magnetic field $\mathbf{B}$.

in Figure 6.2c the effects of intrinsic electron angular momentum and magnetic moment have been disregarded. (If the effect of spin is included, then the three energy levels in Figure 6.2c, for $n = 2$, $l = 1$, become six, that is, each level splits into two. Also, spin causes the single level $n = 1$, $l = 0$ to split into two.) The point at issue here, however, is that atoms known to be in the $n = 2$, $l = 1$ state, when subjected to a magnetic field, reveal three distinct values of M_z. The level splitting caused by the magnetic field is known as the Zeeman effect.

Once again—as in Chapter 5—we see that the observation of the quantity predicted by the expectation value calculation of Postulate V involves disturbing the system under observation. The hydrogen-like wave functions, which we have used as the basis of the calculations in this section, correctly describe the atom when the inhomogeneous magnetic field is not present. The field acts as a probe to interfere with the atom, and cause it to reveal its quantum state.

If the three-dimensional wave functions are expressed in terms of x, y, and z (as for the rectangular box), then the angular momentum operators, in Cartesian coordinates [6–3] through [6–7], can be used directly. Problems 6.6 and 6.7 are concerned with the calculation of the expectation values of some of the angular momentum operators for the rectangular box.

6.3. The expectation value of the magnitude of the angular momentum

Another quantity, which a study of atomic spectra and molecular beams shows to have a discrete value and whose expectation value can be simply calculated, is the square of the angular momentum, M^2.

In Section 6.1, [6–8] (also see Appendix VII), the operator belonging to the square of the angular momentum, M^2, was given to be

$$-\hbar^2\left[\frac{1}{\sin\theta}\frac{\partial}{\partial\theta}\left(\sin\theta\frac{\partial}{\partial\theta}\right) + \frac{1}{\sin^2\theta}\frac{\partial^2}{\partial\phi^2}\right]$$

This operator looks complicated, but actually results in a simple eigenvalue when applied to the hydrogen atom wave functions.

The Θ-equation for the hydrogen atom (Section 4.3, [4–25]) is

$$-\left[\frac{1}{\sin\theta}\frac{\partial}{\partial\theta}\left(\sin\theta\frac{\partial}{\partial\theta}\right) - \frac{m^2}{\sin^2\theta}\right]\Theta = \beta\Theta \qquad [6-15$$

and this equation has well-behaved solutions Θ_{lm} only when $\beta = l(l + 1)$ where l is 0, 1, 2, 3, $\cdots$, and m ranges from $-l$ to $+l$ in integral steps, as was demonstrated in Section 4.5. Thus, the expectation value of M^2 is

$$\overline{M^2} =$$

$$\int\int\int R_{nl}^* \Theta_{lm}^* \Phi_m^* \left\{-\hbar^2\left[\frac{1}{\sin\theta}\frac{\partial}{\partial\theta}\left(\sin\theta\frac{\partial}{\partial\theta}\right) + \frac{1}{\sin^2\theta}\frac{\partial^2}{\partial\phi^2}\right]\right\} R_{nl}\,\Theta_{lm}\,\Phi_m\,d\tau$$

$$[6-16$$

After the operation using $\partial^2/\partial\phi^2$, [6-16] becomes

$$\overline{M^2} = \iiint R_{nl}^* \Theta_{lm}^* \Phi_m^* \left\{ -\hbar^2 \left[\frac{1}{\sin\theta} \frac{\partial}{\partial\theta} \left(\sin\theta \frac{\partial}{\partial\theta} \right) - \frac{m^2}{\sin^2\theta} \right] \right\} R_{nl} \Theta_{lm} \Phi_m \, d\tau$$

$$[6-17$$

since

$$\frac{\partial^2}{\partial\phi^2} e^{im\phi} = -m^2 e^{im\phi}$$

so that

$$\frac{\partial^2}{\partial\phi^2} \Phi_m = -m^2 \Phi_m$$

The calculation in [6-17] is very simple since Θ_{lm} is one of the Θ_{lm} eigenfunctions, so that, by [6-15],

$$\overline{M^2} = \iiint R_{nl}^* \Theta_{lm}^* \Phi_m^* \hbar^2 \, l(l+1) \, R_{nl} \Theta_{lm} \Phi_m \, d\tau$$

and, because $\hbar$ and l are constants and the wave function is normalized,

$$\overline{M^2} = \hbar^2 \, l(l+1) \qquad l = 0, 1, 2, 3, 4, \cdots \qquad [6-18$$

To calculate M^4 it is necessary to apply the operator inside the integrand twice in succession. The result is

$$\overline{M^4} = [\hbar^2 \, l(l+1)]^2 \qquad [6-19$$

so that the standard deviation is zero. The magnitude of the angular momentum,

$$M = \hbar\sqrt{l(l+1)}$$

is therefore an exactly predictable value—if the wave function of the system is known to be a single eigenfunction of the hydrogen atom.

Thus, if either M_z or the *magnitude only* of M are measured, one will in each case observe one of a set of discrete values.

If one calcu ates in the above manner the expectation values of M_x and M_x^2, M_y and M_y^2, etc., one will obtain—even for the case of an eigenfunction— values which must belong to a *continuous* probability distribution. Thus, only one component of M and the magnitude of M can be measured exactly, and there is an irreducible uncertainty in the other two components.[3]

Suppose that Ψ is a superposition of many eigenfunctions of the hydrogen atom, what will be the expectation value of M^2, M^4, etc.? As in the case of W and M_z, we will find that the probability distribution of M^2 is a series of discrete values. For M^2, these values are 0, $2\hbar^2$, $6\hbar^2$, $\cdots$, $l(l+1)\hbar^2$. That is, the determination of the magnitude of M for each atom will always result in one of the values 0, $\sqrt{2}\hbar$, $\sqrt{6}\hbar$, $\cdots$.

---

[3] Another example of the uncertainty principle.

Returning to Figure 6.2c, we see that the state $n = 2$, $l = 1$ of the hydrogen atom (neglecting electron spin), may be characterized by an angular momentum of magnitude $M = \sqrt{2}\hbar$. When a magnetic field is applied, we observe that there are now three distinct states with the z-component of M, having the three different values $\hbar$, 0, $-\hbar$. It is *as if* a vector of length $\sqrt{2}\hbar$, representing the atom's angular momentum, could, in a magnetic field, take on any one of three distinct orientations with respect to the field vector (the z-axis) such that M_z was $\hbar$, 0, or $-\hbar$. This "vector model" is shown in Figure 6.3 for this case. Models of this type in which a vector, representing the total angular momentum of the atom, is permitted to have quantized components along any selected axis, are widely used in the analysis and interpretation of atomic and molecular spectra. When $|M| = \sqrt{2(2+1)}\hbar$, for example, there are five possible values of M_z, ranging from $-2\hbar$ to $+2\hbar$, and, as reference to Appendix VI will show, there are five different eigenfunctions all having the quantum numbers $n = 3$ and $l = 2$, with values of m ranging from -2 to $+2$ in integral steps.

In hydrogen, with only one electron, the electron spin and its associated magnetic moment produce large effects which are superimposed on the effects of the orbital angular momentum with its magnetic moment which we have been discussing. Although the orbital effects do not occur in *isolated form* in a simple system like the hydrogen atom, they can be sorted out and the predictions of the above theory are all substantiated by experiment.

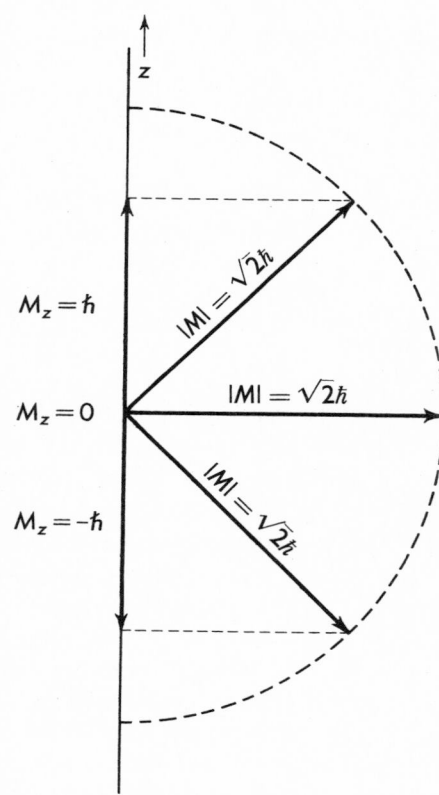

Fig. 6.3. A vector model illustrating the relationship between the magnitude of the angular momentum and its z-component.

When electron spin is included, the principles used in the calculation of wave functions and expectation values are the same, although both the operators and the wave functions are different. In magnetic fields weak enough not to interfere seriously with the atomic structure it is found that the *total* angular momentum has quantized components along the field. The total angular momentum then includes both the orbital and the intrinsic spin angular momentum. (See end of Section 11.7.)

PROBLEMS

Problem 6.1. Show that for a hydrogen atom whose wave function is Ψ_{100} or Ψ_{200}, the expectation values of M_x, M_y, M_z, and M^2 are all zero. The hydrogen atom wave functions are found in [4–52] and [4–53], and also in Appendix VI.

Problem 6.2. Calculate the expectation value of M_x for a hydrogen atom in the state Ψ_{210}. Hint: perform the ϕ-integration first.

Problem 6.3. Calculate the expectation value of M_x^2 for a hydrogen atom in the state Ψ_{210}.

Problem 6.4. Calculate the expectation value of M_x for a hydrogen atom in the state Ψ_{211}.

Problem 6.5. Suppose that the wave function of a hydrogen atom is a linear superposition of the five eigenfunctions belonging to the two lowest energy levels of the atom and, further, that all of these component functions have the same amplitude.
  (a) Calculate the expectation values of M_z and M_z^2.
  (b) Calculate the expectation values of M^2 and M^4.
  (c) Draw a probability distribution of M_z and $|M|$.
  (d) A beam of these atoms transverses the Stern-Gerlach apparatus (Fig. 6.2b). Draw a sketch of the beam intensity *vs* deflection of the atomic beam as it would be received on the detection plate. Neglect electron spin. A simple detection plate (for some types of atoms, although it is not practical for hydrogen) is a cold surface which condenses the atoms. In time, the deposit is visible. (See Problem 6.8 for the calculation of the spacing between the lines on the detection plate.)

Problem 6.6. Calculate $\overline{M}_x$, $\overline{M}_y$, and $\overline{M}_z$ for a particle in an infinite-wall rectangular box whose x, y, and z dimensions are a, b, and c respectively, and where the system is in the single eigenstate $\Psi_{n_x n_y n_z}$, where $n_x = n_y = n_z = 1$ (Section 4.2).

Problem 6.7. Shift the origin of coordinates from one corner of the rectangular box of Problem 6.6 (and Section 4.2) to the center of the box. The eigenfunctions are unchanged with respect to the walls but they must now be expressed differently. For the lowest state, calculate $\overline{M}_z$ and $\overline{M}_z^2$ with respect to the origin.

Problem 6.8. The magnetic moment μ of a current loop is defined, classically, to be $i\mathbf{A}$, where i=current in coulomb/sec and $\mathbf{A}$ = area of the loop (meters)^2. Let a current loop be made of a charge of q coulombs, of mass m_q (kg) rotating at a radius r_0 (meters) with a velocity of v (m/sec). The direction of μ is given in Appendix X.

(a) Show classically that μ has the magnitude $qvr_0/2$. Since $\mathbf{M}$, the angular momentum, has the magnitude $m_q vr_0$, then

$$\mu = \frac{q}{2m_q}\,\mathbf{M}, \text{ and } \mu_z = \frac{q}{2m_q}\,M_z$$

(Note that μ and $\mathbf{M}$ will be oppositely directed if q is a negative charge.)

By quantum mechanics, we know that, for an atomic system, the observed values of M_z can only be $m\hbar$ where m ranges in integral steps from $-l$ to $+l$. Since $M_z = m\hbar$, then if $q = -1.6 \times 10^{-19}$ coulomb, $m_q = 9.1 \times 10^{-31}$ kg, and $\hbar = 1.05 \times 10^{-34}$ joule sec, μ_z will be quantized in integral multiples of $(q\hbar/2m_q) = 0.927 \times 10^{-23}$ joule/ (nt sec/coulomb m). [nt sec/coulomb m = webers/m^2.] A magnetic moment with this magnitude is known as the Bohr magneton. (Since 1 [nt sec/coulomb m] = 10^4 gauss, and 1 joule = 10^7 ergs, the Bohr magneton also equals 0.927×10^{-20} ergs/gauss).

(b) Let $\mathbf{B}$ point along the $+z$-axis, as in the Stern-Gerlach experiment in Figure 6.2b and Problem 6.5, and let B increase from 1,000 to 11,000 gauss in a distance $\Delta z = 1$ cm. Let the magnetic field extend for a distance of 1 m along the path of the hydrogen atoms. Assume that the velocity of the hydrogen atoms is the average velocity, given by kinetic theory, $(\frac{1}{2} mv^2)_{av} = (3/2) kT$, where $T = 100°$ Kelvin. Calculate the spacing between the lines observed on the detection plate in Problem 6.5.

Problem 6.9. Calculate the expectation value of M_z and M_z^2 for the rigid rotator on a fixed axis (see Problem 4.16).

Problem 6.10

(a) Show that the expectation value of M_z is zero for each of the three eigenfunctions $\psi_{n_x n_y}$ belonging to the two lowest

energy levels of the symmetric, two-dimensional harmonic
oscillator (see Problem 4.15).

Note:

$$d\tau = r \, d\phi \, dr$$
$$x^2 + y^2 = r^2$$
$$x = r \cos \phi$$
$$y = r \sin \phi$$
$$\psi_{00} = N_{00} \, e^{-(\alpha/2) \, (x^2+y^2)}$$
$$\psi_{10} = N_{10} \, xe^{-(\alpha/2) \, (x^2+y^2)}$$
$$\psi_{01} = N_{01} \, ye^{-(\alpha/2) \, (x^2+y^2)}$$

The N's are normalizing constants, and $\alpha = 2\pi \, \nu_0 \, m/\hbar$.

(b) Calculate $\bar{x}$ (that is, $\overline{r \cos \phi}$) and $\bar{y}$ (that is, $\overline{r \sin \phi}$) for each
of the three eigenfunctions.

Problem 6.11

(a) Show that if the symmetric, two-dimensional harmonic
oscillator has a wave function which is a particular superposition of two eigenstates,

$$\psi = (1/\sqrt{2}) \, (\psi_{10} + i \, \psi_{01})$$

then the system has a sharply defined angular momentum.

(b) For the above ψ, calculate $\bar{x}$ and $\bar{y}$, and discuss the "particle"
motion inferred.

STEADY-STATE PERTURBATION THEORY. NONDEGENERATE CASE

In Chapters 3 and 4 we found the eigenfunctions of certain simple, highly symmetrical systems. These eigenfunctions correspond to standing-wave patterns of matter waves which resonate within the bounding potential walls much as sound waves resonate in a room with highly reflecting walls, or electromagnetic waves resonate in a conducting cavity. Indeed, the basic techniques of Chapters 3 and 4 will locate the resonant frequencies of any bounded system containing waves. Once the wave equation and the boundary conditions are specified, a set of natural resonant frequencies, each with its characteristic stationary wave pattern, is determined. For example, in a rectangular room with highly reflecting walls, a resonance will occur whenever an integral number of half wavelengths equals one of the sides of the rectangle. In Figure 7.1a, plane waves of sound, whose crests are λ meters apart, are seen moving to the right in a rectangular box. These waves will soon be reflected from the wall on the right and then travel toward the left. If there is an integral number of half wavelengths along the edge (5 half wavelengths are illustrated in the figure), a standing-wave pattern will occur. A closed pipe containing sound waves develops its characteristic frequencies in just this way.

Suppose now, as in Figure 7.1b, the symmetry is destroyed by covering one corner with a small flat, reflecting surface. The plane waves of Figure 7.1a will now no longer be reflected cleanly from the right-hand wall. The simple standing-wave pattern that will occur in the upper diagram depends upon the fact that the plane waves propagating to the right are superimposed upon the reflected plane waves propagating to the left.

What will happen in Figure 7.1b? Clearly, the simple resonance due to plane waves propagating to the right and to the left is upset, for even waves

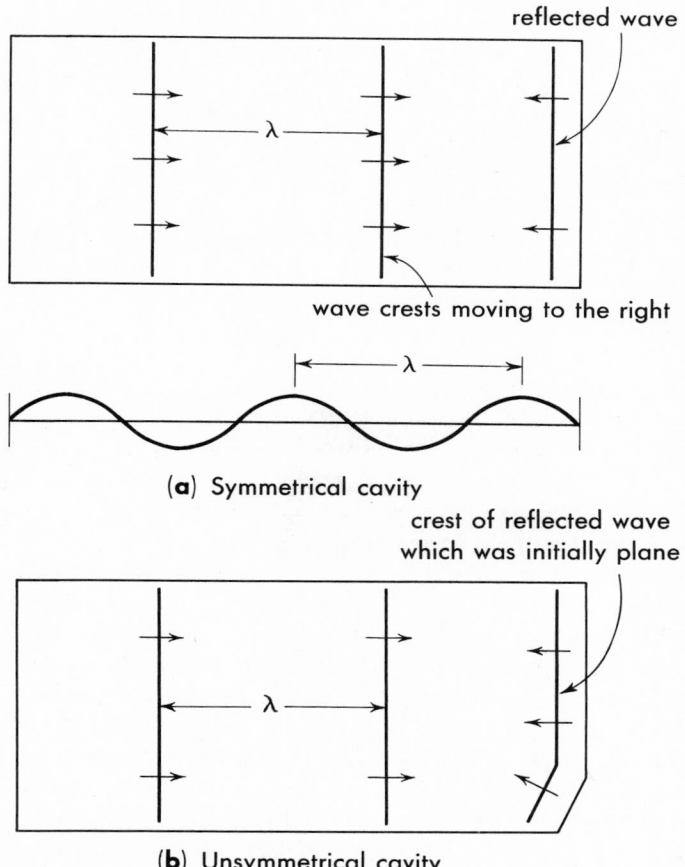

(a) Symmetrical cavity

(b) Unsymmetrical cavity

Fig. 7.1. Waves in cavities with reflecting walls.

that are initially plane will soon be going in many directions owing to the reflections from the odd corner. Rather than solve the problem just posed for sound waves, we will turn to a similar situation involving matter waves and see what changes in the pattern of resonance occur when a small, not necessarily symmetrical, change is made in what was originally a highly symmetrical potential well.

In principle, we can set up, and solve, the exact Schrödinger wave equation including the new term or terms, guided only by the basic postulates. This amounts, as we have seen, to finding certain characteristic functions of space, $\psi_n(x, y, z)$ or $\psi_n(r, \theta, \phi)$, which together with the time factor, $e^{-iWt/\hbar}$, satisfy the requirements of all of the postulates. This process is not particularly simple, even in highly symmetrical systems, and for systems that depart from perfect rectangular or circular symmetry it becomes difficult or impossible. Mathematically, this is often owing to the impossibility of separating the variables. In any case, for only a handful of systems can the eigenfunctions be found in mathematically closed form.[1] This makes the few sets of eigenfunctions that *are* known—such as the hydrogen-like eigenfunctions—of great value. For many systems the exact wave equation contains, in dominant form, the terms that belong to the symmetrical, solvable system, *plus* some terms of relatively small influence. The assumpton is then made that the exact eigenfunctions of the true wave equation do not differ greatly from the known eigenfunctions of the symmetrical, solvable system which is similar to the true system. The known eigenfunctions are used as a starting point, and corrections are then calculated by approximate methods. This technique is often surprisingly successful, even when the corrections are quite large. The terms of relatively small influence in the wave equation which cause it to differ from the equation of a symmetrical, solvable system are called "perturbation terms."

Today, in the applications of quantum mechanics, practically all calculations being made are of the type described above—i.e., perturbation calculations.

In this chapter we shall be concerned with finding the eigenfunctions which belong to systems that have a small, time-independent difference from known, symmetrical systems. In Chapter 10, we will consider perturbations that are not constant in time.

Perturbation theory for the steady state, first applied by Schrödinger in 1926, is based on the reasonable assumption that a small change in the Hamiltonian operator will result in a correspondingly small change in the eigenfunctions of the system. In terms of the acoustical model in Figure 7.1, if the deformation in the corner is very small, the enclosure will resonate at *almost* the same set of frequencies and have *almost* the same standing-wave patterns as when the deformation is entirely missing. As the deformation is made larger and larger, however, the characteristic frequencies and the associated standing-wave patterns will become more and more different from those of the perfectly symmetrical box.

7.1. Perturbation theory, nondegenerate level

Let the exact Hamiltonian H be given by

$$H = H^0 + \lambda H' \qquad\qquad [7\text{--}1$$

---

[1] There are a few other types of symmetry, such as cylindrical and ellipsoidal, which permit separation of variables and exact solutions.

where H^0 is the operator, derived for the unperturbed system with known eigenfunctions ψ_n^0 and eigenvalues W_n^0. That is,

$$H^0\psi_n^0 = W_n^0\psi_n^0 \qquad\qquad [7\text{--}2$$

The term H' is the perturbation term, derived by the usual operator-substitution method of Postulate II. The factor λ is a constant[2] whose value will be set anywhere between 0 and 1. Its purpose is to control the size or magnitude of the perturbation for a reason that will be apparent shortly. We can regard λ as a "control knob" which varies the effect of the perturbation all the way from 0 up to its full value. We look then at any particular eigenvalue W_n and at any particular point in space, x_1, y_1, z_1, where we observe the amplitude ψ of the wave function. How will the eigenvalue, and the eigenfunction (at x_1, y_1, z_1) change as the perturbation is increased from 0 to its full value? We can only suppose that they will vary in some smooth manner from their "starting points" W_n^0, and $\psi_n^0 (x_1, y_1, z_1)$. Whether ψ_n becomes larger or smaller than ψ_n^0 as the magnitude of the perturbation increases depends upon the point (x, y, z) in space where ψ_n is being examined. ψ_n may be unchanged at some points, increase in some regions, and decrease in other regions. Thus, after the perturbation is completely "turned on" (i.e., $\lambda = 1$), we find that the new eigenfunction ψ_n will, in general, be everywhere different from ψ_n^0. There is no reason, furthermore, to expect W_n or $\psi_n (x, y, z)$ to deviate in an exactly linear manner from their "starting points" W_n^0 and $\psi_n^0 (x, y, z)$, so we must allow for some curvature. In Figure 7.2, for each case, we approximate the true curve with a linear term in λ, with a coefficient W_n', or $\psi_n' (x_1, y_1, z_1)$, plus a second-degree term, in λ^2, which has different—and here, smaller—coefficients W'' and $\psi''(x_1, y_1, z_1)$. If the curvature is sharper, it may be necessary to synthesize the true curve with terms dependent upon λ^3, λ^4, etc. We shall be concerned here only with "first-order" approximations. *This means that we shall restrict ourselves to perturbations in which, even when the perturbation is "on" at full intensity* ($\lambda = 1$), *the square-law terms are in all cases small compared to the linear terms.*

The use of λ in this manner is really a mathematical artifice. It is possible to identify, without its use, the different "orders" of the approximation. However, if we regard λ as a "control knob" on the magnitude of the perturbation H', and if we use λ and λ^2 to identify the linear and "square-law" dependence of the correction terms as in Figure 7.2, we will be able to simply and clearly identify the "first-order" and the "second-order" corrections. Eventually we will neglect all terms involving λ^2 (second-order terms), *but first we must identify them.* Thus, during the subsequent calculations we shall retain λ only long enough to determine which part of the corrections to the W_n's and the ψ_n^0's are linear in λ (first-order corrections), and then we will set $\lambda = 1$—i.e., establish the perturbation at its normal magnitude. For certain man-made perturbations,

---

[2] No relationship to wavelength λ.

such as the application of electric or magnetic fields to an atom, one can actually control the size of the perturbation. Perturbations inherent in the system itself—such as the electron-electron interaction of the helium atom—cannot, of

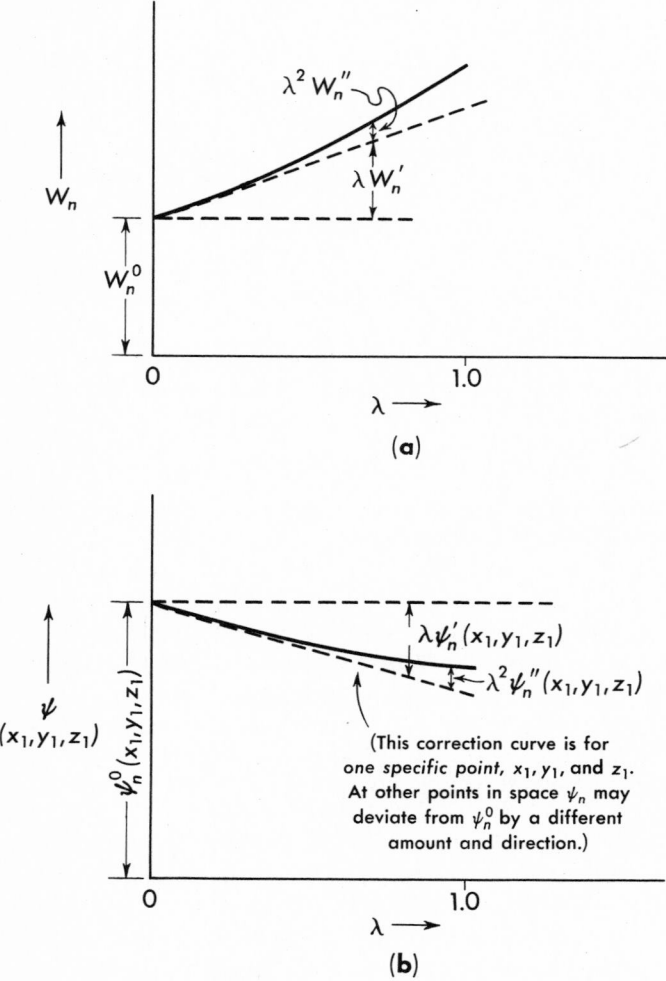

Fig. 7.2. The variation in an eigenvalue W_n and an eigenfunction ψ_n (at a particular point in space) as a function of the magnitude of the perturbation (controlled by λ).

course, be controlled, and if the second-order (λ^2) terms *happen* to be large when $\lambda = 1$ (the only possible value of λ, in reality), there is no alternative but to continue the theory and the calculations to the higher orders. Here, we shall only consider the case where, even when $\lambda = 1$, (i.e., the perturbation is set at the actual magnitude required in the problem), the λ^2 terms in Figure 7.2 are of small magnitude compared to the λ-dependent terms.

The way in which the "true" values of W_n and $\psi_n(x_1 y_1 z_1)$ vary as the perturbation is "turned on" is not initially known. Thus, in Figure 7.2, the "true" curves are arbitrarily drawn. They illustrate that in principle the λ and the λ^2 terms can have coefficients of different magnitude and sign. In fact, it is in general true that at *each point* in space $\psi_n(x, y, z)$ will have a *different* dependence (in both magnitude and direction) upon the intensity of the perturbation (the value of λ). We expect, therefore, that a complete description of the corrections to $\psi_n^0 (x, y, z)$ will be much more elaborate than the description of the correction to W_n^0.

We make the assumptions

$$\psi_n = \psi_n^0 + \lambda\psi_n' + \lambda^2\psi_n'' + \cdots \qquad [7\text{--}3^3]$$

$$W_n = W_n^0 + \lambda W_n' + \lambda^2 W_n'' + \cdots \qquad [7\text{--}4^3]$$

where ψ_n and W_n are the eigenfunctions and eigenvalues, respectively, of the true wave equation,

$$H\Psi = - (\hbar/i)(\partial/\partial t)\,\Psi \qquad [7\text{--}5]$$

which, since H is time independent, separates into two equations in the manner described in Chapter 3. The amplitude equation is

$$H\psi = W\psi \qquad [7\text{--}6]$$

where, as far as the separation of [7–5] is concerned, $W = $ any constant.

For certain discrete values of W, W_n (yet to be found), the true wave equation [7–6] has well-behaved solutions of integrable square, ψ_n (yet to be found), so that, of the infinity of ψ's and W's possible in [7–6], only those which obey

$$H\psi_n = W_n\psi_n \qquad [7\text{--}7]$$

are possible eigenfunctions of real systems. Equation [7–7] is the true wave equation for the system. We know that it must have eigenvalues and eigenfunctions, but there is one practical difficulty—the operator H has such a form that we have no means of solving the problem exactly by standard analytical mathematical methods. It usually happens that the spatial variables in [7–7] cannot be separated, with the result that numerical methods, even with the aid of a large automatic computer, are often not practical. We are forced, therefore, to turn to some method of approximation. We do this, however, *not* because the postulates are deficient—[7–7] *is* the true wave equation and it *does* have exact solutions corresponding precisely to the states of the system

---

[3] Note: Here the primes do *not* mean differentiation. $\psi' (x, y, z)$ gives that part of the correction to $\psi_n^0 (x, y, z)$ at each point in space, which is linear in λ.

it represents—but *only* because, in this case, the mathematical tools are inadequate.

To find an approximate solution to [7–7], therefore, we insert H in the form given by [7–1]. For ψ_n and W_n we substitute the series given by [7–3] and [7–4] respectively. After arranging the terms according to powers of λ, we have

$$(H^0\psi_n^0 - W_n^0\psi_n^0) + \lambda(H^0\psi_n' + H'\psi_n^0 - W_n^0\psi_n' - W_n'\psi_n^0)$$
$$+ \lambda^2(H^0\psi_n'' + H'\psi_n' - W_n^0\psi_n'' - W_n'\psi_n' - W_n''\psi_n^0)$$
$$+ \lambda^3(\cdots) + \cdots$$
$$= 0 \qquad [7\text{–}8]$$

This equation must be true for all values of λ. Providing the series is properly convergent, [7–8] can only be true when each of the coefficients of powers of λ vanish separately. The zero-order equation, obtained by setting the coefficient of λ^0 equal to 0, is

$$H^0\psi_n^0 = W_n^0\psi_n^0$$

which is merely the solvable equation [7–2]. The first-order equation is

$$H^0\psi_n' - W_n^0\psi_n' = (W_n' - H')\,\psi_n^0 \qquad [7\text{–}9]$$

In this equation $\psi_n'(x, y, z)$ and W_n' are both unknown. W_n' is an unknown constant and $\psi_n'(x, y, z)$ is an unknown *function*.

We neglect the equation derived from setting the λ^2 coefficient equal to zero, since we assume that, even when $\lambda = 1$, the corrections to W_n^0 and ψ_n^0, which are dependent upon λ^2, are small compared to those dependent upon λ.

The equation obtained from [7–8] by setting the coefficient of λ^2 equal to zero is the second-order equation. It can be solved by basically the same method shortly to be described for the first-order equation.

Before turning to the mathematical problem of calculating the first-order corrections to the energy and to the wave function that are made necessary by the introduction of a small perturbation, we shall first discuss a simple case graphically, with the aid of Figure 7.3. (Problems 7.1 and 7.2 are concerned with the mathematical analysis of a specific numerical example of a system with the form of Figure 7.3.)

In Figure 7.3a the unperturbed potential energy function forms a one-dimensional box with infinite walls at $x = 0$ and at $x = L$. In between, the potential energy is zero. The lowest eigenstate of the unperturbed system has the normalized wave function $\psi_1^0 = \sqrt{2/L} \sin \pi x/L$, as was found in Chapter 3, and an energy $W_1^0 = \pi^2\hbar^2/2mL^2$.

We now add a potential well, V_1 ergs in depth and B cm in width, centered at $x = L/2$. Thus $H' = -V_1$ in the range $x = (L/2) - B/2$ to $(L/2) + B/2$, and is zero elsewhere inside the box. If B, or V_1, or both, are small enough, we will expect that the true wave function, for the system including the perturbation will differ only slightly from the zero-order wave function, and the true eigenvalue will differ only slightly from the zero-order eigenvalue.

Figure 7.3b shows the correct shape for the true eigenfunction. The shape can be derived qualitatively by simple arguments. Near $x = L/2$, and without

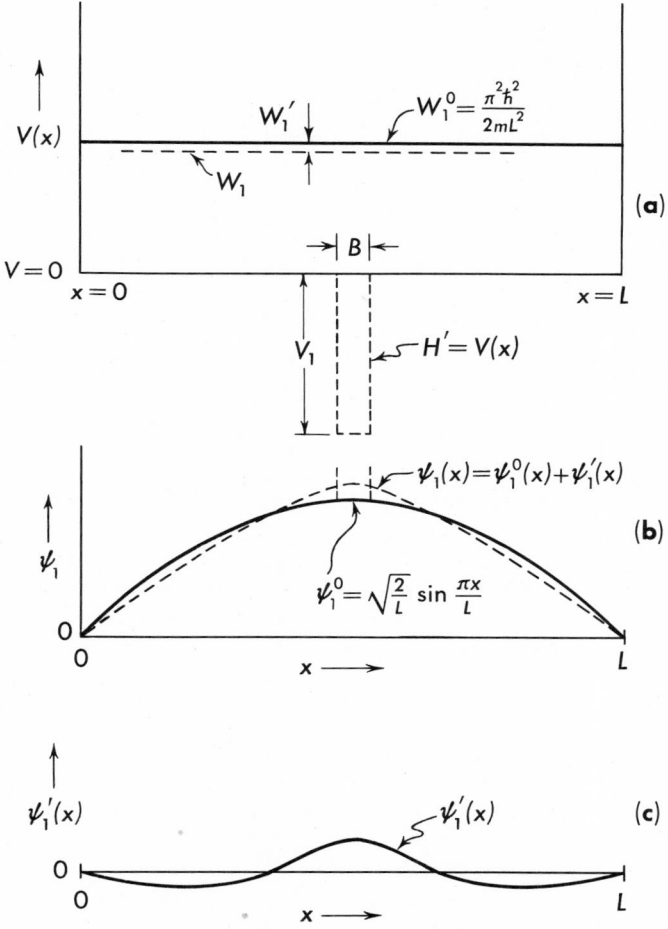

Fig. 7.3. A one-dimensional system containing a small, central potential well.

the perturbing well, the curvature of ψ, $(d^2\psi/dx^2)$ is nearly constant. When the new well is added, the curvature of ψ in the region B must be considerably greater than it was before, and therefore greater than the curvature just outside the well. This occurs since, in the region B, the difference between the potential energy and the total energy is much greater. Inside the region B the true wave function ψ_1 must have the form of a sinusoidal wave, but of short wavelength, with a maximum centered at $x = L/2$. The short wavelength sinusoidal function must, by the postulates, join smoothly (in amplitude and in slope) at *both* boundaries [at $x = (L/2) - (B/2)$ and at $x = (L/2) + (B/2)$] to the rest of the wave function (also of sinusoidal form but of longer wavelength) which exists outside the small potential well. Since the new wave function experiences such sharp curvature in the region of the narrow well, it is clear that *outside* the narrow well the wave function does not need to curve quite as sharply as it did before the narrow well was added. Thus, in spite of its longer wavelength outside the narrow well, the new ψ can still satisfy the boundary conditions (zero amplitude at the infinitely high potential barriers). Since long wavelength is associated with small momentum and thus with small kinetic energy, one should expect the new value of the characteristic energy W_1 (Figure 7.3a) to be lower than the original value W_1^0, and indeed this expectation is quantitatively confirmed by the more detailed calculations which follow.

Figure 7.3c gives the *correction* $\psi_1'(x)$ which must be added to the zero-order wave function ψ_1^0 to produce the true wave function ψ_1. We can see that the *correction* to the zero-order wave function has a different magnitude and sign in different spatial regions.

The over-all magnitude of ψ_1 may be adjusted to make it normalized, i.e. $\int_{-\infty}^{+\infty} \psi_1^* \psi_1 dx = 1$. This has been done, in an approximate manner, for Figure 7.3b. We shall see below, however, that the first-order theory always assumes that the correction terms to ψ are small and that renormalization is not necessary.

The addition of the particular perturbation of Figure 7.3 happens to produce a new system which is exactly solvable, so that it is possible to compare the exact and the approximate solutions. In general, however, this situation does not occur. Suppose, for example, that the added perturbation were not a simple square well, but had some other shape for which there happened to be no closed-form solution. Perturbation theory would still work as well as ever, but the exact solution could not be found, at least by simple mathematical means.

The system in Figure 7.3 gives an example of how, for small perturbations, the true wave function is really much like the zero-order wave function, and the shift in the characteristic energy, from the zero-order energy, is small. It also gives, in graphic form, the nature of the two unknown expressions in the first-order equation [7–9]. W_1' is merely a simple number, but $\psi'(x)$ is an unknown *function* of x. How can we determine this function? The key step is to express $\psi_1'(x)$ as a series of a complete set of orthogonal functions.

It is at this point that the orthogonality of the basic zero-order wave functions becomes indispensable. As we have seen in Chapter 5, almost any function of space can be synthesized by a superposition of a set of appropriate eigenfunctions. We assume, therefore, that the correction ψ_n' to the zero-order wave function ψ_n^0 is given by the series

$$\psi_n' = \sum_j a_j \psi_j^0 \qquad\qquad [7-10]^4$$

That is, the correction terms added to the nth zero-order eigenfunction will be synthesized from a superposition of the complete set of zero-order eigenfunctions. The calculation amounts to finding a particular set of a_j's which will make the synthesis correct. In the example of Figure 7.3, we ask: What amplitudes of the basic functions $\sqrt{2/L}\,\sin j\pi x/L$ ($j = 1, 2, 3, \cdots$) are needed to synthesize the particular function of x shown in Figure 7.3c?

Each system, of course, will have its own "natural set" of basic, or zero-order, functions which are suitable to the problem.

We substitute [7–10] into the first-order equation [7–9]. The term $H^0\psi_n'$ becomes

$$H^0\psi_n' = H^0 \sum_j a_j \psi_j^0 = \sum_j a_j W_j^0 \psi_j^0$$

since $H^0\psi_j^0 = W_j^0 \psi_j^0$. Thus, [7–9] becomes

$$\sum_j a_j(W_j^0 - W_n^0)\,\psi_j^0 = (W_n' - H')\,\psi_n^0 \qquad\qquad [7-11]$$

This equation is a shorthand statement of the equality of a sum of terms on the left to the expression on the right. The student who is not thoroughly familiar with this type of notation should write out at least the first few terms in the series to obtain a better picture of the real nature of the equation. Expressions involving summation signs are often deceptively simple in appearance.

We are here concerned with the perturbations of a nondegenerate state. This is a state which has the characteristic energy W_n^0 to which there belongs only *one* eigenfunction ψ_n^0. For example, the ground state of the hydrogen atom (Section 4.8) has the energy W_1, to which belongs only *one* eigenfunction ψ_{100}, so that this state is nondegenerate. When the characteristic energy is W_2, however, there are *four* different eigenfunctions, and the state is said to be (fourfold) degenerate.

Our first step is to calculate W_n', the correction to the zero-order energy, caused by the addition of the perturbation H' to the zero-order Hamiltonian H^0. We multiply [7–11] from the left by ψ_n^{0*}

$$\sum_j a_j(W_j^0 - W_n^0)\,\psi_n^{0*}\psi_j^0 = W_n'\psi_n^{0*}\psi_n^0 - \psi_n^{0*}H'\psi_n^0$$

In this operation, we have made use of the fact that the a's and the W's are constants and can be interchanged, in order, with ψ_n^{0*}. H', being an operator,

---

[4] The a_j's in [7–10] all have specific values needed to synthesize the correction to a particular zero-order eigenfunction Ψ_n^0. The a's are often written, $a_j^{(n)}$. Here, we concentrate on finding the set of a's which are correct for only one eigenfunction, the nth, and neglect writing the superscript (n).

cannot be interchanged, in order, with the eigenfunction $\psi_n^0{}^*$ (except when H' has certain special forms).

We now multiply each term by the volume element $d\tau$ and integrate each term over the full range of all the coordinates,

$$\sum a_j(W_j^0 - W_n^0)\int \psi_n^0{}^* \psi_j^0 d\tau = W_n' \int \psi_n^0{}^* \psi_n^0 d\tau - \int \psi_n^0{}^* H' \psi_n^0 d\tau$$

Since

$$\int \psi_n^0{}^* \psi_n^0 d\tau = 1 \text{ and } \int \psi_n^0{}^* \psi_j^0 d\tau = 0 \text{ when } j \neq n$$

all of the terms on the left are zero. (The integral is zero when $n \neq j$, and the factor $(W_j^0 - W_n^0)$ is zero when $n = j$.) Thus,

$$W_n' = \int \psi_n^0{}^* H' \psi_n^0 \, d\tau \qquad\qquad [7\text{--}12$$
$$\text{all configuration space}$$

Since H' is given and the zero-order eigenfunction ψ_n^0 is known, the energy correction W_n' to the nth nondegenerate level can be calculated directly from [7–12].

The next step is to find *each* of the a_j's which, in the series [7–10], specify the unknown correction ψ_n'. When ψ_n' is added to ψ_n^0, we have the true (to first-order) wave function ψ belonging to the true (to first-order) energy $W_n = W_n^0 + W_n'$. This is done in the same manner as in the calculation for W_n', except that each term in [7–11] is now multiplied from the left by the complex conjugate of a *different* zero-order eigenfunction, say $\psi_m^0{}^*$. Again, we multiply by the volume element $d\tau$ and integrate over all of the coordinates. Equation [7–11] becomes,

$$\sum_j a_j(W_j^0 - W_n^0)\int \psi_m^0{}^* \psi_j^0 d\tau = W_n' \int \psi_m^0{}^* \psi_n^0 d\tau - \int \psi_m^0{}^* H' \psi_n^0 d\tau$$

The left side of this equation is a sum of terms in each of which j has a different value, identifying, in turn, each of the complete set of the zero-order eigenfunctions. We are in the process of finding the correction to the nth zero-order eigenfunction, so here n is fixed. Also, we have used the complex conjugate of a *particular* zero-order eigenfunction $\psi_m^0{}^*$ to multiply [7–11], so that here m is fixed. Due to the orthogonality of the zero-order eigenfunctions, the left side of the above equation is zero whenever $j \neq m$, leaving, on the left, only one term—for which $j = m$. Since we have specifically assumed that $m \neq n$, the first term on the right is zero. Thus,

$$a_m(W_m^0 - W_n^0) = -\int \psi_m^0{}^* H' \psi_n^0 \, d\tau$$
$$\text{all configuration space}$$

Solving for a_m, the amplitude of the mth component in the *correction* ψ' to the unperturbed eigenfunction ψ_n^0, which is needed to produce the true (to first-order) eigenfunction ψ_n,

$$a_m = -\frac{\int \psi_m^{0*} H' \psi_n^0 \, d\tau}{W_m^0 - W_n^0}, \qquad m \neq n \qquad [7-13$$

There may be an infinite number of these equations if the complete set of zero-order eigenfunctions is infinite in number. Thus, to find the true ψ_n for just *one* of the eigenfunctions of the perturbed system requires a great deal of calculation. Usually only a finite number of the a_m's, calculated by [7-13], have a significant magnitude. Each a_m depends upon the form of the perturbation H' *and* upon the spatial form of the two *different* functions, ψ_m^0 and ψ_n^0, in [7-13].

We see, from [7-13], why it is that this theory is valid only when applied to a nondegenerate level. Suppose that the state whose eigenfunction is ψ_m^0 has the same characteristic energy value as that state whose eigenfunction is ψ_n^0—in other words, two different eigenfunctions belong to the same energy level (we say that this level is twofold degenerate). When this happens a_m will, in general, become infinite, making the correction ψ_m' infinite and therefore unsuitable as part of a wave function. This catastrophy will be avoided only if it also happens that the integral forming the numerator of [7-13] goes to zero whenever the denominator does.

In the next chapter we will discuss the method of avoiding infinite a_m's even though degeneracy exists.

To find the true eigenfunction and the true characteristic energy of some different, nondegenerate level, k, it is necessary to repeat, for the kth level, the complete calculation we have just outlined for the nth level. Thus, a system that has relatively simple, closed-form expressions for its zero-order eigenfunctions will have, after the addition of a perturbation, eigenfunctions that are describable only with the aid of a long table of the a_j's—one *complete list* for *each* of the eigenstates. The new eigenfunctions are still describable in terms of the original ones, but each eigenfunction now appears in the relatively clumsy form of a particular series of the zero-order eigenfunctions. The value of the true (to first-order) W_n is

$$W_n = W_n^0 + H'_{nn} \qquad [7-14$$

where by the symbol H'_{nn} we designate the right side of [7-12],

$$H'_{nn} = \int \psi_n^{0*} H' \psi_n^0 \, d\tau \qquad [7-15$$

By [7-3] and [7-10], the first-order wave function for the nth eigenstate is

$$\psi_n = \psi_n^0 + a_1\psi_1^0 + a_2\psi_2^0 + a_3\psi_3^0 + \cdots + a_{n-1}\psi_{n-1}^0 + a_n\psi_n^0$$
$$+ a_{n+1}\psi_{n+1}^0 + \cdots \qquad [7-16$$

Each of the a_m's ($m = 1, 2, 3, 4, \cdots$) in this equation can be calculated from [7–13] *except* a_n, for which $m = n$, and therefore [7–13] is inapplicable. With this one exception, therefore, [7–13] gives each of the a's

$$a_m = \frac{- H'_{mn}}{(W^0_m - W^0_n)}, \qquad (n \neq m) \qquad\qquad [7\text{–}17$$

where

$$H'_{mn} = \int \psi^0_m{}^* H' \psi^0_n \, d\tau \qquad\qquad [7\text{–}18$$

The symbols H'_{nn} and H'_{mn} are called the matrix elements of the operator H' with respect to the specified eigenfunctions. These expressions, because of their appearance, are easy to confuse with the perturbation operator H', but they are of course very different, since they imply an important operation involving H' and two eigenfunctions.

How can the only undetermined constant, a_n, in [7–16] be found? We have one requirement left—the new wave function ψ_n must be normalized. It is basic to perturbation theory that the amplitude of the perturbed zero-order eigenfunction does not change appreciably, but in first-order theory we regard this amplitude as being constant. To see what limits the normalization of ψ_n sets upon a_n, we write the perturbed eigenfunction

$$\psi_n = \lambda a_1 \psi^0_1 + \lambda a_2 \psi^0_2 + \cdots + (1 + \lambda a_n) \psi^0_n + \cdots \qquad\qquad [7\text{–}19$$

where only a_n is undetermined. We then form the complex conjugate ψ^*_n, multiply it into ψ_n, insert the volume element $d\tau$, integrate term-by-term over all configuration space, and set $\int \psi^*_n \psi_n \, d\tau = 1$, with the result,

$$1 = 1 + \lambda(a^*_n + a_n) + \lambda^2(a^*_1 a_1 + a^*_2 a_2 + \cdots + a^*_n a_n + \cdots) \qquad [7\text{–}20$$

We neglect the second-order (λ^2) terms, and note that [7–20] is true for arbitrary λ if $2 \times$ (real part of a_n) = 0. The undetermined imaginary part is of no physical significance. In actual first-order calculations, one sets $a_n = 0$.

7.2. A sample calculation for a nondegenerate level

To see how the theory in the previous section is applied, we return to the problem of Figure 7.3. In this simple one-dimensional case we were able from general considerations to predict the approximate consequences of the addition of the perturbing potential well in the center of the one-dimensional box. We will now use the theory to calculate the same results.

For a single particle of mass m, in a one-dimensional box, with infinite walls at $x = 0$ and $x = L$, without the perturbing potential, the amplitude eigenfunctions are

$$\psi^0_n = \sqrt{\frac{2}{L}} \sin n\pi x/L$$

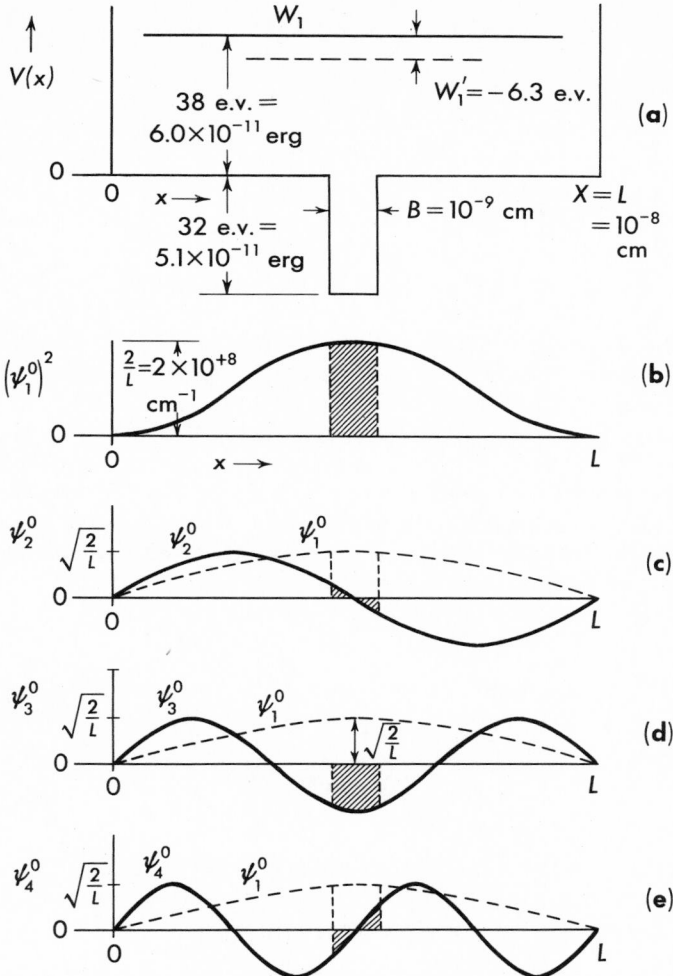

Fig. 7.4. A sample calculation using perturbation theory.

and the energy eigenvalues are,

$$W_n^0 = n^2\pi^2\hbar^2/2mL^2$$

Let the mass $= 9.11 \times 10^{-28}$ gm, $L = 10^{-8}$ cm. Since $\hbar = 1.054 \times 10^{-27}$ erg sec, we have

$$\psi_n^0 = \sqrt{2 \times 10^8} \sin n\pi x/10^{-8} \text{ (cm)}^{-(1/2)}$$

The lowest energy level is[5]

$$W_1^0 = 6\cdot0 \times 10^{-11} \text{ erg, or 38 e.v.}$$

---

[5] If $\hbar = 1.054 \times 10^{-34}$ joule sec, $m = 9.11 \times 10^{-31}$ kg, and $L = 10^{-10}$ m, then $W_1^0 = 6.0 \times 10^{-18}$ joule (1 e.v. $= 1.6 \times 10^{-19}$ joule).

This is plotted on the potential energy diagram at the top of Figure 7.4.

Let $H' = -5.1 \times 10^{-11}$ erg (or -32 e.v.) in an interval B, of 10^{-9} cm, centered at 0.5×10^{-8} cm, and zero elsewhere.

We first calculate H'_{11}, the first-order correction to the energy level W_1^0.

$$H'_{11} = \frac{2}{10^{-8}} \int_{x=4.5 \times 10^{-9}}^{x=5.5 \times 10^{-9}} (-5.1 \times 10^{-11}) \sin^2(\pi x/10^{-8}) \, dx$$

which, from Figure 7.4b, can be seen to be very nearly equal to

$$(2 \times 10^{+8} \text{ cm}^{-1})(-5.1 \times 10^{-11} \text{ erg})(10^{-9} \text{ cm}).$$

Thus,

$$H'_{11} = -10.2 \times 10^{-12} \text{ erg}$$
$$= -6.3 \text{ e.v.}$$

The addition of the potential well lowers the original 38 e.v. level to 31.7 e.v. This lowering of the characteristic energy of the first resonance, or eigenstate, by the addition of the potential well is in agreement with the qualitative arguments used in connection with Figure 7.3.

We next calculate the amplitude of the ψ_2^0 "component" present in the correction to the zero-order wave function. By [7–13],

$$a_2 = \frac{H'_{21}}{W_2^0 - W_1^0} = \frac{-\int \sqrt{\frac{2}{L}} \sin (2\pi x/10^{-8})(-5.1 \times 10^{-11}) \sqrt{\frac{2}{L}} \sin (\pi x/10^{-8}) \, dx}{(2^2 - 1)(6.0 \times 10^{-11})}$$

where the integration runs from

$$x = (5.0 - 0.5) \times 10^{-9}$$

to

$$x = (5.0 + 0.5) \times 10^{-9} \text{ cm},$$

since H' is zero everywhere else. Examination of Figure 7.4c shows at once, however, that the integral H'_{21} will be zero, since the two shaded areas have opposite sign and are equal in magnitude. Thus $a_2 = 0$.

The calculation of a_3 can be performed approximately with the aid of Figure 7.4d, since both functions are essentially constant over the range of integration.

$$H'_{31} \cong \underbrace{(\sqrt{2/L})}_{\psi_3^0}\underbrace{(-5.1 \times 10^{-11})}_{H'}\underbrace{(-\sqrt{2/L})}_{\cong \psi_1^0}\underbrace{(10^{-9})}_{\Delta x}; \quad L = 10^{-8} \text{ cm}$$

$$H'_{31} \cong +1.02 \times 10^{-11} \text{ erg}$$

$$a_3 \cong \frac{-H'_{31}}{W_3^0 - W_1^0} = -\frac{1.02 \times 10^{-11} \text{ erg}}{(3^2 - 1) \, 6.0 \times 10^{-11} \text{ erg}} = -.0208$$

   With the aid of Figure 7.4d, one can see at once that $H'_{41} = 0$, and therefore $a_4 = 0$.

   As higher a_j's are calculated, one should use exact integration in the
calculation of the intensity of the odd-numbered components, because the eigenfunctions vary more rapidly inside the perturbing well, although by symmetery

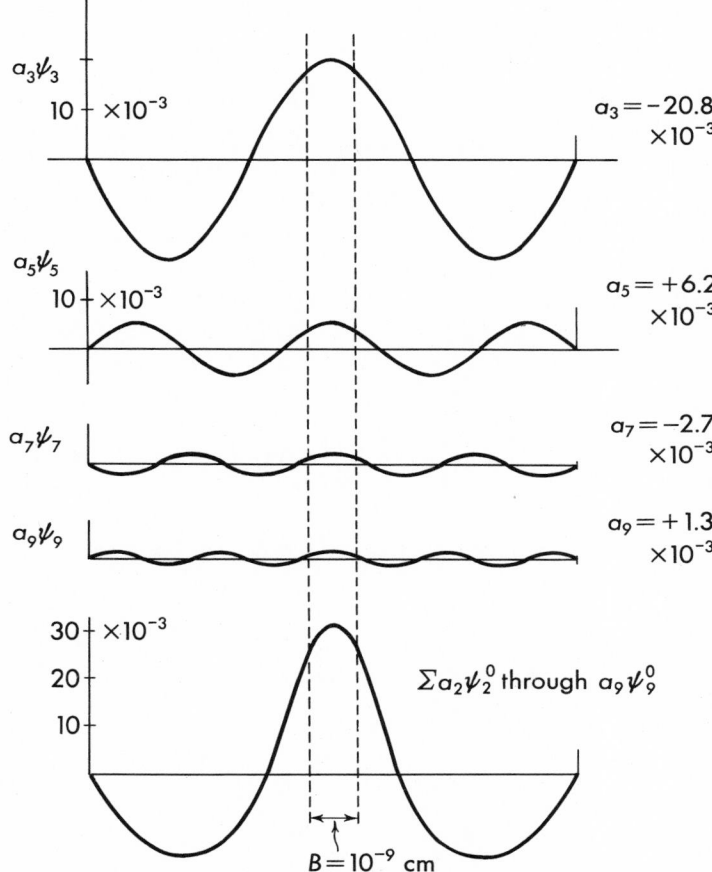

Fig. 7.5.   The calculated corrections to the zero-order state
ψ_1^0 of the system of Figure 7·4.

all of the even-numbered components are always exactly zero. Because the
denominator $W_j^0 - W_1^0$ appears in the calculation of a_j, the magnitude of a_j
becomes smaller with increasing $W_j^0 - W_1^0$.

   Continuing the calculation of the a_j's, we find the amplitude of the terms
up through $n = 9$. These are shown in Figure 7.5. The component wave
functions are drawn to scale, with the correct sign. At the bottom of Figure

7.5 the terms $a_2\psi_2^0$ through $a_9\psi_9^0$ have been added together to give the correction ψ_1' needed to convert the zero-order wave function for this stage, ψ_1^0, into the true (to first-order) wave function, ψ_1. This correction term is seen to have the same shape as the one sketched in Figure 7.3c, which was deduced from general considerations.

Except for the terms for $n = 11$ and higher, which rapidly decrease in amplitude and can be neglected, we now have the true wave function expressed as a superposition of zero-order wave functions.

The normalized, true (to first-order) wave function for the lowest level of the system, including perturbation, is

$$\psi_1 = \psi_1^0 + (-20.8 \times 10^{-3})\,\psi_3^0 + (6.2 \times 10^{-3})\,\psi_5^0$$
$$+ (-2.7 \times 10^{-3})\,\psi_7^0 + (1.3 \times 10^{-3})\,\psi_9^0 + \cdots$$

The characteristic energy belonging to this wave function is

$$W_1 = W_1^0 - 1.02 \times 10^{-11} \text{ erg}$$

A mathematically exact solution of the problem will produce a function $\psi_1(x)$ and a characteristic energy W_1 which are nearly indistinguishable from the above approximate results. Estimating the accuracy of a perturbation calculation is an advanced subject which will not be considered here.

This sample calculation has in it all the essential features of any perturbation calculation for a nondegenerate level in any one-, two-, or three-dimensional system. The only difference in the other systems is that the basic zero-order eigenfunctions in which the true wave function is expressed are different functions of space. One general feature is always present, however. The larger the perturbation, the greater the inaccuracy of the first-order calculations.

In some cases calculations using this theory can be compared with the results of actual experiments. Such a case is the calculation of the lowest energy level of the helium atom, for which $Z = 2$ and for which there are two electrons surrounding the nucleus. The details of this problem can be found in other textbooks[6] and only the main points will be outlined here.

Assume first that for the zero-order system the two electrons do not sense each other's presence in any way but have a potential energy due solely to the presence of the nucleus. The potential energy for the system is then

$$V = -(Ze^2/r_1) - (Ze^2/r_2)$$

where r_1 locates the first electron at x_1, y_1, z_1, and r_2 locates the second electron at x_2, y_2, z_2. Each of the kinetic energy terms is dependent on only three of the six coordinates. We neglect the motion of the nucleus. If the operators are substituted for the dynamical variables according to Postulate II, the resulting zero-order wave equation can be separated into two, one dependent upon

---

[6] See, for example, L. Pauling and E. B. Wilson, *Introduction to Quantum Mechanics* (1935, McGraw-Hill Book Co., Inc., New York): p. 162.

x_1, y_1, z_1, and the other on x_2, y_2, z_2. ψ^0 is the product of two hydrogen-like wave functions, each dependent upon one set of coordinates. The zero-order energy W^0 is the sum of the individual energies of the two electrons, each in the coulomb field of a nucleus with $Z = 2$.

Thus the zero-order wave function and the zero-order energy for each electron in the state ψ_{100} are exactly known.

We now add the perturbation,[7]

$$H' = + e^2/r_{12}$$

where r_{12} is the distance between the two electrons. This is the mutual potential energy of repulsion of the two electrons, each with charge e. This is really a quite large perturbation in the sense that the correction energy W' is comparable to the energy of the unperturbed level, and the results based upon it should not be expected to be extremely accurate. The term

$$r_{12} = \sqrt{(x_1 - x_2)^2 + (y_1 - y_2)^2 + (z_1 - z_2)^2},$$

depending as it does on all six spatial coordinates, does not permit the separation of the exact wave equation. For this reason perturbation methods, or some numerical methods of solution, must be used.

The first-order correction to the energy is

$$W' = \int \psi_{100,100} \, (Ze^2/r_{12}) \, \psi_{100,100} \, d\tau$$

where $\psi_{100,100}$ is merely the product of two ψ_{100} eigenfunctions as given in Appendix VI, one a function of r_1 and the other of r_2. The volume element $d\tau$ is $(r_1^2 \sin \theta_1 \, d\theta_1 \, d\phi_1 \, dr_1)(r_2^2 \sin \theta_2 \, d\theta_2 \, d\phi_2 \, dr_2)$. The above integral yields the result

$$W' = + 33.82 \text{ e.v.}$$

Since the zero-order energy is $- 108.24$ e.v., the perturbation calculation predicts that the lowest energy level of helium will lie at

$$W_1 = - 74.42 \text{ e.v.}$$

Experimentally, the lowest energy level is found to be

$$W_1 = - 78.62 \text{ e.v.}$$

that is, it requires 78.62 e.v. to completely remove both electrons from a helium nucleus, bringing them to rest at infinity.

Thus, the first-order perturbation calculation gives a 27 per cent correction to the zero-order energy and gives a final result which is 5.5 per cent in error from the experimentally determined value.[8]

---

[7] If e is expressed in e.s.u., and r in cm, then H' is in ergs. If e is in coulombs, and r in meters, $H' = (1/4 \pi \varepsilon_0) \, e^2/r$ joules, where $(1/4 \pi \varepsilon_0) = 9 \times 10^9$ nt m²/coulomb².

[8] A more accurate calculation requires that other effects are included such as "exchange symmetry" (Section 11.9).

As Z increases, the relative importance of the electron repulsion becomes less. For example, for quadruply ionized carbon, $Z = 6$, there are two electrons. Here, the correction W' is 10 per cent of the unperturbed energy and the calculated value is only 0.4 per cent in error compared to the experimental value.

The first-order wave functions can also be found by the same principles we have discussed in this section. Due, however, to the geometrical complexity of the hydrogen-like wave functions, and also to the nature of the perturbation H', this calculation is not easy to perform.

We have discussed here only the most simple type of perturbation theory. By extending the method to include the second-order terms in [7–8] (where, for ψ_n'', one substitutes, once again, a series of the basic zero-order eigenfunctions and then proceeds in a manner similar to first-order theory), greatly improved accuracy can often be obtained. In addition to these methods there are many other techniques of approximate calculation that can be found in the more advanced textbooks and in the literature.

7.3. Summary

In this, and in all of the subsequent chapters, the detailed method of presentation loses much of the brevity and essential simplicity of the mathematical argument. Also, for reference purposes, it is convenient to have the key equations brought together. Therefore, we reproduce here, in outline form and with minimum comment, the essential steps in theory developed in this chapter. The equations are identified by the same numbers that are used in the main part of the chapter.

For the nth level, the exact or true wave equation is

$$H\psi_n = W\psi_n, \text{ where } H = H^0 + \lambda H' \qquad \text{[7–6], [7–1}$$

In the true wave equation, we substitute:

$$\psi_n = \psi_n^0 + \lambda\psi_n', \text{ where } \psi_n' = \sum_j a_j \psi_j^0 \qquad \text{[7–3], [7–10}$$

$$W_n = W_n^0 + \lambda W_n' \qquad \text{[7–4}$$

obtaining [7–8] (see text).

We set the coefficient of $\lambda^0 = 0$, obtaining

$$H^0 \psi_n^0 = W_n^0 \psi_n^0, \text{ the zero-order equation} \qquad \text{[7–2}$$

We set the coefficient of $\lambda^1 = 0$, obtaining

$$\sum_j a_j(W_j^0 - W_n^0) \psi_j^0 = (W_n' - H') \psi_n^0, \text{ the first-order equation} \qquad \text{[7–9], [7–11}$$

We multiply the first-order equation from the left by ψ_n^{0*}, insert $d\tau$, and integrate over all configuration space, obtaining *one* equation, which gives the energy *correction* to the *n*th level,

$$W'_n = \int \psi_n^{0*} H' \psi_n^0 \, d\tau \equiv H'_{nn} \qquad [7\text{-}12$$

We repeat the above operation, except using ψ_m^{0*}, $(m \neq n)$, obtaining a *set* of equations which gives, by [7–10], the *correction* to the wave function of the *n*th level,

$$a_m = -\frac{\int \psi_m^{0*} H' \psi_n^0 \, d\tau}{W_m^0 - W_n^0} = \frac{-H'_{mn}}{W_m^0 - W_n^0},$$

$$\text{where } m = 1, 2, 3, \cdots \text{ except, } m \neq n. \qquad [7\text{-}13$$

To first-order, set $a_n = 0$. Since all the above results are true for arbitrary λ, we set $\lambda = 1$. Thus, from [7–3] the first-order energy is

$$W_n = W_n^0 + W'_n \qquad [7\text{-}21$$

where W'_n is given by [7–12].

From [7–4] the first-order wave function belonging to W_n is

$$\psi_n = \psi_n^0 + a_1 \psi_1^0 + a_2 \psi_2^0 + a_3 \psi_3^0 + \cdots + (0) \psi_n^0 + \cdots \qquad [7\text{-}22$$

where each a_m is given by [7–13].

For another level—the *k*th—this whole process must be repeated, resulting in a first-order W_k and ψ_k.

PROBLEMS

Problem 7.1. For the system described in Figure 7.4a find, to first-order, the energy value W_3 and the amplitudes, a_j of the two strongest components in the correction, ψ_3', to the zero-order wave function ψ_3^0.

Problem 7.2. For the system of Figure 7.4a find, to first-order, the energy value W_2 and the amplitudes a_j of the two strongest components in the correction, ψ_2', to the zero-order wave function ψ_2^0. Hint; With the aid of diagrams, make a geometrical analysis of the problem, exploiting symmetry, before doing any quantitative calculations.

Problem 7.3. Classically, a particle bound by a potential such as that in Figure 7.4 would, upon losing energy, settle down into the central potential well. Estimate the necessary depth of the central well in Figure 7.4 in order that the quantum-mechanical particle could be bound inside it.

Problem 7.4.   Move the narrow well from the center, in Figure 7.4, to the left-hand edge—that is, assume that the same well is now located between $x = 0$ and $x = 10^{-9}$ cm. Calculate the new value of W_1. Calculate the a_j's for $j = 2$, 3, 4, and 5. Qualitatively, what has the presence of the well done to the probability of finding the particle inside the region occupied by the small well, as contrasted to the unperturbed system? Compare this situation to the example worked out in the text.

Problem 7.5.   In the hydrogen atom, the potential energy $V(r)$ of the system is $- e^2/r$, and exact energy values and exact eigenfunctions are known. As $r \to 0$, $V(r)$ approaches infinity, since we are assuming a mathematical point charge, $+ e$, at the nucleus. This cannot actually be true, since other evidence shows that the nucleus has a finite radius, of the order of 10^{-13} cm, and the charge is distributed throughout a sphere of this radius. Let us assume, for purposes of simplicity, that the total charge, $+ e$, is in the form of a thin shell of radius 10^{-13} cm. If this were so, then $V(r)$ would reach a maximum negative value at $r_N = 10^{-13}$ cm, and remain constant at the value $- e^2/r_N$ between $x = 0$ and $x = r_N$. Let the perturbation H' be: $(e^2/r) - (e^2/r_N)$ from $x = 0$ to $x = r_N$, and $H' = 0$ for $x > r_N$. Calculate the correction W' to the lowest energy state of the hydrogen atom if the above H' is added to the Hamiltonian based upon the point charge model. Hint: Note that from $r = 0$ to $r = r_N$, $\psi^*\psi \cong$ (const.) and may therefore be taken outside the integral.

Problem 7.6.   The text states that the zero-order energy of the helium atom is $- 108$ e.v.

(a)   Confirm this result.
(b)   How far apart are two classical electrons when they have a mutual potential energy of $+ 29.6$ e.v., the first-order correction to the ground state of helium?
(c)   Compare (b) to the size of a helium atom (in its ground state) whose electrons do not interact. As a measure of size, use the magnitude of the expectation value of r^2.
(d)   Why does not the expectation value of r yield an estimate of size?

Problem 7.7.   Calculate W_5' for the system of Figure 7.4. With the sketches, estimate the amplitude and sign of the terms in ψ_5' involving ψ_3^0, ψ_4^0, ψ_6^0, ψ_7^0.

Problem 7.8.   Show, for the system of Figure 7.4, that when $n \gg 1$, then, to first-order, all the energy levels are perturbed downward by essentially the same amount. What is this amount? Obtain the same result by classical mechanics and the correspondence principle.

Problem 7.9.   Problem 4.16 gives the wave equation and eigen-functions of the free rigid rotator on a fixed axis. The lowest energy state ($M = 0$) is nondegenerate. Add a weak, uniform gravitational field, g, pointing in the $+ x$-direction (Fig. 4.11) and define $H' = r_0$ $(1 - \cos \phi)\, mg$. Let g have such a value that $mgr_0 = (1/10)\, (\hbar^2/2mr_0^2)$, that is, the maximum value of H' is small compared to the smallest spacing between energy levels of the system. For the state $M = 0$,

(a)   Show that $W' = r_0 mg$.
(b)   Show that $a_1 = a_{-1} = (1/20)$. ⎫ Exploit symmetry and anti-
(c)   Show that $a_2 = a_{-2} = 0$.   ⎬   symmetry about $\phi = 0$.
(d)   In two graphs, one above the other, sketch $V(\phi)$ and ⎭

$$\psi_0(\phi) = \psi_0^0 + a_1 \psi_1^0 + a_{-1} \psi_{-1}^0.$$

Does the functional form of ψ_0 agree with the qualitative arguments used on the (essentially identical) physical pen-dulum system analysed in Problem 4.17?

8

STEADY-STATE PERTURBATION THEORY.   DEGENERATE CASE

In the last chapter we found that the first-order perturbation theory breaks down if one tries to analyze a level for which two (or more) distinct wave functions exist. It was shown that some additional requirements had to be placed upon the two different wave functions belonging to the degenerate level in order to avoid an infinite amplitude for one of the components of the correction wave function. In this chapter we shall find, for a twofold degenerate level, what these additional requirements are—at least for certain classes of the perturbation H'. The theory can be readily extended to degeneracy of higher multiplicity, at the price of somewhat increased complexity of notation, but with little additional insight into the significance of the process. The twofold degenerate case has the additional importance of being essential to the understanding of the distinctive quantum effect known as exchange degeneracy—which appears whenever two or more identical particles occupy the same region of space (see Chapter 9).

8.1.   Analysis of a twofold degenerate level

We analyze a system whose zero-order wave equation has, for a particular characteristic energy W^0, two different (linearly independent)[1] eigenfunctions

---

[1] If a relationship exists between ψ_1^0 and ψ_2^0, of the form
$$a_1 \psi_1^0 + a_2 \psi_2^0 = \text{constant}$$
where the a's are constants, then ψ_1^0 and ψ_2^0 are *not* linearly independent. If one is specified, the other is automatically determined.

ψ_1^0 and ψ_2^0. That is,

$$H^0\psi_1^0 = W^0\psi_1^0 \text{ and } H^0\psi_2^0 = W^0\psi_2^0 \qquad [8\text{--}1$$

In Appendix II we can see that the basic wave equation, with auxiliary conditions, automatically guarantees the orthogonality of any pair of eigenfunctions belonging to *different* energy levels, but does not require that eigenfunctions belonging to the *same* energy level be orthogonal. However, as Appendix II shows, it is always possible to form two different linear combinations of the original wave functions which *are* orthogonal. It sometimes happens that the original eigenfunctions belonging to a degenerate level are already orthogonal, even though there is no general requirement to this effect. For example, the four hydrogen eigenfunctions of the energy operator H belonging to the $n = 2$ level (Appendix VI) all happen to be mutually orthogonal.[2]

We shall assume that the two eigenfunctions ψ_1^0 and ψ_2^0 of [8--1], belonging to the degenerate level W^0, are, or have been made, mutually orthogonal. Also, they are individually normalized.

As in Chapter 7, we now assume that a correction term $\lambda H'$ is added to the zero-order Hamiltonian

$$H = H^0 + \lambda H' \qquad [8\text{--}2$$

where λ is used once again to sort out the parts of the resulting corrections to the zero-order energy and zero-order wave function, which are dependent upon λ and λ^2. We again assume that, even when $\lambda = 1$, the first-order corrections to both the energy levels and the wave functions are still much more important than the second-order corrections. The value $\lambda = 1$ corresponds to the perturbation being "turned on" at the full intensity appropriate to the problem.

There is no doubt that the zero-order energy W^0 will be the correct starting point for the perturbation calculation. Thus we assume, as before,

$$W = W^0 + \lambda W' \qquad [8\text{--}3a$$

The problem arises when we try to decide the correct "starting point" for the *wave function*. There are *two* ortho-normal linearly independent functions, ψ_1^0 and ψ_2^0, to choose from. We have seen, using the theory in Chapter 7, that if we take either one of these, we will run into trouble. Thus, we can only *assume that some linear combination of the two eigenfunctions is the correct zero-order or "starting point" function.* Therefore, we assume an initially arbitrary, linear combination, $c_1\psi_1^0 + c_2\psi_2^0$, as the zero-order wave function. For this sum to be a normalized solution to the zero-order wave equation, we

---

[2] As we have seen in Chapter 4, these four eigenfunction of the energy operator all belong to the same energy eigenvalue W_2. The same four functions (see Chapter 6) are *also* eigenfunctions of the operators corresponding to M_z and M^2. When operated on by these latter operators, however, the functions provide eigenvalues which are different. In this chapter, and generally throughout the book, the word "eigenfunction" refers to an eigenfunction of the energy operator.

must require that

$$c_1^* c_1 + c_2^* c_2 = 1 \qquad \text{[8–3b}$$

The true wave function for the perturbed system is

$$\psi = c_1 \psi_1^0 + c_2 \psi_2^0 + \lambda \psi' \qquad \text{[8–4}$$

where ψ' is the sought-after correction to the zero-order wave function caused by the presence of H' in the true wave equation

$$H\psi = W\psi \qquad \text{[8–5a}$$

and c_1 and c_2 are initially unknown constants, except for the condition [8–3b].

The problem is solved as follows: First, the expressions for H, W, and ψ, given by [8–2], [8–3a], and [8–4], are substituted into [8–5a]. Second, we identify the first-order terms, that is, those proportional to λ, and thereafter set $\lambda = 1$. Finally, we find W', ψ', and c_1 and c_2. This is similar to the problem of Chapter 7, except there are two additional numbers, c_1 and c_2, to be found. Making the indicated substitutions into [8–5a], we have,

$$H^0(c_1 \psi_1^0 + c_2 \psi_2^0) + \lambda(H^0 - W^0)\,\psi' + \lambda^2(\ \cdots\ )$$

$$= W^0(c_1 \psi_1^0 + c_2 \psi_2^0)$$
$$+ \lambda[c_1(W' - H')\,\psi_1^0 + c_2(W' - H')\,\psi_2^0] + \lambda^2(\ \cdots\ )\ \text{[8–5b}$$

By [8–1], the terms in λ^0 cancel ($\lambda^0 = 1$)

If the equation is to be true for an *arbitrary* value of λ, it must be separately true for each power of λ. The terms in the first power of λ give the equation,

$$(H^0 - W^0)\,\psi' = c_1(W' - H')\,\psi_1^0 + c_2(W' - H')\,\psi_2^0 \qquad \text{[8–6}$$

upon which all subsequent first-order calculations are based.

As in Chapter 7, we synthesize ψ' from a series of the complete set of basic, ortho-normal eigenfunctions of the zero-order system,

$$\psi' = \sum_j a_j \psi_j^0 \qquad \text{[8–7}$$

so that the calculation of the unknown correction ψ' is complete when we can list each of the a_j's.

In [8–6] there are two functions of the coordinates, $H'\psi_1^0$ and $H'\psi_2^0$, which are actually known (since H' is given and the zero-order wave functions are known). However, rather than express these two functions explicitly in terms of the spatial coordinates (which is possible), we shall express each of them as a series of the basic, ortho-normal eigenfunctions, ψ_j^0, just as we have done in [8–7] for the *unknown* ψ'. Note that the expression $H'\psi_1^0$ can be, in principle, very different from any of the basic ψ_j^0's, since H' can be an expression involving the coordinates, or an operator involving the coordinates.

Therefore, we form two new series

$$H'\psi_1^0 = \sum_j b_j \psi_j^0 \text{ and } H'\psi_2^0 = \sum d_j \psi^0 \qquad [8\text{--}8$$

Since H', ψ_1, and ψ_2 are known, we can calculate the b_j's and the d_j's at once,

$$b_j = H'_{j1}, \text{ where } H'_{j1} = \int \psi_j^{0*} H' \psi_1^0 \, d\tau$$

$$d_j = H'_{j2}, \text{ where } H'_{j2} = \int \psi_j^{0*} H' \psi_2^0 \, d\tau \qquad [8\text{--}9$$

These expressions for the b_j and d_j are found in the usual manner: Multiply each of the equations [8–8] from the left by ψ_j^{0*}, insert the volume element $d\tau$, and integrate over all of the spatial coordinates.

If the substitutions [8–7] and [8–8] are made in the first-order equation [8–6], and $H^0\psi_j^0 = W_j^0\psi_j^0$ is used, we have, upon rearrangement,

$$\sum_j (W_j^0 - W^0)\, a_j \,\psi_j^0 = W'(c_1 \,\psi_1^0 + c_2 \,\psi_2^0) - \sum c_1 \,H'_{j1}\,\psi_j^0 - \sum_j c_2 \,H'_{j2}\,\psi_j^0$$

where $W^0 = W_1^0 = W_2^0$. $\qquad [8\text{--}10$

In this equation, a series of terms in ψ_j^0 on the left is equated to a different series, also in ψ_j^0, on the right. For this to be true for arbitrary H' (which affects the values of H'_{j1} and H'_{j2}) it is necessary that equality in [8–10] exists, term by term. Thus, equating the coefficients of ψ_1^0,

$$0 = c_1 \,W' - c_1 \,H'_{11} - c_2 \,H'_{12}$$

equating the coefficients of ψ_2^0,

$$0 = c_2 \,W' - c_1 \,H'_{21} - c_2 \,H'_{22} \qquad [8\text{--}11$$

equating the coefficients of ψ_3^0,

$$(W_3^0 - W^0)\, a_3 = - c_1 \,H'_{31} - c_2 \,H'_{32}$$

etc.

In general, when $j \neq 1, j \neq 2$, equating the coefficients of ψ_j^0 gives

$$a_j = \frac{c_1 \,H'_{j1} + c_2 \,H'_{j2}}{W^0 - W_j^0} \qquad [8\text{--}12$$

For $j = 1$ and $j = 2$ [8–12] cannot be used. We shall see below, however, that to preserve normalization (to first-order), it is necessary that a_1 and a_2 be zero. (That is, to first-order, the correction term ψ' does not contain any of the components belonging to the level being analyzed.)

Thus, if we can find c_1 and c_2, we will then know *all* of the a_j's since [8–12] gives all of the a_j's for $j > 2$, and, as [8–4] shows, c_1 and c_2 are themselves the amplitudes of ψ_1^0 and ψ_2^0. Thus, we will then know the true (to first-order) wave function ψ, which is being sought.

For an alternative derivation of [8–11] and [8–12], see Problem 8.10.

To find c_1 and c_2, we return to the first two equations of [8–11], which are

$$c_1(H'_{11} - W') + c_2 H'_{12} = 0$$

$$c_1 H'_{21} + c_2(H'_{22} - W') = 0$$

[8–13

$c_1 = c_2 = 0$ is of course a (trivial) solution to these equations, but if a nontrivial solution exists, it is necessary that the determinant of the coefficients vanish,[3]

$$\begin{vmatrix} (H'_{11} - W') & H'_{12} \\ H'_{21} & (H'_{22} - W') \end{vmatrix} = 0$$

[8–14

that is,

$$(H'_{11} - W')(H'_{22} - W') - H'_{21} H'_{12} = 0$$

[8–15

This equation, usually called the "secular equation," has only one unknown, W', but being a second-degree equation there are, in general, two distinct roots,[4] that is, two distinct values of W', which we indicate by W'_a and W'_b. We see at once, therefore, that when a zero-order system is perturbed, an initial, exactly defined energy level W^0, which was twofold degenerate, may be corrected by *either* W'_a or W'_b. If these two numbers are different, as they often are, since they depend on both the zero-order wave functions and also the form of H', one says that "the degeneracy has been removed" by the application of the perturbation H' to the system with characteristic energy W^0. If W'_a and W'_b turn out to be identical, one says that H' does *not* "remove the degeneracy."

The pair of equations [8–13] involves three quantities, originally unknown, W', c_1, and c_2. The determinant equation [8–15] selects possible values of one quantity, W'. When this is done, equations [8–13] are no longer linearly independent and will yield only the ratio c_1/c_2. To [8–13] we add therefore the requirement that the complete first-order wave function,

$$\psi = c_1 \psi_1^0 + c_2 \psi_2^0 + \lambda \sum_j a_j \psi_j^0$$

[8–16a

be normalized, in accordance with the basic postulates. That is, $\int \psi^* \psi \, d\tau = 1$. Since the ψ_j^0's are ortho-normal,

$$1 = c_1^* c_1 + c_2^* c_2 + \lambda(c_1^* a_1 + c_1 a_1^* + c_2^* a_2 + c_2 a_2^*) + \lambda^2 \sum_j a_j^* a_j$$

[8–16b

---

[3] For example, see L. E. Dickson, *First Course in the Theory of Equations* (1922, John Wiley and Sons, Inc., New York): p. 119.

[4] It can be shown that both these roots will be real if H'_{21} and H'_{12} are complex conjugates, that is, $H'_{21} = (H'_{12})^*$, and if H'_{11} and H'_{22} are real (that is, if $H'^*_{11} = H'_{11}$, and $H'^*_{22} = H'_{22}$). See Problem 8.8. If $H'_{12} = H'_{21} = 0$, the matrix is said to be diagonal.

Also note: Only if ψ_1^0 and ψ_2^0 are linearly independent is this solution possible. If, for example, $a\psi + b\psi = 0$, then the first two equations in [8–11] are not independent, and the determinant [8–14] does not exist.

For first-order theory, we neglect the λ^2 terms and note that, since we have already required by [8-3b] that $c_1^* c_1 + c_2^* c_2 = 1$, and since λ is arbitrary, the coefficient of λ must be zero. This is most simply guaranteed for all possible values of c_1 and c_2 if both a_1 and a_2 are zero. Thus, setting $\lambda = 1$, [8-16a] becomes

$$\psi = c_1 \psi_1^0 + c_2 \psi_2^0 + \sum_{j>2} a_j \psi_j^0 \qquad [8\text{-}16c$$

where, as before,

$$c_1^* c_1 + c_2^* c_2 = 1 \qquad [8\text{-}3b$$

That is, the normalization of the first-order wave function is accomplished by setting a_1 and a_2 equal to zero. We are left with the original condition, [8-3b], on c_1 and c_2.

Equations [8-13] and [8-3b] together make three equations involving the three unknowns, c_1, c_2, and W'. c_1 and c_2 are, in general, complex numbers, whereas W' is a real number (a certain number of ergs, for example). Thus, only the magnitudes of c_1 and c_2 can be determined, leaving, in each case, a constant, complex-exponential factor of the form $e^{i\delta}$, called the phase factor, which is undetermined.[5] Since all predictions about the results of experiments are reached through the use of Postulate V, and since δ is a constant, the value of the phase factor is of no practical consequence. The examples which follow will make the role of the phase factor more clear.

We return to the calculation of the two unknown quantities, c_1 and c_2. As before, we designate the two values of W' found from [8-14] or [8-15] by W_a' and W_b'. Each, in turn, is substituted into [8-13], and for each case, we can only obtain a value of the *ratio* of c_1/c_2. Thus,

$$\text{when } W' = W_a', \text{ then } (c_1)_a/(c_2)_a = A$$
$$\text{when } W' = W_b', \text{ then } (c_1)_b/(c_2)_b = B \qquad [8\text{-}17$$

if $(c_2)_a \neq 0$, and $(c_2)_b \neq 0$.
Thus we see how both A and B are completely determined by [8-13].

Consider the case where $W' = W_a'$, then $(c_1)_a = A(c_2)_a$. Making this substitution in [8-12],

$$(a_j)_a = \frac{A(c_2)_a \, H_{j1}' + (c_2)_a \, H_{j2}'}{W^0 - W_j^0} = (c_2)_a \, (K_j)_a \qquad [8\text{-}18$$

where $(K_j)_a$ is the completely determined factor

$$(K_j)_a = \frac{A \, H_{j1}' + H_{j2}'}{W^0 - W_j^0} \qquad [8\text{-}19$$

---

[5] The *relative* phase of c_1 and c_2 is determined, since by [8-17], below, the *ratio* c_1/c_2 is known. If $| c_1 | e^{i\delta_1}/| c_2 | e^{i\delta_2}$ is known, then $e^{i(\delta_1 - \delta_2)}$ is known.

The subscript a means that these K_j's are determined for the case where $W' = W'_a$.

Finally, the magnitude of $(c_2)_a$ is found by combining [8-17] with [8-3b],

$$1 = A^* A(c_2)^*_a (c_2)_a + (c_2)^*_a (c_2)_a, \text{ or } (c_2)^*_a (c_2)_a = \frac{1}{1 + A^* A} \qquad [8-20$$

Thus, for the case $W' = W'_a$,

$$W = W^0 + W'_a$$

and,

$$\psi_a = (c_2)_a \left[A \psi^0_1 + \psi^0_2 + \sum_{j>2} (K_j)_a \psi^0_j \right] \qquad [8-21a$$

where the magnitude of the constant $(c_2)_a$ is given by [8-20]. $(K_j)_a$ is given by [8-19]. A is given by [8-17] and [8-15].

Similarly, for $W' = W'_b$, the other root of the determinant [8-14], we have

$$W = W^0 + W'_b$$

and,

$$\psi_b = (c_2)_b \left[B \psi^0_1 + \psi^0_2 + \sum_{j>2} (K_j)_b \psi^0_j \right] \qquad [8-21b$$

where the magnitude of $(c_2)_b$ is given by the equation corresponding to [8-20], and $(K_j)_b$ by an equation corresponding to [8-19], except that B appears in place of A.

We have now determined the first-order energy and also the wave function for each of the two levels.

The numerical values found in the above calculation are dependent upon the form as well as the magnitude of H', since this operator—representing the perturbation energy—determines the two values of W' through [8-14] and also the two sets of values for the c's. In general, therefore, for *each* different H', added to the zero-order Hamiltonian, there will be *two different true wave functions*, ψ, and two corresponding characteristic energies, W. Each of the new, true wave functions [8-21a] and [8-21b], has as its "starting point," or zero-order function, a *different* combination of ψ^0_1 and ψ^0_2—that is, a particular combination which ψ approaches as the magnitude of the perturbation, H', approaches zero,[6] since, with no perturbation present at all, there is an infinite number of acceptable linear combinations of ψ^0_1 and ψ^0_2 (see Appendix II), it is not surprising that H' should "demand" a *particular* linear combination for each of the two "starting point" or zero-order wave functions.

One speaks of H' as "removing the degeneracy to first-order" when W'_a

---

[6] The fact that the *relative* magnitudes of c_1 and c_2 are independent of the magnitude of H', but the other amplitudes, a_j ($j > 2$), are *not*, is the subject of Problem 8.4. As $H' \to 0$, the relative amounts of ψ^0_1 and ψ^0_2 do not change, but a_3, a_4, a_5, etc. in ψ' all approach zero.

and W_b' are different. If these two energy corrections turn out to be the same in the first-order calculation, then one must look to the terms in λ^2, or second-order, in [8–5b] to "remove the degeneracy." If the perturbation term does not alter the symmetry which was the initial cause of the degeneracy, then the degeneracy cannot be removed.

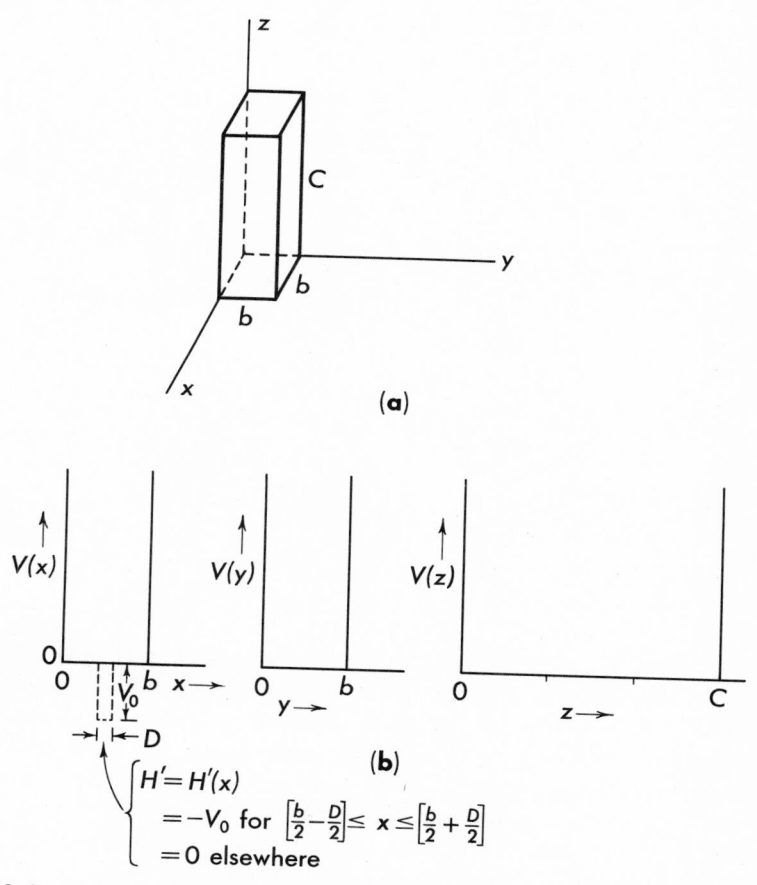

Fig. 8.1. A rectangular box with twofold degenerate levels. The addition of the perturbation H' destroys the $x - y$ symmetry and removes the degeneracy.

8.2. Example: Analysis of a twofold degenerate level for a single particle in a rectangular box

Degeneracy usually arises because of some form of symmetry. For example, in the cubical box, and in the hydrogen atom where there is three-dimensional symmetry, we found energy levels that had three or more eigenfunctions belonging to them. We wish to analyze the simplest case—a twofold degenerate level. We look therefore for a system with symmetry in two dimensions. Consider a rectangular box in which two of the dimensions are the same (Fig. 8.1a). Such a box, with (for simplicity) infinite potential walls, has the (unperturbed) potential energy,

$$V(x, y, z) = 0 \text{ for } 0 \le x \le b; \ 0 \le y \le b; \ 0 \le z \le c$$

$$= \infty, \text{ elsewhere,} \tag{8-22}$$

as shown in Figure 8.1b. We will add a perturbation H', which is a function only of one variable, x, but first we describe the zero-order, or unperturbed, system.

For the box of Figure 8.1, the eigenfunctions are (see Section 4.2)

$$\psi_{n_x n_y n_z} = \sqrt{\frac{8}{b^2 c}} \sin \frac{n_x \pi x}{b} \sin \frac{n_y \pi y}{b} \sin \frac{n_z \pi z}{c} \tag{8-23}$$

and the values of the characteristic energy are

$$W_{n_x n_y n_z} = \frac{\hbar^2 \pi^2}{2m} \left[\frac{n_x^2}{b^2} + \frac{n_y^2}{b^2} + \frac{n_z^2}{c^2} \right] \tag{8-24}$$

For concreteness, we make the additional assumption that the side c is equal to $3b$. This gives the energy-level diagram of Figure 8.2.

The lowest energy level is $n_x = n_y = n_z = 1$,

$$W_{111} = \frac{\hbar^2 \pi^2}{2m} \left[\frac{1}{b^2} + \frac{1}{b^2} + \frac{1}{c^2} \right] \text{ where } c = 3b$$

to which belongs only one eigenfunction, ψ_{111}. The next higher level is $n_x = n_y = 1$ and $n_z = 2$, with energy $W_{112} = 2\frac{4}{9}$ energy units and one eigenfunction, ψ_{112} (one energy unit $= (\hbar^2 \pi^2)/2mb^2$.

The next three levels, whose quantum numbers are 1,1,3, 1,1,4, and 1,1,5, are also nondegenerate. The next highest energy level is $W_{121} = W_{211} = 5\frac{1}{9}$ energy units, and has *two* different eigenfunctions, $\psi(x, y, z)$,

$$\psi_{121} = \sqrt{\frac{8}{b^2 c}} \sin \frac{\pi x}{b} \sin \frac{2\pi y}{b} \sin \frac{\pi z}{c} \tag{8-25}$$

$$\psi_{211} = \sqrt{\frac{8}{b^2 c}} \sin \frac{2\pi x}{b} \sin \frac{\pi y}{b} \sin \frac{\pi z}{c} \tag{8-26}$$

so that this level is twofold degenerate. Its perturbation will be calculated as an example.

There is a second twofold degenerate level at $W_{122} = W_{212} = 5\frac{4}{9}$ energy units, with eigenfunctions ψ_{122} and ψ_{212} and there are many higher levels, some of which are shown in Figure 8.2.

As an example of a perturbation calculation, we will determine the effect,

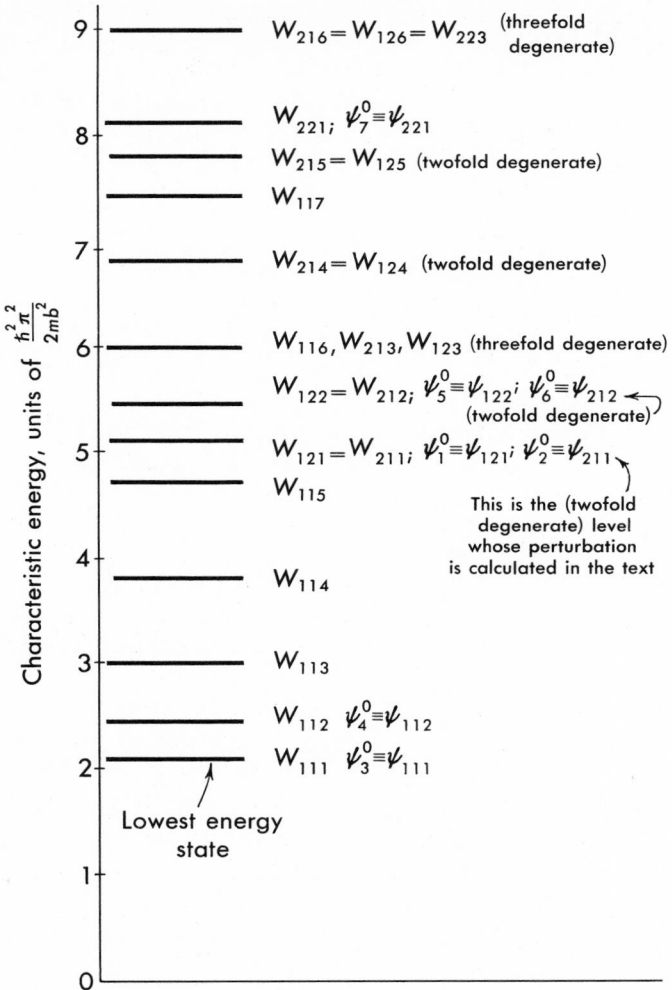

Fig. 8.2. The low-lying zero-order energy levels for the system of Figure 8.1 for the case $c = 3b$.

on the $W_{121} = W_{211}$ level and on the two eigenfunctions which belong to it, of adding the perturbation,

$$H'(x, y, z) = H'(x) = -V_0 \text{ ergs, for } \left(\frac{b}{2} - \frac{D}{2}\right) \leq x \leq \left(\frac{b}{2} + \frac{D}{2}\right)$$

$$[8\text{--}27$$

$$= 0 \text{ elsewhere}$$

Since this purely x-dependent perturbation destroys the symmetry between $V(x)$ and $V(y)$, we shall expect the degeneracy to be removed.

In the theory of the previous section, we identified each eigenfunction by a running subscript, j—that is, to each j there belongs *one* particular eigenfunction. This enumeration is arbitrary, except that to conform to the earlier notation we will identify the eigenfunctions of the degenerate level being analyzed by ψ_1^0 and ψ_2^0, thus,

$$\begin{aligned}\psi_1^0 &= \psi_{121} \ [8\text{-}25] \\ \psi_2^0 &= \psi_{211} \ [8\text{-}26]\end{aligned} \quad \text{and } W^0 = W_{121} = W_{211} \qquad [8\text{-}28]$$

In addition, we make the following arbitrary identifications,

$\psi_3^0 = \psi_{111}$ and $W_3^0 = W_{111}$

$\psi_4^0 = \psi_{112}$ and $W_4^0 = W_{112}$

$\left.\begin{aligned}\psi_5^0 &= \psi_{122} \text{ and } W_5^0 = W_{122} \\ \psi_6^0 &= \psi_{212} \text{ and } W_6^0 = W_{212}\end{aligned}\right\}$ the equality of these two values $\qquad [8\text{-}29]$

does not affect the calculations

$\psi_7^0 = \psi_{221}$ and $W_7^0 = W_{221}$ for the level at W_{121}

etc.

We shall see below that none of the other levels listed on Figure 8.2 "connect" with the perturbed level, $W_{121} = W_{211}$, so it is not necessary to give them a subscript. Each eigenfunction may, however, be identified, as needed, by a single numerical subscript.

In Section 8.1 functions of space were synthesized from a series of *orthogonal* functions, the ψ_j^0's, and we must be sure, before proceeding, that the above ψ_j^0's are in fact orthogonal. Only those belonging to degenerate energy levels need be examined, and one can quickly see, from symmetry, that ψ_1^0 and ψ_2^0 are orthogonal already,[7] that is, $\iiint \psi_1^0 \ \psi_2^0 \ dx \ dy \ dz = 0$. Similarly, ψ_5^0 and ψ_6^0 are orthogonal. If either of these pairs were *not* orthogonal, we would have had to construct pairs that were orthogonal as in Appendix II. (All pairs belonging to *different* energy levels are guaranteed to be orthogonal by the basic postulates. See Appendix II.)

The next step is to calculate the matrix elements, H_{11}', etc., which appear in [8-13], [8-14], and [8-15].

$$H_{11}' = \iiint \psi_1^{0*} \ H'(x) \ \psi_1^0 \ dx \ dy \ dz$$

$$\cong \sqrt{\frac{8}{b^2 c}} (-V_0) \sqrt{\frac{8}{b^2 c}} \cdot \underbrace{D \cdot \frac{b}{2}}_{= \Delta x} \cdot \underbrace{\frac{c}{2}}_{\text{from } y \text{ and } z \text{ integration}} = -\frac{2DV_0}{b}$$

---

[7] Plot, for example, both sin $(\pi x/b)$ and sin $(2\pi x/b)$ between $x = 0$ and $x = b$. Note that the contributions to the integral (the *product* of the two sine functions times Δx) which are equally distant from $x = b/2$ are of equal magnitude but opposite in sign. Thus, the x-integration yields zero.

since we are assuming that D, the width of the potential well, is small compared to the width b of the original potential well with infinite walls at $x = 0$ and $x = b$.

Similarly, using the approximation

$$\sin (2\pi x/b) = - \frac{2\pi(x - b/2)}{b}$$

in the neighborhood of $x = b/2$, we obtain

$$H'_{22} \cong - \frac{2\pi^2 D^3 V_0}{3b^3}$$

With the aid of a graph showing $\sin (\pi x/b)$, $\sin (2\pi x/b)$, and also H' [8–27], one can see at once that $H'_{12} = H'_{21} = 0$. Thus the secular equation [8–15] gives

$$W'_a = H'_{11} \cong - \frac{2DV_0}{b} \qquad \text{ergs} \qquad\qquad [8\text{–}30$$

$$W'_b = H'_{22} \cong - \frac{2}{3} \pi^2 \left(\frac{D}{b}\right)^3 V_0 \text{ ergs (this is very small}$$
$$\text{compared to } W'_a)$$

so that the single level at W^0 is caused by this particular perturbation to split into two different levels. One is very slightly lower in energy than W^0 and the other is depressed a much larger amount (see Fig. 8.3).

We use, in turn, each of the values of W' in [8–13] to obtain a relationship between the amplitudes c_1 and c_2, which define the corresponding zero-order wave function.

For $W' = W'_a = H'_{11}$ we have by the second equations of [8–13] (the first is indeterminate), $(c_2)_a (H'_{22} - H'_{11}) = 0$, that is, $(c_2)_a = 0$. Thus, by [8–3b], $| (c_1)_a |$ is unity.

For the case that $W' = W'_b = H'_{22}$ we have by the first equation [8–13] that $(c_1)_b = 0$, and therefore, for this case, $| (c_2)_b |$ is unity.

For each case we can calculate the set of a_j's [8–12] which determine the correction ψ' needed to change the zero-order wave function into the true (to first-order) wave function. Thus, for the case $W' = W'_a = H'_{11}$, and $j = 3$,

$$a_3 = \frac{(c_1)_a H'_{31} - 0}{W^0 - W_3^0} = \frac{(c_1)_a \iiint \psi_{111}^* H'(x) \psi_{121} \, dx \, dy \, dz}{W_{121} - W_{111}} = 0$$

where the ψ_3^0 function, used in the calculation, is given by [8–29] as ψ_{111}, and W_3^0 is W_{111} (a_3 is zero due to the y-integration).

An examination of the values of a_4 through a_7 will quickly show that each is zero, due to antisymmetry (about the center of the box) in either the x-, y-, or z-dependent factors in the integrand. Also, none of the other states listed in Figure 8.2 are "connected" by H' to the states at W_{121} and W_{211}.

If we define ψ_8^0 to be the function ψ_{321}, we will get a non-zero result:

$$a_8 = \frac{(c_1)_a \iiint \psi_{321}^* \, H'(x) \, \psi_{121} \, dx \, dy \, dz}{W^0 - W_{321}^0} \cong \frac{- (c_1)_a \, 2DV_0/b}{(5\frac{1}{9} - 13\frac{1}{9}) \dfrac{\hbar^2 \, \pi^2}{2mb^2}} \qquad [8\text{-}31$$

$$= (c_1)_a \, K_8$$

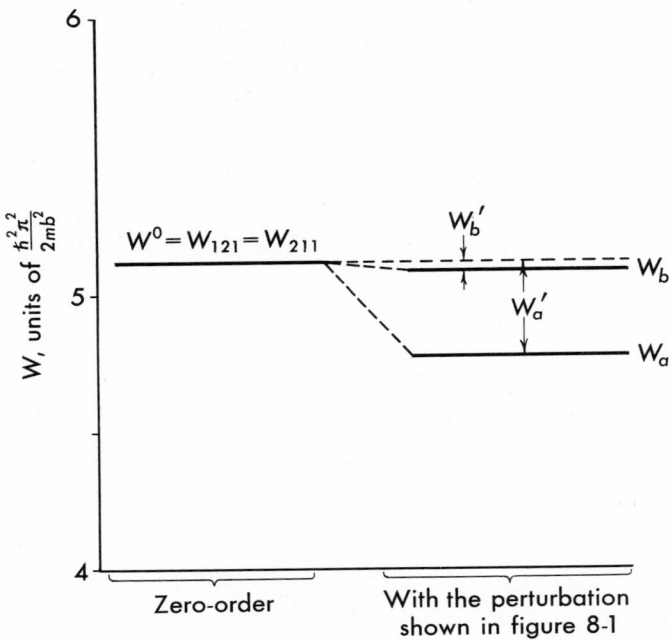

Fig. 8.3. The first-order correction to the degenerate level $W^0 = W_{121} = W_{211}$, caused by the small perturbation H' of Figure 8.1.

where K_8 is the known, constant factor. Thus, the true (to first-order) wave function belonging to the level

$$W_a = W^0 - 2DV_0/b$$

is

$$\psi_a = (c_1)_a \, \psi_{121} + (0) \, \psi_{211} + (0) \, \psi_{111} + \cdots + (c_1)_a \, K_8 \, \psi_{321} + \cdots \quad [8\text{-}32$$

The level at,

$$W_b = W^0 - \frac{2}{3} \, \pi^2 \left(\frac{D}{b}\right)^3 V_0$$

has the wave function,

$$\psi_b = (0)\,\psi_{121} + (c_2)_b\,\psi_{211} + \cdots \qquad [8\text{–}33$$

where the amplitudes of the unlisted terms may all be calculated from [8–12]. Each will involve, as a factor, the constant $(c_2)_b$ which, however, is known, by [8–20], to be unity.

We have, therefore, completely determined the true (to first-order) energy and wave function for each of the two states. Upon the removal of H', each energy level will return to the original energy level $W^0 = W_{121} = W_{211}$. Each wave function will return, as $H' \to 0$, to a particular linear combination[8] of the two original eigenfunctions belonging to W^0. However, without any perturbation, there is an infinite number of acceptable linear combinations—including the two particular ones "selected by the perturbation" as the "starting points" for each of the first-order ψ's. In the example we have been discussing, the perturbation *happens* to have such a spatial form that it selects (for small magnitude of H') either $c_1 = 1$ and $c_2 = 0$, or $c_1 = 0$ and $c_2 = 1$. A different form of perturbation might, for example, select amplitude combinations: $\sqrt{0\cdot6}$, $\sqrt{0\cdot4}$, or $\sqrt{0\cdot1}$, $\sqrt{0\cdot9}$, etc.

8.3. Multiple degeneracy

Suppose that there are three different orthogonal eigenfunctions, ψ_1^0, ψ_2^0, and ψ_3^0, which belong to a given energy value W^0 of the zero-order system. Then the true wave function, as in [8–4], must be regarded, a *priori*, as containing, in zero order, all three of these eigenfunctions. There is no reason to prefer one over another—until, of course, calculations with a particular H' force the selection of certain combinations. Thus,

$$\psi = c_1\,\psi_1^0 + c_2\,\psi_2^0 + c_3\,\psi_3^0 + \lambda\psi' \qquad [8\text{–}34$$

If the three linearly independent eigenfunctions belonging to W^0 were not originally orthogonal, a new set of three that *are* orthogonal will have to be formed before [8–34] is used. As before, $c_1^*c_1 + c_2^*c_2 + c_3^*c_3 = 1$.

There are now three identities in place of [8–8] and [8–9], and the first three equations of [8–11] lead to a 3×3 determinant instead of the 2×2 determinant [8–14]. The determinant has, in general, three roots, W', which give the three different energy corrections. Each one has a particular set of amplitudes, c_1, c_2, and c_3, which identify each of the three zero-order or "starting point" wave functions. Also, each of the three functions ψ' is usually, though not necessarily, different for each of the three W' values.

For a fourfold degenerate level the determinant [8–14] is 4×4, and has, in general, four different "characteristic values," W'.

---

[8] See Problem 8.4.

The characteristic values or eigenvalues of a set of equations such as [8–13] are closely related to the characteristic values of differential equations. Assume first that one has solved the *true* wave equation $H\psi = W\psi$ by mathematically exact methods, using the basic postulates in the manner discussed in earlier chapters. Also assume that one finds α distinct energy levels, W_1, W_2, $\cdots$ W_α, clustered close together. These are the *exact* eigenvalues of the system energy. We further assume (to simplify the discussion) that to each eigenvalue there belongs only one eigenfunction. In practice, the only thing that prevents this direct, exact solution to the wave equation is mathematical difficulty.

If one were forced to use perturbation theory, what would happen? Let us suppose that a term, H', is neglected in the Hamiltonian, leaving it in the form H^0 for which mathematical solutions are known, the ψ_n^0's. We find that the approximate equation has an eigenvalue, W^0, right in the region where we found the cluster of energy eigenvalues when performing the exact computatation. We also find that there are α different eigenfunctions belonging to this *one* eigenvalue W^0, so that the energy level W^0, is α-fold degenerate. By perturbation methods, we set up the α equations corresponding to [8–13] which involve $(\alpha + 1)$ unknowns ($c_1, c_2, \cdots c_\alpha$, *and* W'). We find that these equations have a solution *only* when W' has one of α distinct values, as identified by the $\alpha \times \alpha$ determinant corresponding to [8–14]. One speaks of W_1', W_2', $\cdots$ W_α' as being the "eigenvalues of the set of linear equations" (corresponding to [8–13]) or the "eigenvalues of the matrix" (which represents these equations). Each of these corrections, W_1', W_2', $\cdots$ W_α', is now added, in turn, to W^0, giving α distinct values for the system energy. These will cluster near W^0 and, if first-order theory is adequate to the case, correspond very closely, term by term, to the α *exact* eigenvalues of the system energy in this region. Thus, the eigenvalues of a matrix (a set of linear equations) when added to the zero-order constant W^0, yield (very nearly) the true eigenvalues of the exact differential equation.

The earliest form of quantum mechanics, developed by Heisenberg, used the method of matrices and determinants. It was later shown to be equivalent to the Schrödinger method. The student is referred to the more advanced textbooks for further discussion of matrix calculations in quantum mechanics.

8.4. The unique relationship between H′ and the zero-order eigenfunctions

There is a very important difference in the dependence on the magnitude of H', of c_1 and c_2 on the one hand, and of W and also $a_3, a_4, a_5, \cdots$, on the other. Given any *form* of H', *no matter how small its magnitude*, a ratio of c_1 to c_2 is uniquely determined for each of the two possible energy levels, no matter how closely spaced. (They will be closely spaced as $|H'| \to 0$, since $W' \propto H'$.) The a's also are all proportional to H' and approach zero as

$H' \to 0$. Thus, the two unique values of c_1/c_2 are associated only with the mathematical *form* of the perturbation H', independent of its magnitude (since they are each determined from a ratio of terms, each proportional to H'). On the other hand, the energy corrections and the wave function corrections belonging to each value of c_1/c_2 are not merely associated with the form of H', but they are, in addition, proportional to its magnitude. It is this unique association between the mathematical *form* of H' and the two characteristic values of c_1/c_2 (that is, the two characteristic zero-order ψ's which "belong to" H') that forms the basis of the treatment of identical particles in Chapter 9.

8.5. Summary: First-order perturbation theory for a twofold degenerate state

Consider a particular energy level, W^0, of a system which in zero-order (that is, in the unperturbed condition) has two different eigenfunctions belonging to it:

$$H^0 \psi_1^0 = W_1^0 \psi_1^0, \text{ and } H^0 \psi_2^0 = W_2^0 \psi_2^0; \text{ where } W_1^0 = W_2^0 = W^0 \qquad [8\text{-}1$$

ψ_1^0 and ψ_2^0 are assumed to be orthogonal. The most general normalized wave function belonging to W^0 is

$$\psi = c_1 \psi_1^0 + c_2 \psi_2^0, \text{ where } c_1^* c_1 + c_2^* c_2 = 1 \qquad [8\text{-}3b$$

The true or exact wave equation is,

$$H\psi = W\psi, \text{ where } H = H^0 + \lambda H' \qquad [8\text{-}5a], [8\text{-}2$$

Into the true wave equation, we substitute

$$\psi = c_1 \psi_1 + c_2 \psi_2 + \lambda \psi' \qquad [8\text{-}4$$

and

$$W = W^0 + \lambda W' \qquad [8\text{-}3a$$

obtaining [8–5b] (see text).

Setting the coefficient of $\lambda^0 = 0$ (λ is arbitrary), we obtain the zero-order equation $H^0(c_1 \psi_1^0 + c_2 \psi_2^0) = W^0(c_1 \psi_1^0 + c_2 \psi_2^0)$.

Setting the coefficient of $\lambda^1 = 0$, we obtain the first-order equation

$$(H^0 - W^0)\psi' = c_1(W' - H')\psi_1^0 + c_2(W' - H')\psi_2^0 \qquad [8\text{-}6$$

In the first-order equation we substitute three series composed of the zero-order eigenfunctions:

(a) for the *unknown* ψ' we substitute $\psi' = \sum_j a_j \psi_j^0$

(b) for the two *known* functions $H' \psi_1^0$, and $H' \psi_2^0$, for purely mathematical reasons, we substitute

$$H' \psi_1^0 = \sum_j b_j \psi_j^0 \quad \text{where} \quad b_j = H'_{j1} \int \psi_j^{0*} H' \psi_1^0 \, d\tau \qquad [8-8$$

$$H' \psi_2^0 = \sum_j d_j \psi_j^0 \quad \text{where} \quad d_j = H'_{j2} \int \psi_j^{0*} H' \psi_2^0 \, d\tau \qquad [8-9$$

When the above three series are inserted into the first-order equation [8–6], it becomes,

$$\sum_j (W_j^0 - W^0) a_j \psi_j^0 = W'(c_1 \psi_1^0 + c_2 \psi_2^0) - \sum_j c_1 H'_{j1} \psi_j^0 - \sum_j c_2 H'_{j2} \psi_j^0 \qquad [8-10$$

On the left is one series in ψ_j^0 and on the right is a different series in ψ_j^0. We now make a *key step*: for arbitrary H', these two series can be equal only if the coefficients of ψ_j^0 are equal, term by term.

$$\left. \begin{aligned} \text{For } j = 1, && 0 = c_1 W' - c_1 H'_{11} - c_2 H'_{12} \\ \text{For } j = 2, && 0 = c_2 W' - c_1 H'_{21} - c_2 H'_{22} \end{aligned} \right\} \qquad [8-11$$

$$\text{For } j = 3, 4, 5, \cdots \quad (W_j^0 - W^0) a_j = - c_1 H'_{j1} - c_2 H'_{j2} \qquad [8-12$$

Thus, the single first-order equation [8–10] becomes the *set* of equations, [8–11] and [8–12]. a_1 and a_2 are not determined by set, but are put equal to zero to preserve normalization of the first-order wave function (see [8–16b] and [8–16c]).

The three equations, consisting of [8–11] and $c_1^* c_1 + c_2^* c_2 = 1$ [8–3b], suffice to determine unique values of W', $|c_1|$, and $|c_2|$ in the following manner: W' is determined from the determinant of [8–11],

$$\begin{vmatrix} (H'_{11} - W') & H'_{12} \\ H'_{21} & (H'_{22} - W') \end{vmatrix} = 0 \qquad [8-14$$

since [8–11] is homogeneous. In general, two values, W'_a, and W'_b, result from [8–14]. For *each* value of W', [8–11] and [8–3b] together uniquely specify $|c_1|$ and $|c_2|$.

Once the magnitudes of c_1 and c_2 are known the magnitudes of a_3, a_4, $\cdots$ can be calculated from [8–12]. Thus for each of the two values of W' there belongs a particular $|c_1|$ and $|c_2|$, and also a particular set of a's.

Since λ is arbitrary, we set it equal to unity in [8–3a] and [8–4], and for $W' = W'_a$ we have *one* first-order energy value and its first-order wave function.

$$W_a = W^0 + W'_a$$

$$\psi_a = [1/(1 + A^*A)]^{\frac{1}{2}} \left[A\psi_1^0 + \psi_2^0 + \sum_{j>2} \frac{A H'_{j1} + H'_{j2}}{W^0 - W_j^0} \psi_j^0 \right] e^{i\delta} \qquad [8-21a$$

where $A \equiv c_1/c_2$, as determined from [8–11] when $W' = W'_a$, $\delta = \text{constant}$.

For $W' = W_b'$ we have the other first-order energy value and its first-order wave function. (The expressions are the same as above, except that B replaces A, where $B \equiv c_1/c_2$, obtained from [8–11] for the case $W' = W_b'$.)

Should the two roots of the determinant [8–14] be identical, then "the perturbation does not remove the degeneracy."

PROBLEMS

Problem 8.1

(a) Find the effect of the perturbation of Figure 8.1 upon the energy level at $W_{122} = W_{212}$, and find the zero-order wave function appropriate to each of the new energy levels.

(b) Which of the states, if any, listed in [8–29] will contribute to the first-order wave function?

Problem 8.2. Shift the perturbation of Figure 8.1 to the region $x = 0$ to $x = D$, where $D \ll b$.

(a) Find the new energy levels arising from the original level at $W_{121} = W_{211}$.

(b) Find the corresponding zero-order wave functions.

(c) Find the contribution, if any, to the first-order wave function of the states listed in [8–29].

Problem 8.3. *The Energy Levels of the Lithium Atom*

As an example of the application of perturbation theory to a more realistic problem, we consider the two lowest energy levels of the lithium atom.

The normal lithium atom has three electrons ($Z = 3$), two of which are in an $n = 1$ state near the nucleus, and one in an $n = 2$ state.[9] If the two inner electrons were independent of each other, they would each have a hydrogen-like wave function, ψ_{100}, where $\sigma = 3r/a_0$ (see Appendix VI). This means that they are most likely to be found in the neighborhood of $r = a_1$, where $a_1 = (.528 \times 10^{-8} \text{ cm})/3$. The probability density is ψ_{100}^2, and the probability of observing the electron in a spherical shell of radius r and thickness Δr is $\psi_{100}^2 \, 4\pi r^2 \, \Delta r$. (This latter function is maximum near a_1.) We *assume* that the outer electron experiences a potential of $-e^2/r$ outside $r = a_1$, and a potential of $-3e^2/r$ inside $r = a_1$—that is, that the two inner electrons form a sharp shell of charge at the radius a_1. This is shown in Figure 8.4a. In an actual atom, the potential *gradually* changes from the outer form to the inner form. In the figure we use the abrupt change

---

[9] The description in which each electron has *one* of the states (set of quantum numbers) is not correct. The three identical electrons *share* all occupied states (see Chapter 9).

since it gives a simple form to the perturbation, that is, $H' = -2e^2/r$ for the range $0 \le r \le a_1$ and zero elsewhere. (Actually, due to their mutual repulsion, the two inner electrons are most likely found somewhat further out than at $r = a_1$.)

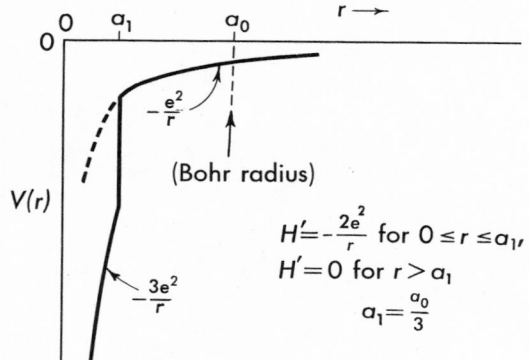

(a) Approximate potential function for outer electron, lithium atom.

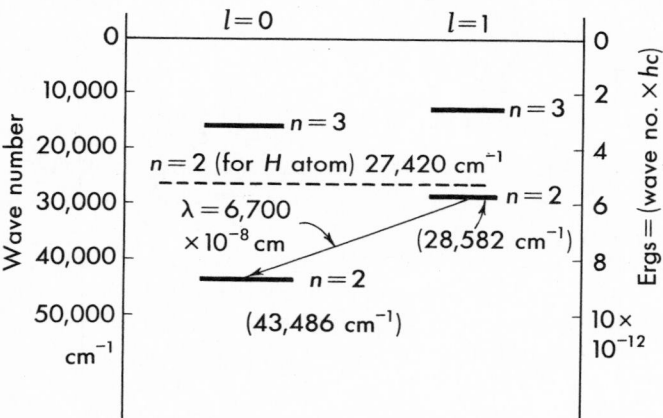

(b) The lithium atom energy levels (experimental)

Fig. 8.4. The calculation of the $n = 2$ energy levels of the lithium atom for $l = 0$ and $l = 1$. The electrostatic "screening" due to the two inner electrons is treated approximately by perturbation theory (Problem 8.3).

The lowest energy state "available to the third electron" is the state for which $n = 2$, since it is impossible for it to assume the state $n = 1$, $l = 0$ of the inner electrons (see section 9.5, The Pauli Exclusion Principle). For the state $n = 2$ there are, in the zero-order

$(V = - e^2/r$ potential), four different eigenfunctions, $\psi_1 = \psi_{200}$, $\psi_2 = \psi_{210}$, $\psi_3 = \psi_{211}$, and $\psi_4 = \psi_{21, -1}$ (see Appendix VI). These are true *hydrogen* wave functions since for them $Z = 1$. All of these have the same energy, $W_2 = 27{,}420$ cm^{-1}, where the unit cm^{-1} is a spectroscopic term called wave number. Energy, in

$$\text{ergs} = (\text{energy in cm}^{-1})\ hc$$
$$= (\text{energy in cm}^{-1}) \times (1.99\ 10^{-16}\ \text{erg per cm}^{-1}).$$

In lithium, the state for which $n = 2$ is perturbed by the presence of $H'(r)$ (Fig. 8.4a). The problem is to calculate the energy correction W' to each of the four states caused by this perturbation. Note that the four zero-order eigenfunctions are already orthogonal to each other (see Problem 4.10).

The determinant, corresponding to [8–14], is

$$
\begin{vmatrix}
(H'_{11} - W') & H'_{12} & H'_{13} & H'_{14} \\
H'_{21} & (H'_{22} - W') & H'_{23} & H'_{24} \\
H'_{31} & H'_{32} & (H'_{33} - W') & H'_{34} \\
H'_{41} & H'_{42} & H'_{43} & (H'_{44} - W')
\end{vmatrix} = 0
$$

(a) Show that all off-diagonal matrix elements are zero for this perturbation.

(b) Calculate H'_{11} and H'_{22}. Also, show that $H'_{33} = H'_{44} = H'_{22}$, so that this particular perturbation does not remove the degeneracy completely. (There are other types of perturbation which will cause all four energy levels to be distinct.) Numerical integration is satisfactory here.

(c) Compare your results on the corrections to the $l = 0$ and $l = 1$ levels with the experimental spectrum in Figure 8.4b.

Problem 8.4. In the discussion following equation [8–21b], it was mentioned that, for a given form of H', the amplitudes c_1 and c_2 (which define one of the two possible zero-order or "starting point" wave functions) are *independent* of the magnitude of H', whereas the other amplitudes a_j $(j > 2)$ are *not* independent of the magnitude of H'.

(a) Show why this is so. Hint: By the secular equation [8–14], show that W' must be proportional to the magnitude of H'. By either of the equations [8–13], therefore, the *ratio* c_1/c_2 must be independent of the magnitude of H'.

(b) Is c_1/c_2 also independent of the spatial form of H'?

Problem 8.5. The first-order wave function written out in equation [8–32] has the property that only those zero-order eigenfunctions appear whose n_y and n_z quantum numbers are 2 and 1 respectively. Is this a general rule?

Problem 8.6. Find the largest correction term, beyond zero-order, in ψ_b [8–33].

Problem 8.7. In the system of Figure 8.1, let $m = 9.1 \times 10^{-28}$ gm, $b = 10^{-8}$ cm, $c = 3 \times 10^{-8}$ cm, $D = 10^{-9}$ cm, and $V_0 = 10 \times 10^{-12}$ erg. In [8–32] and [8–33], calculate the numerical values of W_a, W_b, $(c_1)_a$, and $(c_2)_b$.

Problem 8.8. Prove the statement in footnote 4 in the discussion following [8–15], namely: The secular equation [8–15] has real roots if H'_{21} and H'_{12} are complex conjugates.

Problem 8.9. Problem 4.16 gives the eigenfunctions and energy levels of the free, rigid rotator on a fixed axis, and Problem 7.9 determines the perturbation of the lowest (and nondegenerate) state of this system when a weak gravitational field is applied. The zero-order energy level for which $M^2 = 1$ is twofold degenerate, since it possesses the two eigenfunctions,

$$\psi_1^0 = \sqrt{1/2\pi}\, e^{i\phi}\ (M = 1); \quad \psi_2^0 = \sqrt{1/2\pi}\, e^{-i\phi}\ (M = -1);$$

$$W^0 = W_1^0 = W_{-1}^0 = \hbar^2/2mr_0^2$$

(a) Show that the perturbation produced by the gravitational field, given in Problem 7.9, does *not* remove the degeneracy of the $M^2 = 1$ level.
(b) Calculate the first-order energy for this level.
(c) Calculate the first-order energy for the level $M^2 = 4$.

Problem 8.10 *An alternate derivation of* [8–11] *and* [8–12].

Start with the first-order equation [8–6]. Insert [8–7]. Perform the operation using H^0. Multiply from the left by $\psi_1^0\, d\tau$, and integrate over all configuration space, obtaining the first equation of [8–11]. Multiply from the left by $\psi_2^{0*}\, d\tau$, and integrate, obtaining the second equation of [8–11]. Multiply from the left by $\psi_3^{0*}\, d\tau$, etc., obtaining the third equation of [8–11] and [8–12].

9

IDENTICAL PARTICLES

In the two preceding chapters we observed that symmetry in physical space of the potential function of a system produced degeneracy; that is, to a given characteristic energy value there belong two or more different eigenfunctions. These degenerate functions, such as the two examples in [8–25] and [8–26], or the hydrogen-like functions for the case $n = 2$, differ among themselves because they have distinctly different dependence upon the three coordinates, (x, y, z) or (r, θ, ϕ) respectively.

In Chapter 8, we saw that when degeneracy occurred, a question immediately arose regarding the correct form of the zero-order wave function. We found that for each form of perturbation H', one requires, in general, a different zero-order or "starting point" wave function *for each* of the new characteristic energy values. When $H' \to 0$, for those cases where the degeneracy is completely removed, each first-order wave function reduces to a distinct linear combination of the basic eigenfunctions. This is, of course, the "starting point" for the perturbation calculation of the particular true wave function. However, when $H' = 0$ there is an infinite number of linear combinations of the basic eigenfunctions, belonging to the energy level being analyzed, which are all, *a priori*, equally satisfactory. *One cannot choose among them until H' is defined*, and no energy level shifts occur until H' is allowed to become finite.

In this chapter we are concerned with a new type of symmetry due, not to geometrical symmetry in physical space, but to the indistinguishable nature of the particles composing a system. This results in degeneracy—in zero-order—and therefore we shall have to use the theory of Chapter 8.

205

9.1. Two identical particles in a one-dimensional box

Let us suppose that a one-dimensional box, with infinite walls at $x = 0$ and $x = L$, contains not one but two particles of the same mass, m. We further suppose that, in zero-order, although these particles and the matter waves belonging to them are reflected from the potential barriers, they in no way affect each other. The total energy of the system is

$$(1/2m)\, p_1^2 + (1/2m)\, p_2^2 + V_1(x_1) + V_2(x_2) = W \qquad [9\text{--}1$$

where x_1 is the coordinate and p_1 the momentum of particle number 1, and x_2 is the coordinate and p_2 the momentum of particle number 2. There is no potential-energy term dependent upon the relative positions of particle 1 and 2—that is, the two particles are assumed to be noninteracting.

As in Section 4.1 and Appendix IV, where we also considered a system that consisted of two particles, we once more extend Postulate I to state that $\Psi = \Psi(x_1, y_1, z_1, x_2, y_2, z_2, t)$. That is, the system wave function is assumed to depend upon the six spatial coordinates of the two particles which compose it. In Appendix IV this assumption leads to the prediction that the hydrogen atom, moving as a whole, should show wave properties characterized by the linear momentum of the total atom, while the relative motion of the parts should show the wave properties which determine its internal structure. Both of these predictions—which would be impossible without the sixfold spatial dependence—are fully borne out by experiment. Here, for the case where the two particles are identical, we shall find that the assumption that the system wave function depends upon two sets of spatial coordinates and time also leads to some very important and unusual predictions which are also substantiated by experiment. The limitation of the analysis to the case of one-dimensional motion of the particles does not cause any essential features in the phenomena associated with identical particles to be overlooked, and it simplifies the calculations, but most important of all, it permits the results to be presented in graphical form.

Using Postulate II, we make the operator substitutions,

$$p_1 \to (\hbar/i)\, \partial/\partial x_1;\ p_2 \to (\hbar/i)\, \partial/\partial x_2;\ x_1 \to x_1;\ x_2 \to x_2;\ W \to -(\hbar/i)\, \partial/\partial t \quad [9\text{--}2$$

obtaining from [9–1] the time-dependent wave equation,

$$-(\hbar^2/2m)(\partial^2\Psi/\partial x_1^2) - (\hbar^2/2m)(\partial^2\Psi/\partial x_2^2)$$
$$+ V_1(x_1)\,\Psi + V_2(x_2)\,\Psi = -(\hbar/i)\, \partial\Psi/\partial t$$

where $V_1(x_1) = 0$ for $0 \le x_1 \le L$, ∞ elsewhere $\qquad [9\text{--}3$

$\quad V_2(x_2) = 0$ for $0 \le x_2 \le L$, ∞ elsewhere

$\quad \Psi = \Psi(x_1, x_2, t)$

This equation is separable in the three variables, for if we set,

$$\Psi = \psi_1(x_1)\, \psi_2(x_2)\, \phi(t) \tag{9-4}$$

we have the usual time-dependent equation [3-3], whose solution is

$$\phi(t) = e^{-i\frac{W}{\hbar}t} \tag{9-5}$$

The two coordinate-dependent equations are

$$d^2\,\psi_1/dx_1^2 + (2m/\hbar^2)[W_1 - V_1(x_1)]\,\psi_1 = 0$$
$$d^2\,\psi_2/dx_2^2 + (2m/\hbar^2)[W_2 - V_2(x_2)]\,\psi_2 = 0 \tag{9-6}$$

where

$$W = W_1 + W_2 \tag{9-7}$$

and where both V_1 and V_2 are zero inside the box and ∞ outside.

From Section 3.4 the eigenvalues W_1 and W_2 of equations [9-6] are known to be

$$W_1 = \hbar^2 n^2 \pi^2 / 2mL^2; \;\; W_2 = \hbar^2 k^2 \pi^2 / 2mL^2 \tag{9-8}$$

and the eigenfunctions of the *one-particle* system are

$$\psi_1 = \sqrt{(2/L)}\, \sin\,(n\pi x_1/L) \tag{9-9}$$

$$\psi_2 = \sqrt{(2/L)}\, \sin\,(k\pi x_2/L) \tag{9-10}$$

where $n = 1, 2, 3, 4, \cdots$ and $k = 1, 2, 3, 4, \cdots$

The energy value for the complete system of two noninteracting particles is

$$W^0 = (\hbar^2 \pi^2 / 2mL^2)(n^2 + k^2) \tag{9-11}$$

There are now *two* different *two-particle* amplitude eigenfunctions,

$$\psi_1^0(x_1, x_2) = (2/L)\, \sin\,(n\pi x_1/L)\, \sin\,(k\pi x_2/L) \tag{9-12}$$

$$\psi_2^0(x_1, x_2) = (2/L)\, \sin\,(n\pi x_2/L)\, \sin\,(k\pi x_1/L) \tag{9-13[1]}$$

where $n = 1, 2, 3, \cdots$ and $k = 1, 2, 3, \cdots$ and is therefore twofold degenerate—providing $n \neq k$. The case $n = k$ (for which [9-12] and [9-13] coalesce into *one* eigenfunction) will be discussed shortly.

The reason for this degeneracy lies, not in geometrical symmetry in physical space, but in the "symmetry with respect to the interchange of the two identical particles." If, for example, the two particles did *not* have exactly the same mass, then m could *not* have been separated as a factor in [9-11], with the

---

[1] The ψ's of [9-9] and [9-10] are eigenfunctions of a *one-particle* system, whereas the ψ's of [9-12] and [9-13] are zero-order eigenfunctions of a *two-particle system*. The former has one quantum number and one variable, and the latter has two quantum numbers and two variables.

consequence that W^0 would then depend upon which of the two particles has the quantum number n and which has the quantum number k.

The *two-particle* amplitude functions, $\psi_1^0(x_1, x_2)$ and $\psi_2^0(x_1, x_2)$, are each dependent upon two different variables, x_1 and x_2. Plotted in terms of these

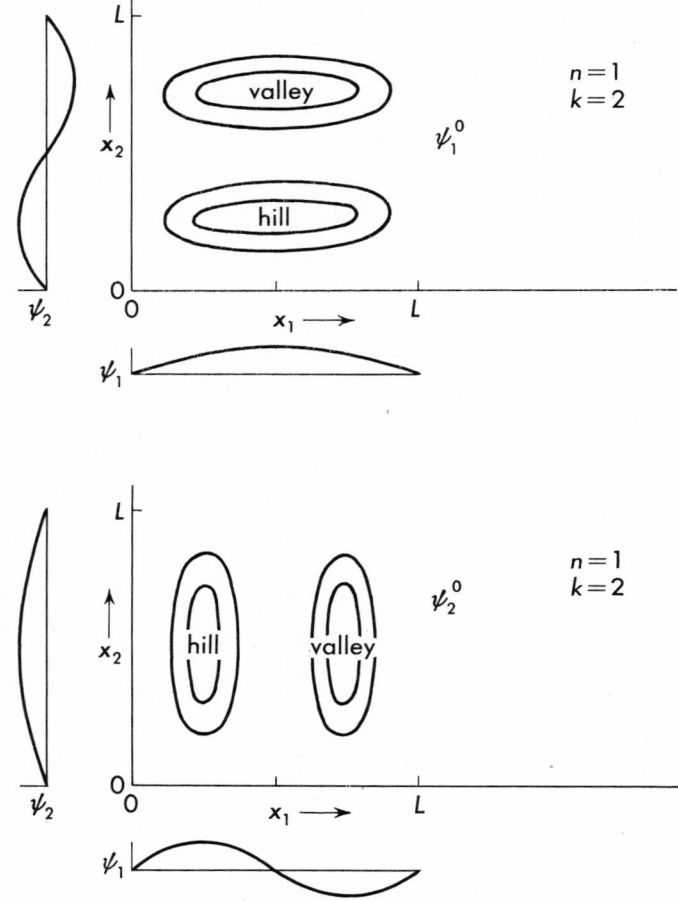

Fig. 9.1. Two exchange-degenerate eigenfunctions, [9–12] and [9–13].

variables, the two functions are differently shaped, as can be seen by referring to Figure 9.1. In the figure, for concreteness, particular values of n and k were chosen. ψ_1^0 and ψ_2^0 are, in each case, plotted normal to the paper, with the positive direction out of the paper. The contour diagrams show that, in terms of the two independent coordinates, the two functions are completely distinct. (In Figure 9.1, $\psi[x_1, x_2]$ is plotted in terms of its two variables, x_1 and x_2, where the two physical dimensions x and y of the figure are used to represent "configuration space.") This is possible, of course, only when the total number of spatial variables upon which ψ depends is three or less. (If

$$\psi = \psi[x_1, y_1, z_1, x_2, y_2, z_2]$$

for example, configuration space has six dimensions, and ψ cannot be adequately represented even in three physical dimensions.)

We now use the perturbation theory of Chapter 8 to determine the consequences of allowing the two identical particles to have a mutual energy of interaction, $H'(x_1, x_2)$, such as the coulomb energy,

$$H' = \frac{e^2}{|x_1 - x_2|} \qquad [9-14$$

which is "symmetric to the interchange of the two coordinates." Here this expression means that the mutual electrostatic potential energy is exactly the same if two interacting particles are interchanged in position. Mathematically, this means: interchange x_1 and x_2. (The only significant coordinate-dependent term in [9–14] is the *magnitude* of the distance separating the two particles.)

The two zero-order wave functions [9–12] and [9–13] are already orthogonal to each other, since $n \neq k$, that is $\int_0^L \int_0^L \psi_1^0 \psi_2^0 \, dx_1 \, dx_2 = 0$, so that we can proceed at once to apply the theory for the twofold degenerate level. Since identical particles produce a type of degeneracy which is *mathematically* identical in form to the degeneracy produced by symmetry in physical space, it is now apparent that, for the proper understanding of the behavior of identical particles, one should first understand the theory of perturbations for degenerate states. As in Chapter 8, the first step is to find the W' values which are the corrections to the unperturbed energy. These are given by the solution of the secular equation [8–14] or [8–15]

$$\begin{vmatrix} (H'_{11} - W') & H'_{12} \\ H'_{21} & (H'_{22} - W') \end{vmatrix} = 0 \qquad [9-15$$

For the zero-order wave functions [9–12] and [9–13] and the perturbation H' given by [9–14], however, we can see at once that

$$H'_{12} = H'_{21} \qquad [9-16$$

since the two integrands, $\psi_1^{0*} H' \psi_2^0$ and $\psi_2^{0*} H' \psi_1^0$, are identical.

Furthermore,

$$H'_{11} = H'_{22} \qquad [9-17$$

since

$$H'_{11} = \int \psi_1^{0*} H' \psi_1^0 \, dx_1 \, dx_2$$

$$= \left(\frac{2}{L}\right)^2 \int\int \sin^2 (n\pi x_1/L) \sin^2 (k\pi x_2/L) \frac{e^2}{|x_1 - x_2|} \, dx_1 \, dx_2$$

and [9–18

$$H'_{22} = \int \psi_2^{0*} H' \psi_2^0 \, dx_1 \, dx_2$$

$$= \left(\frac{2}{L}\right)^2 \int\int \sin^2 (n\pi x_2/L) \sin^2 (k\pi x_1/L) \frac{e^2}{|x_1 - x_2|} \, dx_1 \, dx_2$$

(Relabeling the variables inside the integrands merely turns one integral into the other—an operation which does not affect the value of the integral. The range of integration is from 0 to L for each variable.)

Using the above results, the secular equation becomes

$$(H'_{11} - W')^2 = (H'_{12})^2 \qquad [9\text{--}19$$

so that the two possible values of W' are

$$W' = H'_{11} + H'_{12}, \text{ or } W' = H'_{11} - H'_{12} \qquad [9\text{--}20$$

Inserting these values of W' into the two simultaneous equations [8–13] from which the determinant arose, we have, for $W' = H'_{11} + H'_{12}$, then $c_1 = c_2$, and so

$$\psi = c_1(\psi_1^0 + \psi_2^0) + \sum_{j>2} a_j \psi_j^0 \qquad [9\text{--}21$$

for $W' = H'_{11} - H'_{12}$, then $-c_1 = c_2$, and so

$$\psi = c_1(\psi_1^0 - \psi_2^0) + \sum_{j>2} a_j \psi_j^0 \qquad [9\text{--}22$$

Since we have already required that the zero-order wave function be normalized [8–3b], that is

$$c_1^* c_1 + c_2^* c_2 = 1$$

then, for the case that $c_1 = c_2$, $2c_1^* c_1 = 1$, or $|c_1| = 1/\sqrt{2}$, or $c_1 = (1/\sqrt{2}) e^{i\delta}$. Similarly, when $c_1 = -c_2$, we again have the same result, $2c_1^* c_1 = 1$, or $|c_1| = 1/\sqrt{2}$, or $c_1 = (1/\sqrt{2}) e^{i\delta}$. The undetermined constant δ is the "phase." The phase factor $e^{i\delta}$ disappears in any expectation-value calculation, and thus does not affect predictions about observable quantities.

Ignoring the phase factor, the two possible zero-order wave functions are,

$$\psi_s = (1/\sqrt{2})(\psi_1^0 + \psi_2^0)$$

$$= (1/\sqrt{2})(2/L)\left(\sin \frac{n\pi x_1}{L} \sin \frac{k\pi x_2}{L} + \sin \frac{n\pi x_2}{L} \sin \frac{k\pi x_1}{L}\right) \qquad [9\text{--}23$$

and

$$\psi_a = (1/\sqrt{2})(\psi_1^0 - \psi_2^0)$$

$$= (1/\sqrt{2})(2/L)\left(\sin\frac{n\pi x_1}{L}\sin\frac{k\pi x_2}{L} - \sin\frac{n\pi x_2}{L}\sin\frac{k\pi x_1}{L}\right) \qquad [9\text{–}24$$

where we have used [9–12] and [9–13] to write ψ_1^0 and ψ_2^0 explicitly in terms of the two variables x_1 and x_2. It is clear in [9–23] that interchanging x_1 and x_2 does not change ψ_s in any way, but that in [9–24] the interchange causes ψ_a to reverse sign. (The interchange of x_1 and x_2 causes ψ_1^0 to change into ψ_2^0, and vice versa.)

In quantum-mechanical terminology, the much-used expression, "ψ_s^0 is symmetric to interchange" means: ψ_s^0 does not change in any way when all the position variables associated with particle 1, such as x_1, y_1, and z_1, are exchanged in position with all the variables associated with particle 2, such as x_2, y_2, and z_2.

Similarly, ψ_a^0 is "antisymmetric to interchange," means that this function changes algebraic sign when x_1 and x_2 are exchanged.

When, in equations [9–9] through [9–13], we let $n = k$, there exists only *one* two-particle eigenfunction,

$$\psi^0 = (2/L)(\sin n\pi x_1/L)(\sin n\pi x_2/L) \qquad [9\text{–}25$$

which belongs to the energy level,

$$W^0 = (\hbar^2\pi^2/2mL^2)(2n^2) \qquad [9\text{–}26$$

If x_1 and x_2 are interchanged in [9–25], then ψ^0 does not change in any way— therefore it is symmetric to interchange. (Also, W^0 of [9–26] is a nondegenerate level, since only one eigenfunction belongs to it.)

Any two-particle eigenfunction (for spinless[2] particles) which has its two spatial quantum numbers the *same* (such as in [9–25]) is automatically symmetric. In the next section we will discuss the correction terms which, when added to a zero-order wave function, change it into a first-order wave function. If one of the correction terms is a two-particle eigenfunction for which both of the quantum numbers are the *same*, then, as in [9–25], this particular correction term must be exchange-symmetric. If, however, one of the first-order correction terms is a two-particle eigenfunction for which the two quantum numbers are *different*, then by itself it is neither symmetric nor antisymmetric. (Upon interchange, it turns into a *different* function, as do ψ_1^0 and ψ_2^0 of [9–12] and [9–13].) It turns out (see Section 9.2) that the first-order correction terms always occur in pairs such that the complete first-order wave function *does* have exchange symmetry.

---

[2] By "spinless particle" we mean one whose wave function is a solution of the non-relativistic Schrödinger wave equation as contrasted to the Dirac equation (Chapter 11).

9.2.   The symmetry properties of the first-order wave functions[3]

In the previous section, we have seen that the zero-order wave function for a two-particle system where the two particles share two different quantum numbers, n and k, can be either symmetric or antisymmetric with respect to interchange. We will now show that if the zero-order wave function for the system is symmetric, ψ_s [9–23], then the correction terms $a_j \psi_j^0$ taken together are also symmetric, and, if the zero-order wave function is antisymmetric, ψ_a [9–24], then the correction terms, $a_j \psi_j^0$ taken together will also be antisymmetric.

Let us first consider a correction term containing the "two-particle" eigenfunction ψ_j^0, which has both its quantum numbers (which we will call q and r) the same. Then, as we have seen in [9–25] and [9–26], ψ_j^0 must be unchanged when x_1 and x_2 are interchanged. The amplitude of the jth eigenfunction is given by the fundamental equation [8–12], so that, considering only this one particular correction term, the first-order wave function is either

$$\psi_s = c_1(\psi_1^0 + \psi_2^0) + \cdots + \frac{c_1(H_{j1}' + H_{j2}')}{W^0 - W_j^0}\,\psi_j^0 + \cdots \qquad [9\text{–}27\text{a}$$

or

$$\psi_a = c_1(\psi_1^0 - \psi_2^0) + \cdots + \frac{c_1(H_{j1}' - H_{j2}')}{W^0 - W_j^0}\,\psi_j^0 + \cdots \qquad [9\text{–}27\text{b}$$

depending upon which of the two possible zero-order wave functions is used.

Since ψ_j^0 is itself unaffected by the interchange of x_1 and x_2, and since this interchange turns ψ_1^0 into ψ_2^0, and vice versa, then the interchange causes

$$H_{j1}' = \int\int \psi_j^{0*}\, H'\, \psi_1^0\, dx_1\, dx_2$$

to become

$$\int\int \psi_j^{0*}\, H'\, \psi_2^0\, dx_2\, dx_1$$

but this is merely H_{j2}'. However, interchanging x_1 and x_2 everywhere in the definite intergral H_{j1}' cannot change its value, since this operation merely relabels the variables of integration. Thus, $H_{j1}' = H_{j2}'$, and the term involving ψ_j^0 survives in [9–27a] but has zero amplitude in [9–27b]. Thus we see that an inherently symmetric term (such as ψ_j^0, when $q = r$) can never be a part of a wave function whose zero-order part is antisymmetric.

We next consider a correction term $a_j \psi_j^0$ whose two quantum numbers, q and r, are different. Such a term, by itself, is neither symmetric nor antisymmetric, but it happens to be accompanied by a second term—which we will label as $a_{j+1} \psi_{j+1}^0$—that has the same two quantum numbers, r and q. (ψ_j^0 and ψ_{j+1}^0 are similar to the pair ψ_1^0 and ψ_2^0 in [9–12] and [9–13]. Upon interchange of x_1 and x_2 each is converted into the other.) The two correction terms ψ_j^0

---

[3] This section may be omitted in a first reading.

and ψ_{j+1}^0 both belong to the same energy level,

$$W_j^0 = W_{j+1}^0 = (\hbar^2 \pi^2 / 2mL^2)(q^2 + r^2).$$

What happens to ψ_s and ψ_a when a pair of terms such as ψ_j^0 and ψ_{j+1}^0 form part of the correction to the zero-order wave function?

$$\psi_s = c_1(\psi_1^0 + \psi_2^0) + \cdots$$

$$+ \frac{c_1(H_{j1}' + H_{j2}')}{W^0 - W_j^0} \psi_j^0 + \frac{c_1(H_{j+1,\,1}' + H_{j+1,\,2}')}{W^0 - W_{j+1}^0} \psi_{j+1}^0 + \cdots \qquad \text{[9–28a]}$$

$$\psi_a = c_1(\psi_1^0 - \psi_2^0) + \cdots$$

$$+ \frac{c_1(H_{j1}' - H_{j2}')}{W^0 - W_j^0} \psi_j^0 + \frac{c_1(H_{j+1,\,1}' - H_{j+1,\,2}')}{W^0 - W_{j+1}^0} \psi_{j+1}^0 + \cdots \qquad \text{[9–28b]}$$

Upon interchange of x_1 and x_2:

$$\psi_j^0 \to \psi_{j+1}^0; \text{ and } \psi_{j+1}^0 \to \psi_j^0 \qquad (W_j^0 = W_{j+1}^0)$$

$$\psi_1^0 \to \psi_2^0; \text{ and } \psi_2^0 \to \psi_1^0 \qquad H' \to H'$$

Concentrating upon the term involving ψ_j^0, we indicate in [9–28] by the arrows the consequence of the interchange of x_1 and x_2. We see that in [9–28a] $a_j \psi_j^0$ converts into $+ a_{j+1} \psi_{j+1}^0$, but that in [9–28b], $a_j \psi_j^0$ converts into $- a_{j+1} \psi_{j+1}^0$.

Similarly, the interchange of x_1 and x_2 causes $a_{j+1} \psi_{j+1}^0$ to convert, in the case of ψ_s, into $+ a_j \psi_j^0$, but in the case of ψ_a, into $- a_j \psi_j^0$.

Thus, when a pair of terms, each having quantum numbers q and r, but $q \neq r$, form a correction to ψ_s, the pair is symmetric to interchange. However, when this pair of terms forms a correction to the zero-order ψ_a, the pair is antisymmetric to interchange.

We conclude: *If the zero-order wave function is symmetric, then the first-order wave function is also symmetric. If the zero-order wave function is antisymmetric, then the first-order wave function is also antisymmetric.* This result hinges on two basic features in the Hamiltonian: (a) the zero-order Hamiltonian is symmetric—that is, unaffected by interchange of x_1 and x_2, since the particles are identical—and (b) $H'(x_1 x_2)$ is also symmetric.[4]

It is clear that the symmetry properties are a deep-seated characteristic of a wave function. As we shall see in the next chapter (Problem 10.9), if a wave function is once symmetric, it will forever be symmetric. Similarly, an anti-symmetric function can never be converted into a symmetric one. In both cases, this result once more hinges upon the symmetry of H'—which is true for all known forms of mutual energy storage between two identical particles.

---

[4] If either H or H' was *not* unaffected by interchange, the particles would be distinguishable, and therefore not identical.

Since the exchange-symmetry properties of any wave function can be changed by no known process, we must conclude that if any one type of real particle once possesses a definite exchange symmetry it will *always* have wave functions of this same exchange symmetry.

The basic postulates can lead us only so far. They give us, in the case of two identical particles, two complete sets of wave functions, and they also tell us that there is no bridge between them, but they do not say *which* set belongs to any given particle. However, this question can be answered by experiment and the answer is clear. Electrons, protons, neutrons, and some mesons have antisymmetric wave functions, and certain other mesons, alpha particles, and photons have symmetric wave functions. For the simple hypothetical case of two identical particles in a one-dimensional box, we shall see shortly how symmetric and antisymmetric particles can be distinguished.

We can now see why an understanding of degenerate-level perturbation theory is needed to appreciate properly the symmetry properties of wave functions. These properties are due entirely to the fact that the basic zero-order wave functions (such as ψ_1^0 and ψ_2^0), although different functions of the two space variables x_1 and x_2, belong, because of the identical nature of the particles, to the same energy level. Exchange degeneracy is identical in a formal mathematical sense to degeneracy, caused by spatial symmetry, and therefore may be treated by the same methods.

It is most important to notice that the phenomena of exchange degeneracy are a direct consequence of the basic postulates. The utility of the theory hinges, however, on a key experimental fact: *Completely identical, indistinguishable particles exist.*

9.3. Some consequences of the symmetry properties of wave functions

We shall examine the probability distributions $\Psi^* \Psi$ and the energy levels belonging to the two different states [9–21] and [9–22]

$$W_s = W^0 + H_{11}' + H_{12}'; \quad \psi_s = \frac{1}{\sqrt{2}} (\psi_1^0 + \psi_2^0) + \sum_{j>2} a_j \psi_j^0 \qquad [9\text{–}29$$

$$W_a = W^0 + H_{11}' - H_{12}'; \quad \psi_a = \frac{1}{\sqrt{2}} (\psi_1^0 - \psi_2^0) + \sum_{j>2} a_j \psi_j^0 \qquad [9\text{–}30$$

for the case where correction terms $\sum_{j>2} a_j \psi_j^0$ are small compared to the zero-order terms in the two wave functions. This means that the sum of the $(a_j^* a_j)$'s must be small compared to unity, that is,

$$\Sigma a_j^* a_j \ll 1$$

This can be assured by the smallness of the H_{j1}' and H_{j2}' (since H' is small), and also by the largeness of the denominator terms, $W^0 - W_j^0$. (Even the nearest states are often considerably different in energy from W^0.)

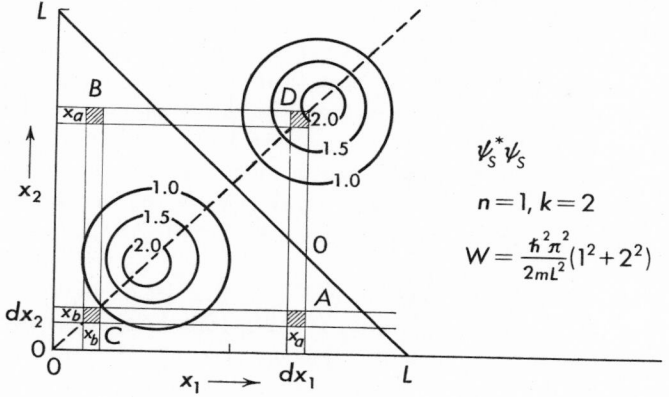

(**a**) Symmetric wave function

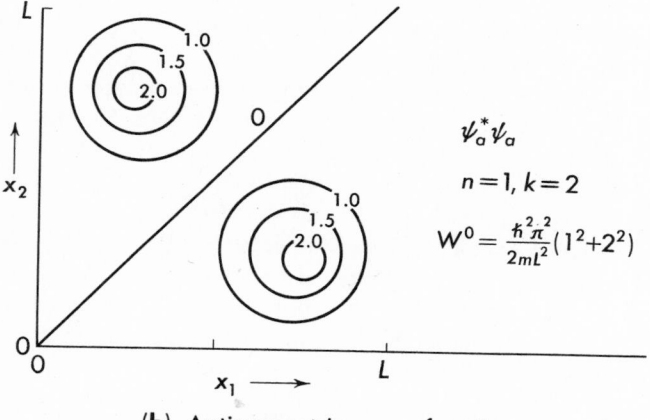

(**b**) Antisymmetric wave function

Fig. 9.2. The probability density $\psi^*\psi$, for symmetric and antisymmetric wave functions for two identical, spinless particles in a one-dimensional potential well.

We choose the same two quantum numbers as in Figure 9.1, $n = 1$ and $k = 2$. Since both ψ_s and ψ_a contain wave functions dependent upon *both* n and k, we can only say, in either case, that the two particles *share* the quantum numbers n and k.

We wish to plot both $\psi_s^* \psi_s$ and $\psi_a^* \psi_a$ against the two space variables x_1

and x_2. The main features of this plot are sketched, in contour form, in Figure 9.2. We see that, for both $\psi_s^* \psi_s$ and $\psi_a^* \psi_a$, the probability density functions appear as two hills, but that there is a striking difference in their locations. For the symmetrical function, the two hills are located on the line $x_1 = x_2$. That is, the particles with symmetrical wave functions tend to be found together in the neighborhood of either $x = L/4$ or $x = 3L/4$. $\psi_s \psi_s(x_1, x_2) \, dx_1 \, dx_2$ is, by definition, the probability that particle 1 will be found in the range between x_1 and $x_1 + dx_1$ and that, simultaneously, particle 2 will be found within the interval x_2 and $x_2 + dx_2$. The cross-hatched square labeled A on the $\psi_s^* \psi_s$ plot shows the area $dx_1 \, dx_2$. This area, multiplied by the vertically plotted intensity of $\psi_s^* \psi_s$, is the volume contained with the cross-hatched region as a base and is the probability $\psi_s^* \psi_s \, dx_1 \, dx_2$.

In order to clarify the interpretation of Figure 9.2, let us assume that two particle detectors, each with an aperture Δx, are placed along the x-axis of the one-dimensional physical system, one at $x = x_a$ and the other at $x = x_b$. At any time t, the detectors may be simultaneously turned on. If a particle is in an aperture, the detector will register 1 particle. If 2 particles are in one aperture, the detector will register 2 particles, and if none are present, it will register 0 particles. Since the two particles are identical, there is no way to distinguish which one causes any given "count" or "particle detection." All a detector can do is to register whether 0, 1, or 2 particles were present in its aperture Δx at the instant of examination.

For example, let $dx_1 = dx_2 = \Delta x$, and let one counter be located at $x = x_a$ and the other at $x = x_b$, as shown in Figure 9.2a, locating the cross-hatched area, A. The volume defined by A (that is, $A\psi^* \psi$, where $A = [\Delta x]^2$) measures the probability that particle 1 will be found in the interval Δx centered at x_a, and that, simultaneously, particle 2 will be found in the interval Δx centered at x_b. In this case, each counter will register 1 particle. However, since the particles are identical, each counter will also register a single particle if the reverse association occurs: particle 1 is recorded at x_b, and particle 2 is recorded at x_a. The probability of this latter event occurring is the volume $(B\psi^* \psi)$, defined by the cross-hatched area B. The sum of the two volumes defined by A and B is the probability that each of the two counters will register *one* particle when the system is examined (and consequently destroyed).

The volume defined by the cross-hatched area C is the probability that the counter located at $x = x_b$ will register 2 particles. When this occurs, it is certain that the counter located at $x = x_a$ will register 0 particles. Similarly, the volume defined by area D is the probability that the detector located at $x = x_a$ will register 2 particles, and that the other will register 0. For the particles with the symmetric wave function, Figure 9.2a, a single detector located either at $x = L/4$ or at $x = 3L/4$ will relatively often register a double detection. This is what we mean when we say that particles with symmetric wave functions "tend to be found together."

Considering the small size of the detector aperture Δx, compared to the length L of the one-dimensional box, the most frequent result of an observation of the system is that no counts are observed in either counter.

The "area" and "volume" which we have been discussing in the above paragraph, are not physical area and volume but refer only to the figure. This figure illustrates the difference between physical space and configuration space. The physical space of the particles is one-dimensional, but in the figure we use the x and the y axes to plot the two independent coordinates, x_1 and x_2, of $\psi(x_1, x_2)$, and the z-axis to plot $\psi^*\psi$ itself. Thus, *the plane of the figure is configuration space.* To each point in the plane belongs a unique value of ψ.

The advantage of representing the complete wave function of the two-particle system in a diagram such as Figure 9.2 is that one can then see at a glance all of its significant features. The very different nature of the symmetric and antisymmetric functions is particularly apparent.

The particles with the antisymmetric wave functions tend to be found *either* with number 1 near $x = L/4$ and number 2 near $x = 3L/4$, *or* with number 1 near $x = 3L/4$ and number 2 near $x = L/4$. They are *never* found at the same point, since $\psi_a^* \psi_a$ is zero along the line $x_1 = x_2$. A detailed contour plot shows, furthermore, that $\psi_a^* \psi_a$ is quite small anywhere in the neighborhood of this line. A single detector with very small aperture, Δx, will never record a double "count".

Thus, the (spinless) particles with symmetric wave functions "like each other," and those with antisymmetric wave functions "avoid each other."

It should be noted that the particles with antisymmetric wave functions avoid each other as assiduously as they avoid the infinite walls at $x = 0$ and $x = L$. The mutual avoidance of the antisymmetric particles and the "clumping together" of the symmetric particles is a unique quantum-mechanical phenomenon. It is *not* dependent upon the magnitude, or even the sign, of any possible physical forces which exist between the two particles! The particles described by Figure 9.2 are assumed to have negligible interparticle *physical* force, $H'(\, |\, x_1 - x_2 \,| \,) \to 0$, so that the remarkably different behavior of those particles possessing symmetric, and of those possessing antisymmetric, wave functions must be due to some very basic, deep-lying quality which is unknown in the world of direct experience.

With respect to the energy of the two different systems, we note from [9–29] and [9–30] that when $H' = 0$, W_s and W_a are identical, namely

$$W^0 = (\hbar^2\, \pi^2/2mL^2)(2^2 + 1^2) \qquad [9\text{–}31|$$

If the mutual potential energy of the two particles in the box is positive (repulsive force)—as is the case when $H' = e^2/\,|\, x_1 - x_2 \,|$—then we shall expect from Figure 9.2 that particles possessing a symmetric wave function which tend to clump together will have a higher system energy than particles (of the same mass and charge) possessing an antisymmetric wave function. Equations [9–29] and [9–30] show quantitatively that this is so. The term H_{11}' (which is equal to H_{22}') is just the expectation value of the energy belonging to the operator H', for either ψ_1^0 or ψ_2^0, [9–12] and [9–13]. The other term, H_{12}' (which also equals H_{21}') is preceded by a *positive* sign for the symmetric state, further increasing the system energy, and is preceded by a *negative* sign for the antisymmetric state, decreasing the system energy. The net result is that whenever H' is positive W_s will always be larger than W_a.[5]

The energy corrections for the symmetric and antisymmetric wave functions may be simply calculated. Using [9–23],

$$\int\int \psi_s^{0*}\, H'\, \psi_s^0\, dx_1\, dx_2 = \int\int \frac{1}{\sqrt{2}}(\psi_1^{0*} + \psi_2^{0*})\, H'\, \frac{1}{\sqrt{2}}(\psi_1^0 + \psi_2^0)\, dx_1\, dx_2$$

$$= \tfrac{1}{2}\Big[\int\int \psi_1^{0*}\, H'\, \psi_1^0\, dx_1\, dx_2 + \int\int \psi_2^{0*}\, H'\, \psi_2^0\, dx_1\, dx_2$$

$$+ \int\int \psi_1^{0*}\, H'\, \psi_2^0\, dx_1\, dx_2 + \int\int \psi_2^{0*}\, H'\, \psi_1^0\, dx_1\, dx_2\Big]$$

and, since $H_{11}' = H_{22}'$, and $H_{12}' = H_{21}'$ (where $H_{11}' = \int \psi_1^{0*}\, H'\, \psi_1^0\, dx_1\, dx_2$, etc.),

$$\int\int \psi_s^{0*}\, H'\, \psi_s^0\, dx_1\, dx_2 = H_{11}' + H_{12}' \qquad\qquad [9\text{–}32$$

Similarly, using [9–24],

$$\int\int \psi_a^{0*}\, H'\, \psi_a^0\, dx_1\, dx_2 = H_{11}' - H_{12}' \qquad\qquad [9\text{–}33$$

Thus, the energy correction to W^0 is merely the expectation value of H' with respect to either the zero-order symmetric, or the zero-order antisymmetric, wave function belonging to the level W^0.

For the state of Figure 9.2, where two identical particles share the quantum numbers 1 and 2, we now assume that H' has the value,

$$H' = V_0 \text{ for } |x_1 - x_2| \le D$$
$$H' = 0 \quad \text{for } |x_1 - x_2| > D \qquad D \ll L \qquad [9\text{–}34$$

This mathematically simple form for H' is not really quite so artificial as it may seem at first sight. For example, two neutrons have a mutual energy which is dependent upon their separation and which is more nearly like [9–34] than the inverse first-power potential to which we are more accustomed. In any case, the H' of [9–34] merely means that we multiply the probability density, $\psi_s^*\psi_s$ or $\psi_a^*\psi_a$, by V_0 whenever both x_1 and x_2 are within D centimeters of the line $x_1 = x_2$, and by zero elsewhere. The result of this operation (for the wave functions of Figure 9.2) is shown in Figure 9.3 in perspective. The volume of the "slice" is directly proportional to the energy correction term in each case. Since the slice goes right through the two "hills" for $\psi_s^*\psi_s$, and brackets

---

[5] W_a does not exist unless the two spinless particles are sharing different quantum numbers, such as 1 and 2 in this example. If the two particles share the same quantum number, 1 for example, the wave function must be symmetric and the system energy much lower.

a zero-intensity contour for $\psi_a^* \psi_a$, it is clear that there is only a very tiny positive shift in the energy in the antisymmetric case, compared to the symmetric.

Quantitative calculations are simple, since $D \ll L$. They are obtained by integrating [9–32] and [9–33] for the ranges: x_1 varies from $x_2 - D$ to $x_2 + D$; and x_2 varies from 0 to L.

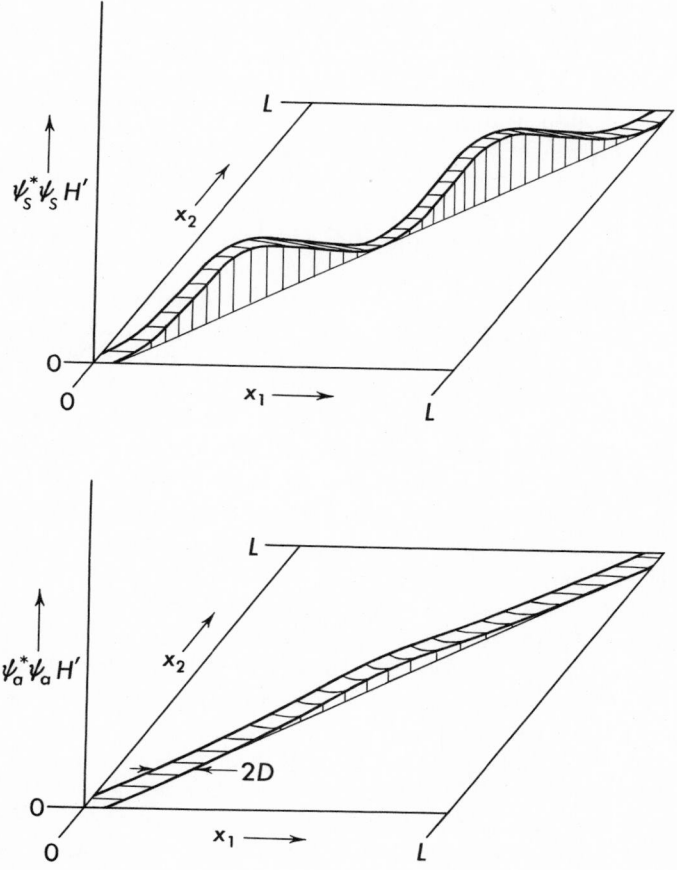

Fig. 9.3. The calculation of the energy correction to the symmetric and antisymmetric systems of Figure 9.2, due to a short-range repulsive force between the two identical (spinless) particles.

It is plain, from Figure 9.3, that the correction term to the energy is always positive if H' is positive—for both symmetric and antisymmetric particles. Similarly, the correction term to the zero-order energy is always negative if H' is negative (the particles attract each other). The difference in the magnitude of the two corrections is due entirely to the fact that symmetric particles tend to clump together and the antisymmetric particles tend to avoid each other as much as the constraining box permits (independent of the interparticle force).[6]

Why do particles with symmetric wave functions tend to clump together, and those with antisymmetric wave functions tend to avoid each other? One is tempted to think of some sort of force that either attracts or repels the particles, but this is not a satisfactory model. All true forces can be measured by (change in energy)/(change in distance). For example, in Problem 3.7 we calculated the force exerted by a trapped particle, or bound matter waves, on the walls of a one-dimensional box. If the length of the one-dimensional box containing the particles of Figure 9.2 is reduced, the two symmetric particles will clump more closely, and also the two antisymmetric particles will be forced closer together. If, as we can assume without changing the symmetry properties of the wave functions, the *ordinary* interaction energy H' between the two particles is negligibly small, the external work done in compressing the box will be exactly the same for the same quantum numbers n and k, whether symmetric or antisymmetric particles are contained inside, and, furthermore, *all* the added work is derived from pressure on the walls. The two types of system had the same energy before compression, and they will have the same energy afterward. Clearly, although we are forcing a change in the average distance between the particles, *there is no increment of work that can be associated with this change.* An increment of work appears of course when $H' \neq 0$, but this is due to the presence of *ordinary forces*, such as, for example, the coulomb force between two electrons. Changes in energy levels *caused* by ordinary potential energy terms, H', but *controlled* in large part by the symmetry properties of the particles' wave functions, are of great practical importance. These "symmetry-controlled" energy changes cause large differences in atomic and molecular energy levels, and are the basis of the periodic system of the elements and of the valence bonds which are of such vital importance in chemistry.

As we shall see shortly, the symmetry properties of the electron wave function (electrons are all antisymmetric) dominate the structure of multi-electron atoms. Without the "avoidance" characteristic of antisymmetric particles, atoms would be unrecognizable to us. The electrons, if they were symmetric, would all clump together in the lowest possible state near the nucleus. What matter in the gross would then be like—if indeed it could exist at all—is hard to imagine.

We are here contemplating one of the most important and profound

---

[6] The expression "symmetric particle" is abbreviated notation for: "that type of particle which, when forming a system with an identical particle, has a system-wave function which is symmetric, that is, ψ is unchanged by the interchange of the spatial variables x_1 and x_2.

Similarly, the expression "antisymmetric particle" means: "that type of particle, which, when forming a system with an identical particle, has a system-wave function which is antisymmetric, that is, ψ changes sign upon the interchange of the spatial variables, x_1 and x_2.

consequences of quantum mechanics—the symmetry, or antisymmetry, of wave functions belonging to particles. We see that symmetry and antisymmetry follow directly from the basic postulates when we apply them to the case of two identical particles located in the same region of physical space. The postulates will not tell us that electrons, for example, will *only* exist in states that are antisymmetric to the interchange of any two electrons—this must be inferred from experiment (see Section 9.5, The Pauli Exclusion Principle)—but they *do tell us exactly how antisymmetric particles (or symmetric particles) must behave, if they exist at all.* The fact that all of the particles of nature fall neatly into one or the other of the two categories provided by the postulates *and* behave as predicted is a great triumph for the theory.

The exchange-symmetry property of the wave functions belonging to particles is one of the most important and fundamental characteristics of matter.

9.4.   Particles with nonoverlapping wave functions

From the beginning of this chapter we have been basing all our analysis upon single-particle eigenfunctions, which are solutions of the separated, zero-order equation, such as ψ_1 and ψ_2 of [9–10]. We originally assumed that particle 1 was in the state with the quantum number n, and particle 2 was in the state with the quantum number k. Only after the exchange-degeneracy had been disclosed by [9–12] and [9–13], and perturbation theory applied (with H' nonzero), did we find that either of two linear combinations of ψ_1^0 and ψ_2^0 could be the correct zero-order wave function of the system. We regarded the two particles as sharing the two states ψ_1 and ψ_2. The particular case we have been considering is shown in Figure 9.4a.

The reason, in Figure 9.4a, why we cannot think of particle 1 as being in state ψ_1 and particle 2 as being in state ψ_2, is that these two wave functions overlap in space and there is no way of knowing how much of either function "belongs" to any one electron. We must not forget that a *single* particle in a box *can* be represented by matter waves resonating at *many* different frequencies. When two identical particles occupy the *same* space we have no way of knowing what fraction of the amplitude of vibration of any particular mode "belongs" to one particle. In contrast to this, consider the two wave functions of Figure 9.4b, which, since they are not pure eigenfunctions (each is a superposition of many eigenfunctions), are time-dependent. At the moment shown in Figure 9.4b they are completely separated in space, but at a later (or earlier) time they might be overlapped, as shown in Figure 9.4c.

For the two nonoverlapping wave functions of Figure 9.4b we form the two (un-normalized) degenerate system wave functions (as in the case of [9–12] and [9–13]),

$$\psi_1^0 = \psi_1(x_1)\,\psi_2(x_2) \text{ and } \psi_2^0 = \psi_1(x_2)\,\psi_2(x_1)$$

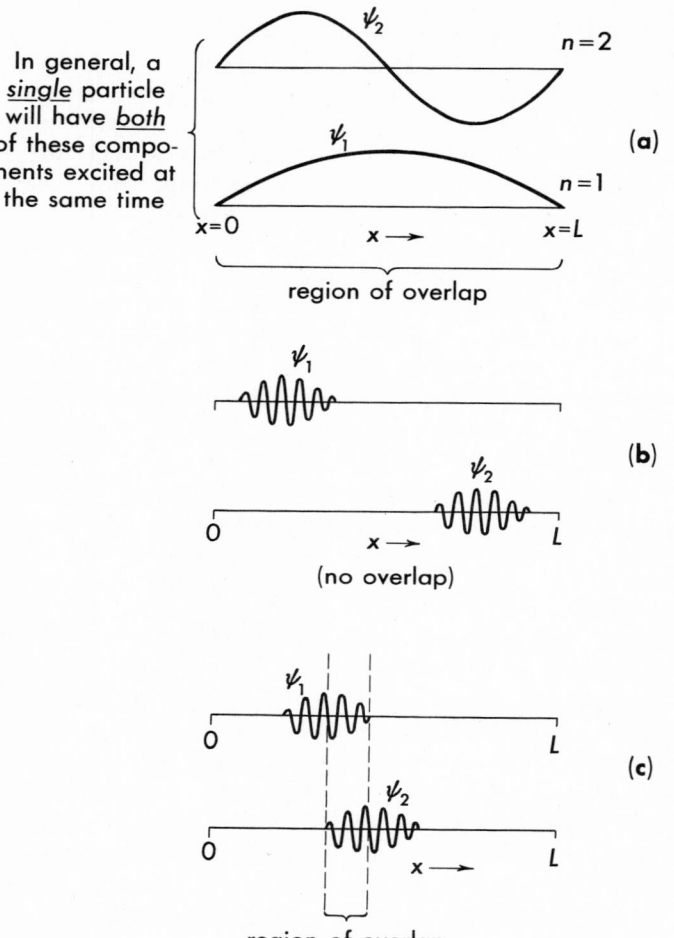

In general, a _single_ particle will have _both_ of these components excited at the same time

Fig. 9.4. Two particles in a box with overlapping and nonoverlapping wave functions.

both belonging to the same energy level, W^0. We now assume an exchange-symmetric interaction H' and find the eigenvalues W' of the determinant [9–15]. Now, however, $H'_{12} = H'_{21} = 0$, since the integral

$$H'_{12} = \int\int \psi_1^*(x_1)\, \psi_2^*(x_2)\, H'\, \psi_1(x_2)\, \psi_2(x_1)\, dx_1\, dx_2 = H'_{21}$$

vanishes. For example, when integrating x_1, $\psi_1(x_1)$ is zero in the region where $\psi_2(x_1)$ is non-zero, and vice versa. Thus the integration with respect to x_1 yields zero. Similarly, the integration with respect to x_2 yields zero. The reason is simple: there is no overlap between the wave form ψ_1 and the wave form ψ_2.

In contrast to this, the integral

$$H'_{11} = \int \int \psi_1^*(x_1)\, \psi_2^*(x_2)\, H'\, \psi_1(x_1)\, \psi_2(x_2)\, dx_1\, dx_2 = H'_{22}$$

is, in general, not zero—providing that $H'(x_1, x_2)$ "reaches" between the two localized particles, as will any potential of the form $1/\,|\,x_1 - x_2\,|$.

Therefore there is only one energy correction, $W' = H'_{11} = H'_{22}$, and the set of equations

$$c_1(H'_{11} - W') + c_2\, H'_{12} = 0$$
$$c_1\, H'_{21} + c_2(H'_{22} - W') = 0$$

[9–35

from which the determinant was derived does not determine either c_1 or c_2. We can therefore take *any* relative amount of ψ_1^0 and ψ_2^0 [9–35], as the zero-order system wave function. We are not limited to only those combinations that are either symmetric or antisymmetric to identical particle interchange. *Thus, when the wave functions belonging to particles are nonoverlapping, the concepts of symmetry and antisymmetry are not needed.* One can think of the two wave "packets" as being isolated in space, and the particles as being uniquely identifiable by their *spatial* position.

When, however, the two wave functions ψ_1 and ψ_2 overlap, as in Figure 9.4c, H_{12} *is no longer zero*, so that [9–35] forces us to accept one of two ratios for c_1/c_2, leading to the immediate result that we must choose only symmetric or antisymmetric combinations of the two degenerate wave functions, ψ_1^0 and ψ_2^0. The energy difference between the symmetric and antisymmetric systems now depends both on the degree of overlap and on the magnitude and form of H', the interaction energy.

In actual fact, the two wave functions of Figure 9.4b must overlap slightly. Only an (artificial) infinite-wall barrier can cause a wave function *literally* to go to zero. According to the theory, even the smallest magnitude for H'_{12} will force the selection of either symmetric or antisymmetric wave functions. Thus, two spinless, antisymmetric, electrically charged particles in a box, apparently localized, will not only sense each other's presence through their mutual coulomb force, but "the tentacles of their wave functions" will at all times reach out and overlap slightly. Since these particles will exist only with an antisymmetric system wave function, they tend to avoid each other—i.e., minimize overlap of their wave functions. Two (spinless) symmetric-type particles, on the other hand, would tend to increase the overlap, that is, clump together as much as possible. Thus, spinless symmetrical particles, if they have a mutual physical force which is repulsive, will have a higher system energy than spinless antisymmetric particles with the same mutual physical force. The calculation for the wave functions of Figure 9.4 is more complex than for the simple, highly overlapped case we have been considering, but the principles are unchanged and the results are qualitatively the same.

For an analysis of the symmetry properties of two nearly isolated systems, see Problem 9.9.

9.5. The Pauli exclusion principle

At the end of Section 9.4 we pointed out that the basic postulates permitted only two types of exchange symmetry for identical particles. The behavior of particles possessing each type of symmetry is clearly predicted, but the postulates themselves do not tell us *which* type of symmetry is characteristic of any particular particle. Pauli was the first to explain why electrons do *not* all clump together, near the nucleus, in the lowest possible energy state. He originally postulated that "no two electrons can have the same four quantum numbers, n, l, m and m_s." (m_s, the "spin" quantum number, can have one of two values, $1/2$ or $-1/2$, two numbers which are used to identify the two independent modes of propagation available to electron waves [see Chapter 11].) As we shall see shortly, Pauli's original form of the principle follows directly from the more general statement of the Exclusion Principle: *Electrons have antisymmetric wave functions.*

We have seen how, according to the basic postulates, systems containing two identical particles must have wave functions which either change sign or do not change sign when the coordinates x_1 and x_2 are interchanged. Let us now assume that two identical (spinless) particles, in a one-dimensional box, obey the Pauli Exclusion Principle, and see what the consequences are. Real electron wave functions are antisymmetric with respect to the complete interchange of both space and spin variables (see Section 11.8). We postulate hypothetical spinless particles which can exist only in an antisymmetric state (with respect to the interchange of x_1 and x_2). We assume that H' is very small, but finite.

We first place only one particle in the box, and imagine that it radiates away any excess energy and settles in the lowest state—the zero-point state, with quantum number 1—as in Figure 9.5a.

Next, we place the second particle in the box, and allow the system to settle into its lowest possible energy state. Since the state wherein both particles have quantum number 1 is a symmetric state, the system cannot assume this energy condition. It must assume, therefore, the antisymmetric state whose energy is at 5 units, as in Figure 9.5b. Actually, the energy is slightly higher than this by $H'_{11} - H'_{12}$, if H' is positive. In this state, we *must* speak of the two particles as sharing the quantum numbers 1 and 2, since the wave functions of the two particles occupy the same region of physical space (see the preceding section).

If, on the other hand, our hypothetical particles had been symmetric, the lowest state, at 2 energy units, would have been occupied. The two particles would have shared the quantum number 1.

Thus we see that, even though the interaction energy of the two particles is very small, their *symmetry or antisymmetry can cause a great difference in the ground-state energy level for the complete system.*

Real electrons in an atom act in basically this same way. As more and more electrons are added (the nuclear charge is assumed to be large enough to hold them all), they do not all clump together down in the lowest possible eigenstate (ψ_{100} of the hydrogen-like wave functions), but "stack up" in a definite pattern,

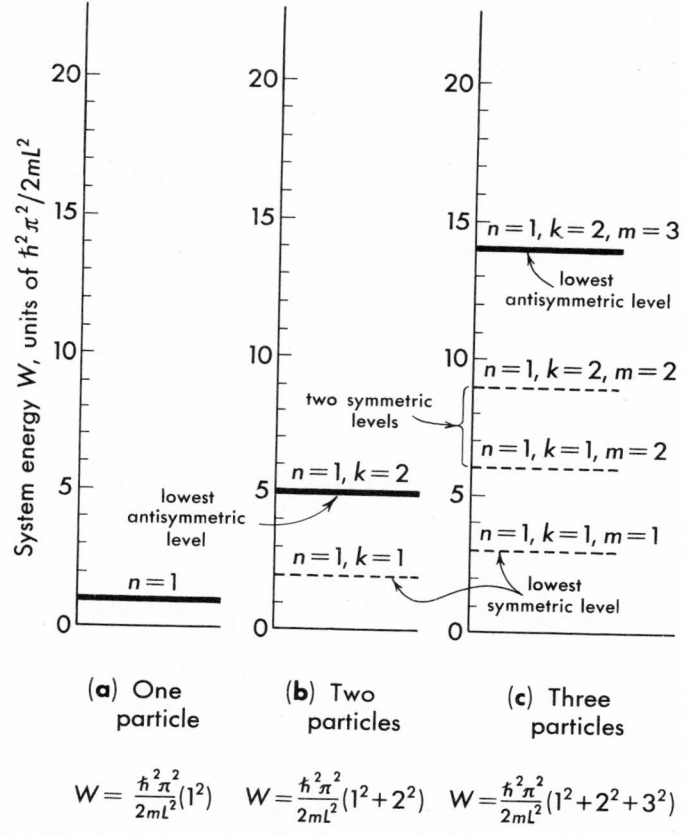

$$W = \frac{\hbar^2\pi^2}{2mL^2}(1^2) \qquad W = \frac{\hbar^2\pi^2}{2mL^2}(1^2+2^2) \qquad W = \frac{\hbar^2\pi^2}{2mL^2}(1^2+2^2+3^2)$$

Fig. 9.5. The lowest system energy levels for antisymmetric and symmetric particles for identical spinless particles in a one-dimensional box.

"sharing" quantum numbers of higher and higher magnitudes. Thus the whole structure of the periodic table and of the chemical elements is a consequence of the antisymmetry of the electron.

Let us imagine a third antisymmetric particle to be added to our one-dimensional system. The lowest possible system energy is now 14 energy units (Fig. 9.5). As we shall see below, the three lower levels are all ignored because, for them, the system function would not be antisymmetric. The level in which the three particles share the quantum numbers 1, 2, and 3 is now the lowest antisymmetric level. One speaks loosely of the third particle "taking the quantum number 3," but this is not really an accurate statement. When the third particle is added to the system, the three particles *share* the quantum numbers, 1, 2, and 3.

To see how this comes about, we list the six wave functions belonging to the level where the system energy W equals 14 units of energy:

The *single-particle* eigenfunctions are

$$\psi_1(x) = \sin(\pi x/L), \quad \psi_2(x) = \sin(2\pi x/L), \quad \psi_3(x) = \sin(3\pi x/L) \qquad [9\text{--}36$$

Then all the possible zero-order *three-particle* eigenfunctions are:

$$\psi_1^0 = \left(\frac{2}{L}\right)^{3/2} \psi_1(x_1)\,\psi_2(x_2)\,\psi_3(x_3)$$

$$\psi_2^0 = \left(\frac{2}{L}\right)^{3/2} \psi_1(x_1)\,\psi_2(x_3)\,\psi_3(x_2)$$

$$\psi_3^0 = \left(\frac{2}{L}\right)^{3/2} \psi_1(x_2)\,\psi_2(x_3)\,\psi_3(x_1)$$

$$\psi_4^0 = \left(\frac{2}{L}\right)^{3/2} \psi_1(x_2)\,\psi_2(x_1)\,\psi_3(x_3) \qquad [9\text{--}37$$

$$\psi_5^0 = \left(\frac{2}{L}\right)^{3/2} \psi_1(x_3)\,\psi_2(x_1)\,\psi_3(x_2)$$

$$\psi_6^0 = \left(\frac{2}{L}\right)^{3/2} \psi_1(x_3)\,\psi_2(x_2)\,\psi_3(x_1)$$

In the absence of symmetry requirements *any* linear combination of these functions is a solution to the zero-order wave equation, and therefore a possible (un-normalized) wave function for the system. It is required by the Pauli Exclusion Principle that the system wave function be antisymmetric in the interchange of any pair of particles. This can be accomplished by forming a particular combination:

$$\psi_a^0 = \psi_1^0 + \psi_3^0 + \psi_5^0 - (\psi_2^0 + \psi_4^0 + \psi_6^0) \qquad [9\text{--}38$$

which, although un-normalized, is antisymmetric, as required. To see that this is so, one observes that if, in [9–38], x_1 is interchanged with x_2, then

$$\psi_1^0 \rightarrow \psi_4^0 \text{ and } \psi_4^0 \rightarrow \psi_1^0$$

$$\psi_3^0 \rightarrow \psi_2^0 \text{ and } \psi_2^0 \rightarrow \psi_3^0$$

$$\psi_5^0 \rightarrow \psi_6^0 \text{ and } \psi_6^0 \rightarrow \psi_5^0$$

Thus, all the positive terms turn into the negative ones, all the negative terms turn into the positive ones, and the sum, ψ_a^0, changes sign. The interchange of any other pair of coordinates, for example x_2 and x_3, produces exactly the same result. ψ_a^0 is called "completely" antisymmetric, since it changes sign upon the interchange of *any* pair of particles.

It should be noted that the most general, completely symmetric (un-normalized) wave function ψ_s^0 is merely the sum of the ψ^0's of [9–37]. Here, the interchange of any pair of the *x*'s will again cause each of the ψ^0's to change into one of the others, but now this reproduces the same function as before, with no sign change.

Suppose that the three wave functions listed in [9–36] had the quantum numbers 1, 2, and 2, instead of 1, 2, and 3. Then $\psi_2(x) = \psi_3(x)$, and the anti-symmetric wave function [9–38] becomes zero. There is therefore *no* anti-symmetric function for the state $n = 1$, $k = 2$, $m = 2$ in Figure 9.5c. The antisymmetric function [9–38] also becomes zero for the other two states which are indicated by dotted lines in Figure 9.5c.

Although we have been discussing zero-order wave functions, we have seen in Section 9.2 that the symmetry properties of the first-order wave functions are the same as for the zero-order functions.

A simple way to find the right form for the antisymmetric wave function [9–38] is to calculate the determinant,

$$\psi_a = \begin{vmatrix} \psi_1(x_1) & \psi_2(x_1) & \psi_3(x_1) \\ \psi_1(x_2) & \psi_2(x_2) & \psi_3(x_2) \\ \psi_1(x_3) & \psi_2(x_3) & \psi_3(x_3) \end{vmatrix}$$

If two of the ψ's are the same (which will occur if two of the quantum numbers which identify the ψ's are the same), then the determinant will have two identical columns and automatically give a zero value for ψ_a.

Since a symmetric wave function can always be formed from the sum of the ψ's [9–37], and it does not vanish no matter how many ψ's are the same, all the levels identified in Figure 9.5 can be occupied by any number of sym-metric particles. For example, if the three particles in Figure 9.5c were sym-metric and were allowed to seek the lowest possible system energy, they would all be in the state with quantum number 1, for which the wavelength is $2L$, and the system energy is three units.

The exchange symmetry of the wave function describing a system of particles has important consequences regarding the aggregate behavior of the system. We have already seen, for the three particles of Figure 9.5c, that the lowest possible value of the total system energy is strikingly different for the two types of symmetry, even though the particles have the same mass and are inside identical boxes. Suppose there are N identical particles in a one-dimen-sional box. Figure 9.6a shows that the system composed of symmetric particles has a much lower value for the lowest possible system energy than does the antisymmetric system. A system having the lowest possible value of total system energy is, thermodynamically speaking, at absolute zero, since it cannot lose energy under *any* circumstances.

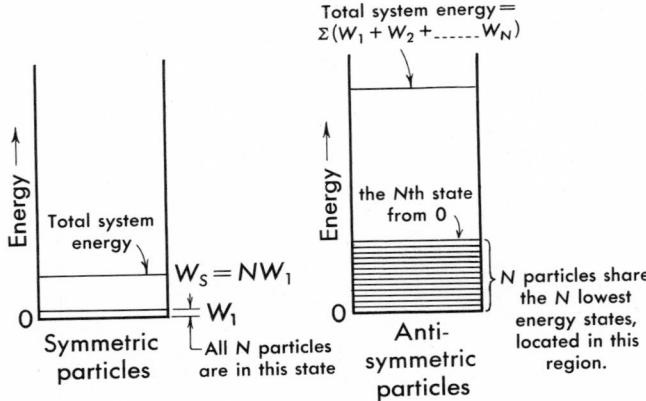

(**a**) Lowest possible state of a system
($T = 0$, absolute zero).

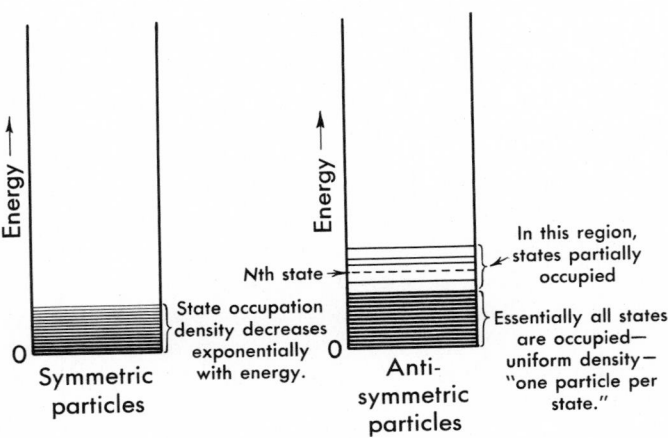

(**b**) Total system energy ($T > 0$).

Fig. 9.6. Energy levels of one-dimensional systems for N symmetric or antisymmetric particles (without spin).

In Figure 9.6b we imagine that the two systems each have been brought into contact with a source of energy that has caused them to increase their total system energy. The symmetric system may now have many states excited besides the lowest one, which was the only one originally occupied. The antisymmetrical system will now have, in an unoccupied condition, some of its originally occupied states (below the *N*th state from zero energy), while above the *N*th state there will be some newly occupied states. (If the *j*th state is unoccupied, there is *no* excitation of the matter waves of the frequency $[W_j/h]$ characteristic of the state. If the *j*th state is occupied, the matter waves of frequency $[W_j/h]$ are excited to some degree—very intensely, if the waves of many particles are superimposed—which only happens in the symmetric case.)

The "filled-up sea of states" for the antisymmetric system lying, in general, below the *N*th state, is often called the "Fermi sea of states." Electrons in metals are found to behave as if they "stacked up" in an array of states of just this type.[7] The statistical analysis of large aggregates of antisymmetric particles, such as electrons, is described by the term "Fermi-Dirac statistics." Clearly some understanding of the basic quantum-mechanical principles of exchange symmetry is essential for an adequate understanding of systems of antisymmetric particles.

Systems of symmetric particles, such as those on the left side of Figure 9.6, may also be treated in the aggregate by statistical methods. These methods are described by the term "Bose-Einstein statistics." For example, helium atoms in a physical box behave in the manner of symmetric particles.

Photons, in a box with perfectly reflecting walls, have resonances similar to matter waves. They act like symmetric particles, however, since any number of them can have the same wavelength—that is, the same quantum number. For example, electromagnetic waves in a resonant cavity have a set of distinct resonant frequencies. It is quite possible to get billions of photons of microwave frequency to occupy any resonance. Indeed, the energy per photon, $h\nu$, is so low, due to low frequency, that only large numbers of photons will produce enough energy to permit detection.

The discussion respecting electrons has avoided one important feature, the electron "spin." Taking this into account, one finds that the Fermi sea of states contains not merely one electron, but *two* electrons for each of the states; otherwise there is no change in the consequences of the electron's symmetry properties. In Sections 11.8 and 11.9 we shall re-analyze the one-dimensional system we have been discussing, but will take full account of the electron "spin," or, alternatively, of the "two independent modes of vibration of electron matter waves."

9.6. Summary

The significant features of exchange symmetry are displayed by simple systems such as, for example, two identical, spinless particles in a one-dimensional box. We assume initially that the two particles are noninteracting, that

---

[7] More precisely, the *N* electrons *share* the whole array of states. See L. I. Schiff, *Quantum Mechanics* (1949, McGraw-Hill Book Co., Inc., New York; also, R. C. Tolman, *The Principles of Statistical Mechanics* (1938, Oxford U. Press, Oxford): Chapter X.

each has a mass m, and that they are in an infinite-wall, one-dimensional box of length L. The Schrödinger wave equation for this system is

$$\left[-\left(\frac{\hbar^2}{2m}\frac{\partial^2}{\partial x_1^2}\right)-\left(\frac{\hbar^2}{2m}\frac{\partial^2}{\partial x_2^2}\right)+V_1(x_1)+V_2(x_2)\right]\Psi(x_1, x_2, t)$$
$$=-\frac{\hbar}{i}\frac{\partial}{\partial t}\Psi(x_1, x_2, t) \qquad [9\text{--}3$$

where both $V_1(x_1)$ and $V_2(x_2)$ are zero in the range $0 \leq x \leq L$ and infinite outside.

Equation [9--3] can be separated into three equations, in the usual manner, by assuming

$$\Psi = \psi_1(x_1)\,\psi_2(x_2)\,\phi(t) \qquad [9\text{--}4$$

obtaining thereby the time-dependent equation [9--5] and two one-particle space-dependent equations in each of the two variables x_1 and x_2 [9--6].

The *one-particle* eigenfunctions are:

$$\psi_1(x_1) = \sqrt{\frac{2}{L}}\sin\frac{n\pi x_1}{L}, \qquad n = 1, 2, 3, \cdots \qquad [9\text{--}9$$

$$\psi_2(x_2) = \sqrt{\frac{2}{L}}\sin\frac{k\pi x_2}{L}, \qquad k = 1, 2, 3, \cdots \qquad [9\text{--}10$$

Therefore, the two-particle, space-dependent equation (the spatial part of [9--3]), has, for $n \neq k$, two *two-particle* eigenfunctions:

$$\psi_1^0(x_1, x_2) = \frac{2}{L}\sin\frac{n\pi x_1}{L}\sin\frac{k\pi x_2}{L} \qquad [9\text{--}12$$

$$\psi_2^0(x_1, x_2) = \frac{2}{L}\sin\frac{n\pi x_2}{L}\sin\frac{k\pi x_1}{L} \qquad [9\text{--}13$$

These two functions have different spatial form, but both belong to the same energy level,

$$W^0 = \frac{\hbar^2\,\pi^2}{2mL^2}(n^2 + k^2) \qquad [9\text{--}11$$

and are, therefore, degenerate.

As long as there is no mutual interaction between the two particles, there is no way of choosing between either of the two degenerate eigenfunctions [9--12] or [9--13], or *any* (normalized) linear combination of the two. Each of these alternatives is a solution to the wave equation, is well behaved, and possesses an integrable square. If, however, there is some mutual potential energy, $H'(x_1, x_2)$, however small, between the two identical particles (which appears to be true for all known particles), and if $H'(x_1, x_2)$ is unchanged in sign or magnitude upon the interchange of x_1 and x_2 (which must be true if the particles are identical), then *there are only two possible choices for the zero-order wave function for the two-particle system*:

$$\psi_s = \frac{1}{\sqrt{2}} (\psi_1^0 + \psi_2^0)$$

$$= \frac{1}{\sqrt{2}} \frac{2}{L} \left[\sin \frac{n\pi x_1}{L} \sin \frac{k\pi x_2}{L} + \sin \frac{n\pi x_2}{L} \sin \frac{k\pi x_1}{L} \right] \qquad [9\text{-}23]$$

$$\psi_a = \frac{1}{\sqrt{2}} (\psi_1^0 - \psi_2^0)$$

$$= \frac{1}{\sqrt{2}} \frac{2}{L} \left[\sin \frac{n\pi x_1}{L} \sin \frac{k\pi x_2}{L} - \sin \frac{n\pi x_2}{L} \sin \frac{k\pi x_1}{L} \right] \qquad [9\text{-}24$$

This result follows directly from the solution to the secular equation (obtained from the mathematically identical case of degeneracy arising from spatial symmetry),

$$\begin{vmatrix} (H_{11}' - W') & H_{12}' \\ H_{21}' & (H_{22}' - W') \end{vmatrix} = 0 \qquad [9\text{-}15$$

where

$$H_{11}' = \int \psi_1^{0*} H' \psi_1^0 \, dx_1 \, dx_2, \text{ etc.}$$

Due to the symmetry properties of $H'(x_1, x_2)$ (see [9-16] and [9-18]), $H_{12}' = H_{21}'$, and $H_{11}' = H_{22}'$, so that the determinant [9-15] becomes

$$(H_{11}' - W')^2 = (H_{12}')^2 \qquad [9\text{-}19$$

The selection of the root $W' = H_{11}' + H_{12}'$ *forces* the selection of the (exchange-symmetric) linear combination [9-23] as the zero-order wave function for the two-particle system.

The selection of the root $W' = H_{11}' - H_{12}'$ *forces* the selection of the (exchange-antisymmetric) linear combination [9-24] as the zero-order wave function for the two-particle system.

These results are not changed (see Chapter 8), even though

$$| H'(x_1, x_2) | \to 0$$

Also, as Section 9:2 shows, the first-order wave functions possess the same exchange symmetry as the zero-order wave functions. Exchange symmetry is a very basic and deep-seated property of a class of particles.

In Section 9.4 we show that if the two *one-particle* wave functions do not overlap in any region, then the secular equation [9-15] becomes indeterminant and we are no longer forced to accept either [9-12] or [9-13] as the zero-order wave function for the system. Each particle may be regarded as having an independent existence.

If $n = k$, the antisymmetric wave function ψ_a vanishes. That is, two (spinless) particles with antisymmetric wave functions *cannot* share a single state (that is, share one quantum number, or, more generally, share any one set of spatial quantum numbers). Any number of symmetric particles, however, can share one state.

If the two particles differed in some manner by even the smallest conceivable amount (in mass, for example), the two two-particle eigenfunctions [9–12] and [9–13] would *not* belong to the same energy level, and no question could arise regarding the form of the zero-order wave function for the system—there would be just one function belonging to each level.

The postulates tell us that *if there are identical particles, they must be either symmetric or antisymmetric to exchange.*

Observation of nature tells us that: (1) *Identical particles exist*, and (2) *Electrons* (and protons, and neutrons) *have antisymmetric wave functions* (the Pauli Exclusion Principle).

For the case of n identical particles inside a potential well, a practical problem arises in finding a linear combination of the *n-particle*, zero-order eigenfunctions which is antisymmetric to the interchange of any pair of coordinates. If ψ_1, ψ_2, ψ_3, $\cdots$, ψ_n are the *one-particle* zero-order eigenfunctions, then a zero-order (un-normalized) antisymmetric wave function for the n-particle system may be obtained from the determinant,

$$\psi_a = \begin{vmatrix} \psi_1(x_1) & \psi_2(x_1) & \cdots & \psi_n(x_1) \\ \psi_1(x_2) & \psi_2(x_2) & & \psi_n(x_2) \\ \psi_1(x_3) & \psi_2(x_3) & & \psi_n(x_3) \\ \cdot & \cdot & & \cdot \\ \cdot & \cdot & & \cdot \\ \cdot & \cdot & & \cdot \\ \psi_1(x_n) & \psi_2(x_n) & & \psi_n(x_n) \end{vmatrix}$$

This wave function is completely antisymmetric—that is, it changes sign upon the interchange of any pair of variables. Also, it vanishes if the functions in any two columns are identical—that is, if any two of the *one-particle* states have the same spatial dependence (the same quantum number). A symmetric (un-normalized) wave function can be formed from the above merely by using only $+$ signs in the sum formed from the determinant.

When spin is taken into account (see Sections 11.8 and 11.9) *it is possible for two electrons to share the same spatial quantum number and still possess an exchange-antisymmetric wave function.* Thus, the principle effect of spin is to double the "occupation" of the levels. More accurately, when spin is included, it is possible for as many as $2n$ electrons to *share* n sets of spatial quantum numbers (distinct spatial functions).

PROBLEMS

Problem 9.1. Two spinless, noninteracting particles whose masses are m and $(1.0001)\,m$ respectively are placed in a one-dimensional box of length L. The first is in the state for which $n = 1$ and the second in the state for which $n = 2$. Derive formulas for the total system energy, and the complete system wave function (normalized and time-dependent). Compare your derivation step by step with the corresponding one for the case where two *identical* particles *share* the states for which $n = 1$ and $n = 2$. Plot $\psi^* \psi$ in configuration space and compare with Figure 9.2. Discuss.

Problem 9.2. Sketch the principal features of the probability density functions, $\psi_s^* \psi_s$ and $\psi_a^* \psi_a$, for two identical particles sharing the states $n = 1$ and $k = 3$. See Figure 9.2.

Problem 9.3. Consider the system in the states sketched in Figures 9.2 and 9.3. Let $L = 10^{-8}$ cm, $D = 10^{-10}$ cm, $V_0 = 1.6 \times 10^{-10}$ erg, and $m = 9.1 \times 10^{-28}$ gm. Calculate the energy shift of the symmetric system from the zero-order energy level.

Problem 9.4. Consider the three-dimensional, rectangular box of Figures 8.1 and 8.2, without the small well. Let $b = 1 \times 10^{-8}$ cm and $c = 3 \times 10^{-8}$ cm. Two identical, spinless, weakly interacting particles of electronic mass are enclosed inside the box. In zero order, what is the wave function and the characteristic energy of the lowest state of the system for (a) symmetric particles, and (b) antisymmetric particles?

Problem 9.5. Consider two one-dimensional boxes, each of length $L = 10^{-8}$ cm and each containing three identical, noninteracting, spinless particles of electronic mass. Let one box contain symmetric particles and the other antisymmetric particles.

(a) What is the lowest possible total system energy for each type of particle?

(b) What additional energy would be needed to raise each system to the next highest value of system energy?

(c) Write out in full the wave functions, including time, representing each of the two types of system when they have the lowest possible system energy, and also when their system energy is at the next highest value, as in (a) and (b).

(d) For the symmetric system only, sketch, in three-dimensional perspective, the probability density as a function of x_1, x_2, and x_3, representing these configuration-space variables by the three physical dimensions x, y, and z of the sketch. Use shading to indicate the magnitude of the probability density. Also, draw a cross section of the three-dimensional sketch consisting of the plane $x_1 = 10^{-8}/2$, and sketch, in approximate contours, some lines of constant probability density.

Problem 9.6. Consider a rectangular box that is cubical in form and is very nearly 1 cm on each edge. Imagine that 10^9 spinless, noninteracting particles of electronic mass are introduced into the box, and that the system is allowed to seek, and attain, its lowest possible value of total system energy.

(a) What is the value of the lowest possible system energy if the particles are symmetric?

(b) What is the value of the lowest possible system energy if the particles are antisymmetric?

Discussion of Problem 9.6b: Since the system consists of m particles ($m = 10^9$), the lowest energy state will occur when the m particles share the m lowest states. These m lowest energy states may be identified in the following manner: The energy of any state with quantum numbers n_x, n_y, and n_z, is

$$W = (\hbar^2 \pi^2 / 2\, ma^2)(n_x^2 + n_y^2 + n_z^2)$$

In Figure 9.7a we plot a point for each possible state of the system, using the x, y, and z axes to plot the integral values of the quantum numbers n_x, n_y, and n_z, respectively. We next define

$$N^2 = n_x^2 + n_y^2 + n_z^2$$

so that

$$W(N) = (\hbar^2 \pi^2 / 2\, ma^2)\, N^2$$

which shows that energy of each state, identified by one point, is proportional to the square of the radial distance of the point from the origin of coordinates in Figure 9.7a.

We now let N become very large compared to 1 and, in Figure 9.7b, draw one octant of a sphere of radius $N_{\max}$, inside of which are 10^9 points, each representing one possible state. (The n's can only be positive, so that we use only one octant of the sphere.) Each point on (or very near) the spherical surface has (nearly) the same energy, W_{max}, although each point has a different set of quantum numbers. W_{max} is called the top of the "Fermi sea of states." The total energy of the system of the m spinless, antisymmetric particles is just the sum of the energy values of the characteristic energies of the m states

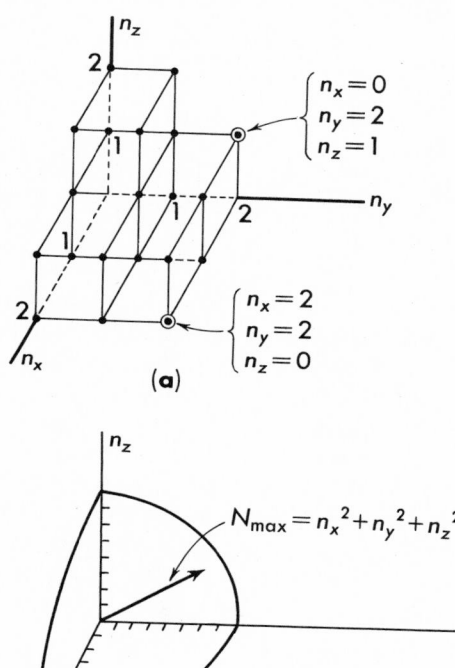

(a)

$N_{max} = n_x{}^2 + n_y{}^2 + n_z{}^2$

$\text{Volume} = \frac{1}{8} \cdot \frac{4}{3} \pi N_{max}^3$

(b)

Fig. 9.7. The calculation of the number of states in a system consisting of m antisymmetric (spinless) particles.

inside the "Fermi surface." To calculate the energy, we must first find N_{max}:

$m = $ total number of particles

$= $ total number of one-particle states shared

$= $ total number of dots inside surface bounded by N_{max}

$= (1/8)(4/3) \, \pi \, N_{max}^3$

The total system energy is then calculated from,

$$W_{total} = \int_{N=1}^{N=N_{max}} W(N)\,(1/8)\,4\,\pi\,N^2\,dN$$

$\underbrace{W(N)}$ energy of state with quantum number N. $\underbrace{(1/8)\,4\,\pi\,N^2\,dN}$ the fraction of all states which have total quantum number between N and $N + dN$.

[It is also possible to calculate the average energy per state, obtaining $\overline{W} = (3/5)\,W_{max}$.]

Problem 9.7. Two identical spinless, noninteracting particles, with $m = 0.9 \times 10^{-27}$ gm, are in a two-dimensional infinite-wall box whose sides are of length a (along the x-axis) and b (along the y-axis). $a = 10^{-8}$ cm and $b = 2 \times 10^{-8}$ cm.

(a) Write a formula for the *single-particle* eigenfunctions.
(b) If the two particles are symmetric to interchange, what is the energy of the lowest state and what is the normalized, *two-particle* wave function, ψ_s, belonging to this state?
(c) If the two particles are antisymmetric to interchange, what is the energy of the lowest state, and what is the normalized, *two-particle* wave function, ψ_a, belonging to this state?

Problem 9.8. Describe atomic structure qualitatively if electrons were spinless particles with exchange-symmetric wave functions.

Problem 9.9. Particles in nearly isolated potential wells.
A spinless particle of mass 10^{-27} gm occupies the one-dimensional well shown in Figure 9.8.

(a) Show from general considerations that the two states whose eigenfunctions are sketched in the figure are the two lowest energy states, and that they both have an energy slightly less than 55×10^{-12} erg. Show that ψ_2 must be slightly higher in energy than ψ_1.
(b) If the single particle is in a state which is an equal superposition of ψ_1 and ψ_2, what must the particle be doing? Discuss in classical terms.

A second, identical, spinless particle is now added to the potential well. The two particles have a repulsive force with a resulting potential energy of interaction

$$H' = 2 \times 10^{-22}/\,|\,x_1 - x_2\,|\ \text{erg}$$

where x is in cm.

(c) If the two particles are exchange-antisymmetric, *estimate* the correction ΔW to the zero-order energy level, $W_1^0 + W_2^0$, of the lowest state caused by the interaction H'. Describe the

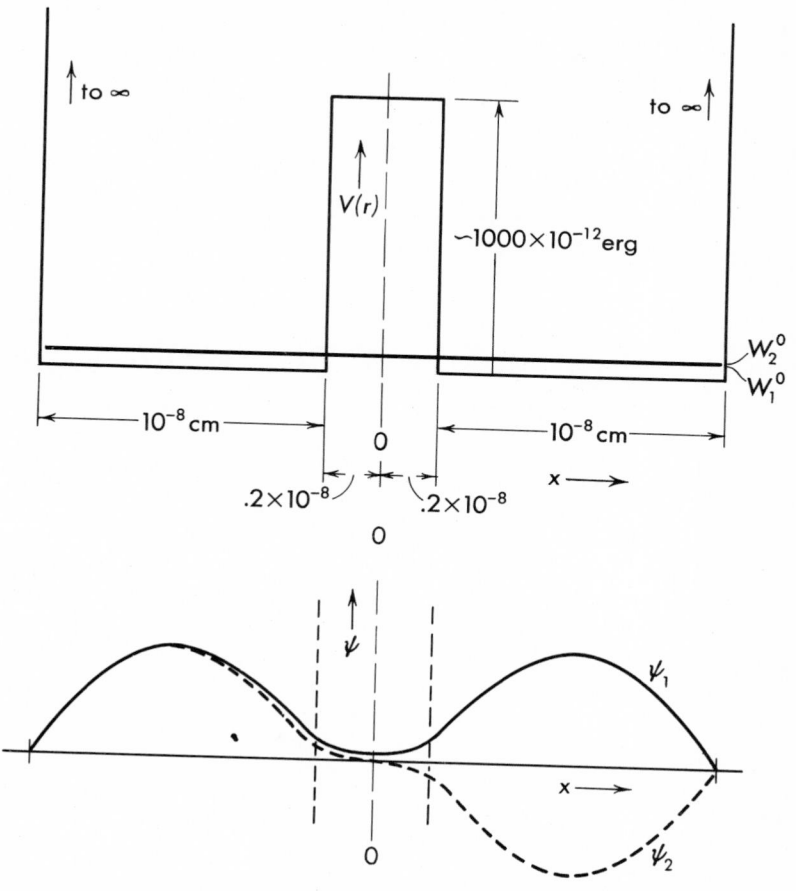

Fig. 9.8. Two identical particles sharing two nearly isolated potential wells.

possible results of observing these particles with particle detectors.

(d) If the two particles are exchange-symmetric, make a *rough* estimate of the correction, ΔW, to the zero-order system energy, $2W_1^0$, of the lowest state caused by H'.

(e) Discuss the following hypothetical situation: There are only two electrons in the universe, but both share a potential well

such as that in Figure 9.8, where the barrier is 10^{10} cm wide
and 10^{10} erg high. Is it possible for them to have a system
wave function which is antisymmetric to interchange?

(f) Suppose that the coordinates of an electron on the earth
were interchanged with those of an electron on the sun.
Would the wave function representing the present state of
the universe change sign?

TIME-DEPENDENT
PERTURBATION THEORY

Up to now, all the quantitative calculations have been concerned with the Hamiltonian functions which are independent of time—and therefore with Hamiltonian operators, H, which are independent of time. In a real sense, however, all that we have done so far is a mathematical exercise, because when the Hamiltonian is time-independent, *nothing observable ever happens*.

Consider first a system in the pure vibration of a stationary state. Its probability density, $\Psi^*\Psi$, is constant in time. The expectation value of the system energy is constant. If it is a three-dimensional system, such as the hydrogen atom in the $l = 1$ state, the expectation value of the magnitude of its angular momentum is constant and, along any specified axis, the component of its angular momentum is a constant—depending upon which of the m-quantum numbers appears in its eigenfunction. Such a state of affairs will go on forever unless the system is interfered with in some way. In the earlier chapters we performed imaginary experiments which consisted of *interfering with the system*, usually in some rather violent manner. For example, we imagined that, to locate the particle, we inserted a series of slits into the space occupied by the system and turned on some accelerating potential that pulled the particle through the nearest slit (thus locating it). Then, after much magnification, we observed a macroscopic pulse of current which implied that the amplifier in question received the particle at its input. This process can scarcely be described by a time-independent system energy (Hamiltonian) with its corresponding time-independent operator. Clearly, the results of laboratory experiments cannot be predicted unless the system energy is, in some manner, time-dependent.

Consider next a system in an arbitrary superposition of its pure vibrations, that is, eigenstates. We can *calculate*, as in Section 5.1, that the probability density is now changing with time, but to observe where the particle *is* requires, once again, interference with the system, so that this changing probability does not lead to any observable consequences. We saw in Chapter 5 that for "mixed" states, including wave packets, the amplitude of each pure vibration remained constant with time. The systematic changes in $\Psi^*\Psi$ are due merely to the "beating together" of the "proper" or pure resonant frequencies, each of constant amplitude, which characterize the system. The expectation value of the energy is still constant with time, although it is now the weighted sum of the characteristic energies of the pure vibrations. The weighting factor is merely $a_j^* a_j$—which measures the intensity of the jth proper vibration. Until we interfere with the system, we will never be able to find out what the intensities of the different possible vibrations actually are.

The expectation-value formula of Postulate V provides the link between theory and observation, but when it is used with stationary-state wave functions and time-independent operators its predictions cannot be verified. There is no way to observe a completely isolated atomic system.

Thus, when the Hamiltonian is time-independent, nothing observable ever happens.

Clearly, then, the practical uses of quantum mechanics must be intimately associated with time-dependent Hamiltonian operators, and also with much larger systems—such as one consisting of N atoms, an optical grating, and a photographic plate—in some definite geometrical arrangement. At $t = 0$ the atoms are excited by a pulse of electrons, and the photographic plate is blank. At some later time, the atoms are in their ground states, and the photographic plate has dark lines on it in certain measurable places and with certain measurable intensities. This realistic, complete system is certainly not in any stationary state, or in a superposition of stationary states.

It may come as something of a shock to discover, after nine chapters, that we have yet to get down to the business of predicting experiments in a realistic, logically consistent way. Nonetheless, only with a thorough grasp of the formal mathematics of the stationary states can we deal with time-varying Hamiltonians. As we shall see, only with the aid of the familiar ortho-normal eigenfunctions can the time-dependent wave equation be made tractable.

This textbook seeks primarily to teach what quantum mechanics *is*, and not to explore the intriguing (and very important) byways of philosophical interpretation. We have diverged from this principle here only to highlight the great importance of time-dependent calculations. Even though it comes late in the textbook it is, in a sense, the very heart of the theory. We shall be content to limit time-dependent calculations to only one or two of the theory's

most simple applications, since these will suffice to illuminate the important concepts.

10.1.　Time-dependent perturbation theory

　　Basically, we are looking for solutions, $\Psi(x, y, z, t)$, of the wave equation
of Postulate II,

$$H\Psi = -(\hbar/i)(\partial/\partial t)\,\Psi \qquad\qquad [10\text{--}1$$

which, at all times, are well behaved and possess an integrable square, as required by Postulates III and IV. Unfortunately, for even a single particle, when
H is a function of t the dependence of Ψ upon the four variables x, y, z, and t
usually makes the direct solution of the equation very difficult.[1] We fall back,
therefore, upon some set of known stationary-state eigenfunctions which, because of their ortho-normality, provide a tractable means of describing the
true Ψ's of [10–1]. In an artificial manner, therefore, we split the true Hamiltonian into two parts.

$$H = H^0(x, y, z, p_x, p_y, p_z) + H'(x, y, z, p_x, p_y, p_z, t) \qquad [10\text{--}2$$

where H^0 is time independent and has eigenfunctions Ψ_n^0, which are either
known or can be found. These eigenfunction are found by the same method
that we have used on many occasions. The equation to be solved is:

$$H^0\Psi = -(\hbar/i)(\partial/\partial t)\,\Psi \qquad\qquad [10\text{--}3$$

We set $\Psi = \psi(x, y, z)\,e^{-i(W/\hbar)t}$, and separate [10–3] into two equations. The
space-dependent equation is

$$H^0\psi = W\psi$$

which has, of course, a solution for every value of W, the separation constant.
It possesses *well-behaved* solutions of *integrable square*, ψ_n^0, only when W has
certain valies, W_n^0. Thus, each of the set of eigenfunctions obeys an equation.

$$H^0\,\psi_n^0 = W_n^0\,\psi_n^0$$

or

$$H^0\Psi_n^0 = -(\hbar/i)\,\partial\Psi_n^0/\partial t = W_n^0\Psi_n^0 \qquad\qquad [10\text{--}3a$$

Each ψ_n^0 is an eigenfunction of the operator H^0, corresponding to the eigenvalue W_n^0. The most general well-behaved solution to [10–3] is a linear combination of the complete set of Ψ_n^0's,

$$\Psi^0 = \sum_n a_n \Psi_n^0$$

---

[1] Since now [10–1] cannot, in general, be "separated" into two equations, one space-
dependent, and the other time-dependent.

where

$$\Psi_n^0 = \psi_n^0 \, e^{-i\frac{W_n}{\hbar}t} \quad \text{and} \quad \sum_n a_n^* a_n = 1 \tag{10–4}$$

From the foregoing, which is a brief review of time-independent theory, we turn to the problem of time dependence. The part of the true Hamiltonian H (which makes the wave equation intractable) has all been lumped into H'. H' can depend upon position, momentum, and time. For example, an electromagnetic wave, passing through an atom, will not have the same influence at all points at a given instant since it is varying in both time and space. Also, electrons with velocity (momentum) will be affected by the magnetic field as well as by the electric field, but the electric field is the only one experienced by electrons momentarily at rest. Thus, H' can depend upon the momentum operators p_x, p_y, and p_z, as well as position and time.

Writing H in two parts, as in [10–2], the true wave equation [10–1], becomes

$$(H^0 + H')\,\Psi = -\,(\hbar/i)(\partial/\partial t)\,\Psi \tag{10–5}$$

At all times, Ψ must meet the requirements of the basic postulates. Let us suppose, as in Section 5.1, that at $t = t_0$, Ψ has some given form, $\Psi(x, t_0)$. Our objective is to find Ψ at some later time, where Ψ is at all times governed by [10–5]. $\Psi(x, t_0)$ provides the initial conditions without which specific solutions to a partial differential equation are impossible. For example, each specific solution of a second-order *ordinary* differential equation is determined by two numbers at $t = t_0$, the value of the variable and the value of slope. We shall see shortly, that if a partial differential equation of the type [10–5] is given a *whole function*, $\Psi(x, t_0)$, for its initial conditions, then at all later (or earlier) times, the equation determines a unique function, $\Psi(x, t)$. We have already seen, in Section 5.1, a simple example of this type of calculation. There we had a Hamiltonian operator H which was independent of t. This form of H simplified the computations, but the basic process we have just been discussing occurred. The argument in Section 5.1 can be summarized as follows: We were given an initial function $\Psi(x, t_0)$ [5–8], which we then synthesized by the series of orthogonal functions, $\sum_n a_n(t_0)\,\Psi_n^0 \,(x, t_0)$ [5–9]. We then found, by substitution into the wave equation

$$H\Psi = -\,(\hbar/i)(\partial/\partial t)\,\Psi \tag{5–1}$$

that

$$\Psi(x, t) = \sum_n a_n(t_0)\,\Psi_n^0 \,(x, t) \tag{5–15}$$

is a solution to the wave equation at *any* time t and reduces, of course, when $t = t_0$, to the initial function. The problem at hand differs from the one of Section 5.1 only in the fact that H is now time-dependent. The time dependence of H will cause differences in the method of analysis of the problem, but the basic principles employed will be the same. In particular, we will use, once

again, a series of orthogonal functions to synthesize both the initial wave
function $\Psi(x, t_0)$ and also $\Psi(x, t)$. For simplicity we continue to use a one-
dimensional system, and in Figure 10.1a we draw, schematically, the wave
function $\Psi(x, t_0)$, plotted against x. (We assume here that $\Psi(x, t_0)$ is real, so

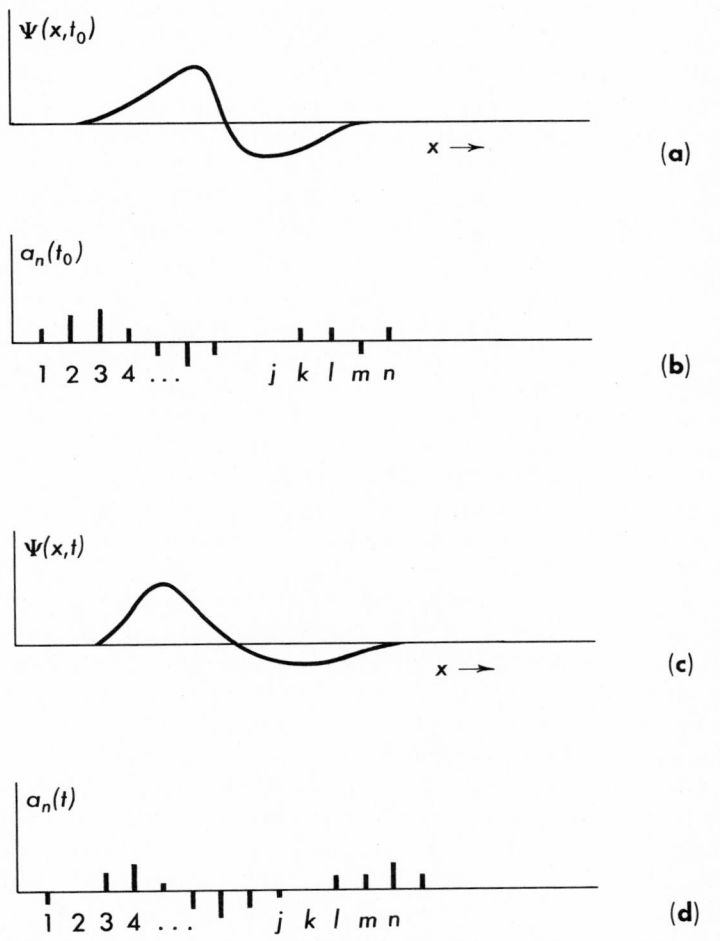

Fig. 10.1. The wave function of a system at two different times, $t = t_0$ and
$t = t$, and the amplitude spectra of the eigenfunctions needed to synthesize
each of the two different functions of x.

that it can be plotted in two dimensions.) As we have seen in Section 5.1, as
long as $\Psi(x, t_0)$ is a bounded function, we have almost complete freedom in
assuming any shape for it, such as that in Figure 10.1. We can synthesize any
reasonable shape from the right combination of the complete set of orthogonal

eigenfunctions, whose domain in space covers the entire region where the function to be synthesized is non-zero. Thus, we set

$$\Psi(x, t_0) = \sum_n a_n(t_0) \Psi_n^0(x, t_0)$$

[10-6

where the $a_n(t_0)$'s are given by

$$a_n(t_0) = \int \Psi_n^{0*}(x, t_0) \Psi(x, t_0) \, dx$$

[10-7

and where, since $\Psi(x, t_0)$ is normalized,

$$\sum_n a_n(t_0)^* a_n(t_0) = 1$$

[10-8

In schematic form, Figure 10.1b gives the "spectrum" of $\Psi(x, t_0)$ in terms of the amplitudes of its components. Each amplitude is calculated by [10-7].

At a different time, t, the solution to [10-5] will, in general, have a different form, such as in Figure 10.1c. This too can be synthesized from the basic Ψ_n^0's. Since it has a different shape it will, in general, have different amplitudes, $a_n(t)$, of the basic Ψ_n^0's, as sketched in Figure 10.1d. We see that, by merely specifying the a_n's at any time, we can describe the general solution $\Psi(x, t)$. The theory is concerned, therefore, with the calculation of the $a_n(t)$'s in the general expansion,

$$\Psi(x, t) = \sum_n a_n(t) \Psi_n^0(x, t)$$

[10-9

The step we have just taken is very important. What we have done is this: we have given up any effort to handle $\Psi(x, t)$ directly in terms of its spatial variable x. *From here on, we shall describe the wave function $\Psi(x, t)$ in terms of the amplitudes of the components of the orthogonal series expansion which are needed to synthesize it.* Since H is time dependent the spatial form of Ψ is changing from moment to moment, and the amplitudes of the components that are needed to synthesize Ψ must *also* be changing from moment to moment. For this reason, we must regard the a_n's functions of time, as is indicated in [10-9] and illustrated in Figure 10.1. The method of describing a function by means of the *time* variation of its components may seem indirect and perhaps unnecessarily complicated, but it is really simple compared to trying to work *directly* with the unknown function of space and time. A partial differential equation, even more than an ordinary differential equation, can look deceptively simple and yet be extremely difficult to solve. The method of the "variation of constants" which we use here is very powerful and general.

Substituting the series [10-9] for Ψ in the complete wave equation [10-5], we have,[2]

$$\sum_n a_n(t) H^0 \Psi_n^0 + \sum_n a_n(t) H' \Psi_n^0 = -\frac{\hbar}{i} \sum_n \left[\frac{d}{dt} a_n(t) \right] \Psi_n^0 - \frac{\hbar}{i} \sum_n a_n(t) \frac{\partial \Psi_n^0}{\partial t}$$

[10-10

---

[2] Note: $H'(t)$ cannot involve the operator $\partial/\partial t$, as this operator is used in representing the *total* energy.

The sum of terms on the extreme left equals, term by term, the sum of terms on the extreme right, so that these two parts of [10–10] cancel. Multiplying the rest of [10–10] by Ψ_m^{0*}, integrating with respect to the spatial coordinates $d\tau$, and using the orthogonality of the Ψ_m^0's,

$$\frac{d}{dt} a_m(t) = -\frac{i}{\hbar} \sum_{n=1}^{\infty} a_n(t) \int \Psi_m^{0*} H' \Psi_n^0 \, d\tau \qquad [10\text{--}11$$

where $m = 1, 2, 3, 4, \cdots$.

This is the basic law of time-dependent perturbation theory. It gives the rate of change of the *m*th component of the expansion [10–9], which describes the true, time-varying wave function of the system. The rate of change of the amplitude a_m depends upon the magnitude of the other amplitudes and also upon a set of matrix elements, $\int \Psi_m^{0*} H' \Psi_n^0 \, d\tau$, which "connect," by means of H', the pure state Ψ_m^0 with each of the other pure states Ψ_n^0.[3]

We must visualize a vibrating system that has many modes or pure vibrations excited simultaneously. The time-dependent operator H' causes the amplitude of each of the pure vibrations to change in some definite manner. Some will increase with time and others must decrease—since at *all* times $\sum_n a_n^* a_n = 1$, and any amplitude can increase only at the expense of some, or all, of the others.

The fundamental equation [10–11] looks deceptively simple. It stands for a whole set of equations (in general, an infinite set) *each* of which has a large number of terms (in general, an infinite number). We write out these equations (in part) to provide a better appreciation of their nature.

$$-\frac{\hbar}{i}\frac{da_1}{dt} = a_1 \int \Psi_1^{0*} H' \Psi_1^0 d\tau + a_2 \int \Psi_1^{0*} H' \Psi_2^0 d\tau + \cdots + a_k \int \Psi_1^{0*} H' \Psi_k^0 d\tau + \cdots$$

$$-\frac{\hbar}{i}\frac{da_2}{dt} = a_1 \int \Psi_2^{0*} H' \Psi_1^0 d\tau + a_2 \int \Psi_2^{0*} H' \Psi_2^0 d\tau + \cdots + a_k \int \Psi_2^{0*} H' \Psi_k^0 d\tau + \cdots$$

$$-\frac{\hbar}{i}\frac{da_k}{dt} = a_1 \int \Psi_k^{0*} H' \Psi_1^0 d\tau + a_2 \int \Psi_k^{0*} H' \Psi_2^0 d\tau + \cdots + a_k \int \Psi_k^{0*} H' \Psi_k^0 d\tau + \cdots$$

$$[10\text{--}12$$

---

[3] If, in addition to H^0, H contains a time-independent term H'(space) as well as a time-dependent term H'(space, time), one first applies time-independent perturbation theory to get the corrected wave functions, and then uses these wave functions in the time-dependent theory. This process is illustrated below in Sec. 10.5.

Since the number of basic eigenfunctions is, in general, infinite, the set of equations [10–12] is infinite in size and has an infinite number of unknowns, $a_1, a_2, a_3, \cdots$. The equations are all first-order, ordinary differential equations, and we assume, or are given, the value of each of the a_j's at $t = t_0$. Since all of the Ψ_j^0's are known and H' is given, there is enough information to determine all of the a_j's at any time t. Note that if $H'(t) = 0$, all of the a_j's are constants.[4]

Up to this point there has been no approximation, and [10–12] *is fully equivalent to the original wave equation* [10–1] or [10–5]. H^0 does not appear explicitly in [10–12], but it is there nonetheless, due to the selection of the basic Ψ_j^0's as the set of functions used to synthesize the true wave function. The choice of the particular set of Ψ_j^0's as the basic functions used in the expansion [10–9] is often refered to as "the choice of representation."

So formidable a set of equations as [10–12] cannot, in general, be easily solved without some simplifying conditions and approximations. We shall assume that the effect of H' on the system is small compared to that of H^0, that is, we shall now regard H' as a perturbation. We than develop a new form of perturbation theory appropriate to the time-dependent nature of the perturbing term.

As in Chapter 7, we imagine that the intensity of the perturbation H' can be controlled by multiplying it by a parameter λ. We therefore set

$$H = H^0 + \lambda H' \qquad\qquad [10\text{–}13$$

and allow λ to vary from 0 to 1.[5] As this occurs, we expect each of the a's to vary, but not necessarily in a purely linear manner, with λ. Thus, we assume that

$$a_m = a_m^0 + \lambda a_m' + \lambda^2 a_m'' + \cdots \qquad\qquad [10\text{–}14$$

This is the same type of variation as that of ψ in Figure 7.2. We are interested in the *linear* part of this variation and, for a good first-order approximation, we require, as in Figure 7.2, that even when $\lambda = 1$ the square term $\lambda^2 a_m'$ is small compared to the linear term $\lambda a_m'$.

We substitute [10–14] for the a_m, and $\lambda H'$ for H' into [10–12]. The kth equation of the set becomes

$$-\frac{\hbar}{i}\frac{d}{dt}\left(a_k^0 + \lambda a_k' + \lambda^2 a_k'' \right) = (a_1^0 + \lambda a_1' + \lambda^2 a_1'')$$

$$\int \Psi_k^{0*} \lambda H' \Psi_1^0 \, d\tau + \cdots$$

$$+ (a_k^0 + \lambda a_k' + \lambda^2 a_k'')$$

$$\int \Psi_k^{0*} \lambda H' \Psi_k^0 \, d\tau + \cdots \qquad\qquad [10\text{–}12a$$

---

[4] It is a common practice to denote the set of quantities, $a_1\, a_2\, a_3, \ldots$ etc., by the expression "the a_j's." Equivalent expressions are "the a_k's" or "the a_m's". The letter subscript is merely a "running index" and is of no significance in itself. Similarly the expression, "the Ψ_j^0's" is equivalent to "the Ψ_k^0's", etc.

[5] As in Chapter 7, λ is a mathematical device whose purpose is to make easier the "sorting out" of the different orders of approximation.

We equate separately each power of λ. For zero order,

$$(d/dt)\, a_1^0 = 0;\quad (d/dt)\, a_2^0 = 0;\quad \cdots \quad ;\quad (d/dt)\, a_k^0 = 0;\quad \cdots \qquad [10\text{--}15$$

That is, if the time-dependent part of the Hamiltonian is zero, then each a_m (which determines the amplitude of the component Ψ_m^0 of the complete wave function Ψ), if determined at one time, is unchanged for any other time. This same result, for the time-independent Hamiltonian, was obtained in Chapter 7.

Equating all terms of λ^1, we have the set of equations

$$-\frac{\hbar}{i}\frac{da_1'}{dt} = a_1^0 \int \Psi_1^{0*} H' \Psi_1^0 d\tau + a_2^0 \int \Psi_1^{0*} H' \Psi_2^0 d\tau + \cdots + a_k^0 \int \Psi_1^{0*} H' \Psi_k^0 d\tau + \cdots$$

$$-\frac{\hbar}{i}\frac{da_2'}{dt} = a_1^0 \int \Psi_2^{0*} H' \Psi_1^0 d\tau + a_2^0 \int \Psi_2^{0*} H' \Psi_2^0 d\tau + \cdots + a_k^0 \int \Psi_2^{0*} H' \Psi_k^0 d\tau + \cdots$$

$$\cdot \qquad\qquad \cdot \qquad\qquad \cdot \qquad\qquad \cdot$$
$$\cdot \qquad\qquad \cdot \qquad\qquad \cdot \qquad\qquad \cdot$$
$$\cdot \qquad\qquad \cdot \qquad\qquad \cdot \qquad\qquad \cdot$$

$$-\frac{\hbar}{i}\frac{da_k'}{dt} = a_1^0 \int \Psi_k^{0*} H' \Psi_1^0 d\tau + a_2^0 \int \Psi_k^{0*} H' \Psi_2^0 d\tau + \cdots + a_k^0 \int \Psi_k^{0*} H' \Psi_k^0 d\tau + \cdots$$

$$\cdot \qquad\qquad \cdot \qquad\qquad \cdot \qquad\qquad \cdot$$
$$\cdot \qquad\qquad \cdot \qquad\qquad \cdot \qquad\qquad \cdot$$
$$\cdot \qquad\qquad \cdot \qquad\qquad \cdot \qquad\qquad \cdot$$

$$\qquad\qquad\qquad\qquad\qquad\qquad\qquad\qquad\qquad\qquad [10\text{--}16$$

This set of *approximate* equations differs from the exact set [10–12] by the presence, on the right, of the constant zero-order coefficients a_m^0 and by the presence, on the left, of the *corrections*, a_m', to the zero-order coefficients a_m^0. The a_m^0's are merely the initial conditions. They measure the intensity of vibration of all of the modes of the unperturbed system that are needed to form the actual wave function at $t = t_0$. The equations [10–16] give the growth or decline of the amplitude of vibration of each of the natural modes of the system. Since H' is assumed to be small, the corrections to the amplitudes, a_m', are also small. Thus, although all the vibrations can either grow or decrease as time proceeds, the changes from their initial values will not be very large.

One speaks of a typical mode of vibration, or "proper" vibration (such as that represented by Ψ_1^0, as being "connected," via H', to each of the other modes. The exact equation [10–12] shows that, as time proceeds, the state Ψ_k^0 "feeds amplitude" into the state Ψ_1^0 at a rate given by $a_k \int \Psi_1^{0*} H' \Psi_k^0 d\tau$, and that the reverse process goes on at a rate given by $a_1 \int \Psi_k^{0*} H' \Psi_1^0 d\tau$. This is a completely continuous process. *The perturbation H' acts constantly to reshuffle the degree of excitation of the modes. If it is suddenly terminated the* system remains, thereafter, with exactly constant amplitudes for each proper vibration. In the first-order equations [10–16], however, we permit the re-shuffling process to proceed only a relatively small amount from the initial set of amplitudes. (See the discussion following [10–17], below.)

10.2. Constant perturbation

The set of first-order differential equations [10–16] takes on a particularly simple form for the case where $a_k^0 = 1$ and all the other a_m^0's are zero—that is, where the initial state of the system is the pure state Ψ_k^0. Only *one* column of terms, the kth column, survives. Furthermore, we will assume for the first example that H' is independent of time.[6] However, H' must depend upon space, since otherwise all of the off-diagonal matrix elements would be zero. Thus, we let $H' = f(x)$. We ask what the amplitudes will be at some later time, t_1. As before, we symbolize $\int \psi_m^{0*} H' \psi_k^0 \, d\tau$ by H'_{mk}, the "matrix element" of the operator H' with respect to the two eigenfunctions ψ_m^0 and ψ_k^0. The integrand involves space, and perhaps the momentum operators, but not time.

For these conditions, since only the kth column in [10–16] survives, and since $\Psi_m^0 = \psi_m^0 \, e^{-i\frac{W_m}{\hbar}t}$, the set of equations becomes

$$- (\hbar/i)(d/dt) \, a_1' = H'_{1k} \, e^{i\omega_{1k}t}$$

$$- (\hbar/i)(d/dt) \, a_2' = H'_{2k} \, e^{i\omega_{2k}t}$$

$$a_k' = 0$$

$$- (\hbar/i)(d/dt) \, a_m' = H'_{mk} \, e^{i\omega_{mk}t} \qquad [10\text{--}17$$

where $\omega_{mk} = (W_m^0 - W_k^0)/\hbar$; $H'_{mk} = \int \psi_m^{0*} H' \psi_k^0 \, d\tau = \int \psi_m^{0*} f(x) \psi_k^0 \, d\tau$. a_k' must be zero since, in first-order, our basic assumption is that a_k not only equals unity at $t = 0$, but also does not deviate appreciably from unity at later times.

Each of the above equations has the solution, when each $a_m' = 0$ at $t = 0$,

$$a_m'(t_1) = - \frac{H'_{mk}}{\hbar} \frac{e^{i\omega_{mk}t_1} - 1}{\omega_{mk}} \qquad \begin{matrix} m = 1, 2, 3, \cdots \\ m \neq k \end{matrix} \qquad [10\text{--}18$$

Thus, after time t_1 has elapsed, the amplitudes of all of the states (which were originally zero) are now, in general, not zero. We assume that a_k still has the value of unity at $t = t_1$. The a_m' (although necessarily small compared to one) are now the actual amplitudes of the states. (Normalization of the new wave function is preserved, to first-order, by the assumption: $|a_k^0(t_1)| = 1$.)

---

[6] H' is time-dependent in the sense that it may be regarded as being "turned on" at $t = 0$, and continuing, at constant value, as long as necessary. It is therefore a step function in time.

In the calculation of the expectation values, the term $(a'_m)^*(a'_m)$ will appear. It measures the probability of finding the system in the state with energy W^0_m or, alternatively, it measures the probability of occurrence of the value W^0_m in computing the average energy of the system (see Section 5.2). From [10–18] we calculate[7]

$$(a'_m)^*(a'_m) = \frac{(H'_{mk})^*(H_{mk}) \sin^2 (\frac{1}{2} \omega_{mk} t_1)}{\hbar^2 (\omega_{mk}/2)^2}, \qquad m \neq k$$

[10–19

This equation tells how the intensities of the proper vibrations change with time—for the special case where only one level, the kth, was initially excited and where the spatial perturbation H' is constant from $t = 0$ to $t = t_1$. In Figure 10.2 a sequence of diagrams shows how the intensity of each of the proper vibrations would appear if the system were examined at $t = t_1$, $t = 2t_1$ and $t = 3t_1$. In Figure 10.2a we show, schematically, a sequence of equally spaced system energy levels. (In most systems, the energy levels are not equally spaced but, over a small range of energy, equal spacing often happens to be a good approximation. In any case, the equal spacing has no basic effect on the principles involved in the discussion.) At $t = 0$, by hypothesis, only one level, the kth, is occupied—so that $a^*_k a_k = 1$. During the subsequent intervals, we know that $a^*_k a_k$ must actually decrease slightly, but in the first-order calculation H' has so small an influence that the fractional change in $a^*_k a_k$ is *assumed to be zero*.

In Figure 10.2b we see that, after the perturbation has been effective for t_1 seconds, a broad range of energy levels[8] have developed a finite vibration amplitude, although the levels with energy near W^0_k are the most strongly affected and there are definite nulls at those energy levels for which

$$(W^0_m - W^0_k) t_1/\hbar = 2\pi$$

[10–20

The intensity curve is controlled by the factor

$$\frac{\sin^2 (\omega_{mk}/2) t}{(\omega_{mk}/2)^2}$$

[10–21a

which is plotted in Figure 10.2. The peak of this function has the magnitude t^2, since

$$\lim_{y \to 0} \left(\frac{\sin^2 yt}{y^2} \right) = t^2$$

[10–21b

At a later time $2t_1$, as in Figure 10.2c, the curve giving the distribution of intensity of excitation of vibration is, because of [10–20], twice as narrow, and

---

[7] Using the identities $(1 - e^{ix})^* (1 - e^{ix}) = 2 - e^{ix} - e^{-ix}$, $\sin x = (1/2) (e^{ix} - e^{-ix})$, and $\sin^2 x = (1/4) (2 - e^{2ix} - e^{-2ix})$, we have $(1 - e^{ix})^* (1 - e^{ix}) = 4 \sin^2 \frac{x}{2}$.

[8] The continuous curves of Figure 10.2 will give the actual degree of excitation of the levels only if H'_{mk} is the same for each level, W^0_m.

because of [10–21b] four times as high. At a later time $3t_1$, the curve is three times narrower and nine times higher than the same curve at $t = t_1$. The area under the curve—which measures the total excitation in levels other than the kth—is thus increasing in proportion to t. The excitation "piles up" in those

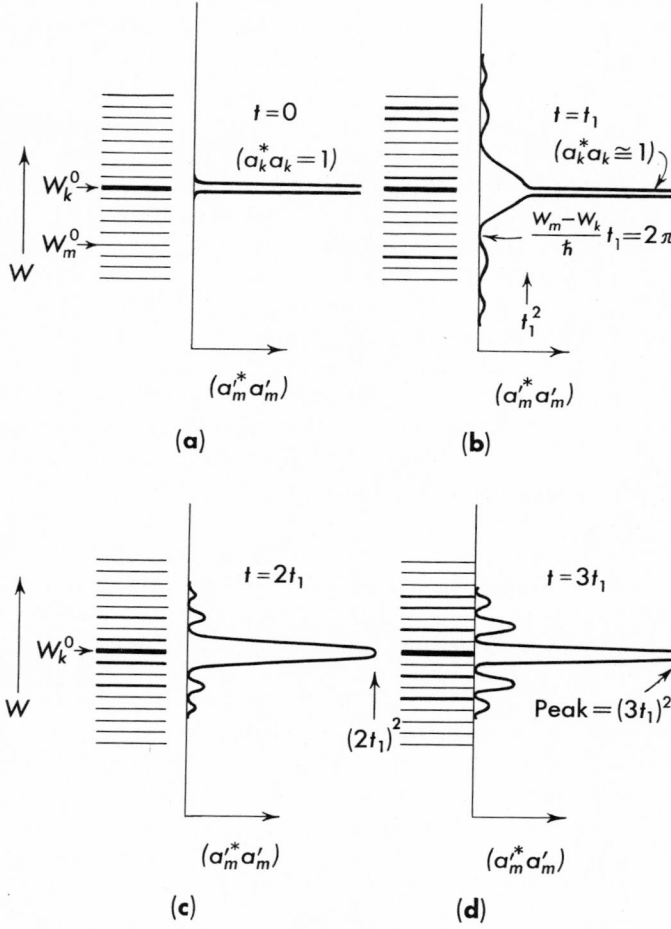

Fig. 10.2. The time variation of the excitation of the proper vibrations (eigenfunctions) caused by the constant perturbation, starting at $t = 0$. The density of the horizontal lines indicates the degree of excitation of the level or state.

levels nearest W_k^0, the effect being more pronounced the longer the perturbation is allowed to continue.

The detailed picture of the excitation process is complicated, except for those levels very near to W_k^0, which show a steady growth of excitation with t^2.

At greater distances from W_k^0 the degree of excitation of the levels increases, decreases, increases, etc., with time, in a relatively complicated manner. Those levels far from W_k^0 finally end up with relatively small excitation compared to those very near W_k^0, which grow steadily.

Unless the perturbation "connects" the mth state to the kth—that is, unless $H'_{mk} \neq 0$—there will, of course, be no excitation of the mth level at *any* time. This selectivity of coupling is dependent upon both H' itself and on the two eigenfunctions that are involved.

H'_{mk} is the source of the "selection rules" of atomic and nuclear spectra. If the perturbation H' is strong enough, or if it is allowed to proceed long enough, then the amplitude of vibration of the levels away from W_k^0 will become so large that the first-order theory is no longer accurate. Excitation will now begin to "feed" from one newly excited level to another, and also from the newly excited levels back to the original level, at W_k^0. These secondary effects will always be relatively small as long as $a_k^* a_k$ is close to unity, since the "flow" of excitation will then be predominantly *from* this one level.

The progressive narrowing of the region of excitation with time as shown in Figure 10.2 provides another example of the uncertainty principle, here relating the accuracy between the measurements of the two "canonically conjugate" variables, energy W, and time t. In Figure 10.2b (and equation [10–20]) the location of the null in the band of excited energy levels is located at W_m, a distance on the energy scale of $|W_m - W_k| \equiv \Delta W$ from the center of the excitation peak. Thus, the full width at half intensity of the peak is about ΔW. Let $\Delta t \equiv t_1$, the duration of the excitation, then by [10–20],

$$\Delta W \, \Delta t = h \qquad\qquad [10\text{–}21\text{c}]$$

This equation may be interpreted as follows: Many identical systems are all initially in the state k. At $t = 0$ the perturbation H' is suddenly applied, and then removed Δt seconds later. All the systems are then examined to determine their energy. Most of them will still have the original energy W_k, but there will be a number with different energies, spread about the center value, with a half-width of about $\Delta W = 2\pi\hbar/\Delta t$. Of those that "made the transition sometime within the interval, Δt," there is a spread, ΔW, in the resulting characteristic energy. This spread is independent of any system parameters, and depends only upon h and some numerical constant, here unity. If the time of application of the perturbation is doubled, the uncertainty in the energy values of the systems making the transition is halved, etc. Thus, as the uncertainty of the "time of transition" increases (that is, the perturbation is *on* for a longer period of time), the uncertainty in the energy of the affected systems progressively decreases.

10.3. Harmonic perturbation

The set of first-order equations [10–17] takes a particularly simple form when the perturbation is a pure sine wave of angular frequency ω_0, and which is constant in amplitude from $t = 0$ to $t = t_1$.

$$H' = A(x) \sin \omega_0 t \text{ for } 0 \leq t \leq t_1 \qquad [10\text{-}22$$

$$A(x) = \text{constant with respect to time.}$$

The mth equation of set [10-16] becomes

$$-\frac{\hbar}{i} \frac{d}{dt} a'_m = H'_{mk} e^{i\omega_{mk}t} \underbrace{\left(-\frac{i}{2}\right)(e^{i\omega_0 t} - e^{-i\omega_0 t})}_{= \sin \omega_0 t} \qquad [10\text{-}23$$

$$m = 1, 2, 3, \cdots, \qquad m \neq k$$

where

$$H'_{mk} = \int \psi_m^{0*} A(x) \psi_k^0 \, d\tau \qquad [10\text{-}24$$

If $a'_m = 0$ when $t = 0$, the integral of [10-23] from 0 to t_1 is

$$-\frac{\hbar}{i} a'_m(t_1) = -\frac{H'_{mk}}{2} \left[\frac{e^{i(\omega_{mk}+\omega_0)t_1} - 1}{\omega_{mk} + \omega_0} - \frac{e^{i(\omega_{mk}-\omega_0)t_1} - 1}{\omega_{mk} - \omega_0} \right] \qquad [10\text{-}25$$

It is clear from this equation that the magnitude of $a'_m(t_1)$ is going to be unusually large in two regions—at $\omega_{mk} = \omega_0$ and at $\omega_{mk} = -\omega_0$. Thus the states that will be most affected by the perturbation of frequency ω_0 will have a characteristic energy lying either in the region $W_m^0 = W_k^0 + \hbar\omega_0$ or in the region $W_m^0 = W_k^0 - \hbar\omega_0$. The states between (and beyond) these two regions of excitation will be excited, but not very strongly.

To determine the magnitude of excitation of the mth state at time t_1, we must calculate $a'_m(t_1)^* \, a'_m(t_1)$. If we change the sign of i wherever it appears in [10-25] and multiply the result into [10-25], we obtain four terms. There are two "resonance" terms, one with $(\omega_{mk} + \omega_0)^2$ in the denominator, and one with $(\omega_{mk} - \omega_0)^2$ in the denominator. There are two "cross" terms, each with $(\omega_{mk} + \omega_0)(\omega_{mk} - \omega_0)$ in the denominator. In Problem 10.2, we see that near either of the resonance regions the cross terms are very small, and also the *other* resonance term is small. Thus, near $W_m^0 = W_k^0 + \hbar\omega_0$,

$$[a'_m(t_1)]^*[a'_m(t_1)] \cong \frac{H'^*_{mk} H'_{mk}}{(2\hbar)^2} \frac{\sin^2 [(\omega_{mk} - \omega_0) t_1/2]}{[(\omega_{mk} - \omega_0)/2]^2} \qquad [10\text{-}26$$

and, near $W_m^0 = W_k^0 - \hbar\omega_0$,

$$[a'_m(t_1)]^*[a'_m(t_1)] \cong \frac{H'^*_{mk} H'_{mk}}{(2\hbar)^2} \frac{\sin^2 [(\omega_{mk} + \omega_0) t_1/2]}{[(\omega_{mk} + \omega_0)/2]^2} \qquad [10\text{-}27$$

These two resonance curves are plotted in Figure 10.3. In Figure 10.3a we see the initial condition. Only one state, the kth, is occupied. In Figure 10.3b the states near the two resonance regions are beginning to increase their amplitudes of vibration. At still later times, Figures 10.3c and 10.3d, the resonance regions are getting narrower (as $1/t$) and more intense at their maxima (as t^2). *Thus the total excitation of each resonance region grows in proportion to t, the duration of the perturbation.* (In these figures we assume, for con-

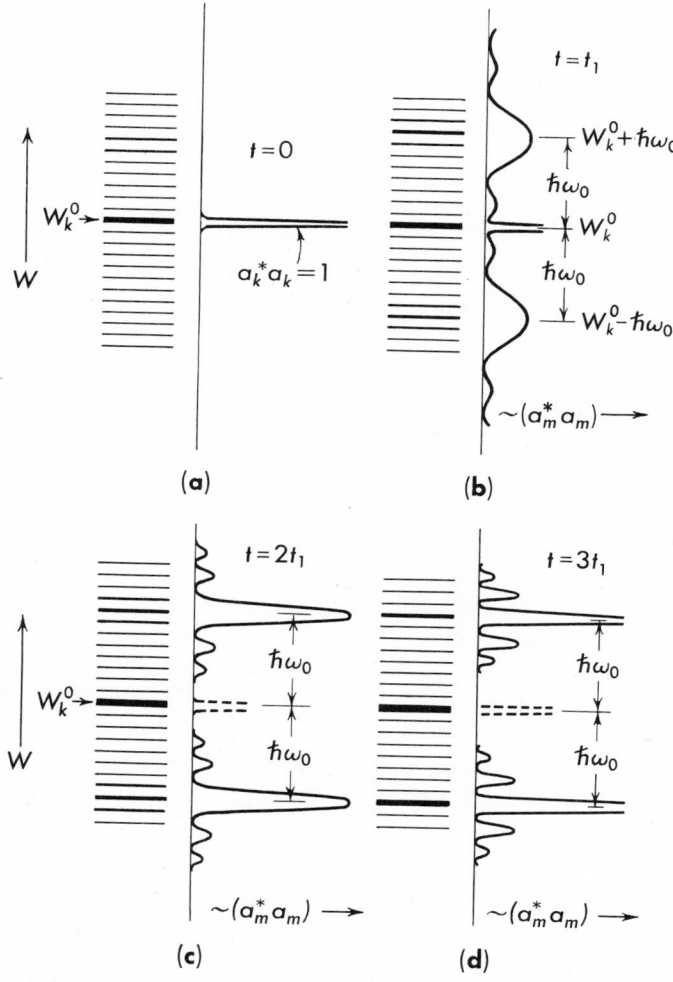

Fig. 10.3. The time variation of the excitation of the proper vibrations caused by a harmonic perturbation, starting at $t = 0$. The density of the horizontal lines indicates qualitatively the degree of excitation of the level or state.

venience, that the matrix elements connecting k to all other states are the same. Actually, of course, the matrix elements can, and do, exert a strong selective effect over and above the basic resonance effects. The matrix elements

$\int \psi_m^{0*} \, H' \, \psi_k^0 \, d\tau$ are the source of the selection rules of atomic and nuclear transitions for harmonic perturbations.)

Again, after H' has been on for Δt seconds, the half-width of each peak is ΔW, where, by [10–21c], $\Delta W \, \Delta t = h$.

This case is very similar to that in which an atom is excited by the application of external radiation. Suppose an atom is in its ground state, and an electromagnetic wave of frequency ω_0 is applied, with some definite direction of propagation and polarization. There is no state at the lower of the two resonance regions, but if there is a state whose characteristic energy lies $\hbar\omega_0$ ergs *above* the ground state, *and* if the matrix element of the electromagnetic field "connects" the two states—that is, H_{jk}' is not zero—then this state will experience a steady build-up in amplitude.

If one shines monochromatic light on a group of atoms for a definite (short) *time*, many atoms will be found in whatever excited states occur near the resonance level. (Generally, they re-radiate this energy as "resonance radiation.")

An almost perfect macroscopic model of the process of resonance excitation by a harmonic perturbation starting at $t = 0$, is provided by a bank of reed filters. Figure 10.4 shows photographs, taken at intervals of 1/16th second, of a bank of filters (each 2 cps wide) centered at 180 cps. The input signal is coupled uniformly to each of the filters (each state has the same "matrix element"). At $t = 0$, the first photograph (upper left) shows the small square "flags" on the ends of the unexcited reeds at $t = 0$ when the constant-amplitude 180-cps signal is initiated. At $t = 1/16$ second very little change has occured, but by $t = 2/16$ second, a broad band of excitation, which is centered at 180 cps but has nulls at 168 and at 192 cps, is observed. This picture corresponds to either of the two resonance regions sketched in Figure 10.3b. As time passes, the reeds near 180 cps continue to increase in amplitude (limited, unfortunately, by mechanical constraints), but the off-resonance reeds fluctuate in their state of excitation. For example, at $t = 5/16$ second (lower left) the reeds at 184 cps and at 176 cps are seen to have no vibration, whereas at earlier and later times they had observable excitation. At $t = 5/16$ second, moreover, a small but definite peak of intensity is observed at 186 cps, and also at 174 cps. This picture corresponds to Figure 10.3c. Finally, in the last picture ($t = 11/16$ second) only the one reed at 180 cps has appreciable excitation although, due to mechanical constraints, the excitation is much smaller than would be expected in a perfect system. In Figure 10.4 the steady narrowing of the region of excitation, with time, is very apparent.

Due to friction, the reeds have a natural decay time constant of about 1/2 second, so that they lose energy in proportion to their state of vibration. This too is analogous to the behavior of atoms which, while in the process of absorbing energy (from a light wave, for example) may *also* at the same time be re-radiating energy. If resonance radiation partially excites a hydrogen atom

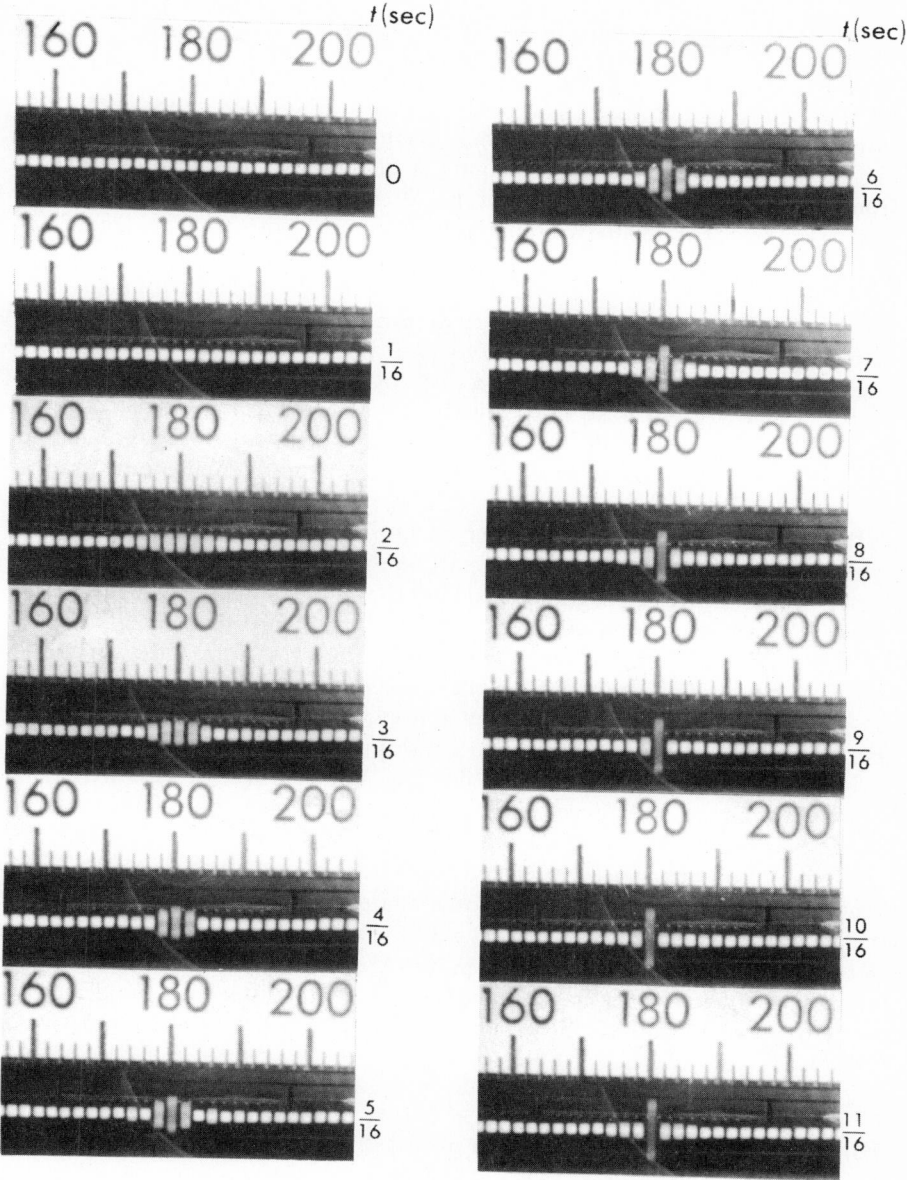

Fig. 10.4. Sequential photographs of a bank of reed filters. At $t = 0$, a constant-amplitude 180 cps signal is coupled equally to each of the reeds.

into its first excited state and then the perturbation is stopped, the excitation of the atom is observed to decay with a time constant of the order of 10^{-8} second. However, when atoms radiate light waves whose wavelength is thousands of times their diameter (as is the case for hydrogen) they lose only a small fraction of their energy in any one cycle. They require a total of about 10^7 cycles to lose an appreciable fraction of their energy (time constant $\simeq 10^{-8}$ second, and period of vibration $\simeq 10^{-15}$ second). A quantitative treatment of radiation from atomic-sized systems will not be attempted here since, for adequate analysis, one needs relativistic quantum theory for both particles and fields. We do consider, however, in the next section, the manner in which an externally applied, time-varying electric field can both excite and de-excite atoms.

The model with the vibrating reeds can help interpret the constant, or "step-function" perturbation of Section 10.2 and Figure 10.2. The equipment could be prepared so that just one reed is excited, for example, the one at 180 cps. At $t = 0$ very weak springs, all identical, are connected from the excited reed to each of the other reeds in the array. (This corresponds to the uniform-magnitude matrix elements which "connect" the kth state to each of the other states.) As time progresses, some excitation will be transfered to all the other reeds, at the expense, of course, of a decrease in amplitude of vibration of the original reed at 180 cps. Shortly after the connections occur at $t = 0$, there will be a broad region of excitation in the neighbourhood of 180 cps, but as time progresses the region of excitation will narrow, as in Figure 10.2. The two reeds, on either side of 180 will eventually develop the largest amplitudes, since they are most closely in resonance with the 180-cps driving signal coming through the very weak springs, but even they will eventually reach a maximum value and then decrease to zero, increase to a maximum once again, decrease to zero, etc., as *all* off-resonance reeds must do. During this whole process we assume that the amplitude of the reed at 180 cps has not changed appreciably, and that there are no decay-effects associated with energy loss.

Thus, "constant perturbation" merely means that the kth state is suddenly "connected" to one or more of the other states of the system with a constant, that is, a time-independent, coupling, with the result that a part of the vibration of the kth state is transferred to the other states. Since none of the other states is assumed to be *exactly* in resonance with the kth state, their amplitudes of vibration do not continuously increase, but each fluctuates periodically as required by [10–19].

10.4. The harmonic oscillator in a periodic electric field

As a simple example of how a time-varying electric field can cause a system to make a "transition to a higher energy state" or, alternatively, "to increase the amplitude, a_m, of the matter-wave vibrations characteristic of a higher energy state," we consider the system in Figure 10.5a. A sinusoidally varying potential source of frequency ω_0 is connected to the two parallel plate conductors C causing, therefore, a time-varying electric field[9] along the x-axis,

$$E_x(t) = E_x^0 \sin \omega_0 t; \quad \omega_0 = 2\pi\nu_0 \qquad [10\text{--}28$$

At any time t the electric field is everywhere constant in the region where the

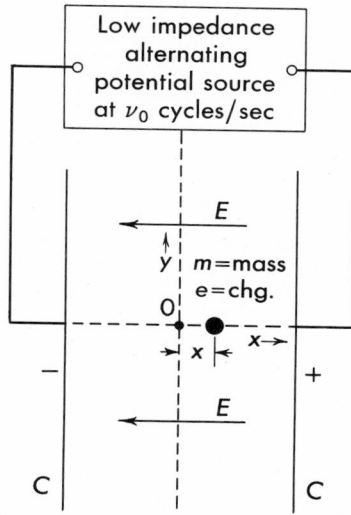

(a) Harmonic oscillator in a time-varying electric field

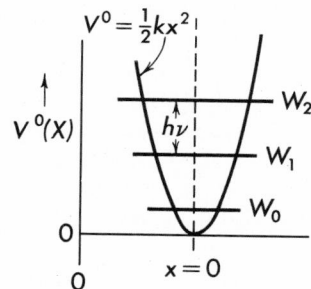

(b) Energy levels of oscillator (zero-order)

mass m, of charge e, is executing harmonic motion along the x-axis, about **0**, as shown in the figure. (That is, over the region where $\Psi^*\Psi$ has any appreciable

---

[9] The operators belonging to the electromagnetic radiation field are discussed in advanced textbooks on quantum mechanics. See, for example, H. Eyring, J. Walter, and G. E. Kimball, *Quantum Chemistry* (1944, John Wiley & Sons, Inc., New York): p. 108. For our purposes here the essential feature of an electromagnetic wave is its time-dependence—it produces a *periodic* variation in the total energy of any charged particle, or magnetic moment (current loop), present in its fields (see Section 10.5).

magnitude, E_x is independent of x.) Without E_x, the perturbing field, the harmonic oscillator is governed by the constant (in time) potential,

$$V^0 = (1/2) \, kx^2$$

where k is the "spring constant" of the oscillator. We assume that this constant potential is derived (indirectly) from an electric charge, fixed at 0, of opposite sign to e, the vibrating charge. Thus the harmonic oscillator is electrically neutral. In the potential V^0, the oscillator has the zero-order energy levels shown in Figure 10.5b since for

$$H^0 = \frac{p^2}{2m} + \tfrac{1}{2}kx^2,$$

the energy levels are equally spaced (Section 3.2).

In a spatially uniform electric field a charge e has at any time, t, the potential energy

$$V(t) = e \, \underbrace{E_x^0(t)}_{\text{force}} \, \underbrace{(x - x_0)}_{\text{distance}} \qquad [10\text{--}29$$

where V is defined to be zero at $x = x_0$. Since the zero value for the potential energy can be arbitrarily chosen, we shall define the perturbing potential energy to be zero when $x = 0$, that is, we chose $x_0 = 0$. (In Problem 10.5 we see that any constant value for x_0 is equally satisfactory.) Thus, the perturbation H' is given by[10]

$$H' = exE_x^0 \sin \omega_0 t \qquad [10\text{--}30$$

This new H' has the same time dependence as the perturbation [10–22] which we discussed in the previous section. Now, however, *there is present a new factor, x, which causes the perturbation to have a particular spatial dependence*, even though E_x is itself uniform throughout the spatial extent of the oscillator. (The same situation occurs when the wavelength of a light wave is large compared to the physical dimensions of the atom which it is perturbing, so that the electric field in the wave is, at any instant, substantially constant throughout the atom.) The term ex is the classical dipole moment of a charge e, displaced a distance x from an equal charge of opposite sign. For this reason, the oscillator transitions caused by the perturbation [10–30] are called "electric dipole transitions."

If we use the perturbation [10–30], we obtain the same results as given in [10–27] through [10–31], except that now the matrix element [10–24] has the particular form

$$H'_{mk} = e \, E_x^0 \int_{-\infty}^{+\infty} \psi_m^{0*} \, x \, \psi_k^0 \, dx \qquad [10\text{--}31$$

---

[10] H' is in ergs if x is in cm, e is in esu, and $E_x^0 = E_x^0$ (volts/cm)/300. H' is in joules if x is in meters, e is in coulombs, and E_x^0 is in volts/m or nt/coulomb.

The time-dependent part of the calculation is unchanged. If $\omega_{mk} = \pm\, \omega_0$, there will be a continuous growth proportional to t^2 (see [10–21b]), in the magnitude of the amplitude a_m of the mth state. (We assume, again, that the system is initially in the pure state, ψ_k^0.) As before, if $\omega_{mk} \neq \omega_0$ the "final state" ψ_m^0 will, at most, develop a small, fluctuating amplitude. It is "off-resonance."

The growth of the intensity of the mth state, measured by $(a_m')^* (a_m')$ [10–26] and [10–27], is, as before, dependent upon $H_{mk}'^* H_{mk}'$, the square of the matrix element. If the perturbation H' is given by [10–31] we find that certain transitions are allowed and certain ones are forbidden. As an example of these "section rules for dipole transitions" we will calculate two simple cases for the harmonic oscillator. Let the oscillator be initially in its zero-point state, that is, k (the quantum number) $= 0$. The zero-order wave function ψ_0^0 belonging to this state is plotted in Figure 10.6, and below it is plotted $x = x$, and also $x\, \psi_0^0$. We wish to calculate

$$H_{10}' = e\, E_x^0 \int_{-\infty}^{+\infty} \psi_1^{0*}\, x\, \psi_0^0\, dx$$

With the aid of the graph of ψ_1^0, also given in Figure 10.6, we can see at once that the integral $\int \psi_1^0\, x\, \psi_0^0\, dx$ is not zero, since the integrand is everywhere positive. In contrast to this,

$$H_{20}' = e\, E_x^0 \int_{-\infty}^{+\infty} \psi_2^{0*}\, x\, \psi_0^0\, dx = 0$$

since the contribution to the integral from the positive-x region exactly cancels the contribution from the negative-x region. Thus, if n is the quantum number of the initial state of the harmonic oscillator, we find (for these two special cases) that $\Delta n = 1$ is allowed, and $\Delta n = 2$ is forbidden. That is, if the system of Figure 10.5 is originally in its lowest states, $n = 0$, the oscillating electric field can cause it to "jump" to the state $n = 1$ or, alternatively, the intensity of the vibrations characteristic of $n = 1$ will increase but will *not* cause the system to "jump" to the state for which $n = 2$ (or, the intensity of the vibrations characteristic of $n = 2$ will *not* increase).

The two examples we have just been discussing are included in the general rule for electric dipole transitions for the harmonic oscillator, $\Delta n = \pm\, 1$. This general rule can be derived from the properties of the Hermite functions. Specifically, it can be shown[11] that

$$H_{k-1,\, k}' = e\, E_x^0 \sqrt{k/2a} \quad \text{(downward transitions)}$$

$$H_{k+1,\, k}' = e\, E_x^0 \sqrt{(k+1)/2a} \quad \text{(upward transitions)} \qquad [10\text{–}32$$

$$H_{m,\, k}' = 0 \quad \text{for all other values of } m.$$

---

[11] See, for example, L. Pauling and E. B. Wilson, *Introduction to Quantum Mechanics* (1935, McGraw-Hill Book Co., Inc., New York): pp. 77 and 306.

$a = 2\pi m v / \hbar$. (For $k = 0$, of course, there can be no downward transition.) The initial state (by convention, the right-hand subscript on a matrix element symbol) is k.

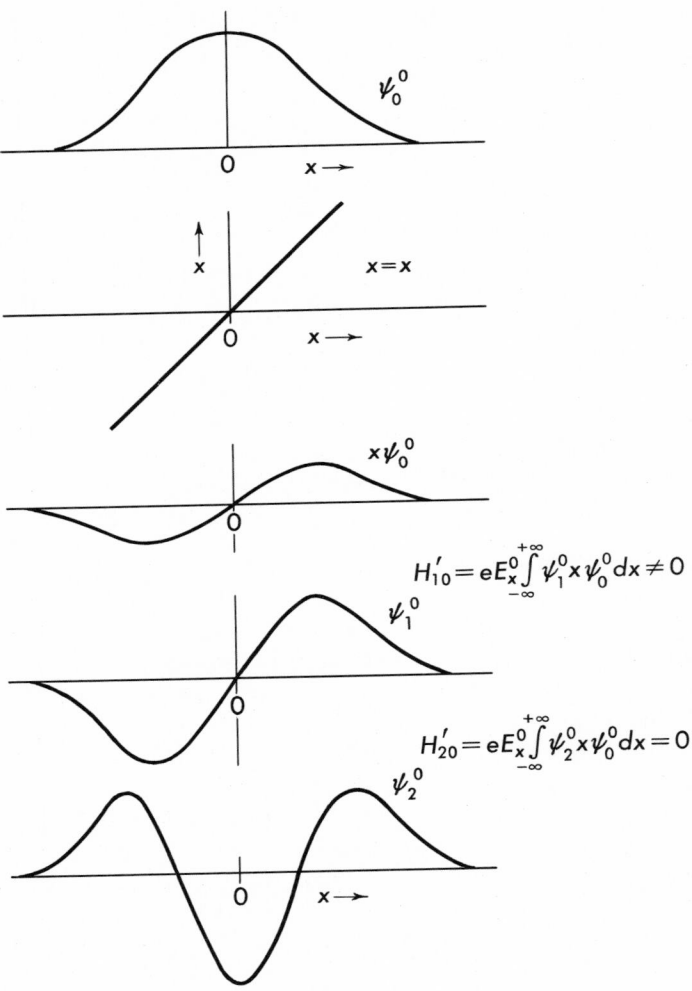

$$\psi_0^0$$

$$x = x$$

$$x\psi_0^0$$

$$H_{10}' = eE_x^0 \int_{-\infty}^{+\infty} \psi_1^0 x \psi_0^0 \, dx \neq 0$$

$$\psi_1^0$$

$$H_{20}' = eE_x^0 \int_{-\infty}^{+\infty} \psi_2^0 x \psi_0^0 \, dx = 0$$

$$\psi_2^0$$

Fig. 10.6. Electric dipole transitions of the harmonic oscillator.

Suppose that the oscillator in Figure 10.5 is initially in an excited state, k. The periodic electric field now causes the amplitudes of *both* the $k + 1$ and the $k - 1$ states to increase (if $v = v_0$). Since, by [10–32], the higher energy state $k + 1$ will increase in amplitude more rapidly than the lower state, the expectation value of the energy of the oscillator will increase with time. (See Problem 10.6, where this effect is calculated for a specific case.)

We are using first-order perturbation theory and must, therefore, always require that the amplitude of initial state a_k remains (essentially) at unity. For a system with only two states involved in the resonance, it is possible to solve the time-dependent wave equation exactly[12] and, given the amplitudes of the two states at any initial time, find (without restriction) the new amplitudes at any later (or earlier) time. It is found that if one state alone is initially excited, the other state gradually increases in amplitude until it finally has all of the excitation—the system is now certain to be found in the second state. If the perturbation is continued, the second-state vibrations die down and the original-state vibrations build up. The shift of excitation from one state to the other is sinusoidal. (The t^2-dependence of the build-up of the intensity of a resonant state [10–21a] is just the beginning of this process, starting from the case where one state has all of the excitation.) Transitions of this type are encountered in "nuclear resonance," where an external harmonic perturbation causes the relative population of two spin states to shift continuously.

The calculation of the x-component of the dipole moment matrix element [10–31] is intimately related to the already familiar calculation of the expectation value of ex, using Postulate V, for the case where the system is in a super-position of two pure states, Ψ_m and Ψ_k. As a simple example, let

$$\Psi = a_m \psi_m e^{-i\omega_m t} + a_k \psi_k e^{-i\omega_k t}, \quad a_m^2 + a_k^2 = 1, \quad \omega_m = \frac{W_m}{\hbar}, \quad \omega_k = \frac{W_k}{\hbar}$$

$$[10–33$$

where the a's and the ψ's are both real. Using this superposition for the wave function, we find by Postulate V (see Problem 10.8)

$$\overline{ex} = \text{constant} \cdot H'_{mk} \cdot 2 \cos(\omega_k - \omega_m) t + (\text{const.})[\bar{x}_m + \bar{x}_k] \quad [10–34$$

where H'_{mk} is exactly the matrix element of [10–31]. In other words, a system in certain mixed states but *without* an external perturbation may possess, quite naturally, a time-varying expectation value of its dipole moment. Classically, this means that electric charge is being accelerated, so that radiation will occur at the frequency $(\omega_k - \omega_m)$. We may expect, therefore, for those mixed states which possess a time-varying electric dipole moment,[13] that energy should be radiated away, and the system should have a continually increasing probability of being found in the state of lower energy. We will not discuss "spontaneous radiation" any further here. It can be adequately treated only with more advanced theory. We see once again, however, that H'_{mk} is intimately associated with transitions from one state to another.

---

[12] L. D. Landau and E. M. Lifshitz (tr. by J. B. Sykes and J. S. Bell), *Quantum Mechanics, Non-Relativistic Theory* (1958, Pergamon Press & Addison Wesley Press, Reading, Mass.): p. 143.

[13] For a *pure* state, $\overline{ex}$ = constant in time.

Returning to our oscillator problem, we note that we have considered only the effect of the electric field on the oscillator. From Maxwell's equations, in a region of space where **E** is uniform spatially but varying in time, we know that there must be an associated magnetic field, **B**, $B = E/c$, perpendicular to **E**, and also varying in time with the same frequency.

Let us consider a system (such as a hydrogen atom in an $l = 1$ state) that has a magnetic moment μ. (See the discussion in Problem 6.8.) In contrast to the harmonic oscillator, this system has motion in at least two dimensions, and has a magnetic moment. A current loop, or magnet, has, in a magnetic field, an orientation-dependent energy,[14]

$$H' = -\mu \cos \theta \, B = -\mu \cos \theta \, B^0 \sin \omega_0 t \qquad [10\text{--}35$$

where θ is the angle between the direction of μ and the direction of **B**. In Problem 6.8 we found that a charge of e coulombs, moving in a circle of radius r_0 meters with a velocity v m/sec, has, classically, a magnetic moment of magnitude $\mu = evr_0/2$; so that

$$H' = (evr_0/2)[\cos \theta](E/c) \qquad [10\text{--}36$$

If we call er_0 the electric dipole moment of the point charge e (r_0 is a distance characteristic of the size of the structure), and if we consider $\cos \theta$ and 2 to be approximately unity, we have,

$$H'(\text{magnetic}) \cong \left(\frac{v}{c}\right) \cdot H'(\text{electric dipole}) \qquad [10\text{--}37$$

Thus, since transition rates are proportional to $|H'|^2$, the effectiveness of the magnetic field on a rotating point charge is about $(v/c)^2$ times that of the electric field. In typical atoms, electrons have energies of a few tens of electron volts, and therefore have velocities of less than .01 times the velocity of light, so that the "magnetic dipole transitions" which we have been discussing are, in general, about 10^4 times weaker than electric dipole transitions. The integration involved in the matrix elements for the magnetic perturbation is different from that for the electric dipole perturbation, so that the selection rules are different. Thus it often happens that H'_{mk} (electric) is zero, but H'_{mk} (magnetic) $\neq 0$. Thus, a "transition can proceed by a magnetic dipole perturbation" even though it is forbidden by the electric dipole matrix element.[15] For the transition to proceed rapidly, however, it needs (in addition to a favorable matrix element) a very powerful time-varying magnetic field, due to the inherent smallness of the magnetic force on a charge moving at velocities small compared to that of light.

In Figure 10.5 we considered the case where the perturbing electric field

---

[14] See Section 6.1.
[15] A classical model of this case would be a *uniform current loop* of magnetic moment μ. Its H' (magnetic) would be $\mu \, B \cos \theta$, the same as above, while with respect to an origin in the center of the loop, the electric dipole moment—along any axis—is zero.

was produced with the aid of an alternating voltage source of fixed maximum amplitude. Let us consider a slightly different arrangement, in Figure 10.7, where the parallel plates are forming the capacitance C, connected to an (ideal) inductance L. The L-C circuit is set into free oscillation. As before, the oscillating electric field is produced between the plates, the energy storage of the

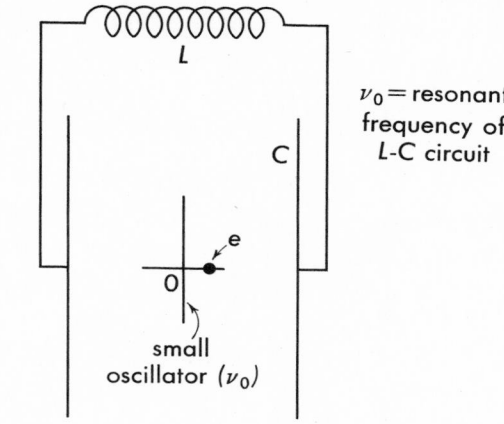

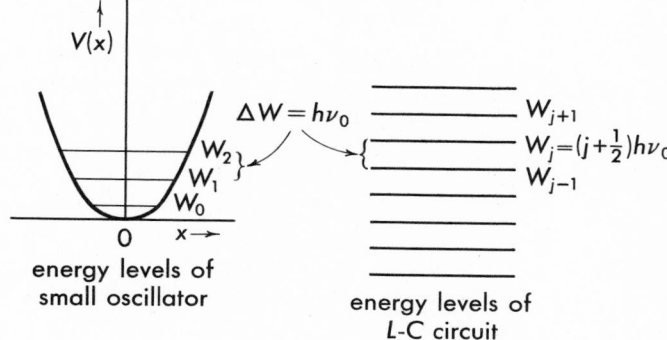

Fig. 10.7. The coupling of an atomic oscillator and a macroscopic oscillator by means of the electric field.

L-C circuit shifting rhythmically between the electric field of the capacitor and the magnetic field of the inductance. This has the basic features of a harmonic oscillator, so that we may expect the circuit to have similar energy levels—even though it is a macroscopic system. These levels are sketched in Figure 10.7 and, because the natural frequency of the L-C circuit is the same as the small oscillator, the levels of the two systems are drawn equally spaced. If we regard the *L-C* circuit as being in a state (or a superposition of states) of high quantum number, then the small oscillator experiences the same perturbing electric field as before. Should the expectation value of the energy of the small system decrease, however, we must expect the energy so released to appear in the *L-C* circuit by raising its energy. That is, the system as a whole maintains a constant energy. We can regard the energy H' [10–30] as being a perturbation on either system, and as being the mechanism for shifting the energy from one system to the other. We see that when macroscopic oscillators such as *L-C* circuits or a resonant microwave cavity exchange energy with atomic systems, it is convenient to regard the circuits—along with their associated electric and magnetic fields—as being quantized.

A particularly interesting case (see Problem 10.7) is one in which an atomic system, known to be in its first excited state which is $h\nu_0$ ergs above the ground state, is suddenly inserted into a microwave cavity, or *L-C* circuit, in a state of high quantum number, resonating at ν_0 cycles per sec. The electric field causes the amplitude of the ground state (of the small oscillator) to increase. If the small system does *not* have another resonance $h\nu_0$ ergs *above* the first excited state, the small system cannot make transitions to higher energy. The higher states that do exist are "off-resonance." One speaks of the oscillating field in the cavity as "stimulating emission" in the atomic oscillators. Thus the oscillators "unload" their energy of excitation into the cavity which increases the amplitudes of its higher quantum number states. In this manner, atomic oscillators "drive" a macroscopic resonant circuit. If excited atomic oscillators are inserted into the cavity at a high enough rate, a stable, detectable oscillation can be maintained entirely from this source.[16] After being "unloaded" the atomic oscillators must be removed; otherwise, after reaching the ground state, they would start to develop excitation in the first excited state once again, and so take back the energy they had once given up.

Even in the simple system of Figure 10.7 we can see the inadequacy of the perturbation concept. We have regarded the small oscillator and the *L-C* circuit as each having its "own" characteristic modes of vibration, whose amplitudes are shifted by the perturbation. In short, we have regarded each system as having a separate existence. Clearly, however, there is only *one* system—the small oscillator *plus* the circuit. If the zero-order wave equation [10–3] for the *complete* system is solved exactly, one finds a set of the *true* resonant modes [10–4] whose relative amplitudes shift in some exactly predictable and continuous manner according to [10–12], the *exact* time-dependent equation, from some given initial state. The conceptual problems of thinking about systems of this sort are discussed in a most interesting manner by Schrödinger in a reference given in Section 10.6.

---

[16] A system of this type (called a "Maser"), using excited NH_3 molecules (selected by deflection in a molecular beam—the excited and non-excited molecules are deflected differently) has been constructed by J. P. Gordon, H. J. Zeiger, and C. H. Townes, *Phys. Rev.*, 99: 1264, 1955.

The discussion here of the interaction of quantum-mechanical systems with electromagnetic fields is a very brief introduction to a very important subject. The electromagnetic field can be introduced into the classical Hamiltonian, and into the wave equation in a more general, although "semiclassical," manner.[17] A more complete treatment, which involves the quantization of the electromagnetic field itself, requires, as a basis, the relativistic quantum theory.

10.5.   An example: The vibration spectrum of the diatomic molecule

In Section 3.2 and Figure 3.6 it was shown that, in the vibration spectrum of the diatomic molecule, the energy levels are not exactly evenly spaced by the amount $h\nu_0$ as in the perfect harmonic oscillator. Furthermore, the selection rule, $\Delta n = \pm 1$ [10–32], is not exactly obeyed since molecules are observed to absorb energy directly from the ground state[18] ($n = 0$) into the $n = 2$, $n = 3$, $\cdots$, states. As an example of the application of both steady-state and time-dependent perturbation theory, we will show how both of these types of deviation may be explained.

The potential energy is

$$V(x) = (1/2)\,kx^2 + f(x); \quad x = r - r_0 \qquad\qquad [10\text{–}38$$

where r_0 is the equilibrium separation of the two atoms. We will assume the perturbing term is

$$f(x) = bx^3 + cx^4 \qquad\qquad [10\text{–}39$$

and we will specifically consider the effects of this perturbation on the $n = 2$ state. We will find, using first-order perturbation theory for the steady state, that not only is the energy level of this state shifted, but, in addition, the spatial form of the wave function is different from that of the zero-order eigenfunction ψ_2^0. Using the correct wave function, time-dependent perturbation theory will then show that dipole absorption and radiation is permitted, although at a reduced intensity, between the $n = 0$ and the $n = 2$ levels.

By [7–12] the first-order energy for the $n = 2$ state is

$$W_2 = W_2^0 + \int\limits_{-\infty}^{+\infty} \psi_2^{0*}\, f(x)\, \psi_2^0\, dx \qquad\qquad [10\text{–}40$$

---

[17] An excellent introduction to the semiclassical treatment of radiation may be found in H. Eyring, J. Walter, and G. E. Kimball, *loc. cit.*

[18] For the HCl spectrum of Figure 3.6, the first excited state is 2880 cm^{-1}, or $(2880)/(5 \times 10^{15}) = 3/5 \times 10^{-21}$ erg, above the zero-point state. At room temperature, the mean vibrational energy is $kT = 1.36 \times 10^{-16} \times 300 = 0.04 \times 10^{-12}$ erg, which is ~ 15 times smaller than the level spacing. Thus, using the Boltzmann factor, $e^{-15} \cong 10^{-6}$, we see that at room temperature only about 1 molecule in 10^6 will be found in the $n = 1$ state, 1 in 10^{12} in the $n = 2$ state, etc.

where

$$W_2^0 = 2h\,\nu_0, \text{ and } \nu_0 = (1/2\pi)\sqrt{k/m} \qquad [10\text{-}41$$

The theory also gives the first-order wave function for the $n = 2$ level,

$$\psi_2 = \psi_2^0 + a_0\,\psi_0^0 + a_1\,\psi_1^0 + (0)\,\psi_2^0 + a_3\,\psi_3^0 + \cdots \qquad [10\text{-}42$$

Each of the a_j's is given by [7-13],

$$a_j = -\left[\int_{-\infty}^{+\infty} \psi_j^{0*} f(x)\,\psi_2^0\,dx\right]\bigg/\left[W_j^0 - W_2^0\right] \qquad [10\text{-}42a$$

We are interested, however, in explaining the transition from $n = 0$ to the $n = 2$ state due to a time-varying electric field near the frequency $2\nu_0$. It is apparent that the presence of the $a_1\,\psi_1^0$ term in the first-order wave function belonging to the level at $n = 2$ will explain the weak transition in question since

$$\int \psi_1^{0*}\,x\,\psi_0^0\,dx \neq 0$$

and when we use time-dependent theory to calculate the normally forbidden transition from the $n = 0$ state to the $n = 2$ state (see [10-26] and [10-31]).

$$H_{20}' = eE_x^0\int_{-\infty}^{+\infty} \psi_2^*\,x\,\psi_0\,dx \qquad [10\text{-}43a$$

We will obtain a non-zero result.[19] Even if the matrix element [10-43a] is $\neq 0$, the amplitude a_2 of the $n = 2$ state will not grow steadily ($\sim t^2$) unless, *in addition*, the resonance requirement [10-26]

$$E_x = E_x^0 \sin\,\omega_{20}\,t, \text{ where } \omega_{20} = (W_2 - W_0)/\hbar \qquad [10\text{-}43b$$

is also satisfied. ψ_2 and ψ_0 are the *true* wave functions belonging to the final state and the initial state respectively. *Neither* are exact harmonic oscillator eigenfunctions.

Since ψ_0 is the lowest state, however, it will be *nearly* the pure state,

$$\psi_0^0 = (\sqrt{a/\pi})^{\frac{1}{2}}\,e^{-ax^2/2}; \quad a = 2\pi\,\nu_0\,m/\hbar \qquad [10\text{-}44^{20}$$

because $f(x)$ is small at low vibrational amplitude. For simplicity, we assume that [10-44] is the exact form of the wave function for the ground state. When the first-order wave function [10-42] is used in the calculation of the matrix element H_{20}' of [10-43a], we see by [10-32] that only one term will be non-zero—the one involving ψ_1^0 and ψ_0^0. Thus,

$$H_{20}' = eE_x^0\int_{-\infty}^{+\infty} a_1^*\,\psi_1^{0*}\,x\,\psi_0^0\,dx = a_1^*\,H_{10}' = eE_x^0\,a_1^*\,\sqrt{1/a} \qquad [10\text{-}45$$

---

[19] A small amount of Ψ_2^0 present in Ψ_0 (the ground-state wave function) *also* contributes the $n = 0 \to n = 2$ transition.　See Problem 10.11.
[20] See Appendix I.

Thus, the absorption line from $n = 0$ to $n = 2$ whose intensity is proportional to $|H'_{20}|^2$, is $|a_1|^2$ times as intense as the main absorption line, which is proportional to $|H'_{10}|^2$, and since, in practice, $a_1 \ll 1$, the absorption line near $2\nu_0$ is much weaker than the one at ν_0.

By steady-state perturbation theory for a nondegenerate level [7–13],

$$a_1 = \frac{- \int \psi_1^{0*} f(x)\, \psi_2^0 \, dx}{W_1^0 - W_2^0}, \quad \text{where} \quad W_1^0 - W_2^0 = -h\nu_0 \qquad [10\text{–}46$$

Thus, if the deviation $f(x)$ from a parabolic potential energy curve of the ideal harmonic oscillator has such a form that it "mixes" some of the $n = 1$ state with the $n = 2$ state (that is, if a_1 is not zero), then the dipole transition from the $n = 0$ to the $n = 2$ state is no longer rigorously forbidden.

The same $f(x)$, used in [10–40], must explain the experimental fact that W_2 is slightly smaller than the value $2h\nu_0$ predicted for the case of the ideal oscillator.

From Appendix I, the zero-order wave functions for $n = 1$ and $n = 2$ are

$$\psi_1^0 = [(1/2)(\sqrt{a/\pi})]^{\frac{1}{2}} (2\sqrt{a}\, x)\, e^{-ax^2/2},$$

$$\psi_2^0 = [(1/8)(\sqrt{a/\pi})]^{\frac{1}{2}} (4ax^2 - 2)\, e^{-ax^2/2} \qquad [10\text{–}47$$

Making use of the definite integral,

$$\int_{-\infty}^{+\infty} x^{2n} e^{-ax^2} \, dx = \frac{1 \cdot 3 \cdot 5 \, \cdots \, (2n-1)}{2^n \, a^n} \sqrt{\frac{\pi}{a}}, \quad n = \text{a positive integer} \qquad [10\text{–}48$$

we have, using [10–40],

$$W_2 = W_2^0 + (49\, c)/(4a^2) \qquad [10\text{–}49$$

The bx^3 term does not contribute, since it is odd with respect to $x = 0$, and $\psi_2^{0*}\, \psi_2^0$ is even.

From [10–46] we obtain for the amplitude of ψ_1^0 present in ψ_2,

$$a_1 = -(3b)/(a)^{3/2} (h\nu_0) \qquad [10\text{–}50$$

The cx^4 term does not contribute here due to symmetry properties. Thus the absorption line whose energy is

$$W_2 - W_0 = 2h\,\nu_0 + (49\, c)/(4a^2) \qquad [10\text{–}51$$

(since $W_2^0 = (5/2)\, h\nu_0$ and $W_0 \simeq W_0^0 = h\nu_0$) has a lower intensity than the main resonance, by the factor a_1^2.

We note that the bx^3 term in the perturbation $f(x)$ accounts for the $n = 0$ to $n = 2$ absorption line, while the cx^4 term accounts for the energy shift in the $n = 2$ level. Since experimentally the correction to W_2 is negative, c must be negative—that is, the x^4 term "flattens out" the potential well.

From the experimental HCl spectrum of Figure 3.6 we see, using [10–45], that a_1 is $\sim \sqrt{60}$ and, using [10–50], we can find the constant b.

Hertzberg[21] gives the experimental value of the $n = 2$ energy level as 5668 cm^{-1} which is 1.8 per cent lower than twice the main resonance at 2886 cm^{-1}. If we assume that the latter value (converted to ergs and divided by h) is the characteristic frequency ν_0 of the ideal harmonic oscillator, we can use [10–51] to obtain the value of the constant c. Pauling and Wilson[22] derive a general formula for the energy level corrections, which depends only upon the constant c.

It has been found that quantum theory gives a consistent account of the vibration spectrum, including many other effects not mentioned here, such as the rotational energy levels, the influence of the nuclei (particularly when they are identical isotopes and show exchange-symmetry properties), etc.

We close this section by pointing out that it is also possible for a classical perturbed oscillator to absorb energy at about twice its (low-amplitude) resonance frequency. Suppose that the oscillator is vibrating at an appreciable amplitude. The mass point of an *ideal* oscillator will have its velocity proportional to an exact sinusoidal function such as $\cos 2\pi \nu_0 t$, but the nonideal potential will cause the velocity, although exactly periodic with period T near $(1/\nu_0)$, to deviate from a pure sinusoidal form, the deviation being expressible as a Fourier series,

$$v(t) = a_1 \cos (2\pi/T)\, t + a_2 \cos 2(2\pi/T)\, t + a_3 \cos 3(2\pi/T)\, t + \cdots \qquad [10\text{–}52$$

where, for small deformations of the potential from $1/2\, kx^2$, a_2 and a_3 are small compared to a_1. If a force along the x-axis,

$$F(t) = F_x^0 \cos 2(2\pi/T)\, t \qquad [10\text{–}53$$

which is periodic, with *twice* the basic frequency of the oscillator, is applied to the mass, work *may* be done on the mass. Over one complete period T,

$$\text{work} = \int_0^T F(t)\, v(t)\, dt \qquad [10\text{–}54$$

where $v\, dt = dx$, the distance moved in the time dt.

If [10–53] is the force and [10–52] is the velocity, then the integral in [10–54] is non-zero for one term,

$$a_2 F_x^0 \int_0^T \cos^2 2(2\pi/T)\, t\, dt$$

---

[21] G. Hertzberg, *Molecular Spectra and Molecular Structure* (1939, Prentice-Hall, Inc., New York). I: Diatomic Molecules, p. 58.
[22] L. Pauling and E. B. Wilson, *op. cit.*, p. 160.

Thus, it is possible for the mass to absorb energy (or, release energy) at twice its basic frequency $1/T$, providing that its velocity is not purely sinusoidal in such a way that $a_2 \neq 0*$.[23] For the HCl molecule, however, we have seen that at room temperature only one molecule in 10^6 has an energy equal to the first quantum level, and only one molecule in 10^{12} has an energy equal to the second quantum level, so that, even if $a_1 \cong a_2$ for molecules whose energy is in the range of $h\nu_0$ (a *very* large nonlinearity), the classically predicted absorption line near $2\nu_0$ is *much* weaker than the experimental value. In addition, the classical line should be broadened in frequency—due to the lack of quantization—in contrast to the sharp experimental value.

The diatomic molecule vibration spectrum provides an excellent example of the application of both stationary and time-dependent perturbation theory to a case of physical interest and, in addition, shows the distinctive differences between the (experimentally verified) quantum theory and the incorrect classical theory.

10.6.　The importance of time-dependent perturbations

We see, then, that time-dependent perturbations can cause a system to change its wave function in a significant and observable manner. These perturbations can cause either increases or decreases in the expectation value of the energy of a system, implying either an inflow of energy to the system or an outflow of energy from the system.

Similarly, time-dependent perturbations can cause the expectation value of the magnitude of the angular momentum, or the magnitude of the z-component of the angular momentum, to change. In either case, the system is interchanging angular momentum with its environment, since the angular momentum vector is not constant in time.

Thus, it is through time-dependent perturbations that a system "interacts with its environment." This, of course, is the realm of experiment and observation, so that the great importance of the theory is clear.

But what is the environment? Is it not another system with its own zero-order vibrations and resonant modes? If energy flows out of "the system under observation" which we have been analyzing, it must flow into the system making up the environment. The environmental system is usually large—for example, a box containing slits, an optical grating, and a photographic film—so that it generally has many, closely spaced resonant modes. As the amplitudes of vibraton of two of the modes of the atomic wave functions shift, causing the expectation value of the energy of the atomic system energy to drop, we expect that there will be some corresponding shift among the amplitudes of the many modes of the environment, causing its energy to rise a corresponding

---

[23] Note: $1/T$ will in general differ slightly from ν_0, the frequency of oscillation at very low amplitude.

amount. Suppose, for example, that there were many atoms, originally in a pure state with energy W_k^0. A perturbation causes these atoms to build up some finite amplitude of the state of energy, W_m^0, with a consequent loss (or gain) in the expectation value of the atomic energy. During this process, the electromagnetic vibrations in the environment of frequency, $\omega_{km}/2\pi$, will become more intense (or less intense). If the atoms are losing energy, the electromagnetic vibrations will interact with the grating, and finally result in a black line on the photographic plate at the place where the grating causes the electromagnetic waves to superimpose in phase. Once permanent, macroscopic changes are made (such as the exposed photographic film), the environmental system can be examined at will without altering it significantly. Thus, observation, considered carefully, is a very complex process.

This very brief outline of a typical experiment shows the many problems involved in a really complete quantum-mechanical theory of experiment. The student is referred to other sources for a further discussion of this important and interesting problem.[24]

There are many interesting discussions of the nature of measurement and the philosophical implications of quantum mechanics which the student is now in a position to appreciate. One of them is an extremely interesting article, "Are There Quantum Jumps, ?"[25] by Erwin Schrödinger.

Some of the other founders of the theory of quantum mechanics explain their attitude toward the quantum phenomena in the following relatively non-mathematical articles and books:

Niels Bohr, "Discussion with Einstein on Epistemological Problems in Atomic Physics," Paul A. Schelpp (ed.), in *Albert Einstein, Philosopher-Scientist* (1949, The Library of Living Philosophers, Evanston, Illinois): p. 201.

Louis de Broglie, *The Revolution in Physics* (1953, The Noonday Press, New York).

Max Born, *Physics in my Generation* (1956, Pergamon Press, London).

There are two technical books of both historical and current interest:

E. Schrödinger, *Four Lectures on Wave Mechanics* (1929, Blackie and Son, Ltd., London).

W. Heisenberg (Tr. by C. Eckart & F. Hoyt), *The Physical Principles of Quantum Theory* (1930, University of Chicago Press, Chicago, Ill., also Dover Publications Inc., New York).

There are few subjects so fascinating and so puzzling as the interpretation of quantum phenomena, and it is clear that the last word has not yet been said. Now that the student has been introduced to what quantum mechanics *is*, he will find the study of what it *means* both stimulating and rewarding.

---

[24] D. Bohm, *Quantum Theory* (1951, Prentice-Hall, Inc., New York): p. 583.

[25] E. Schrödinger, *"What Is Life,"* *and Other Scientific Essays* (1956, Doubleday Anchor Co., Garden City, New York): p. 132. (Originally published in the *Brit. J. Phil. Sci.*, **3**: nos. 10 & 11, 1952.)

10.7. Summary

The complete time-dependent wave equation is

$$(H^0 + H')\,\Psi = -\,(\hbar/i)\,\partial\Psi/\partial t \qquad\qquad [10\text{--}5$$

where H' may depend upon space, momentum, and time, and where the time-independent part of the equation is

$$H^0\,\psi_n^0 = -\,(\hbar/i)\,\partial\Psi_n^0/\partial t = W_n^0\,\Psi_n^0,\ \text{since}\ \Psi_n^0 = \psi_n^0\,e^{-iW_n^0 t/\hbar} \qquad [10\text{--}3\text{a}$$

In order to solve the wave equation [10–5] when H' is time-dependent, it is necessary to be given the wave function $\Psi(x, t_0)$ at some time $t = t_0$. Any reasonable form of $\Psi(x, t_0)$ can be synthesized by the orthogonal series

$$\Psi(x, t_0) = \sum_n a_n(t_0)\,\Psi_n^0(x, t_0) \qquad\qquad [5\text{--}9$$

where

$$a_n(t_0) = \int\Psi_n^0(x, t_0)\,\Psi(x, t_0)\,dx \qquad\qquad [5\text{--}12$$

The complete list of a_n's, at $t = t_0$, gives an exact description of the wave function at $t = t_0$.

At any time t the (well-behaved and bounded) wave function may be characterized by some particular set of a_n's which will synthesize $\Psi(x, t)$ at that instant,

$$\Psi(x, t) = \sum_n a_n(t)\,\Psi_n^0(x, t) \qquad\qquad [10\text{--}9$$

The objective of the calculation is this: Given a set of a_n's at t_0, find the *new* set of a_n's at any arbitrary time t. To find the a_n's at t, we substitute [10–9] into the true wave equation [10–5], giving

$$\sum_n a_n(t)\,H^0\Psi_n^0 + \sum_n a_n(t)\,H'\Psi_n^0 = -\,\frac{\hbar}{i}\sum_n\left[\frac{d}{dt}\,a_n(t)\right]\Psi_n^0 - \frac{\hbar}{i}\sum_n a_n(t)\,\frac{\partial\Psi_n^0}{\partial t}$$

$$[10\text{--}10$$

The sums on the extreme left and the extreme right cancel term by term (by the zero-order equation [10–3a]). Multiplying the remainder of [10–10] from the left by $\Psi_m^0{}^*$, and performing the operation $\int d\tau$ on each term, [10–10] becomes the set of equations,

$$\frac{d}{dt}\,a_m(t) = -\,\frac{i}{\hbar}\sum_n a_n(t)\int\Psi_m^0{}^*\,H'\,\Psi_n^0\,d\tau \qquad\qquad [10\text{--}11$$

$$m = 1, 2, 3, \cdots$$

There is one equation [10–11] for each value of m, and for each equation, n ranges over all the values needed to identify each member of the complete set of eigenfunctions of the time-independent equation [10–3a]. There is no approximation in the set of equations [10–11]. It is fully equivalent to the wave equation [10–5]. The set is written out in more detail in [10–12]. Given all the a_n's at $t = 0$, it is possible to integrate the set of differential equations [10–11] from $t = 0$ to t, obtaining, thereby, each of the a_n's at t. In practice this operation is difficult mathematically, and so we turn to a first-order perturbation calculation.

If we substitute

$$H = H^0 + \lambda H' \qquad [10\text{–}13$$

and

$$a_m(t) = a_m^0 + \lambda a_m' \qquad [10\text{–}14$$

in [10–11] or [10–12], we obtain, equating the coefficients of λ^0, the result that all the a_m^0's are constant in time. Equating the coefficients of λ, we obtain the set of first-order equations,

$$- (\hbar/i)\, da_m'/dt = \sum_n a_n^0 \int \Psi_m^{0*} H' \Psi_n^{0} \, d\tau, \qquad m = 1, 2, 3, \cdots \qquad [10\text{–}16$$

which are written out more fully in Section 10.1. This set of approximate equations may be most easily solved for the case where, at $t = 0$, $a_k^0 = 1$ and all the other a_m^0's are zero. For one dimension, $d\tau = dx$. Since at $t = 0$ all the a_m^0's (except a_k) are zero, $a_m'(t) = a_m(t)$, and the integral of [10–16] is:

$$a_m(t) = \int_0^t \left[-\frac{i}{\hbar} \int_{\text{space}} \psi_m^{0*} \, e^{iW_m^0 t/\hbar} \, H'\left(x, \frac{\partial}{\partial x}, t\right) \psi_k^0 \, e^{-iW_k^0 t/\hbar} \, dx \right] dt$$

where H' may depend upon x, $\partial/\partial x$ (i.e., momentum) or t. There is the usual first-order restriction $|a_m(t)| \ll 1$.

$a_m(t)$ is calculated for two different forms for H':

(a) $H' = f(x)$, a constant perturbation, starting at $t = 0$, then

$$a_m(t) = - \frac{H_{mk}'}{\hbar} \frac{(e^{i\omega_{mk}t} - 1)}{\omega_{mk}} \qquad [10\text{–}18$$

$m = 1, 2, 3, \cdots$, $m \neq k$, $\omega_{mk} = (W_m^0 - W_k^0)/\hbar$, $H_{mk}' \equiv \int \psi_m^{0*} f(x) \psi_k^0 \, dx$

(b) $H' = A(x) \sin \omega_0 t$, starting at $t = 0$, then

$$a_m(t) = \frac{- H_{mk}'}{2\hbar} \left[\frac{(e^{i(\omega_{mk}+\omega_0)t} - 1)}{\omega_{mk} + \omega_0} - \frac{(e^{i(\omega_{mk}-\omega_0)t} - 1)}{\omega_{mk} - \omega_0} \right] \qquad [10\text{–}25$$

$m = 1, 2, 3, \cdots$, $m \neq k$, $\omega_{mk} = (W_m^0 - W_k^0)/\hbar$,

and

$$H_{mk}' \equiv \int \psi_m^{0*} A(x) \psi_k^0 \, dx$$

PROBLEMS

Problem 10.1.   A particle of mass $= 9 \times 10^{-28}$ gm is trapped in an infinite-wall, one-dimensional box of width $a = 1 \times 10^{-8}$ cm. The lowest state of this system ($n = 1$) has a characteristic energy $W^0_1 = 38$ e.v. Also, $W^0_2 = 152$ e.v., $W^0_3 = 342$ e.v., and $W^0_4 = 608$ e.v.

At $t = 0$, the particle is known to be in the state for which $n = 1$.

(a) At $t = 0$, a rectangular potential well, $V_0 = -10^4$ e.v., centered at $a/2$ and of width 10^{-12} cm, is suddenly introduced into the well and kept there for 5×10^{-18} second, at which time it is removed. After removal of the perturbation, what is the chance that the system will be found in each of the states $n = 2$, $n = 3$, and $n = 4$? (The height and width of the potential well is characteristic of a neutron interacting with an electron.)

(b) Let the above perturbation continue for a sequence of different time intervals, ranging up to 30 or 40×10^{-18} sec. Plot the $|\,\text{amplitude}\,|^2$ of the $n = 3$ state over this interval. What would be the result of an experiment designed to identify the presence of the $n = 3$ state, if it were performed about 27×10^{-18} sec after the onset of the perturbation?

Problem 10.2

(a) Using the identity, $2 \cos x = e^{ix} + e^{-ix}$, show that the cross terms, neglected in both [10–26] and [10–27] (time-dependent part, only), are equal to

$$(-2)\,\frac{\cos 2\omega_0 t_1 + 1 - \cos (\omega_{mk} - \omega_0) t_1 - \cos (\omega_{mk} + \omega_0) t_1}{(\omega_{mk} - \omega_0)(\omega_{mk} + \omega_0)}$$

(b) Show that when $\omega_{mk} - \omega_0 \ll 1$, the cross terms become, approximately,

$$-\frac{(\omega_{mk} - \omega_0)}{(\omega_{mk} + \omega_0)}\,t_1^2$$

(c) Under what conditions, therefore, are [10–26] and [10–27] good approximations?

Problem 10.3.   Consider, once again, the system of Problem 10.1 where the particle is known to be initially in the state $n = 1$. Now, however, the potential well is perfectly flat from $x = 0$ to $x = a$. Add a perturbation, $H' = A \sin \omega_0 t$, from $t = 0$ to $t = t_1$, where A is a constant, equal to 1 e.v. ($= 1.60 \times 10^{-12}$ erg), *independent of both x and t*. This causes the entire bottom of the well to be raised and lowered sinusoidally with the frequency $v_0 = \omega_0/2\pi$. Assume that the frequency v_0 is $2.8 \times 10^{+16}$ cps [so that $hv_0 = 114$ e.v., the energy needed to reach the first excited state at $(n = 2)$]. Show that no excitation will occur either for $n = 2$ or for any other level.

Problem 10.4. Change the perturbation of Problem 10.3 into the following,

$$H' = A(x) \sin \omega_0 t$$

where

$$A(x) = -1 \text{ e.v. from } x = 0 \text{ to } x = a/2$$
$$A(x) = +1 \text{ e.v. from } x = a/2 \text{ to } x = a$$

and where v_0 is still $2.8 \times 10^{+16}$ cps, the difference in characteristic frequency between the $n = 1$ and the $n = 2$ states.

Let the above perturbation continue for 3.56×10^{-16} second, that is, for 10 complete cycles, and then be removed.

Find $|$ amplitude $|^2$ of vibration of (a) the $n = 2$ state, (b) the $n = 3$ state, and (c) the $n = 4$ state.

Problem 10.5. Equation [10–29] gives the potential energy of a charge e in an electric field E_x, as $eE_x(x - x_0)$, where x_0 is a constant. In Section 10.4 we set $x_0 = 0$, but suppose that this had not been done, so that $H' = e(x - x_0) E_x^0 \sin \omega_0 t$, rather than [10–30]. Show in the two cases discussed in Figure 10.4 that the presence of x_0 in H' does not change the predictions regarding the shifts in excitation of the states of the oscillator.

Problem 10.6. The harmonic oscillator of natural frequency v of Figure 10.4 is assumed to be initially in the pure state ψ_1^0, and experiences an electric field, along the x-axis, whose frequency is equal to v. According to [10–32], the vibrations in the upper state, for which $m = 2$, should grow more rapidly than those in the ground state $m = 0$.

(a) Using the harmonic oscillator eigenfunctions given in Section 3.5, show, for this case, that [10–32] is correct. (The integrals involved are composed of the gamma functions, $\Gamma(n + \frac{1}{2})$, which can be found in a table of definite integrals.)

(b) Let $v = v_0 = 10^{10}$ cycles per second, $e = 1.6 \times 10^{-19}$ coulomb, $m = 20 \times 10^{-27}$ kg (the approximate mass of a nitrogen atom), and $E_x^0 = 100$ volt/m, or nt/coulomb. Calculate the time needed for the most strongly excited of the two states to build up to an intensity of 1 per cent of the excitation of the initial state.

(c) Show that in this problem $H'(\text{max.}) \ll h\nu$, that is, the maximum value of the perturbation energy is small compared to the energy difference between levels. [Suggestion: estimate the maximum value of x from the harmonic oscillator wave function (see Figure 3.10). Does this value of $x(\text{max.})$ agree with the known size of small molecules (2 or 3×10^{-8} cm)?] [Note: NH_3 has a mode of vibration at about 3×10^{10} cps—referred to at the end of Section 3.3 in connection with barrier penetration. The N atom vibrates from one side of the triangular H_3 structure to the other, through a barrier, so it is not a harmonic oscillator, but it does have an electric dipole moment and can, therefore, react with the electric field of the cavity. It is used in Townes's "Maser" (see footnote in Section 10.4).]

Problem 10.7.   We consider a particle of mass 20×10^{-27} kg and charge $e = 1.6 \times 10^{-19}$ coulombs to be in an infinite-wall, one-dimensional box of length L.

(a) What must be the value of L in order that the first excited state lie an amount $h\nu$ above the ground state, where $\nu = 10^{10}$ cps?

(b) This system, initially in its first excited state, is introduced, at $t = 0$, into a microwave cavity which is resonating at 10^{10} cps. In the region occupied by the small system, the electric field (assumed to be parallel to the x-axis of the small system) has the amplitude $E_x^0 = 100$ volt/m. How long will it take for the ground-state vibrations to attain an intensity of 1 percent of the initial state vibrations? (Suggestion: It is convenient, although not essential, to let $x = 0$ in the center of the one-dimensional box and re-write the eigenfunctions accordingly.)

(c) At the time calculated in (b), what is the intensity of vibration of the *second* excited state? (Assume that [10–26] holds, although it cannot be strictly correct owing to the distance from resonance.) What must be happening to the expectation value of the system energy for the small oscillator?

Problem 10.8

(a) Show that a system whose wave function is the superposition of two pure states Ψ_m and Ψ_k, given in [10–33], has the periodically varying electric dipole moment given in [10–34].

(b) Show that if a charged particle in a one-dimensional infinite-wall box is in a superposition of Ψ'_1 and Ψ'_2, one should expect radiation to occur.

(c) What would one expect if the system were in a superposition of Ψ'_1 and Ψ'_3? (Suggestion: Place the origin in the center of the box.)

Problem 10.9. In Chapter 9 it was mentioned that any system which originally has a given exchange symmetry must keep it always. Let the perturbation H' be unchanged by the interchange of x_1 and x_2, the coordinates of two identical particles. Let the initial state of the system be $\Psi'_k(x_1, x_2)$, and the final state be $\Psi'_m(x_1, x_2)$. Assume that one of these states is symmetrical to interchange of x_1 and x_2, while the other is antisymmetrical. Show that if this is true,

$$H'_{mk} = \iint \Psi'_m(x_1, x_2) \, H' \, \Psi'_k(x_1, x_2) \, dx_1 \, dx_2$$

must equal zero, that is, transitions between states of different exchange symmetry do not occur. (Hints: Interchange of variables in a definite integral cannot change its value. When a number equals its own negative, it must be zero.)

Problem 10.10. Using the theory in Section 10.5, calculate the numerical values of b and c for the HCl molecule. (Let ν_0 be given by $h\nu_0 = 2886/(5 \times 10^{15})$ erg and let m, the reduced mass, be 1.6×10^{-24} gm.)

Problem 10.11. Using the perturbation $f(x) = bx^3 + cx^4$ for the harmonic oscillator:

(a) Calculate an expression giving the correction to the energy of the $n = 0$ state.

(b) Calculate an expression for the amplitude $a_1^{(0)}$ of the $n = 1$ state which is "mixed" into ψ_0 by the perturbation above.

(c) Calculate the contribution to the absorption line located near $2h\nu_0$ of the term $a_1^{(0)} \psi_1^0$, present in ψ_0. (Note: The a_1, used in Section 10.5, should more properly be written $a_1^{(2)}$, since it refers to the amplitude of ψ_1^0 present in the first-order wave function ψ_2, for which $n = 2$.)

Proplem 10.12. A particle of mass $m = 10^{-27}$ gm and charge, $e = 4.8 \times 10^{-10}$ esu forms a harmonic oscillator whose resonant frequency is $\nu_0 = 1.0 \times 10^{14}$ cps. At $t = 0$, the oscillator is known to be in the state $n = 0$, and an electric field,

$$E = E_0 \sin 2\pi f t, \, f = 1.1 \times 10^{14} \text{ cps}$$

parallel to the axis of vibration of the oscillator, is applied to the system. $E_0 = 100$ stat-volts/cm. (Note: stat-volts times esu = ergs.)

   (a) At $t = 5 \times 10^{-14}$ sec, what is the probability that the system will be found in the state $n = 1$?

   (b) At $t = 10 \times 10^{-14}$ sec, what is the probability that the system will be found in the state $n = 1$?

   (c) On the average, how much energy does this "off-resonance" system absorb from the electric radiation field?

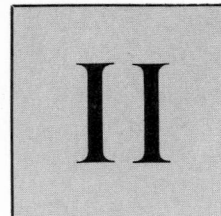

THE RELATIVISTIC WAVE EQUATION AND THE ORIGIN OF ELECTRON SPIN

11.1. The relationship between energy, momentum, and mass in the special theory of relativity

Since the publication of Einstein's special, or restricted, theory of relativity in 1905,[1] it has been clear that Newtonian mechanics is an approximation which is accurate only for laboratory velocities small compared to that of light, $c = 3 \times 10^{10}$ cm/sec. Our principal concern has been with particles of low velocity. For example, in the ground state of the hydrogen atom, the electron at rest at infinity is allowed to drop to an energy level of about -13 e.v. The released potential energy appears as the kinetic energy of the electron. Such electrons have a velocity which is only about 2×10^{-3} c. This is a very small velocity and, since the effects of relativity always appear in proportion to v^2/c^2, one would *expect* that taking special relativity into account would produce extremely small effects in the theory of atomic structure. Such is not the case, however, and when Dirac in 1928 found a way to solve the Schrödinger wave equation, allowing for relativity, he found that the concept of matter waves, even those belonging to low-velocity particles, required significant modification.

---

[1] A. Einstein, *Ann. Physik*, **17**: 891, 1905.

The consequences of including relativity were all out of proportion to those expected on the basis of the low velocity of the electron and were related to the intrinsic structure of the electron. These effects are referred to as the "electron spin," first postulated by Uhlenbeck and Goudsmit[2] in 1925 to interpret certain features of atomic spectra.

In contemplating spin, one is tempted to have a mental picture of an electric charge spinning about an axis through the charge, but—at least for high velocity—the Dirac theory shows that this simple picture cannot be valid. The Dirac theory has been completely successful in accounting for the behavior of both low- and high-energy electrons.

In an introductory treatment of quantum mechanics it is very difficult to give a really adequate account of electron spin, and this chapter, therefore, is something of an experiment. One can readily argue that the title promises more than is actually delivered. For example, the idea of spin is intimately associated with the concept of rotation, and yet we do not succeed in demonstrating the connection between spin and ordinary angular momentum. (At the end of Section 11.7, however, we do outline the argument which leads to this association, and make reference to the more complete theory.) None the less, there *are* certain significant phenomena associated with spin which we demonstrate here. We shall explain the doubling of the occupation of the states for particles with antisymmetric wave functions, discussed at the end of Section 9.5, and also the "singlet" and "triplet" states which always appear whenever systems are composed of two electrons. Both are clearly demonstrated in one-dimensional systems where ordinary angular momentum cannot even be defined. Since some of the important features due to spin appear without any reference to ordinary angular momentum, the "intrinsic angular momentum" associated with spin must be regarded as only *one* of the several aspects demonstrated by the matter waves of the Dirac theory. Since, in this chapter, we do not venture beyond one-dimensional systems, we shall have to be content with a description of only those aspects of spin which appear in these simple cases.

The broad applicability of the basic postulates is highlighted by the Dirac theory, since the whole set of phenomena associated with "electron spin" is an automatic result of these same postulates when using the exact (relativistic) relationship between total energy W, the momentum $\mathbf{p}$, and the rest mass m. For a free particle, this relationship is

$$W^2/c^2 = p_x^2 + p_y^2 + p_z^2 + m^2c^2 \qquad [11-1]$$

In Appendix IX this relationship is derived from two starting points,[3]

---

[2] G. Uhlenbeck and S. Goudsmit, *Naturwiss.*, **13**: 593, 1925; *Nature*, **117**: 263, 1926.

[3] For a short introduction to the theory of relativity, see F. K. Richtmyer, E. H. Kennard, and T. Lauritsen, *Introduction to Modern Physics* (McGraw-Hill Book Co., Inc., New York, any edition, 1928–1955). For a more complete discussion, see P. Bergman, *Introduction to the Theory of Relativity* (1946, Prentice-Hall, Inc., New York), or M. Born (tr. by H. L. Brose), *Einstein's Theory of Relativity* (1924, Methuen Co., London).

(1) M (inertial mass of a particle moving in the laboratory, with velocity v)

$$= \frac{m}{\sqrt{1 - v^2/c^2}} \qquad [11-2$$

and (2) Newton's Second Law, in its original and most basic form,

$$\mathbf{F} = (d/dt)(M \mathbf{v}) \qquad [11-3$$

The truth of [11–2] follows, after a considerable chain of reasoning, from Einstein's basic assumption that in any "inertial" (i.e., unaccelerated) frame of reference all the laws of physical phenomena are identical in form,[4] including the (observed) constancy of the velocity of light. The relation [11–2] has, however, been subjected to accurate experimental verification. As the measured velocity of electrons increases, it becomes more and more difficult to make them curve in a magnetic field. It is not simply that v (in Mv) is increasing, but also one must regard M as increasing as in [11–2]. Starting from m, the rest mass at low velocities M increases at first slowly and then very rapidly, as v approaches c. If we define force as the time rate of change of momentum and regard [11–2] as an experimental observation, we are led to the relation (see Appendix IX)

$$W \text{ (the total energy)} = \pm c\sqrt{p_x^2 + p_y^2 + p_z^2 + m^2 c^2} \qquad [11-4$$

which permits both positive and negative values of the total energy W.

Equation [11–4], or [11–1] to which it is equivalent, is the relativistice expression analogous to

$$W = (p_x^2 + p_y^2 + p_z^2)/2m$$

of the nonrelativistic case. We can now develop a relativistic quantum theory by applying Postulate II to [11–4] just as we did in the nonrelativistic case. By this process we will obtain the Dirac equation which is the relativistic version of the Schrödinger equation. The solutions to the Dirac equation must be well behaved and possess an integrable square as required by Postulates III and IV. Similarly, we shall calculate expectation values using Postulate V.

We shall see that although the Dirac theory starts off naturally enough from the familiar Postulates, almost immediately one finds oneself on a very strange path (mathematically speaking), which, with great ingenuity, Dirac succeeded in following to its surprising end.

By Postulate II, the expression [11–4] for the total energy is converted into the time-dependent wave equation by the operator substitutions

$$p_x \to (\hbar/i)\, \partial/\partial x, \text{ etc., and } W \to - (\hbar/i)\, \partial/\partial t$$

giving the wave equation

$$- (\hbar/i)(\partial/\partial t)\, \Psi = \pm c\sqrt{- \hbar^2(\partial^2/\partial x^2 + \partial^2/\partial y^2 + \partial^2/\partial z^2) + m^2 c^2}\ \Psi \qquad [11-5$$

---

[4] This is Einstein's "principle of covariance."

Here one is brought to a halt by the failure of the mathematical symbolism. What, if anything, is the meaning of a linear set of second-order derivatives inside the radical? Are the basic postulates in error, leading to a nonmeaningful result, or are they not being applied correctly? Dirac found the way out of the dilemma. He ignored [11–5] and went back to the basic Hamiltonian [11–4]. He concluded that [11–4] must *first* be freed from the radical before it could be converted into the wave-mechanical operator. The balance of this chapter is concerned with the method Dirac used to accomplish this seemingly impossible task, and with some of the simpler of the many consequences that ensue when this is done.

11.2. The relativistic Hamiltonian in linear form

Undeterred by the apparently impossible problem of expressing

$$p_x^2 + p_y^2 + p_z^2 + m^2 c^2 \qquad\qquad [11–6$$

as a perfect square, Dirac boldly wrote down the relationship

$$p_x^2 + p_y^2 + p_z^2 + m^2 c^2 = (a_x p_x + a_y p_y + a_z p_z + \beta mc)^2 \qquad [11–7$$

and asked what conditions must be placed upon a_x, a_y, a_z, and β in order for this to be true.

Multiplying out the expression on the right side of [11–7], and preserving the order of the factors in each term, we have

$$(a_x p_x + a_y p_y + a_z p_z + \beta mc)^2 =$$
$$a_x^2 p_x^2 + a_x a_y p_x p_y + a_x a_z p_x p_z + a_x \beta p_x mc$$
$$+ a_y a_x p_y p_x + a_y^2 p_y^2 + a_y a_z p_y p_z + a_y \beta p_y mc$$
$$+ a_z a_x p_z p_x + a_z a_y p_z p_y + a_z^2 p_z^2 + a_z \beta p_z mc \qquad [11–8$$
$$+ \beta a_x mc p_x + \beta a_y mc p_y + \beta a_z mc p_z + \beta^2 m^2 c^2$$

It is clear that the a's and β cannot be ordinary numbers since, if they were, all the cross-product terms present on the right side of [11–8] would prevent it from being equal to the left side of [11–7]. If [11–7] and [11–8] are to both hold, then it is necessary, first of all, that

$$a_x^2 = a_y^2 = a_z^2 = \beta^2 = 1 \qquad\qquad [11–9$$

In addition, all the cross terms must add up to zero. This can be accomplished by requiring that terms symmetrically disposed about the diagonal from the upper left corner to the lower right corner of [11–8] should add up, pair by pair, to zero. For example, $a_x a_y + a_y a_x = 0$ would dispose of the two cross terms nearest the upper left-hand corner—providing that $p_x p_y = p_y p_x$. This requirement is met, however, since p_x and p_y, when converted into their operator forms $(\hbar/i)(\partial/\partial x)$ and $(\hbar/i)(\partial/\partial y)$, are "commuting operators"—that is they obey the rule

$$[- \hbar^2(\partial/\partial x)(\partial/\partial y) \, \psi] - [- \hbar^2(\partial/\partial y)(\partial/\partial x) \, \psi] = 0 \qquad [11\text{--}10]$$

All of the off-diagonal terms in [11–8] cancel, pair by pair, if the α's and β "anticommute," that is, if

$$\alpha_x \alpha_y = - \alpha_y \alpha_x, \; \alpha_x \alpha_z = - \alpha_z \alpha_x, \; \alpha_x \beta = - \beta \alpha_x$$
$$\alpha_y \alpha_z = - \alpha_z \alpha_y, \; \; \alpha_y \beta = - \beta \alpha_y, \; \; \alpha_z \beta = - \beta \alpha_z \qquad [11\text{--}11]$$

Since p_x, p_y, and p_z will be converted into differential operators by Postulate II, it is reasonable also to regard the α's and β as operators which will "operate on" the wave function ψ, along with $- (\hbar/i)(\partial/\partial x)$, etc.

Thus, if the α's and β obey [11–9] and [11–11], and the p's obey [11–10], equation [11–8] becomes an identity, and the relativistic Hamiltonian [11–4] becomes

$$W \text{ (the total energy)} = c \, \alpha_x \, p_x + c \, \alpha_y \, p_y + c \, \alpha_z \, p_z + \beta \, mc^2 \quad [11\text{--}12]$$

or, equally well,

$$W = - c \, \alpha_x \, p_x - c \, \alpha_y \, p_y - c \, \alpha_z \, p_z - \beta \, mc^2 \qquad [11\text{--}13]$$

since replacing, everywhere in [11–9] and [11–10], each α by $-\alpha$ and each β by $-\beta$, does not change these operator relationships.

Having removed the radical in the relativistic Hamiltonian of a free particle, [11–4], we now make the usual quantum-mechanical operator substitutions into either [11–12] or [11–13]. Dirac chose to use [11–13]:

$$- (\hbar/i)(\partial/\partial t) \, \Psi = - [(c\hbar/i) \, \alpha_x(\partial/\partial x) + (c\hbar/i) \, \alpha_y(\partial/\partial y)$$
$$+ (c\hbar/i) \, \alpha_z(\partial/\partial z) + \beta \, mc^2] \, \Psi \qquad [11\text{--}13a]$$

We separate the equation into time and space equations in the usual way by setting

$$\Psi = \psi(x, y, z) \, \phi(t) \qquad [11\text{--}14]$$

If the α's and β are constants—that is, if they do not depend upon x, y, z, p_x, p_y, p_z, or t—the wave equation [11–13a] becomes two separated equations (see Section 3.1).

The time-dependent equation has the solution,

$$\phi(t) = e^{-i\frac{W}{\hbar}t} \qquad [11\text{--}15]$$

where W is the separation constant. As in nonrelativistic theory, when $\psi(x, y, z)$ is an eigenfunction, W turns out to be the expectation value of the energy operator.

The amplitude equation becomes

$$H \, \psi = W \, \psi; \; H = - \frac{c\hbar}{i} \left(\alpha_x \frac{\partial}{\partial x} + \alpha_y \frac{\partial}{\partial y} + \alpha_z \frac{\partial}{\partial z} \right) - \beta \, mc^2 \qquad [11\text{--}16]$$

where H is the operator on the right side of [11–13a] and W is the separation constant. The equation $H\psi = W\psi$ looks familiar, but there is a very important new feature. H contains not only the familiar spatial derivatives, such as $\partial/\partial x$ (now in first order only), but also the mysterious α's and β, which must obey the commutation rules [11–11], as well as the condition [11–9].

The α's and β cannot be simple, first-order, differential operators, since these do not anticommute but rather commute—as, for example, the operators $\partial/\partial x$ and $\partial/\partial y$ in [11–10].

There is, however, a type of operator, called a matrix operator, which can be made to have exactly the commutation rules required of the α's and β. These operators have long been known to mathematicians. In addition, they played a key role in Heisenberg's "matrix formulation" of quantum mechanics. In the next section we will describe some of the elementary principles of operation with matrices and show that operators can be found which meet the requirements [11–9] and [11–11].

11.3.   Matrix operators[5]

A mathematical operator is a symbol, which, when placed to the left of some mathematical function or other expression, converts it, by means of specific rules, into a different function or expression.

The familiar operator d/dx converts any function $f(x)$ into some other function $g(x)$, by means of certain definite rules. Suppose, rather than to convert one function into another, that the problem is to convert an ordered set of numbers—such as the components of a vector—into another ordered set of numbers. This can be done in many different ways, but a particularly simple method of converting two numbers x_1 and x_2 into some other pair of numbers y_1 and y_2 is by means of the linear equations,

$$a_{11} x_1 + a_{12} x_2 = y_1$$
$$a_{21} x_1 + a_{22} x_2 = y_2$$

[11–17

where the a's are constants. Given any ordered pair (x_1, x_2), one can produce, using [11–17], a second ordered pair (y_1, y_2). We use the set of linear equations [11–17] to "operate on" one set of numbers (x_1, x_2) to produce a second set of numbers (y_1, y_2). Once we limit ourselves to using linear equations, such as [11–17], the only distinctive thing about the equations is the set of a's.

By writing the a's in an array—paralleling their positions in the set of equations—and by writing the x's and y's in a special array consisting of one column, we can reconstruct the set of equations. The arrays, representing

---

[5] For an excellent introduction to matrix operators, see V. Rojansky, *Introductory Quantum Mechanics* (1942, Prentice-Hall, Inc., New York): p. 285.

[11–17], are

$$-\begin{pmatrix} a_{11} & a_{12} \\ a_{21} & a_{22} \end{pmatrix} \rightarrow \begin{pmatrix} x_1 \\ x_2 \end{pmatrix} = \begin{pmatrix} y_1 \\ y_2 \end{pmatrix}$$

[11–18

The square array of the *a*'s is called a 2-by-2 matrix. The arrays of the *x*'s and the *y*'s are called column symbols, or one-column matrices, or "spinors." The two lines with arrowheads are not part of the symbolism but are aids used in describing the operation of the matrix upon the column symbol

$$\begin{pmatrix} x_1 \\ x_2 \end{pmatrix}$$

producing thereby the column symbol

$$\begin{pmatrix} y_1 \\ y_2 \end{pmatrix}$$

The two lines drawn in [11–18] would intersect at the position of x_1, the top position in the column symbol. They are concerned with the calculation of y_1, which has the top position in the column symbol and is identified by the dotted circle. The rule for calculating y_1 is apparent from [11–17]. The first *a* in the row (identified by the horizontal arrow) is multiplied into the first *x* in the column symbol. To this result is added the product of the second *a* in the row and the second *x* in the column. The symbols at the tails of the arrows are always multiplied together first, and then the next pair, in order, until finally one multiplies together the two symbols nearest the heads of the arrows. Thus,

$$y_1 = a_{11} x_1 + a_{12} x_2$$

Imagine the arrow to be removed from the top row of the matrix and drawn through the bottom row. The two lines now would intersect at the position of x_2 and are, therefore, concerned with the calculation of the second term y_2 in the resulting column symbol. Again, the first *a*, identified by the line through the matrix, is multiplied into the first (the top) *x*, and the second *a* is multiplied into the second *x*. Thus,

$$y_2 = a_{21} x_1 + a_{22} x_2$$

In this manner the matrix of the *a*'s operates on one ordered pair (the *x*'s) and produces a *new* ordered pair (the *y*'s). This matrix operation is identical to the two linear equations [11–17].

Suppose that a 3-by-3 matrix operates on a column symbol of three components.

$$\begin{pmatrix} a_{11} & a_{12} & a_{13} \\ a_{21} & a_{22} & a_{23} \\ a_{31} & a_{32} & a_{33} \end{pmatrix} \rightarrow \begin{pmatrix} x_1 \\ x_2 \\ x_3 \end{pmatrix} = \begin{pmatrix} y_1 \\ y_2 \\ y_3 \end{pmatrix}$$

Here the lines are drawn to aid in the calculation of y_2, which is identified by intersection of the two arrows and marked with the dotted circle. Thus,

$$y_2 = a_{21} x_1 + a_{22} x_2 + a_{23} x_3$$

Similarly,

$$y_1 = a_{11} x_1 + a_{12} x_2 + a_{13} x_3 \text{ and } y_3 = a_{31} x_1 + a_{32} x_2 + a_{33} x_3$$

Thus, an ordered triplet of x's has been converted into another ordered triplet, the y's. If, for example, the three x's are the three components of a vector, then the matrix of the a's (which we shall symbolize by A) operates on the vector **x**, producing thereby a new vector, **y**; $(A\,\mathbf{x} = \mathbf{y})$.[6]

Returning to [11–18], we ask what will happen if both sides are operated on (necessarily, from the left) by a second 2-by-2 matrix,

$$B = \begin{pmatrix} b_{11} & b_{12} \\ b_{21} & b_{22} \end{pmatrix}$$

We first calculate the right side of [11–18], since this is covered by the rules already stated,

$$\begin{pmatrix} b_{11} & b_{12} \\ b_{21} & b_{22} \end{pmatrix} \begin{pmatrix} y_1 \\ y_2 \end{pmatrix} = \begin{pmatrix} b_{11} & b_{12} \\ b_{21} & b_{22} \end{pmatrix} \underbrace{\begin{pmatrix} [a_{11}x_1 + a_{12}x_2] \\ [a_{21}x_1 + a_{22}x_2] \end{pmatrix}}_{\text{the column symbol } \binom{y_1}{y_2} \text{ from [11-18]}}$$

$$= \underbrace{\begin{pmatrix} [b_{11}(a_{11}x_1 + a_{12}x_2) + b_{12}(a_{21}x_1 + a_{22}x_2)] \\ [b_{21}(a_{11}x_1 + a_{12}x_2) + b_{22}(a_{21}x_1 + a_{22}x_2)] \end{pmatrix}}_{\text{the column symbol } \binom{z_1}{z_2}} \qquad [11\text{–}19$$

The final result is the column symbol

$$\begin{pmatrix} z_1 \\ z_2 \end{pmatrix}$$

The left side of [11–18] is

$$-\begin{pmatrix} b_{11}\!-\!b_{12} \\ b_{21} & b_{22} \end{pmatrix} \rightarrow \begin{pmatrix} a_{11} & a_{12} \\ a_{21} & a_{22} \end{pmatrix} \begin{pmatrix} x_1 \\ x_2 \end{pmatrix} = \begin{pmatrix} c_{11} & c_{12} \\ c_{21} & c_{22} \end{pmatrix} \begin{pmatrix} x_1 \\ x_2 \end{pmatrix} \qquad [11\text{–}20$$

where again we have drawn two lines to aid in the calculation of the product of the two matrices, A and B. We shall state the rule for forming this product and then see that it leads to the same result as we have already obtained for the right side of [11–18].

---

[6] For example, the operator " curl," or $(\nabla \times)$, converts one vector into another.

The intersection of the two arrows identifies the location, in the product matrix C, of the calculations: The first b times the first (the top) a, plus the second b times the second a. For the lines drawn in [11–20] this sum is the matrix element c_{11} which appears in the dotted circle in the upper left-hand corner of the new matrix, C. Thus, $c_{11} = b_{11} a_{11} + b_{12} a_{21}$. Shifting the vertical arrow, through A, so as to go vertically through the *second* column, we obtain the matrix element, c_{12}, in the upper right-hand corner of C. Thus,

$$c_{12} = b_{11} a_{12} + b_{12} a_{22}$$

Shifting the horizontal arrow through B to the bottom row, we can obtain the two c's in the bottom row, thus,

$$\underbrace{\begin{pmatrix} (b_{11} a_{11} + b_{12} a_{21}) & (b_{11} a_{12} + b_{12} a_{22}) \\ (b_{21} a_{11} + b_{22} a_{21}) & (b_{21} a_{12} + b_{22} a_{22}) \end{pmatrix}}_{= C} \begin{pmatrix} x_1 \\ x_2 \end{pmatrix} \qquad [11\text{--}21$$

The new matrix, C, now operates upon the column symbol

$$\begin{pmatrix} x_1 \\ x_2 \end{pmatrix}$$

giving the final column symbol

$$\begin{pmatrix} z_1 \\ z_2 \end{pmatrix}$$

$$\begin{pmatrix} (b_{11} a_{11} + b_{12} a_{21}) x_1 + (b_{11} a_{12} + b_{12} a_{22}) x_2 \\ (b_{21} a_{11} + b_{22} a_{21}) x_1 + (b_{21} a_{21} + b_{22} a_{22}) x_2 \end{pmatrix} = \begin{pmatrix} z_1 \\ z_2 \end{pmatrix} \qquad [11\text{--}22$$

which is identical to [11–19]. Thus the rule for multiplying matrices leads to the same final result as was obtained by operating twice in succession upon the original column symbol

$$\begin{pmatrix} x_1 \\ x_2 \end{pmatrix}$$

Each of these basic operations is just a shorthand description of a calculation using a set of linear equations such as [11–17].

As a second example of matrix multiplication, we calculate the central term in the right-hand column of the product matrix of

$$-\begin{pmatrix} b_{11} & b_{12} & b_{13} \\ b_{21}\!\!-\!\!b_{22}\!\!-\!\!b_{23}\!\!- \\ b_{31} & b_{32} & b_{33} \end{pmatrix} \rightarrow \begin{pmatrix} a_{11} & a_{12} & a_{13} \\ a_{21} & a_{22} & a_{23} \\ a_{31} & a_{32} & a_{33} \end{pmatrix} = \begin{pmatrix} c_{11} & c_{12} & c_{13} \\ c_{21} & c_{22} & (c_{23}) \\ c_{31} & c_{32} & c_{33} \end{pmatrix}$$

with the result,

$$c_{23} = b_{21} a_{13} + b_{22} a_{23} + b_{23} a_{33}$$

To multiply a matrix by a constant, one merely multiplies each of the elements by the constant. Thus, a constant k can be written as the matrix

$$\begin{pmatrix} k & 0 & 0 \\ 0 & k & 0 \\ 0 & 0 & k \end{pmatrix}$$

since

$$\begin{pmatrix} k & 0 & 0 \\ 0 & k & 0 \\ 0 & 0 & k \end{pmatrix} \begin{pmatrix} a_{11} & a_{12} & a_{13} \\ a_{21} & a_{22} & a_{23} \\ a_{31} & a_{32} & a_{33} \end{pmatrix} = \begin{pmatrix} ka_{11} & ka_{12} & ka_{13} \\ ka_{21} & ka_{22} & ka_{23} \\ ka_{31} & ka_{32} & ka_{33} \end{pmatrix}$$

The elements of a matrix may consist of complex numbers. The set of linear equations, which are thereby summarized, have complex coefficients and, in general, the column symbols have complex "components."

Dirac showed that the α's and the β needed to linearize the Hamiltonian could be represented by 4-by-4 matrices. By a proper choice of elements (there is more than one set of choices), the α's and the β will obey the commutation rules [11–11] and also will meet the normalization requirements of [11–9]. Rather than take arbitrary examples of matrices to demonstrate the complete multiplication process, we shall use Dirac's four matrices and show by multiplication that they have the required characteristics.

11.4. The Dirac matrices

The four Dirac matrices are

$$\beta = \begin{pmatrix} 1 & 0 & 0 & 0 \\ 0 & 1 & 0 & 0 \\ 0 & 0 & -1 & 0 \\ 0 & 0 & 0 & -1 \end{pmatrix} \qquad \alpha_x = \begin{pmatrix} 0 & 0 & 0 & 1 \\ 0 & 0 & 1 & 0 \\ 0 & 1 & 0 & 0 \\ 1 & 0 & 0 & 0 \end{pmatrix}$$

$$\alpha_y = \begin{pmatrix} 0 & 0 & 0 & -i \\ 0 & 0 & i & 0 \\ 0 & -i & 0 & 0 \\ i & 0 & 0 & 0 \end{pmatrix} \qquad \alpha_z = \begin{pmatrix} 0 & 0 & 1 & 0 \\ 0 & 0 & 0 & -1 \\ 1 & 0 & 0 & 0 \\ 0 & -1 & 0 & 0 \end{pmatrix} \quad [11\text{--}23$$

First, we show that each matrix multiplied by itself turns into the unit matrix

$$\begin{pmatrix} 1 & 0 & 0 & 0 \\ 0 & 1 & 0 & 0 \\ 0 & 0 & 1 & 0 \\ 0 & 0 & 0 & 1 \end{pmatrix}$$

which is the matrix symbol for unity. The reason for this can be seen by noting that when the unit matrix operates on any column symbol, it merely transforms the column symbol into itself—that is, it multiplies it by 1.

As an example, we calculate β^2:

$$\begin{pmatrix} 1 & 0 & 0 & 0 \\ 0 & 1 & 0 & 0 \\ 0 & 0 & -1 & 0 \\ 0 & 0 & 0 & -1 \end{pmatrix} \begin{pmatrix} 1 & 0 & 0 & 0 \\ 0 & 1 & 0 & 0 \\ 0 & 0 & -1 & 0 \\ 0 & 0 & 0 & -1 \end{pmatrix} = \begin{pmatrix} 1 & 0 & 0 & 0 \\ 0 & 1 & 0 & 0 \\ 0 & 0 & 1 & 0 \\ 0 & 0 & 0 & 1 \end{pmatrix}$$

Similarly, by writing, twice, each of the Dirac matrices [11–23], it is easy to see that the product will always give the unit matrix.

In addition to the requirement that the square of each matrix is unity, the four matrices must anticommute. As an example, consider a_x and a_y.

$$a_x\, a_y = \begin{pmatrix} 0 & 0 & 0 & 1 \\ 0 & 0 & 1 & 0 \\ 0 & 1 & 0 & 0 \\ 1 & 0 & 0 & 0 \end{pmatrix} \begin{pmatrix} 0 & 0 & 0 & -i \\ 0 & 0 & i & 0 \\ 0 & -i & 0 & 0 \\ i & 0 & 0 & 0 \end{pmatrix} = \begin{pmatrix} i & 0 & 0 & 0 \\ 0 & -i & 0 & 0 \\ 0 & 0 & i & 0 \\ 0 & 0 & 0 & -i \end{pmatrix}$$

but

$$a_y\, a_x = \begin{pmatrix} 0 & 0 & 0 & -i \\ 0 & 0 & i & 0 \\ 0 & -i & 0 & 0 \\ i & 0 & 0 & 0 \end{pmatrix} \begin{pmatrix} 0 & 0 & 0 & 1 \\ 0 & 0 & 1 & 0 \\ 0 & 1 & 0 & 0 \\ 1 & 0 & 0 & 0 \end{pmatrix} = \begin{pmatrix} -i & 0 & 0 & 0 \\ 0 & i & 0 & 0 \\ 0 & 0 & -i & 0 \\ 0 & 0 & 0 & i \end{pmatrix}$$

so

$$a_x\, a_y = (-1)\, a_y\, a_x$$

In a similar manner to this one can quickly show that any pair of the matrices [11–23] anticommute.

Dirac showed that there does not exist any set of four 2-by-2 or four 3-by-3 matrices that meet the requirements on the a's and β. Now, the purpose of this whole effort is to find a well-behaved solution, of integrable square, to the amplitude wave equation [11–16]

$$- c\,(a_x\, p_x + a_y\, p_y + a_z\, p_z + \beta mc)\, \psi = W\psi \qquad [11\text{–}24$$

where the p's are the differential operators $(\hbar/i)(\partial/\partial x)$, etc. Dirac was forced to go to 4-by-4 matrices in order to find some a's and β which made [11–24] possible. What does this mean?

The operation with a 4-by-4 matrix cannot be performed unless the operand is a four-component quantity, such as a column symbol. Dirac concluded, therefore, that the wave function amplitude, which in nonrelativistic theory is a simple scalar quantity, must now be regarded as a four-component quantity,

$$\psi(x, y, z) = \begin{pmatrix} \psi_1(x, y, z) \\ \psi_2(x, y, z) \\ \psi_3(x, y, z) \\ \psi_4(x, y, z) \end{pmatrix} \qquad [11\text{–}24a$$

An ordinary vector can only be described with an ordered set of three numbers, such as its Cartesian coordinates, x, y, and z. In relativity, due to the interdependence of space and time, an ordered set of four quantities such as x, y, z, and ict describes the location of an event in space-time. It is not surprising, therefore, to find that the Ψ-waves belonging to the relativistic Hamiltonian *can* have an amplitude ψ, with a "vector-like" character.[7] It is exactly this vector quality of the ψ-wave which is needed to explain the phenomena associated with electron "spin." For example, the electromagnetic field must be described by at least four quantities—the scalar and vector potentials, ϕ, A_x, A_y, and A_z, or the two vectors, **E** and **B** (six quantities, but with interdependence which reduces the independent quantities to four). The ψ-waves, determined by the Dirac Hamiltonian, are much more complicated than those of the nonrelativistic Hamiltonian. Fortunately, as we shall see in Section 11.10, for velocities small compared to the velocity of light, the ψ-waves are quite accurately describable in terms of only two of the four components.

Once we admit the necessity of four-component ψ functions, a step of great significance, [11–24] becomes *four* equations. The equality sign in [11–24] signifies the identity of two four-component column symbols, and, as in the case of the equation between two vectors **A** = **B**, we have the requirement that each of the corresponding components are equal. For vectors, this means $A_x = B_x$, $A_y = B_y$, and $A_z = B_z$.

11.5. The Dirac wave equation for a free particle

As in the case of an ordinary vector, the derivative of a column symbol is

$$\frac{\partial}{\partial x}\begin{pmatrix} \psi_1 \\ \psi_2 \\ \psi_3 \\ \psi_4 \end{pmatrix} = \begin{pmatrix} \frac{\partial}{\partial x} & 0 & 0 & 0 \\ 0 & \frac{\partial}{\partial x} & 0 & 0 \\ 0 & 0 & \frac{\partial}{\partial x} & 0 \\ 0 & 0 & 0 & \frac{\partial}{\partial x} \end{pmatrix}\begin{pmatrix} \psi_1 \\ \psi_2 \\ \psi_3 \\ \psi_4 \end{pmatrix} = \begin{pmatrix} \frac{\partial}{\partial x}\psi_1 \\ \frac{\partial}{\partial x}\psi_2 \\ \frac{\partial}{\partial x}\psi_3 \\ \frac{\partial}{\partial x}\psi_4 \end{pmatrix}$$

that is, *each* of the components is operated on by the differential operator.

We are now ready to convert [11–24] into a wave equation using the Dirac matrix operators, and the column symbols [11–24a] for the amplitude ψ of the

---

[7] The Schrödinger relativistic wave equation is obtained by making the standard operator substitutions directly into [11–1]. The ψ-waves obtained from this relativistic wave equation— see L. I. Schiff, *Quantum Mechanics* (1949, McGraw-Hill Book Co., Inc., New York): p. 306 —have a *single* component amplitude, ψ. These waves do not apply to electrons since they do not account for the effects of spin, and also they do not give the correct energy levels (fine structure) of the hydrogen atom.

wave function. Writing out [11–24] in full, we have

$$- (c\hbar/i) \begin{pmatrix} 0 & 0 & 0 & 1 \\ 0 & 0 & 1 & 0 \\ 0 & 1 & 0 & 0 \\ 1 & 0 & 0 & 0 \end{pmatrix} \begin{pmatrix} \dfrac{\partial}{\partial x} \psi_1 \\ \dfrac{\partial}{\partial x} \psi_2 \\ \dfrac{\partial}{\partial x} \psi_3 \\ \dfrac{\partial}{\partial x} \psi_4 \end{pmatrix}$$

$$- (c\hbar/i) \begin{pmatrix} 0 & 0 & 0 & -i \\ 0 & 0 & i & 0 \\ 0 & -i & 0 & 0 \\ i & 0 & 0 & 0 \end{pmatrix} \begin{pmatrix} \dfrac{\partial}{\partial y} \psi_1 \\ \dfrac{\partial}{\partial y} \psi_2 \\ \dfrac{\partial}{\partial y} \psi_3 \\ \dfrac{\partial}{\partial y} \psi_4 \end{pmatrix}$$

$$- (c\hbar/i) \begin{pmatrix} 0 & 0 & 1 & 0 \\ 0 & 0 & 0 & -1 \\ 1 & 0 & 0 & 0 \\ 0 & -1 & 0 & 0 \end{pmatrix} \begin{pmatrix} \dfrac{\partial}{\partial z} \psi_1 \\ \dfrac{\partial}{\partial z} \psi_2 \\ \dfrac{\partial}{\partial z} \psi_3 \\ \dfrac{\partial}{\partial z} \psi_4 \end{pmatrix}$$

$$- mc^2 \begin{pmatrix} 1 & 0 & 0 & 0 \\ 0 & 1 & 0 & 0 \\ 0 & 0 & -1 & 0 \\ 0 & 0 & 0 & -1 \end{pmatrix} \begin{pmatrix} \psi_1 \\ \psi_2 \\ \psi_3 \\ \psi_4 \end{pmatrix} = W \begin{pmatrix} \psi_1 \\ \psi_2 \\ \psi_3 \\ \psi_4 \end{pmatrix} \quad [11\text{–}25$$

Using each of the matrix operators on the column symbol to its right, [11–25] becomes an equation involving five column symbols,

$$
-\frac{c\hbar}{i}\begin{pmatrix}\dfrac{\partial}{\partial x}\psi_4\\[4pt]\dfrac{\partial}{\partial x}\psi_3\\[4pt]\dfrac{\partial}{\partial x}\psi_2\\[4pt]\dfrac{\partial}{\partial x}\psi_1\end{pmatrix}
-\frac{c\hbar}{i}\begin{pmatrix}-i\dfrac{\partial}{\partial y}\psi_4\\[4pt]+i\dfrac{\partial}{\partial y}\psi_3\\[4pt]-i\dfrac{\partial}{\partial y}\psi_2\\[4pt]+i\dfrac{\partial}{\partial y}\psi_1\end{pmatrix}
-\frac{c\hbar}{i}\begin{pmatrix}+\dfrac{\partial}{\partial z}\psi_3\\[4pt]-\dfrac{\partial}{\partial z}\psi_4\\[4pt]+\dfrac{\partial}{\partial z}\psi_1\\[4pt]-\dfrac{\partial}{\partial z}\psi_2\end{pmatrix}
$$

$$
-mc^2\begin{pmatrix}\psi_1\\\psi_2\\-\psi_3\\-\psi_4\end{pmatrix}-W\begin{pmatrix}\psi_1\\\psi_2\\\psi_3\\\psi_4\end{pmatrix}=0
$$

$$[11\text{-}26$$

Just as the vector equation $\mathbf{A}+\mathbf{B}=\mathbf{C}$ means that $A_x+B_x=C_x$, $A_y+B_y=C_y$, etc., so an equation between column symbols means that the same relationship holds for *each* of the four components. Thus, the top component in each of the column symbols yields the equation,

$$
\frac{c\hbar}{i}\frac{\partial}{\partial x}\psi_4-i\frac{c\hbar}{i}\frac{\partial}{\partial y}\psi_4+\frac{c\hbar}{i}\frac{\partial}{\partial z}\psi_3+mc^2\psi_1+W\psi_1=0
$$

The second component of the column symbols yields another equation, etc. Written in order, the four equations obtained by equating corresponding components are:

$$
(W+mc^2)\psi_1 \;+\; 0 \;+\; (c\hbar/i)\frac{\partial}{\partial z}\psi_3 \;+\; \left(\frac{c\hbar}{i}\right)\left(\frac{\partial}{\partial x}-i\frac{\partial}{\partial y}\right)\psi_4=0
$$

$$
0 \;+\; (W+mc^2)\psi_2 \;+\;\frac{c\hbar}{i}\left(\frac{\partial}{\partial x}+i\frac{\partial}{\partial y}\right)\psi_3 \;-\;\frac{c\hbar}{i}\frac{\partial}{\partial z}\psi_4 \;=0
$$

$$
\frac{c\hbar}{i}\frac{\partial}{\partial z}\psi_1 \;+\;\frac{c\hbar}{i}\left(\frac{\partial}{\partial x}-i\frac{\partial}{\partial y}\right)\psi_2+ \;(W-mc^2)\psi_3 \;+\; 0 \;=0
$$

$$
\frac{c\hbar}{i}\left(\frac{\partial}{\partial x}+i\frac{\partial}{\partial y}\right)\psi_1-\;\frac{c\hbar}{i}\frac{\partial}{\partial z}\psi_2 \;+\; 0 \;+\; (W-mc^2)\psi_4 \;=0
$$

$$[11\text{-}27$$

This set of linear, partial differential equations is the Dirac wave equation. Here it tells how the four components of ψ—the matter waves of a free particle— must vary in space. If the new ψ is to be well behaved, *each* of its components must be well behaved, and if it is to have an integrable square, *each* of its components must have an integrable square. For ψ to be a nontrivial solution of [11–27], at least one of its components must be non zero.

For comparison, we write the nonrelativistic amplitude equation for a free particle [4–7],

$$[(\partial^2/\partial x^2) + (\partial^2/\partial y^2) + (\partial^2/\partial z^2)]\,\psi + (2m/\hbar^2)\,W\,\psi = 0$$

and we see that starting with the relativistic Hamiltonian makes a *very* great difference in our description of matter waves.

It is not surprising to discover that finding solutions to [11–27] is generally more difficult than finding solutions to the nonrelativistic Schrödinger equation. For this reason we are going to study a very simple case. We shall assume that the solution to [11–27] has the form of a plane wave, propagating along the x-axis. To have a bounded wave, all of the components of ψ must approach zero for both large positive and negative values of all three spatial coordinates. We assume, however, that

$$\Psi = \psi(x)\,e^{-i\frac{W}{\hbar}t}; \quad \psi = \begin{pmatrix} A_1\,e^{i\frac{2\pi}{\lambda}x} \\ A_2\,e^{i\frac{2\pi}{\lambda}x} \\ A_3\,e^{i\frac{2\pi}{\lambda}x} \\ A_4\,e^{i\frac{2\pi}{\lambda}x} \end{pmatrix} \qquad [11–28$$

This form for Ψ implies that the waves are at any instant t the same for all values of y and z (out to $+\infty$ and $-\infty$) and that they are sinusoidal in form, along the x-axis, from $-\infty$ to $+\infty$. Whenever x changes by the distance λ, then *each* of the four components of ψ returns to its initial value. Each component of [11–28] is a periodic wave form, of wavelength λ, propagating in the positive x-direction.[8] Using periodic boundary conditions, as in Section 5.6, superpositions of the waves [11–28] can form wave packets representing localized particles. For the pure wave [11–28], however, the expectation value of p_x and p_x^2 is "sharp" (see Appendix XII), since

$$\overline{p_x} = h/\lambda, \text{ and } \overline{p_x^2} = (h/\lambda)^2 \qquad [11–28a$$

so that, by the uncertainty principle, the x-position of the particle is completely undetermined. By itself, [11–28] does not satisfy Postulate IV (the integrable square) so that it is not an acceptable wave function. None the less, the study of this solution gives useful information about Dirac matter waves.

In [11–28] all the A's are constants. The substitution of the purely x-depen-

---

[8] See Problem 11.1.

dent ψ [11–28] into the wave equation (or rather, set of equations) [11–27] gives the result:

$$(W + mc^2) A_1 + \quad 0 \quad + \quad 0 \quad + \left(\frac{c\hbar}{i} A_4 \frac{2\pi i}{\lambda} \right) = 0$$

$$0 \quad + (W + mc^2) A_2 + \frac{c\hbar}{i} A_3 \left(\frac{2\pi i}{\lambda} \right) + \quad 0 \quad = 0$$

$$0 \quad + \quad \frac{c\hbar}{i} A_2 \frac{2\pi i}{\lambda} \quad + (W - mc^2) A_3 + \quad 0 \quad = 0$$

$$\frac{c\hbar}{i} A_1 \frac{2\pi i}{\lambda} \quad + \quad 0 \quad + \quad 0 \quad + (W - mc^2) A_4 \quad = 0$$

$$[11–29$$

The terms involving $\partial/\partial y$ and $\partial/\partial z$ disappear, since we are considering a wave whose amplitude is dependent only on x.

Equation [11–29] is a set of homogeneous ordinary equations in the four variables A_1, A_2, A_3, and A_4. The theory of equations tells us that a nontrivial solution exists only if the determinant of the coefficients of the A's vanishes. Performing this calculation,[9] we find that

$$W^2 - m^2 c^4 - (ch/\lambda)^2 = 0 \qquad [11–30]$$

that is,

$$W = \pm \sqrt{(ch/\lambda)^2 + m^2 c^4} \text{ or } \pm \sqrt{c^2 p_x^2 + m^2 c^4} \text{ (since } p_x = h/\lambda) \quad [11–31]$$

which is exactly the basic relationship between energy, momentum, and rest mass required by the theory of relativity, and which formed the starting point for the wave equation.

We may take either the positive or the negative sign for the total energy. It turns out that the positive sign gives wave functions which correctly predict the behavior of the electron, and the negative sign gives wave functions which are used to correctly predict the behavior of the positron—the "antiparticle" belonging to the electron, which is one of the great successes of the theory. The theoretical basis of the positron was established before its actual discovery by Anderson in 1932.

Taking the positive sign for the constant W, and signifying

$$+ \sqrt{(ch/\lambda)^2 + m^2 c^4}$$

---

[9] This may be done most easily by noting that only equations 1 and 4 of [11–29] involve A_1 and A_4. The determinant of this pair, when set equal to 0, is [11–30]. Similarly, equations 2 and 3, involving only A_2 and A_3, also yield [11–30].

by $+\sqrt{}$ equations [11–29] become:

$$(+\sqrt{}+mc^2)\,A_1+ \qquad 0 \qquad + \qquad 0 \qquad + \qquad \frac{ch}{\lambda}\,A_4 \qquad =0$$

$$0 \qquad +(+\sqrt{}+mc^2)A_2+ \qquad \frac{ch}{\lambda}\,A_3 \qquad + \qquad 0 \qquad =0$$

$$0 \qquad + \qquad \frac{ch}{\lambda}\,A_2 \qquad +(+\sqrt{}-mc^2)\,A_3+ \qquad 0 \qquad =0$$

$$\frac{ch}{\lambda}\,A_1 \qquad + \qquad 0 \qquad + \qquad 0 \qquad +(+\sqrt{}-mc^2)\,A_4=0$$

$$[11\text{–}32$$

Equations 1 and 4 (counting from the top) in [11–32] involve only A_1 and A_4. Solving either one, we obtain,

$$A_1 = \frac{-\,ch/\lambda}{\sqrt{(ch/\lambda)^2 + m^2\,c^4} + mc^2}\,A_4 \left.\begin{array}{c} \\ \\ \\ \\ \end{array}\right\}$$

and either of equations 2 or 3 gives,

$$A_2 = \frac{-\,ch/\lambda}{\sqrt{(ch/\lambda)^2 + m^2\,c^4} + mc^2}\,A_3$$

$$[11\text{–}33$$

where $h/\lambda = p_x$, the momentum of the particle.

It is not possible to obtain any more information about the A's. Two of the unknowns simply cannot be determined by the equations. As far as the theory is concerned, therefore, they may have arbitrary values. However, once A_3 and A_4 are specified then the other two A_1 and A_2, are given by [11–33]. Conversely, given A_1 and A_2, then A_3 and A_4 are determined.

We could set $A_3 = A_4$, for example, and calculate A_2 and A_3 (which will then also be equal to each other), and the resulting amplitudes of the matter wave [11–28] will satisfy the Dirac wave equation. This wave will have "excitation" in all four of its components. A different assumption about the relative magnitudes of A_3 and A_4 will give another matter wave with all four components "excited," but with different relative intensities than in the first case.

There are two particular selections of the values of A_3 and A_4 which give a great deal of insight into the nature of the matter waves. These selections are

I. $A_4 = 0$, $A_3 = A_3$, so that $A_1 = 0$ and $A_2 = \dfrac{-\,cp_x\,A_3}{\sqrt{c^2\,p_x^2 + m^2\,c^4} + mc^2}$

$$[11\text{–}33a$$

II. $A_3 = 0$, $A_4 = A_4$, so that $A_2 = 0$ and $A_1 = \dfrac{-\,cp_x\,A_4}{\sqrt{c^2\,p_x^2 + m^2\,c^4} + mc^2}$

where p_x is the actual momentum of the particle "to which the waves belong,"

m is the rest mass of the particle, and c is the velocity of light. The particle is moving at constant (average) speed v along the x-axis, with momentum

$$p_x = \frac{mv}{\sqrt{1 - (v/c)^2}}$$

[11–2], and the (plane) waves are propagating in the $+x$-direction.

For $W = + \sqrt{(ch/\lambda)^2 + m^2 c^4}$, the wave functions for the two modes of propagation are, by [11–28],

$$\Psi_{II} = A_4 \begin{pmatrix} \dfrac{- ch/\lambda}{W + mc^2} \\ 0 \\ 0 \\ 1 \end{pmatrix} e^{i\left(\frac{2\pi}{\lambda} x - \frac{W}{\hbar} t\right)}; \quad \Psi_{I} = A_3 \begin{pmatrix} 0 \\ \dfrac{- ch/\lambda}{W + mc^2} \\ 1 \\ 0 \end{pmatrix} e^{i\left(\frac{2\pi}{\lambda} x - \frac{W}{\hbar} t\right)}$$

$$[11\text{–}34$$

The constants A_4 and A_3 may be determined by the normalization requirement (see Appendix XII).

The reason these two particular modes, I and II, are so important is that they are orthogonal—that is, they do not interfere with each other. To see how this comes about, we refer to Figure 11.1a, where the two matter waves, I and II, are shown at one instant of time. (We look at only the real component, $\cos (2\pi x/\lambda)$, of the complex wave $Ae^{i2\pi x/\lambda} = A(\cos 2\pi x/\lambda + i \sin 2\pi x/\lambda)$ of equation [11–28].)

When $p_x \ll mc$, as is the case for the low-velocity electrons in atoms, the denominators in A_2 and A_1 of [11–33a] become approximately equal to $2mc^2$, so that A_2 and A_1 are each approximately $-(v/2c)$ times the large components, A_3 and A_4 respectively.

In Figure 11.1a, wave I, we see a large vibration or excitation of the third component, and a small excitation of the second component, since we are considering the waves of low-momentum electrons. For wave I we see that the first and the fourth components are *completely* unexcited.

For wave II, Figure 11.1a, on the other hand, we see that the fourth component has a large excitation, the first component has a small excitation, and the other two components are completely unexcited. Since *both* I and II are fully satisfactory solutions to the wave equation (each wave can be bounded in space by requiring that each component has an integrable square), we conclude that either of these two distinctive types of wave may belong to a real electron. (Also, a single electron can have any superposition of these two—i.e., it can have *all four* components excited.) Also, we conclude (see Sections 11.8 and 11.9) that *two* electrons—each represented by one of the pure modes—can both propagate along the x-axis with exactly the same energy and wavelength without affecting each other (aside from their normal electrostatic repulsion).

In other words, a perfectly satisfactory wave can exist with excitation in *only* two of its four possible components. Another wave can exist just as well with only the *other* two components excited.

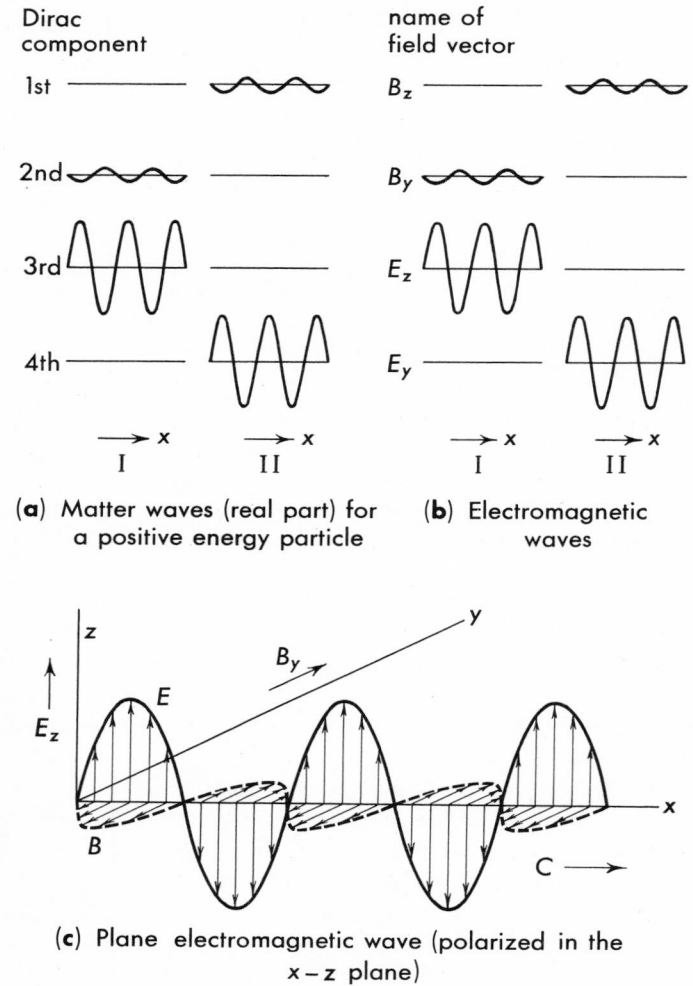

(**a**) Matter waves (real part) for a positive energy particle

(**b**) Electromagnetic waves

(**c**) Plane electromagnetic wave (polarized in the x – z plane)

Fig. 11.1. The formal similarity of Dirac matter waves and electromagnetic waves.

To give this rather abstract discussion a little more reality, we compare these two Dirac matter waves with the more familiar electromagnetic waves. There are some striking similarities, as reference to Figure 11.1b shows. There are two plane-polarized, electromagnetic waves, each propagating along the x-axis. At some instant of time they would appear in space as shown.

Wave I has its E-vector vibrating in the x–z plane. This is the case drawn in perspective in Figure 11.1c. The B-vector of wave I is vibrating in the x–y plane. It has a magnitude $|E|/c$, and it is so directed that $\mathbf{E} \times \mathbf{B}$ (the Poynting vector, giving the direction of propagation) is directed to the right. (In Problem 11.1 we show that the matter waves [11–28], which we are here discussing, are *also* propagating to the right.)

We see that the electromagnetic wave I is very similar to the matter wave I. Even the relative phase of the large component (A_3 or E_z) with respect to the small component (A_2 or B_y) is the same.

Similarly, electromagnetic wave II corresponds closely to Dirac matter wave II.

Both types of waves are true "relativistic" phenomena. That is, each is fully in accord with the principle that, described in terms of any other coordinate system in uniform motion with respect to the one we have been assuming, it will obey an equation of identical form.

There are, of course, differences between these waves. Most important is the fact that there is no evidence that matter waves actually consist of transverse vibrations. Also, each of the two component vibrations constituting the "plane-polarized" matter waves is describable only by an ordered pair, a complex number $A(\sin 2\pi x/\lambda + i \cos 2\pi x/\lambda)$. The matter waves are associated with a "particle" of rest mass m, whereas the electromagnetic waves are not associated with an entity describable as a particle with rest mass. Furthermore, as we see in Problem 11.1, the phase velocity of the matter wave is greater than c (although the average *particle* velocity is always less than c).[10] Electromagnetic waves, in free space, always travel with the velocity c.

The real advantage of comparing the Dirac waves and the electromagnetic waves lies in the vivid picture that can be drawn. We can easily *imagine* what an electromagnetic wave looks like. The drawing in Figure 11.1c is an example of one method of visualization. Diagrams of matter waves (Dirac particles) can be drawn so as to appear much like their electromagnetic counterparts. For example, in Figure 11.2a we draw the real parts of the Dirac wave for a nonrelativistic particle, $p_x \ll mc$, traveling in the x-direction.

If, in Figure 11.2, we plotted the imaginary part of each Dirac component, we would again have wave forms that look like those already shown.

We note that in Figure 11.2 the vector product of ψ_3 and ψ_2 (regarded as ordinary vectors, vibrating in normal planes) points in the direction of the wave velocity, and also the particle velocity. This is analogous to $\mathbf{E} \times \mathbf{B}$ pointing in the direction of propagation of the energy and momentum regarded as being transmitted by an electromagnetic wave. In other words, even the relative phase of the large component ψ_3 and the small component ψ_2 is the same as

---

[10] It can be shown—see J. Frenkel, *Wave Mechanics* (1943, Oxford U. Press: pp. 311–329)—that the eigenvalues of the operator representing velocity are $\pm c$. It is as if the "instantaneous value" of the electron's velocity is either $+ c$ or $- c$, but the frequencies of occurrence are so weighted that the *average* velocity is less than c, and with a definite sign.

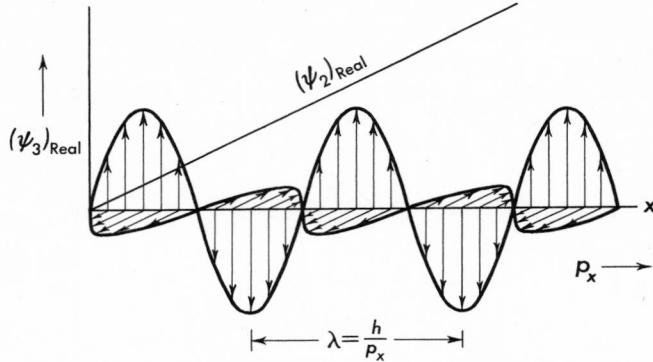

(a) Dirac matter wave for a free particle (average
velocity of particle $\ll C$, so that $A_2 \ll A_3$)

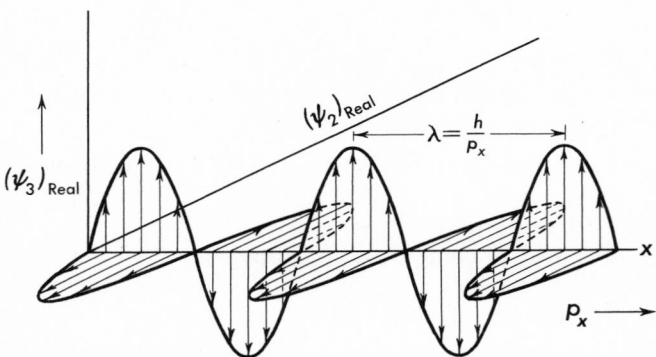

(b) Dirac matter wave for a free particle (average
velocity of particle $\simeq C$, so that $A_2 \simeq A_3$)
[These waves have a *much* shorter wavelength
than the waves in (a).]

Fig. 11.2. Geometrical representation of Dirac matter waves of a
positive-energy particle. **Note:** Only the x-dimension corresponds to
physical space.

the relative phase of **E** and **B**. Again, we must emphasize that the similarity
between Dirac waves and electromagnetic waves is only formal.

Thus far, we have exploited graphical plots and also the analogy with
electromagnetic waves to illustrate how the two modes of propagation of
matter waves (I and II of [11–34] and Figure 11.1a) can be independent.
How can this idea be given a more exact mathematical form?

The amplitude ψ of the matter waves [11–28] is an ordered set of four quantities—a column symbol. An ordinary vector is an ordered set of three quantities. If we speak of two ordinary vectors **A** and **B** as being linearly independent or orthogonal, we mean that the scalar product is zero, that is,

$$\mathbf{A}\cdot\mathbf{B} = A_x\,B_x + A_y\,B_y + A_z\,B_z = 0$$

Thinking of four-component column symbols, u and v, as four-component vectors, and allowing for the fact that the components of the column symbols are complex numbers, we define the condition for linear independence, or orthogonality, as,

$$u_1^*\,v_1 + u_2^*\,v_2 + u_3^*\,v_3 + u_4^*\,v_4 = 0 \qquad\qquad [11\text{--}34a$$

If u is an ordinary column symbol, we write u^* as the "row symbol"

$$u^* = (u_1^*,\,u_2^*,\,u_3^*,\,u_4^*),\ \text{where}\ u = \begin{pmatrix} u_1 \\ u_2 \\ u_3 \\ u_4 \end{pmatrix} \qquad [11\text{--}34b$$

v^* and v are similarly written. To multiply a column symbol by a row symbol, one multiplies the first terms in each, the second terms in each, etc., and then adds the four quantities. Thus, for example,

$$u^*\,u = u_1^*\,u_1 + u_2^*\,u_2 + u_3^*\,u_3 + u_4^*\,u_4$$

(a plain number, or scalar) is the square of the magnitude of the four-component column symbol u, and is zero only if all four terms in the sum are zero. If $u^*\,u = 1$, u is said to be normalized.

We can see at once that the two matter wave modes of [11–34] are linearly independent, or orthogonal. For convenience we write the magnitude of the "small component" of each wave as s, that is

$$s \equiv \frac{-\,cp_x}{\sqrt{c^2\,p_x^2 + m^2\,c^4} + mc^2}$$

Then the complex conjugate of mode I, a row symbol, times mode II, a column symbol, is

$$A_4^*\,A_3\,(0,\ se^{-i\frac{2\pi}{\lambda}x},\ e^{-i\frac{2\pi}{\lambda}x},\ 0) \begin{pmatrix} se^{i\frac{2\pi}{\lambda}x} \\ 0 \\ 0 \\ e^{i\frac{2\pi}{\lambda}x} \end{pmatrix} = 0 \qquad [11\text{--}34c$$

so that the two modes are independent. Suppose, however, that one wave had excitation in all four components. Then the scalar product [10–34c] would *not* be zero. It would contain two terms which will not, in general, cancel each other. The new wave is not linearly independent of the other.

The two independent modes of propagation may be shown to be the basis of the phenomena associated with electron spin. See the end of Section 11.8. The fact that "spin effects" appear in plane waves implies that one should not regard "spin" as an independent kinematical property of the electron, but rather as an essential aspect of its translational motion.

11.6. Particles with negative total energy

If, in the determinant equation [11–31], we take the solution

$$W = - \sqrt{c^2 p_x^2 + m^2 c^4}$$

which has a negative total energy, we obtain, by exactly the same process just discussed, two *new* orthogonal modes for a plane wave of an electron now with negative energy, propagating along the x-axis,

$$A_1 = A_1, A_2 = 0, A_3 = 0, A_4 = \frac{+ cp_x A_1}{\sqrt{c^2 p_x^2 + m^2 c^4} + mc^2} \qquad [11–35$$

$$A_1 = 0, A_2 = A_2, A_3 = \frac{+ cp_x A_2}{\sqrt{c^2 p_x^2 + m^2 c^4} + mc^2}, A_4 = 0$$

Again, a single electron can have any superposition of these two modes.

If, for electrons of negative energy, $c^2 p_x^2 \ll m^2 c^4$, then we can see directly from [11–35] that either the A_3 or the A_4 component is now the small one—of order $p_x/2mc$. Thus electrons in the negative energy states are distinguished by having large excitation in one of the *upper* two components in the column symbol, which is just the reverse of the case for the positive energy electrons.[11]

The negative energy states are very mysterious. If they exist, why do not all electrons drop down into these states? The complete theory shows that there exist matrix elements which "connect" the positive energy states to the negative energy states, so it is not for lack of a mechanism (a suitable time-dependent perturbation) that positive energy electrons do not immediately make transitions to the negative energy states which are at a much lower energy.

Dirac proposed the bold hypothesis that all the negative energy states are already occupied! Each of the negative energy levels already has two electrons with their vibrations in the two orthogonal modes [11–35], and, by the Pauli exclusion principle, no more electrons can share this energy level. (See Sections 11.7 and 11.8.)

The concept of an "infinite sea of negative energy electrons filling all of space" is difficult even to contemplate. This great assembly of electrons is

---

[11] These waves are propagating in the $- x$-direction (see [11–28], use $- W$).

assumed to have no gravitational or electromagnetic effects. There is one event, however, which would produce observable phenomena. If one of the negative energy electrons were given sufficient energy to raise it to an available positive energy state, then it would leave behind an unoccupied state of negative energy. Dirac showed that such a "hole" would act as if it were a positively charged particle with positive energy and with rest mass equal to that of the electron. In this manner, the theory of the positron comes automatically from the relativistic Hamiltonian of Dirac.

11.7.   The Dirac particle in the one-dimensional well

Inside a flat, one-dimensional potential well with infinite walls the particle is free—that is, the basic wave equation for the free particle [11–27] should apply. At the walls we imagine the potential energy to rise abruptly from zero to a very large value. It is reasonable to assume that the matter waves can exist inside the well but must have zero amplitude outside the well. Instead of free electron waves, we will now be considering standing waves (waves propagating from both directions, reflecting from the walls). Stationary states will occur (as in any resonating system, such as a room with sound waves or a resonant cavity containing electromagnetic waves) when the wavelength of the waves bears some integral relationship to the length of the box.

The method of introducing a potential energy term into the original Hamiltonian [11–1] is beyond the scope of this book. The problem is to add a term in such a manner that the relativistic invariance is not affected—that is, when described in terms of a second coordinate system in uniform relative motion to the first, the equation, *including the potential energy term*, must be unchanged in form. It is found that if, in [11–1], instead of the term W^2 one places the term $(W - V)^2$ [where $V(x, y, z)$ is the electrostatic potential energy], the relativistic invariance is not changed. When this is done, the free-particle wave equation [11–27] is changed only by replacing W everywhere by

$$W - V(x, y, z)$$

As before, W is the total energy.

Let us imagine an electron to be inside a rectangular box with the y- and z-dimensions very much larger than the x-dimension. We shall consider waves moving along the x-axis near the center of the box. Waves must also be propagating in the y and z directions, but we shall assume them to have very long wavelengths. We can assume, for example, that for these waves the standing-wave pattern has one half wavelength along each of the long dimensions. Near the center of box, therefore, the waves propagating back and forth in the x-direction are very nearly plane waves, and have no appreciable y- or z-dependence. Because of this, real waves, near the center of the flat rectangular box just described and propagating along the x-axis, are going to be essentially the same as those of our idealized, one-dimensional system.

What happens at the boundaries? We assume a very large (repulsive) electrostatic field, so the (charged) "particle" will certainly be reflected, and all wave amplitudes must be zero to the left of $x = 0$ and to the right of $x = L$ (Fig. 11.3a). If we followed the postulates literally, we must look for solutions

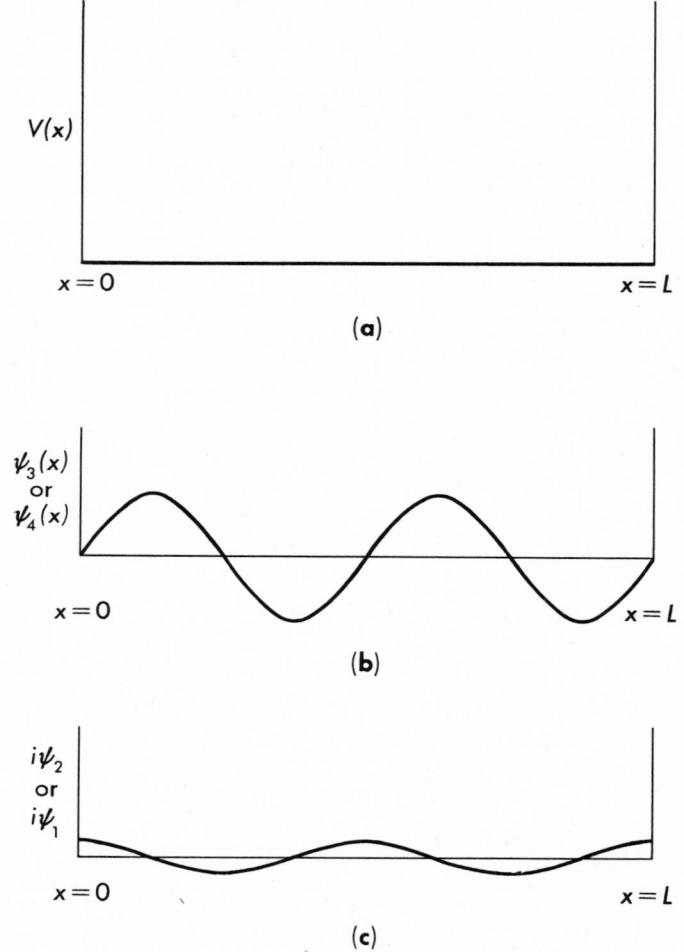

Fig. 11.3. The Dirac particle in a one-dimensional, infinite-wall box.

to the wave equation for which each component is everywhere continuous, has everywhere a continuous slope, and possesses an integrable square. However, as we shall see, the insertion of a term of infinite magnitude at the place in the equation where W appears can cause discontinuities in the slope of the large component and even in the *magnitude* of the small component. In other words, the artificial, infinite barrier can cause a deviation from the strict interpretation of the continuity requirements of the postulates.

Let us assume once again that

$$\Psi = \psi(x)\, e^{-i\frac{W}{\hbar}t} \quad \text{where } \psi = \begin{pmatrix} \psi_1(x) \\ \psi_2(x) \\ \psi_3(x) \\ \psi_4(x) \end{pmatrix} \qquad [11\text{-}36$$

With this assumption, in the region from $x = 0$ to $x = L$, the Dirac wave equation [11–27] becomes

$$(W + mc^2)\,\psi_1 + \qquad 0 \qquad + \qquad 0 \qquad + \frac{c\hbar}{i}\frac{d}{dx}\psi_4 \; = 0$$

$$0 \qquad + (W + mc^2)\,\psi_2 + \frac{c\hbar}{i}\frac{d}{dx}\psi_3 \; + \qquad 0 \qquad = 0$$

$$0 \qquad + \frac{c\hbar}{i}\frac{d}{dx}\psi_2 \; + (W - mc^2)\,\psi_3 + \qquad 0 \qquad = 0$$

$$\frac{c\hbar}{i}\frac{d}{dx}\psi_1 \; + \qquad 0 \qquad + \qquad 0 \qquad + (W - mc^2)\,\psi_4 = 0$$

$$[11\text{-}37$$

We add the boundary condition that ψ_3 and ψ_4, the large components, must be zero at $x = 0$ and $x = L$. This can be accomplished if we assume

$$\psi_3 = A_3 \sin\,(k\pi x/L)$$
$$\psi_4 = A_4 \sin\,(k\pi x/L) \qquad [11\text{-}38$$

where $k = 1, 2, 3, \cdots$.

This wave form is shown in Figure 11.3b. It certainly has an integrable square, although, as in the nonrelativistic case, it does have a discontinuity in slope at $x = 0$ and at $x = L$.

We start with an explicit assumption about the nature of one component of the eigenfunction, since this simplifies the solution of the simultaneous first-order differential equations [11–37].

Given ψ_4, what is ψ_1?

From the first equation in the set,

$$\psi_1 = - \frac{\dfrac{c\hbar}{i}\dfrac{k\pi}{L} A_4 \cos \dfrac{k\pi x}{L}}{W + mc^2} \qquad [11\text{-}39a$$

and from the fourth equation in the set, we obtain, by integration,

$$\psi_1 = \frac{i}{\hbar c}(W - mc^2)\frac{L}{k\pi} A_4 \cos \frac{k\pi x}{L} + \text{constant} \qquad [11\text{-}39b$$

These two results can *both* be true only if the constant of integration [11–39b] is zero and if

$$-\frac{\dfrac{c\hbar}{i}\dfrac{k\pi}{L}}{W+mc^2} = \frac{i}{\hbar c}\frac{L}{k\pi}(W-mc^2)$$

that is,

$$W^2 = m^2 c^4 + \left(\frac{c\hbar\,k\pi}{L}\right)^2 \qquad [11\text{–}40$$

Figure 11.3c shows the appearance of ψ_1 for the case where the particle momentum is small compared to mc.

We see that the small component ψ_1 has a discontinuity in its magnitude at both $x = 0$ and $x = L$. This discontinuity is very small for particles of atomic-scale energy (ψ_1 is of the order of p_x/mc), but it cannot be avoided if we insist that the large component, ψ_3 or ψ_4, be zero at the two limits.

In [11–40], when $(c\hbar k\pi/L)^2 \ll m^2 c^4$ (using $\sqrt{1+x} \cong 1 + x/2$ for $x \ll 1$), we have

$$W \cong \pm \left(mc^2 + \frac{\hbar^2 k^2 \pi^2}{2\,m\,L^2}\right) \qquad [11\text{–}41$$

The second term on the right in [11–41] is familiar. It is just the energy W_k of a nonrelativistic particle of mass m in an infinite-wall box of length L (see [3–23]).

$$W_k = \hbar^2 k^2 \pi^2/2mL^2 \qquad [11\text{–}42$$

It is shown in Appendix XI that if the walls of the box correspond to a positive potential energy, then bound states with the usual discrete energy values exist only when W in [11–41] has the positive sign. These states occur, however, *above* mc^2, as Figure 11.4 shows.

Since mc^2 is 0.51×10^6 e.v., or 8.16×10^{-7} erg, ordinary atomic systems which have binding energies of a few electron volts have energy levels which lie, on the scale of Figure 11.4, an indistinguishable amount above mc^2. Since the usual atomic physics experiments involve only transitions between the various positive energy levels, the constant mc^2 has no effect. Only energy *differences* are observed.

For the positive energy state $W \cong mc^2 + W_k$ (where $W_k \ll mc^2$), we see that for the quantum number k there are two different eigenfunctions.

Let $A_3 = 0$, then by [11–39a] (and by [11–41] which tells us that $W \cong mc^2$),

$$\psi_1 \cong \frac{-\hbar\,k\pi}{i\,2mc\,L} A_4 \cos \frac{k\pi x}{L} \qquad [11\text{–}42a$$

By [11–38], $\psi_4 = A_4 \sin (k\pi x/L)$, so *one* of the positive energy-state wave functions belonging to the level $W = mc^2 + W_k$ is

$$\Psi_\downarrow \cong A_4 \begin{pmatrix} i\,\dfrac{\hbar k\pi}{2\,mc\,L}\cos\dfrac{k\pi x}{L} \\ 0 \\ 0 \\ \sin\dfrac{k\pi x}{L} \end{pmatrix} e^{-i(mc^2 + W_k)t/\hbar}$$

[11–43¹²]

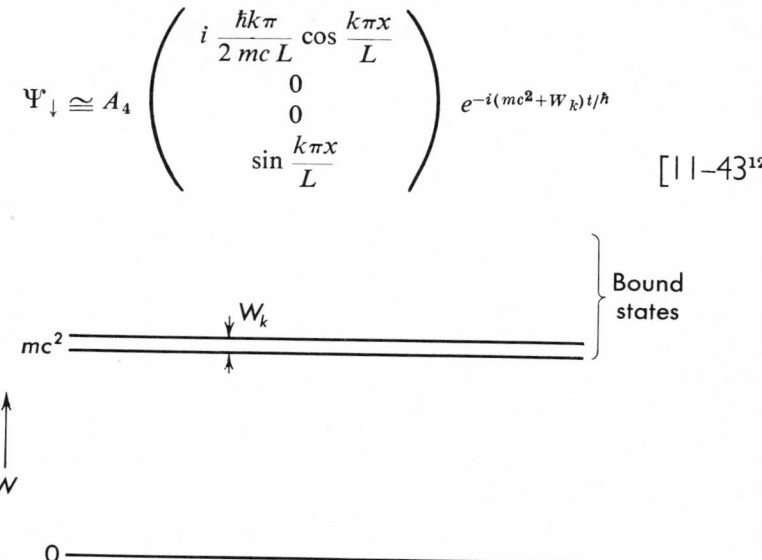

Fig. 11.4. Energy levels of a positive-energy Dirac particle in a positive-energy, infinite-wall, one-dimensional box.

On the other hand, if we set $A_4 = 0$ in [11–38], then

$$\Psi_\uparrow \cong A_3 \begin{pmatrix} 0 \\ i\,\dfrac{\hbar k\pi}{2\,mc\,L}\cos\dfrac{k\pi x}{L} \\ \sin\dfrac{k\pi x}{L} \\ 0 \end{pmatrix} e^{-i(mc^2 + W_k)t/\hbar}$$

[11–44¹²]

where k can have any of the integral values, 1, 2, 3, 4, $\cdots$.

These two distinct eigenfunctions, or "standing waves," have a different appearance from the free-running waves of Figure 11.2. The amplitudes $\psi_\downarrow$ and $\psi_\uparrow$ of the two orthogonal eigenfunctions, by [11–34a], are plotted in Figures 11.5a and 11.5b. In the upper figure, we imagine the large component ψ_4 to be a vector vibrating in the z-direction (of the *figure*), and in the lower figure we imagine the large component ψ_3 to be a vector vibrating in the y-direction (of the *figure*). As with the E vectors of two cross-polarized electromagnetic

---

¹² Note that for the exact form of [11–43] or [11–44], ψ_1 or ψ_2 is given by [11–39a], and the time-dependent term is $e^{-iW/\hbar}$, where W is the positive root of [11–40].

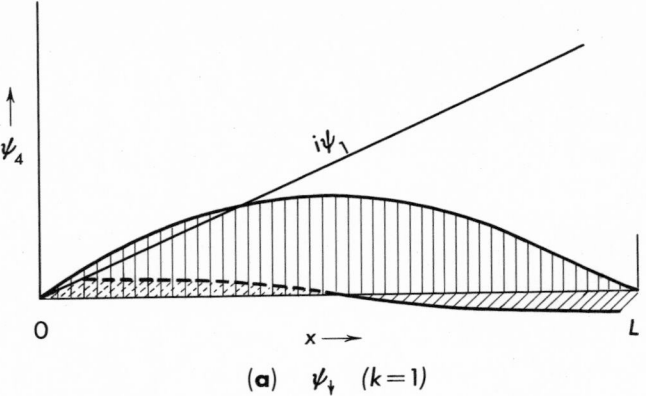

(**a**) $\psi_\downarrow$ $(k=1)$

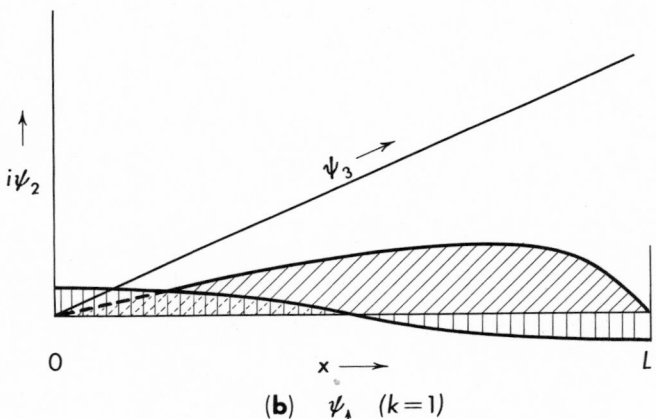

(**b**) $\psi_\uparrow$ $(k=1)$

Fig. 11.5. The two orthogonal eigenfunctions for a Dirac particle in a one-dimensional, infinite wall box for the state $k = 1$. **Note:** Only the x-direction corresponds to physical space.

waves, these two components are noninterfering. Again, the analogy is only formal.

Similarly, in the upper figure we use the *y*-axis to display the complex part of ψ_1. (It is a pure imaginary in contrast to the free-running waves, where ψ_1 has both real and imaginary components.) In the lower figure we use the *z*-axis to display ψ_2. Again, as with the *B* vectors of two cross-polarized electromagnetic waves, the *small* components can be *imagined* as vibrating in perpendicular planes.

In Appendix XII, some typical calculations are performed using the wave functions [11–43] and [11–44].

In using the arrows to designate the two states whose amplitudes are the column symbols $\psi_\downarrow$ and $\psi_\uparrow$, we refer to "spin up" by $\uparrow$ (3rd component excited) and "spin down" by $\downarrow$ (4th component excited). Clearly, the use of the word "spin" implies that these two different solutions are somehow related to angular momentum. For this interpretation to be made, it is necessary to consider a system—such as the hydrogen atom—where there is more than one-dimensional motion, so that angular momentum can be defined. When this is done, one finds that a new operator, J_z, plays the role formerly played by M_z. In the paragraphs immediately following, the mathematical form of J_z is stated, and reference is made to the more advanced theory needed to demonstrate its important properties.

Rojansky[13] shows that for the electron in the electrostatic field $V(r)$, the expectation value of the operator,

$$
J_z =
\begin{pmatrix}
\dfrac{\hbar}{i}\dfrac{\partial}{\partial\phi}+\dfrac{1}{2}\hbar & 0 & 0 & 0 \\[2ex]
0 & \dfrac{\hbar}{i}\dfrac{\partial}{\partial\phi}-\dfrac{1}{2}\hbar & 0 & 0 \\[2ex]
0 & 0 & \dfrac{\hbar}{i}\dfrac{\partial}{\partial\phi}+\dfrac{1}{2}\hbar & 0 \\[2ex]
0 & 0 & 0 & \dfrac{\hbar}{i}\dfrac{\partial}{\partial\phi}-\dfrac{1}{2}\hbar
\end{pmatrix}
\qquad [11\text{–}45a
$$

is *constant in time*, but that the expectation value of the operator representing the z-component of the orbital angular momentum,

$$
M_z =
\begin{pmatrix}
\dfrac{\hbar}{i}\dfrac{\partial}{\partial\phi} & 0 & 0 & 0 \\[2ex]
0 & \dfrac{\hbar}{i}\dfrac{\partial}{\partial\phi} & 0 & 0 \\[2ex]
0 & 0 & \dfrac{\hbar}{i}\dfrac{\partial}{\partial\phi} & 0 \\[2ex]
0 & 0 & 0 & \dfrac{\hbar}{i}\dfrac{\partial}{\partial\phi}
\end{pmatrix}
\qquad [11\text{–}45b
$$

is *time-varying*. In nonrelativistic theory (see Section 6.2) $\overline{M}_z = constant$.

When the expectation value of an operator is constant, the dynamical variable represented by the operator is said to be a "constant of motion" of the system.[14] Since M_z represents the z-component of the *orbital* angular

---

[13] V. Rojansky, *op. cit.* p. 513.
[14] *Ibid.*, pp. 252–255.

momentum, by *analogy* one speaks of the operator J_z as representing the z-component of the *total* angular momentum, and the operator

$$S_z = \tfrac{1}{2}\hbar \begin{pmatrix} 1 & 0 & 0 & 0 \\ 0 & -1 & 0 & 0 \\ 0 & 0 & 1 & 0 \\ 0 & 0 & 0 & -1 \end{pmatrix} \qquad [11\text{--}45c$$

as representing the z-component of the *spin* angular momentum. No question arises regarding any spinning motion of the electron. The use of the Dirac Hamiltonian automatically forces the intimate association between the two operators M_z and s_z. It is *as if* the z-components of two angular momentum vectors are being added together, since the operator

$$J_z = M_z + s_z \qquad \text{(matrix equation)} \qquad [11\text{--}45d$$

plays the role formerly played in nonrelativistic theory by M_z, alone.

We will not attempt to elaborate upon the results quoted above, since this requires the further development of the theory referred to in Rojansky. Our immediate goal is to become familiar with the vector-like nature of the Dirac waves. We will be content with the observation that this nature is essential to the proper understanding of the group of phenomena associated with electron spin.

11.8. Identical Dirac particles, and the exclusion principle for electrons

Let us add a second electron to the potential well of Figure 11.3.

We must go back to the basic postulates and derive the wave equation for two particles, starting, of course, with the relativistic Hamiltonian for the system.

We assume as a first approximation that the two electrons do not interact, and we will obtain, therefore, the zero-order wave equation.

Each of the two electrons has its total energy given by the relativistic expression [11–1]

$$\begin{aligned} W_1^2 &= c^2(p_{x_1}^2 + p_{y_1}^2 + p_{z_1}^2 + m^2 c^2) \\ W_2^2 &= c^2(p_{x_2}^2 + p_{y_2}^2 + p_{z_2}^2 + m^2 c^2) \end{aligned} \qquad [11\text{--}46a$$

where W_1 is the total energy of the electron whose coordinates are x_1, y_1, z_1, and W_2 is the total energy of the electron whose coordinates are x_2, y_2, and z_2.

There is assumed to be no mutual interaction energy, thus the total system energy is

$$W = W_1 + W_2 \qquad\qquad [11\text{-}46b$$

Using Dirac's method, the square root of each of the two expressions in [11–46a] is (again taking the negative sign),

$$W_1 = - c(a_x p_{x_1} + a_y p_{y_1} + a_z p_{z_1} + \beta mc)$$
$$W_2 = - c(a_x p_{x_2} + a_y p_{y_2} + a_z p_{z_2} + \beta mc) \qquad [11\text{-}47$$

where the a's and the β are the same numerical matrices used before [11–23].

Inserting these expressions for W_1 and W_2 into [11–46b], we have the basic expression for the total system energy W, from which the wave equation is to be derived. We replace W by $-(\hbar/i)(\partial/\partial t)$, p_{x_1} by $(\hbar/i)(\partial/\partial x_1)$, p_{x_2} by $(\hbar/i)(\partial/\partial x_2)$, etc., and obtain the wave equation

$$- \frac{\hbar}{i}\frac{\partial}{\partial t}\Psi = \left\{ - \frac{c\hbar}{i}\left[a_x \frac{\partial}{\partial x_1} + a_y \frac{\partial}{\partial y_1} + a_z \frac{\partial}{\partial z_1} \right] - \beta mc^2 \right\}\Psi$$
$$+ \left\{ - \frac{c\hbar}{i}\left[a_x \frac{\partial}{\partial x_2} + a_y \frac{\partial}{\partial y_2} + a_z \frac{\partial}{\partial z_2} \right] - \beta mc^2 \right\}\Psi \qquad [11\text{-}48$$

where Ψ is a function of x_1, y_1, z_1, x_2, y_2, z_2, and t.[15] (Ψ must, of course, consist of column symbols, since this is required by the presence of the 4-by-4 matrices.)

To "separate" this equation, we let

$$\Psi = u(x_1, y_1, z_1)\, v(x_2, y_2, z_2)\, \phi(t) \qquad [11\text{-}49$$

Substituting this expression into [11–48] and dividing through by Ψ, the equation [11–48] consists of three parts. One is dependent only on t, one only on x_1, y_1, z_1, and the third only on x_2, y_2, z_2. Each part must equal a constant: W, W_1, and W_2, respectively; thus, $W = W_1 + W_2$. The time-dependent equation has the solution identical to [11–15], except that $W_1 + W_2$ appears in place of W. Each of the space-dependent equations are identical in form to [11–16], whose solutions we have obtained in the previous sections.

We are concerned with the one-dimensional case, so we have for the complete system wave function

$$\Psi(x_1, x_2, t) = \begin{pmatrix} u_1(x_1) \\ u_2(x_1) \\ u_3(x_1) \\ u_4(x_1) \end{pmatrix} \begin{pmatrix} v_1(x_2) \\ v_2(x_2) \\ v_3(x_2) \\ v_4(x_2) \end{pmatrix} e^{-i\frac{W_1 + W_2}{\hbar}t} \qquad [11\text{-}50$$

where the first column symbol is $u(x_1)$ and the second one is $v(x_2)$.

It should be pointed out that the product (called the "symbolic product")

---

[15] Strictly speaking, t is not exactly the same for both particles since they are in relative motion, but here $v \ll c$.

of two column symbols such as appears in [11–50] does not imply any actual mathematical manipulation. There will never be any need to "multiply out" the two symbols $u(x_1)$ and $v(x_2)$. In any quantum-mechanical calculations which predict, by Postulate V, the results of experiment, only terms of the form

$$u(x_1)^* \, v(x_2)^* \text{ (operator) } u(x_1) \, v(x_2) \qquad [11\text{–}51]$$

appear. The operator in [11–51] is a "double operator"—part acts on u and part on v since they are dependent upon different sets of variables in configuration space. An analogous example is the operation

$$\left(\frac{\partial}{\partial x}\right)\left(\frac{\partial}{\partial y}\right)[f(x)\, g(y)]$$

where $\dfrac{\partial}{\partial x}$ acts *only* on $f(x)$, and $\dfrac{\partial}{\partial y}$ acts *only* on $g(y)$.

As we have seen in [10–34b], the complex conjugate of $u(x_1)$ is the row symbol,

$$u = (u_1^*, \, u_2^*, \, u_3^*, \, u_4^*)$$

and the operation of multiplying the row symbol into its corresponding column symbol (now changed into a new column symbol u' by the operation) is

$$(u_1^*, u_2^*, u_3^*, u_4^*)\begin{pmatrix} u_1' \\ u_2' \\ u_3' \\ u_4' \end{pmatrix} = \text{the plain number} \atop u_1^* \, u_1' + u_2^* \, u_2' + u_3^* \, u_3' + u_4^* \, u_4' \qquad [11\text{–}51a]$$

Thus, in [11–51] the u's and the v's, depending as they do upon different sets of coordinates, are separately multiplied as in [11–51a]. After this is completed, ordinary spatial integration may be performed upon each term.

In the previous section, where we considered a single particle, we found that u and v can each have two distinct forms—the column symbols in [11–43] and [11–44]—which can be pictured as orthogonal vibrations and which are mathematically independent. (This is because u and v *each* obey an equation of the same form as [11–37], obtained in the separation of [11–48].)

Let $u(x_1)$ have the quantum number k, and let $v(x_2)$ have the quantum number n. By [11–43] and [11–44], when the spatial quantum number[16] is k,

---

[16] The "spatial quantum number" is generated by the familiar requirements of "well-behavedness" and the integrable square in configuration space, here of x_1 and x_2. The arrows in [11–52] symbolize which of the two possible modes in "spin space" are excited. Instead of the arrows in [11–52] and [11–53] the "spin quantum numbers" $(1/2) (= \uparrow)$ and $-(1/2) (= \downarrow)$ are often used. Whatever the shorthand notation, however, [11–52] and [11–53] give the actual mathematical forms of u and v.

$u(x_1)$ can have two linearly independent forms,

$$[u_k(x_1)]_\downarrow = \begin{pmatrix} ibk \cos \dfrac{k\pi x_1}{L} \\\\ 0 \\\\ 0 \\\\ \sin \dfrac{k\pi x_1}{L} \end{pmatrix} \quad \text{or} \quad [u_k(x_1)]_\uparrow = \begin{pmatrix} 0 \\\\ ibk \cos \dfrac{k\pi x_1}{L} \\\\ \sin \dfrac{k\pi x_1}{L} \\\\ 0 \end{pmatrix}$$

[11–52

where $b = \hbar\pi/2mcL$. Since $b \ll 1$, we ignore the exact normalization requirement. Similarly, for the state with spatial quantum number n,

$$[v_n(x_2)]_\downarrow = \begin{pmatrix} ibn \cos \dfrac{n\pi x_2}{L} \\\\ 0 \\\\ 0 \\\\ \sin \dfrac{n\pi x_2}{L} \end{pmatrix} \quad \text{or} \quad [v_n(x_2)]_\uparrow = \begin{pmatrix} 0 \\\\ ibn \cos \dfrac{n\pi x_2}{L} \\\\ \sin \dfrac{n\pi x_2}{L} \\\\ 0 \end{pmatrix}$$

[11–53

Four more (different) functions may be obtained from [11–52] and [11–53] by interchanging x_1 and x_2.

Any u times any v, when multiplied by the time-dependent term,

$$e^{-i\frac{W_1+W_2}{\hbar}t} \cong e^{-i\frac{W_k+W_n+2mc^2}{\hbar}t}$$

[11–54

[where

$$W_1 = +\sqrt{(c\hbar\,k\pi/L)^2 + m^2\,c^4} \cong mc^2 + \frac{\hbar^2\,k^2\,\pi^2}{2mL^2} = mc^2 + W_k,$$

and similarly,

$$W_2 \cong mc^2 + W_n]$$

is a solution to the two-electron wave equation [11–48]. *For example, when* $n \neq k$, $[u_k(x_1)]_\downarrow\,[v_n(x_2)]_\uparrow$ *is one of the eight[17] possible products. In this product*

---

[17] The eight possible two-particle eigenfunctions arise as follows: In the first member of the product there are two choices for the quantum number (n or k), two choices for the coordinate (x_1 or x_2), and two choices for the functional form (symbolized by ↑ or ↓), making, as we have seen above, eight different functions. The second member of the product must have the other quantum number and it must have the other variable. Thus, for the second member of the pair, there are only two choices, ↑ or ↓. This makes sixteen ways of forming the pair, but the order is inconsequential, so that there is an arrangement factor of 2!, making 16/2! different products which can be formed from the eight one-particle eigenfunctions.

one speaks of the first term as having the spatial quantum number k, and the spin quantum number $-(1/2)$ or, alternatively, as "spin down." Also, since the wave equation is linear, any *sum* composed of the $(u)(v)$ products (which are the individual solutions) is also a solution. (This is true, as we have seen, for the nonrelativistic equation. For example, if ψ_m is an eigenfunction, and ψ_n is a different eigenfunction, then $\psi_m + \psi_n$ is also a solution, although not an eigenfunction.)

What will happen if both $u(x)$ and $v(x)$ have the same quantum number k? This means that the two particles will have the same number of half wavelengths across the box of length L. For example, if $k = 1$, both particles will be in the lowest energy state. This was not possible for the Schrödinger particles of Chapter 9, *if* one insists upon a system wave function which is antisymmetric to the interchange of the two coordinates, x_1 and x_2. Now, however, even with $k = 1$ in *both* eigenfunctions we can form a solution of the two-electron Dirac equation [11–48], which *is* antisymmetric: Setting $n = k$, and using only two of the eight possible $(u)(v)$ products obtainable from [11–52] and [11–53], we form a *particular* linear combination:

$$\psi_{s=0} = [u_k(x_1)]_\downarrow \, [v_k(x_2)]_\uparrow - [u_k(x_1)]_\uparrow \, [v_k(x_2)]_\downarrow \qquad [11\text{–}55a$$

or, writing these terms out in full,

$$\psi_{s=0} = \begin{pmatrix} ibk \cos \dfrac{k\pi x_1}{L} \\ 0 \\ 0 \\ \sin \dfrac{k\pi x_1}{L} \end{pmatrix} \begin{pmatrix} 0 \\ ibk \cos \dfrac{k\pi x_2}{L} \\ \sin \dfrac{k\pi x_2}{L} \\ 0 \end{pmatrix}$$

$$- \begin{pmatrix} 0 \\ ibk \cos \dfrac{k\pi x_1}{L} \\ \sin \dfrac{k\pi x_1}{L} \\ 0 \end{pmatrix} \begin{pmatrix} ibk \cos \dfrac{k\pi x_2}{L} \\ 0 \\ 0 \\ \sin \dfrac{k\pi x_2}{L} \end{pmatrix} \qquad [11\text{–}55b$$

The reason that the designation $S = 0$ is used to identify the state whose wave function is [11–55b] will be explained in the next section.

If, in [11–55b], one everywhere interchanges x_1 and x_2, then $\psi_{S=0}$ will change sign—as it must if it is to be an electron wave function. Or if, in [11-55a], one everywhere interchanges the spatial coordinates x_1 and x_2, and also interchanges the "spin space coordinates" ↑ and ↓, $\psi_{S=0}$ will change sign. Equation [11-55b] could be made symmetric to interchange by using a + sign, but all known Dirac particles—electrons, protons, neutrons—have antisymmetric wave functions.

In [11-55b] (which is the actual mathematical form of $\psi_{S=0}$), when we interchange x_1 and x_2 we are *forced* to interchange the "spin space coordinates," that is, to interchange the modes of excitation. In the shorthand notation of [11-55a] we keep track of the mode of excitation by the arrow symbols. The complete wave function does this automatically for us when we interchange x_1 and x_2.

We see once again how the idea of spin is intimately tied up with the four-component nature of the Dirac wave functions, or "spinors." The different spin states of each particle are simply spinor functions with different components excited. The automatic interchange of spin, which occurs when we interchange space coordinates, is a feature which is naturally built in to the Dirac spinors. The solutions of the Schrödinger equation could never give these spin characteristics because the Schrödinger functions have only a one-component nature. It is the triumph of Dirac theory that it exhibits the experimentally observed consequences of spin in a natural way.

The order of appearance of *u* and *v* in the symbolic product (*u*)(*v*) does not affect the calculations of any results. (Note that only when the rest mass *m*, which appears in the constant *b*, is the *same* for the two particles will $\psi_{S=0}$ merely change its algebraic sign. *The particles must be identical.*)

Thus the intrinsic nature of the Dirac waves permits two electrons (whose wave functions must always be antisymmetric to interchange) *to share the same spatial quantum number*. This same result holds for the three-dimensional potential well of the atom. The Dirac theory permits two electrons in the lowest state ($n = 1$, $l = 0$, $m = 0$). It is *as if* the two "spin states" provided a fourth dimension, with a fourth quantum number m_s, which can have two values designated by ↑ and by ↓. Thus, three quantum numbers can be the same if the fourth is different. The column symbols, or spinors, as they are also called, depend upon r, θ, and ϕ rather than upon x, as in the simple example which we have been discussing above, but the same effect occurs—there are *two* linearly independent modes of vibration for any particular set of spatial quantum numbers, n, l, and m.

The first term in [11-55b] is the symbolic product of two zero-order terms, which can be described by saying that electron 1 has spin down, and electron 2 has spin up. The reverse is true for the second term. Thus when the two electrons "share the state k," one *cannot* regard one electron as having its large component uniquely in one polarization, or mode, and the second electron as having, uniquely, the other polarization. One must think, rather, of the two electrons as not merely sharing the quantum number k, but *also as sharing both modes of orthogonal vibration.* Only thus can one obtain the antisymmetric wave function [11–55a] or [11–55b].

11.9. Singlet and triplet states

In the previous section we sought an antisymmetric wave function for two electrons that were "sharing the state k." We found that there was one linear combination [11–55b] of the products of the individual u's and the v's [11–52] and [11–53], which would meet the requirement of antisymmetry. We shall see shortly that [11–55b] is the *only* combination. In this state, one can think of the electrons as sharing wave functions having *opposing* spins or, alternatively, sharing the two independent modes of vibration.

We now ask: What combinations of the basic u's and v's will give antisymmetric wave functions when $n \neq k$?

Before writing out these combinations, we will condense the notation. Let kx_1 symbolize $\sin k\pi x_1/L$, etc., and let S symbolize the small component. Thus,

$$\begin{pmatrix} 0 \\ ibk \cos \dfrac{k\pi x_1}{L} \\ \sin \dfrac{k\pi x_1}{L} \\ 0 \end{pmatrix} = \begin{pmatrix} 0 \\ S \\ kx_1 \\ 0 \end{pmatrix};$$

$$\begin{pmatrix} ibn \cos \dfrac{n\pi x_2}{L} \\ 0 \\ 0 \\ \sin \dfrac{n\pi x_2}{L} \end{pmatrix} = \begin{pmatrix} S \\ 0 \\ 0 \\ nx_2 \end{pmatrix}; \cdots \qquad \text{[11–56}$$

when $n \neq k$ there are four linear combinations of the products of the u's and v's of [11–52] and [11–53] which are antisymmetric.

As in the previous section, we do not concern ourselves with the normalization of the wave function. This merely involves a constant chosen so that

$$\int \psi^* \psi \, dx_1 \, dx_2 = 1$$

(For example, see Appendix XII, equation 2.)

When $n \neq k$, the four linear combinations, antisymmetric to interchange, of the zero-order eigenfunctions are:

$$\psi_{\Sigma=+1} = \begin{pmatrix} 0 \\ S \\ kx_1 \\ 0 \end{pmatrix} \begin{pmatrix} 0 \\ S \\ nx_2 \\ 0 \end{pmatrix} - \begin{pmatrix} 0 \\ S \\ nx_1 \\ 0 \end{pmatrix} \begin{pmatrix} 0 \\ S \\ kx_2 \\ 0 \end{pmatrix} \qquad [11\text{-}57$$

"both spins up"

$$\psi_{\Sigma=-1} = \begin{pmatrix} S \\ 0 \\ 0 \\ kx_1 \end{pmatrix} \begin{pmatrix} S \\ 0 \\ 0 \\ nx_2 \end{pmatrix} - \begin{pmatrix} S \\ 0 \\ 0 \\ nx_1 \end{pmatrix} \begin{pmatrix} S \\ 0 \\ 0 \\ kx_2 \end{pmatrix} \qquad [11\text{-}58$$

"both spins down"

$$\psi_{\Sigma=0} = \begin{pmatrix} 0 \\ S \\ nx_1 \\ 0 \end{pmatrix} \begin{pmatrix} S \\ 0 \\ 0 \\ kx_2 \end{pmatrix} + \begin{pmatrix} S \\ 0 \\ 0 \\ nx_1 \end{pmatrix} \begin{pmatrix} 0 \\ S \\ kx_2 \\ 0 \end{pmatrix}$$

"spins opposed"

$$- \begin{pmatrix} S \\ 0 \\ 0 \\ kx_1 \end{pmatrix} \begin{pmatrix} 0 \\ S \\ nx_2 \\ 0 \end{pmatrix} - \begin{pmatrix} 0 \\ S \\ kx_1 \\ 0 \end{pmatrix} \begin{pmatrix} S \\ 0 \\ 0 \\ nx_2 \end{pmatrix} \qquad [11\text{-}59$$

$$\psi_{S=0} = \begin{pmatrix} 0 \\ S \\ nx_1 \\ 0 \end{pmatrix} \begin{pmatrix} S \\ 0 \\ 0 \\ kx_2 \end{pmatrix} + \begin{pmatrix} 0 \\ S \\ kx_1 \\ 0 \end{pmatrix} \begin{pmatrix} S \\ 0 \\ 0 \\ nx_2 \end{pmatrix}$$

"spins opposed"

$$- \begin{pmatrix} S \\ 0 \\ 0 \\ kx_1 \end{pmatrix} \begin{pmatrix} 0 \\ S \\ nx_2 \\ 0 \end{pmatrix} - \begin{pmatrix} S \\ 0 \\ 0 \\ nx_1 \end{pmatrix} \begin{pmatrix} 0 \\ S \\ kx_2 \\ 0 \end{pmatrix} \qquad [11\text{-}60$$

In the wave functions above it is easy to see that if x_1 and x_2 are everywhere interchanged, then each of the wave functions changes sign. Also, if products are formed, such as, for example

$$(\psi^*_{\Sigma=+1})(\psi_{\Sigma=-1})$$

then, using the rule [11–51a], the result will always be zero. Thus the four combinations are mutually orthogonal (see Problems 11.3 and 11.4).

There are no other antisymmetric combinations.

All four of these different states have the *same* characteristic energy (positive),

$$W \simeq 2mc^2 + (\hbar^2 \, \pi^2 / 2mL^2)(k^2 + n^2) \qquad [11\text{-}61$$

since the u's and the v's are individually solutions to the single-particle equation [11–37], which has the energy values [11–41].

There are no bound negative energy states.

The combination [11–60] is labeled $S = 0$ since, if we let $n = k$, we note that this wave function is just two times the wave function $\psi_{S=0}$ of [11–55]. The Σ states and the $S = 0$ state are very different, since all of the wave functions labeled with the Σ's simply vanish when we let $n = k$. *These states cannot exist unless the two electrons are "sharing two different quantum numbers, n and k."*

This phenomenon occurs in atomic structure. If, for example, the two electrons in helium are in (i.e., share) the lowest or $n = 1$ state, then they *must* have "opposite spins," or rather, independent modes of vibration. However, if "one electron" is excited—more exactly, two electrons now share two *different* spatial quantum numbers—then there are four distinct states, one for each of the four wave functions listed above. (See the discussion later in this section.) It is a difference only in detail that the wave functions are dependent upon the spatial variables r_1, θ_1, and ϕ_1, and r_2, θ_2, and ϕ_2, rather than only on x_1 and x_2.

In atoms, one can imagine these Dirac waves to be "wrapped around" the central electric charged nucleus—diffracted by the electric field—but they still possess the ability to form the two orthogonal modes of vibration.

If there is no electrostatic or other interaction between the two electrons, then all four of the states [11–57] through [11–60] are degenerate.

If, however, as in Chapter 9, we introduce a perturbation term H', which depends upon the relative distance between the two electrons, we will find that the three Σ terms will, together, have their characteristic energy raised slightly. In contrast to this, the wave function $\psi_{S=0}$ will have a relatively large increase in its characteristic energy.

To see how this energy difference arises between the three Σ states, called the triplet states, and $S = 0$, or "singlet" state of the same system, we first calculate the probability density function (dependent upon x_1 and x_2) for the four wave functions [11–57] through [11–60]. Using the operation [11–51a], we find[18] that all three of the ψ_Σ states have the *same* probability density

$$\psi_\Sigma \, \psi_\Sigma = \left[\sin \frac{n\pi x_1}{L} \sin \frac{k\pi x_2}{L} - \sin \frac{k\pi x_1}{L} \sin \frac{n\pi x_2}{L} \right]^2 \qquad [11–62$$

---

[18] As an example, consider two typical operations, which are among those needed in performing this calculation. (We neglect the small component since its magnitude is $\sim p_x/mc$.)

$$\left(0, 0, \sin \frac{k\pi x_1}{L}, 0\right) \left(0, 0, \sin \frac{n\pi x_2}{L}, 0\right) \begin{pmatrix} 0 \\ 0 \\ \sin \frac{k\pi x_1}{L} \\ 0 \end{pmatrix} \begin{pmatrix} 0 \\ 0 \\ \sin \frac{n\pi x_2}{L} \\ 0 \end{pmatrix} = \sin^2 \frac{k\pi x_1}{L} \sin^2 \frac{n\pi x_2}{L}$$

Another case:

$$\left(0, 0, \sin \frac{n\pi x_1}{L}, 0\right) \left(0, 0, 0, \sin \frac{k\pi x_2}{L}\right) \begin{pmatrix} 0 \\ 0 \\ 0 \\ \sin \frac{k\pi x_1}{L} \end{pmatrix} \begin{pmatrix} 0 \\ 0 \\ \sin \frac{n\pi x_2}{L} \\ 0 \end{pmatrix} = 0$$

and the $S = 0$ state has the probability density

$$\psi_{S=0}^* \, \psi_{S=0} = \left[\sin \frac{n\pi x_1}{L} \sin \frac{k\pi x_2}{L} + \sin \frac{k\pi x_1}{L} \sin \frac{n\pi x_2}{L} \right]^2 \quad [11\text{-}63]$$

where we neglect a constant factor, since the original wave functions are not normalized. We are concerned here only with the spatial dependence of the probability distributions (see Problem 11.3).

We can see at once, from [11-62] and [11-63], that for the Σ states the probability density (the probability of simultaneously finding one electron in the range x_1 to $x_1 + dx_1$, and the other in the range x_2 to $x_2 + dx_2$) is exactly zero whenever $x_1 = x_2$. In other words, these electrons are "avoiding each other in space." Also, $\psi_\Sigma^* \, \psi_\Sigma$ vanishes when $n = k$.

On the other hand, the two electrons in the singlet state, designated by $S = 0$, usually have an exceptionally large probability density function whenever $x_1 = x_2$. These electrons tend to "clump together in space." $\psi_{S=0}^* \, \psi_{S=0}$ exists for both $n = k$, and $n \neq k$.

In *both* singlet and triplet states, however, the system wave function is antisymmetric to the interchange of the two coordinates x_1 and x_2, a situation which is possible only because the Dirac waves have two independent modes of vibration.

If now we introduce an electrostatic repulsion between the two electrons, we can see that, in the triplet states, where the electrons are "avoiding each other," there will be a relatively small increase in system energy over the zero-order value. In the singlet state, where the electrons are "clumping together in space," we will expect a relatively large increase in system energy.

To illustrate this situation graphically, we take the specific case where $n = 1$ and $k = 2$ and, in Figure 11.6, plot contour diagrams of the two different probability density functions. We see that for the singlet state there are two hills centered along the line $x_1 = x_2$. Here, *both* the electrons are most likely to be found near $x = L/4$, or *both* near $x = 3L/4$. They tend to clump together in space.

In contrast to this, the electrons in the triplet states are most likely to be found as follows: one near $x = L/4$ and the other near $x = 3L/4$, or the reverse: they "avoid" each other. In Chapter 9 we considered the similar problem of two identical particles in a one-dimensional, infinite-wall box, but with a nonrelativistic Hamiltonian. There, in Figure 9.2, we plotted the symmetric and the antisymmetric wave functions. The diagrams in Figure 9.2 look very similar to those in Figure 11.6—indeed, they are mathematically the same—but there is an important difference in the nature of the "particles" being described. In Chapter 9 we considered particles which, obeying the nonrelativistic wave equation, could not have "spin," or two independent modes of vibration. The system wave function for these imaginary particles could be antisymmetric *only* in the case where they were avoiding each other (lower diagram, Fig. 9.2).

In contrast, we see by Figure 11.6 that two real electrons can have an antisymmetric system wave function whether or not they are "avoiding each other." The reason is basically because of the existence of the two independent

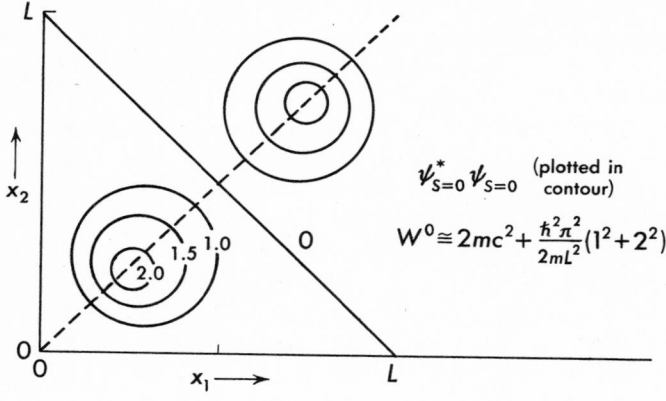

SINGLET STATE

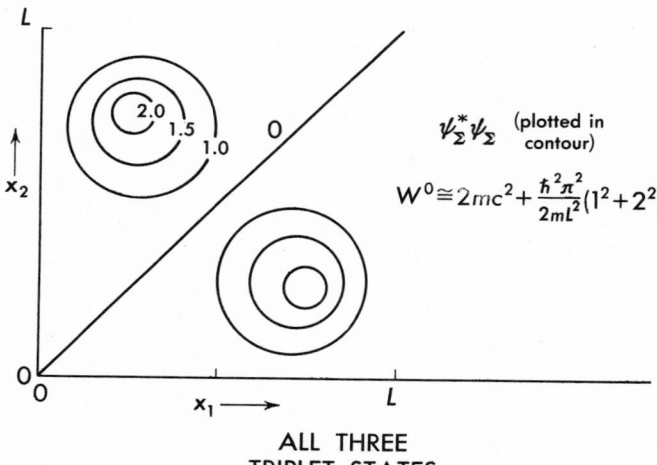

ALL THREE
TRIPLET STATES

Fig. 11.6. Probability density contour plots for the singlet and triplet states for two identical noninteracting Dirac particles in a one-dimensional, infinite-wall box. Both types of state are antisymmetric to interchange of identical particle . Case: $n = 1$, $k = 2$.

modes of vibration required by the Dirac Hamiltonian. Now, even though the electrons are "clumping together in space," their vibrations are independent and their wave functions do not overlap at all!

If the electrons in Figure 11.6 have a mutual potential energy due to their electrostatic repulsion, then, as Figure 11.7a shows, the singlet state will be raised much higher above the zero-order energy level than are the three triplet states. An examination of the energy levels of the helium atom discussed below shows a similar situation.

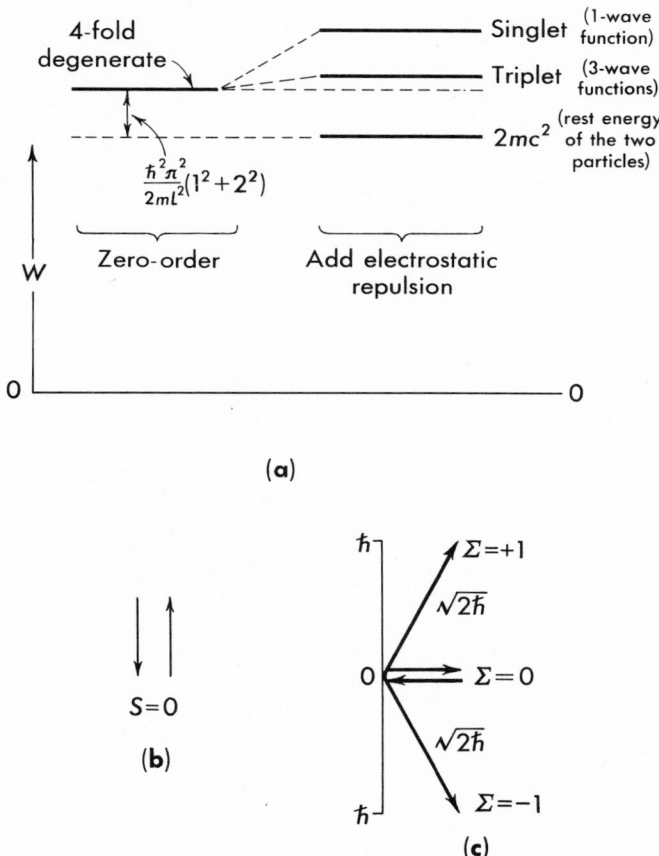

(a)

(b)

(c)

Fig. 11.7. **a.** The energy levels for singlet and triplet states for two identical particles in a one-dimensional, infinite-wall box. **b.** In the singlet state, "the electron spins are opposed." **c.** In the triplet state, "the electron spins are parallel." The resultant vector can have three possible values of M_z.

The complete theory shows that if a magnetic field is imposed upon a system containing a single electron, there will be two energy levels, one for each of the two "orthogonal vibrations" or "spins." If a magnetic field were superimposed upon the two-electron, one-dimensional system (perpendicular to x), we would find that the singlet state is unaffected, but that the triplet-state energy level would split into three—one higher, one unchanged, and one lower. The complete theory shows that each electron acts as if it possessed a spin vector of magnitude $(1/2) \hbar$ and an associated magnetic moment of one Bohr magneton.[19] Using these terms, the vector diagrams of Figures 11.7b and c illustrate the differences between the singlet and triplet states. For the singlet state (Fig. 11.7b) the "spins are opposed." The addition of the magnetic field increases the energy of one electron and decreases the energy of the other, making a total system energy change of zero.

If, on the other hand, the "spins are both up" [11–57], where by "up" we mean that the angular momentum vector is parallel to B, then the system energy is increased.[20] If the "spins are both down" [11–58], then the system energy is decreased. For [11–59] the "spins are opposed" once more, and there is no change in the system energy.

In the artificial, one-dimensional system which we are analyzing one can not properly speak of angular momentum since, with only one degree of freedom, this quantity can not be defined. The three triplet states are here identified by the essentially arbitrary labels $\Sigma = 1, \Sigma = 0, \Sigma = -1$. In the conventional notation of spectroscopy, all three triplets are identified by the notation $S = 1$, and, in a magnetic field, S (which is regarded as an angular momentum vector whose magnitude is always $\sqrt{2} \, \hbar$) takes on discrete spatial orientations which have the components $+ \hbar, 0, - \hbar$ along the direction of the magnetic field. The fact that the singlet and triplet states occur under conditions where angular momentun can not be defined indicates that the distinctive angular momentum effects associated with the two different types of states are secondary features. The four-component wave functions with their two independent modes of propagation are the real basis of the singlet and triplet states which always appear when two electrons share a single potential well.

In atoms with two active electrons, such as helium, the triplet states are not degenerate. The reason for this is found in the magnetic field due to the "orbital motion" of the electrons. In this field, the three $S = 1$ states are spread apart slightly in energy, while the $S = 0$ state is unaffected.

The main structure of the helium energy level diagram[21] shown in Figure 11.8 can be understood in terms of the simpler, one-dimensional, two-electron system which we have been discussing. We note first that in Figure 11.8 there are two complete sets of energy levels, singlet and triplet. In the triplet system, as in the one-dimensional case of Figure 11.7 (with a weak magnetic field), each of the energy levels is a closely spaced triplet.

---

[19] See Problem 6.8 and Appendix X.

[20] When the angular momentum is pointing *parallel* to B, the magnetic moment of a "spinning, negative charge" is pointing against (opposite to) the field, so the system energy is high.

[21] See, for example, G. Hertzberg, *Atomic Spectra and Atomic Structure* (1937, Prentice-Hall, Inc., and Dover Publications, New York): p. 65.

The lowest state of the system, the true ground state, is the $n = 1$ singlet level. Since both the one-particle eigenfunctions, whose products form the two-particle wave function, have the same ($n = 1$, $l = 0$, $m = 0$) *spatial* function, it is necessary that the spins be opposed. Thus, the ground-state wave function is similar to [11–55b]. The ground state must be singlet, since there is only *one* antisymmetric wave function which has this energy.

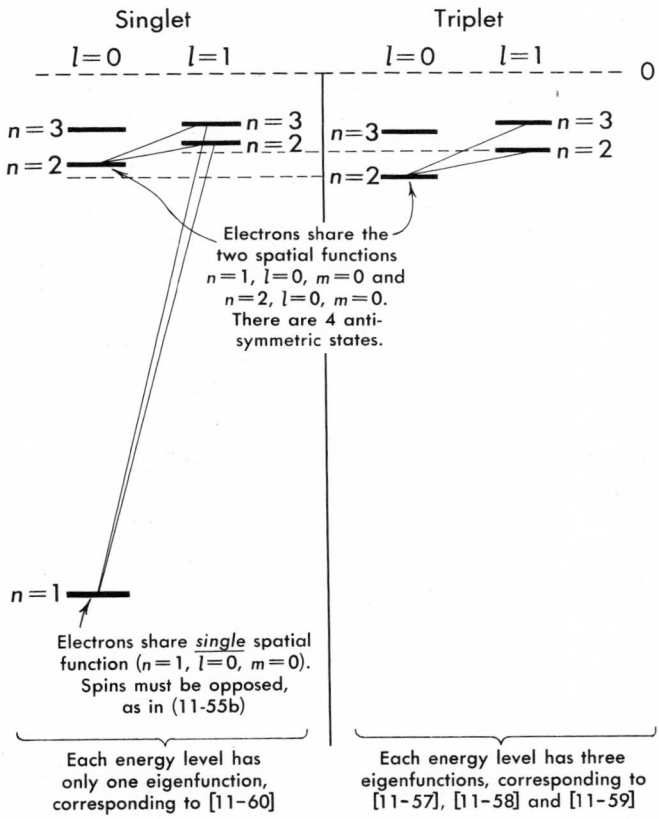

Fig. 11.8. The energy-level diagram of helium, and some of the transitions producing spectral lines.

If the two electrons share the two sets of spatial quantum numbers or wave functions, designated by $n = 1$, $l = 0$, $m = 0$, and $n = 2$, $l = 0$, $m = 0$, one can form a singlet wave function, corresponding to [11–60], and also three triplet wave functions, corresponding to [11–57], [11–58], and [11–59]. In the helium atom, as in the one-dimensional example, the singlet state has a probability density in which the electrons tend to clump together in space,

while, for the triplet states, the electrons tend to avoid each other in space
Thus, as in the one-dimensional case of Figure 11.7, each singlet state of
helium (see Fig. 11.8) has a slightly higher energy than the corresponding
triplet states.

Problem 11.9 is concerned with showing how, for low-energy particles,
dipole transitions are forbidden between the singlet and triplet states of the
one-dimensional box. Similarly, the helium spectrum shows no radiative transitions occuring between singlet and triplet systems of levels. Early investigators
thought that there were two types of helium, para (which we now understand
to be electrons in a singlet state, including the true ground state), and ortho
(the electrons in a triplet state, including the very long-lived or metastable
state, identified on the diagram as $n = 2$, $l = 0$). Within each system, however,
dipole transitions occur in the normal manner, as indicated on the diagram by
the lines connecting the levels. The transition between the metastable triplet
state $n = 2$, $l = 0$, $m = 0$ and the ground state is usually effected by a "spin-
flipping" interaction with foreign atoms.

11.10. The nonrelativistic spin wave functions

In Section 11.7 we found two orthogonal relativistic wave functions for a
particle in an infinite-wall box, [11–43] and [11–44]. The small component of
each wave function is the order of $p_x/mc = v_x/c$ and therefore is of little consequence in the calculations for atomic systems, where $v_x = 10^{-3}c$. We note,
furthermore, that the large component, ψ_3 or ψ_4, has the same spatial dependence
as in nonrelativistic theory. If we ignore the time-dependent factor $e^{-imc^2t/\hbar}$
associated with the rest mass, and write only the ψ_3 and ψ_4 components—since
ψ_1 and ψ_2 are negligible—the pair of wave functions [11–43] and [11–44] may
be written as two-component spinors.

$$\Psi_\uparrow = \begin{pmatrix} 1 \\ 0 \end{pmatrix}\sqrt{\frac{2}{L}}\sin\frac{k\pi x}{L}\,e^{-iW_kt/\hbar}, \;\; \Psi_\downarrow = \begin{pmatrix} 0 \\ 1 \end{pmatrix}\sqrt{\frac{2}{L}}\sin\frac{k\pi x}{L}\,e^{-iW_kt/\hbar} \qquad [11-64$$

The time-dependent term containing the constant energy mc^2 does not influence
(to first order) the calculation of the *difference* between two expectation values
of the system energy, which is the quantity observed in atomic physics experiments. One expects, therefore, that two-component (spinor) functions of the
type in [11–64] will give a fairly accurate description of the phenomena in
atomic physics. Before the appearance of the Dirac theory, Pauli[22] showed that
functions of the above type permitted the incorporation of electron spin,
initially proposed by Goudsmit and Uhlenbeck,[23] into the nonrelativistic theory
of Heisenberg and Schrödinger. Starting with the Dirac theory in the one-

---

[22] W. Pauli, *Zeits. f. Physik*, **43**: 601, 1927.
[23] G. E. Uhlenbeck and S. Goudsmit, *Naturwiss.*, **13**: 953, 1925, and *Nature*, **117**: 264,
1926.

dimensional case discussed above, and *then* going to the nonrelativistic limit ($v \ll c$), we find ourselves back to ordinary Schrödinger wave functions, except that we must regard them as having a two-component, vector-like nature. In other words, the two spin modes, arising automatically from the relativistic theory, do *not* disappear when $v \to 0$, in contrast to the other observable relativistic phenomena. (The rest energy mc^2 also does not disappear when $v \to 0$ but, as we have already noted, it does not produce appreciable consequencies at low energies.)

To find the form of the Pauli spin wave functions [11–64] in a more general case, we show, starting with the Dirac equation [11–27], that when $v \ll c$, ψ_3 and ψ_4 are each solutions to Schrödinger's nonrelativistic amplitude equation.

We start with [11–27], except, as described earlier in the chapter, we replace W by $W - V$, where V is the electrostatic potential energy. We now require that the *classical* total energy (K.E. + P.E.), which we now designate by W', is small compared to the rest energy. When this is true, then W, the *relativistic* total energy [11–1], is given approximately by

$$W \cong mc^2 + W'; \quad W' = (\text{K.E.} + \text{P.E.})_{\text{classical}} \qquad [11\text{–}65$$

Thus,

$$(W - V) + mc^2 \cong 2mc^2, \quad \text{and} \quad (W - V) - mc^2 \cong (W' - V) \qquad [11\text{–}66$$

When these expressions are substituted into the first two equations of [11–27], we have

$$2mc^2\,\psi_1 + \quad 0 \quad + \quad \frac{c\hbar}{i}\frac{\partial}{\partial z}\,\psi_3 \quad + \frac{c\hbar}{i}\left(\frac{\partial}{\partial x} - i\frac{\partial}{\partial y}\right)\psi_4 = 0$$

$$0 \quad + 2mc^2\,\psi_2 + \frac{c\hbar}{i}\left(\frac{\partial}{\partial x} + i\frac{\partial}{\partial y}\right)\psi_3 - \frac{c\hbar}{i}\frac{\partial}{\partial z}\,\psi_4 \quad\quad = 0 \qquad [11\text{–}67$$

which give both ψ_1 and ψ_2 explicitly in terms of ψ_3 and ψ_4. If ψ_1 and ψ_2 are substituted into the third and fourth equations of the set [11–27], we have

$$\left(\frac{\partial^2}{\partial x^2} + \frac{\partial^2}{\partial y^2} + \frac{\partial^2}{\partial z^2}\right)\psi_3 + \frac{2m}{\hbar^2}(W' - V)\,\psi_3 = 0$$

$$\left(\frac{\partial^2}{\partial x^2} + \frac{\partial^2}{\partial y^2} + \frac{\partial^2}{\partial z^2}\right)\psi_4 + \frac{2m}{\hbar^2}(W' - V)\,\psi_4 = 0 \qquad [11\text{–}68$$

Thus, when the classical total energy W' is small compared to the rest energy mc^2, ψ_1 and ψ_2 become very small, and the pair of surviving components, ψ_3 and ψ_4, each becomes a solution to the nonrelativistic Schrödinger equation. We see then that in the nonrelativistic limit, Dirac's equation gives the familiar *spatial* dependence of the electron wave functions, but it adds a two-component structure to the Schrödinger functions, corresponding to spin states.[24]

---

[24] See, for example, V. Rojansky, *op. cit.*, p. 477.

11.11. Summary

The total energy of a free particle, of rest mass m, is

$$W = \pm c\sqrt{p_x^2 + p_y^2 + p_z^2 + m^2 c^2} \qquad [11\text{--}4$$

Before making the standard operator substitutions for W and for p_x, p_y, and p_z, it is necessary to remove the radical. This is possible if

$$p_x^2 + p_y^2 + p_z^2 + m^2 c^2 = (a_x p_x + a_y p_y + a_z p_z + \beta mc)^2 \qquad [11\text{--}7$$

which is true if

$$a_x^2 = a_y^2 = a_z^2 = \beta^2 = 1 \qquad [11\text{--}9$$

and if the a's and β anticommute, [11–11]. Choosing the negative square root, [11–4] becomes

$$W = - c(a_x p_x + a_y p_y + a_z p_z + \beta mc) \qquad [11\text{--}13$$

Now that the radical is removed, operator substitutions may be made, and the wave function inserted in accordance with Postulate II.

$$-\frac{\hbar}{i}\frac{\partial}{\partial t}\Psi = -\left[\frac{ch}{i}\left(a_x\frac{\partial}{\partial x} + a_y\frac{\partial}{\partial y} + a_z\frac{\partial}{\partial z}\right) + \beta mc^2\right]\Psi \qquad [11\text{--}13a$$

We now assume

$$\Psi = \psi(x, y, z)\,\phi(t) \qquad [11\text{--}14$$

and we have, by the usual separation-of-variables process (see Section 3.1), the amplitude equation

$$\left[-\frac{ch}{i}\left(a_x\frac{\partial}{\partial x} + a_y\frac{\partial}{\partial y} + a_z\frac{\partial}{\partial z}\right) - \beta mc^2\right]\psi = W\psi \qquad [11\text{--}16$$

where W is the separation constant.

Using the four Dirac matrices for the a's and β, inserting the unit matrix in front of W, and writing ψ as a four-component column symbol, [11–16] becomes

$$\left[-\frac{ch}{i}\left(a_x\frac{\partial}{\partial x} + a_y\frac{\partial}{\partial y} + a_z\frac{\partial}{\partial z}\right) - \beta mc^2\right]\begin{pmatrix}\psi_1\\\psi_2\\\psi_3\\\psi_4\end{pmatrix} = W\begin{pmatrix}\psi_1\\\psi_2\\\psi_3\\\psi_4\end{pmatrix}$$

$$[11\text{--}25$$

where

$$a_x = \begin{pmatrix} 0 & 0 & 0 & 1 \\ 0 & 0 & 1 & 0 \\ 0 & 1 & 0 & 0 \\ 1 & 0 & 0 & 0 \end{pmatrix} \quad ; \quad a_y = \begin{pmatrix} 0 & 0 & 0 & -i \\ 0 & 0 & i & 0 \\ 0 & -i & 0 & 0 \\ i & 0 & 0 & 0 \end{pmatrix} ;$$

$$a_z = \begin{pmatrix} 0 & 0 & 1 & 0 \\ 0 & 0 & 0 & -1 \\ 1 & 0 & 0 & 0 \\ 0 & -1 & 0 & 0 \end{pmatrix} \quad ; \quad \beta = \begin{pmatrix} 1 & 0 & 0 & 0 \\ 0 & 1 & 0 & 0 \\ 0 & 0 & -1 & 0 \\ 0 & 0 & 0 & -1 \end{pmatrix}$$

[11–23

which is the Dirac amplitude equation for a free particle. Performing the matrix operations, and equating components separately, as in vector equations, we have the set of four linear, partial-differential equations [11–27] which is equivalent to [11–25].

If $\psi = \psi(x)$, and we write $(W - V)$ in place of W (where $V(x)$ is a purely electrostatic potential energy), [11–25] becomes

$$[(W - V) + mc^2]\,\psi_1 + \frac{c\hbar}{i}\frac{\partial}{\partial x}\psi_4 = 0$$

$$[(W - V) + mc^2]\,\psi_2 + \frac{c\hbar}{i}\frac{\partial}{\partial x}\psi_3 = 0$$

$$\frac{c\hbar}{i}\frac{\partial}{\partial x}\psi_2 + [(W - V) - mc^2]\,\psi_3 = 0$$

$$\frac{c\hbar}{i}\frac{\partial}{\partial x}\psi_1 + [(W - V) - mc^2]\,\psi_4 = 0$$

[11–27a

which is the Dirac equation for a particle in a one-dimensional, electrostatic potential well $V(x)$.

This equation is solved for three cases.

(1) The Free Particle

For this case, $V = 0$ everywhere. We assume a solution of the form,

$$\psi(x) = \begin{pmatrix} A_1 \\ A_2 \\ A_3 \\ A_4 \end{pmatrix} e^{i2\pi x/\lambda}, \text{ and } \Psi = \psi(x)\,e^{-iWt/\hbar}$$

[11–28

where the A's are constants. The substitution of [11–28] into [11–27a] will lead to a nontrivial solution only if

$$W = \pm\sqrt{(ch/\lambda)^2 + m^2c^4}$$

[11–31

For $W = +\sqrt{(ch/\lambda)^2 + m^2 c^4}$, there are two independent solutions, depending upon whether A_3 or A_4 is set equal to zero,

$$\Psi'_{\downarrow} = A_4 \begin{pmatrix} \dfrac{-ch/\lambda}{W + mc^2} \\ 0 \\ 0 \\ 1 \end{pmatrix} e^{i\left(\frac{2\pi}{\lambda}x - \frac{W}{\hbar}t\right)}; \quad \Psi'_{\uparrow} = A_3 \begin{pmatrix} 0 \\ \dfrac{-ch/\lambda}{W + mc^2} \\ 1 \\ 0 \end{pmatrix} e^{i\left(\frac{2\pi}{\lambda}x - \frac{W}{\hbar}t\right)} \qquad [11\text{--}34$$

where, for low-energy particles (states near mc^2), the magnitude of the first or the second component is much less than the magnitude of the third or fourth. The two modes are orthogonal, since $\Psi'^*_{\downarrow} \cdot \Psi'_{\uparrow} = 0$.

For $W = -\sqrt{(ch/\lambda)^2 + m^2 c^4}$, there are also two independent solutions, similar to [11--34], except that now the first and second components are the large ones, and components three and four are smaller. These negative energy states are considered to be completely filled, except for an occasional vacancy produced by the elevation of a particle to one of the available positive energy states. The *vacancy* constitutes the antiparticle.

(2) The Particle in the One-Dimensional Well, Infinite Walls

For this case, $V = 0$ inside the well and becomes infinite at the boundaries at $x = 0$ and $x = L$. (In Appendix XI, the case of finite potential walls is examined.)

If we assume that $\psi_4 = A_4 \sin(k\pi x/L)$, and set $\psi_3 = 0$, we obtain $\psi_2 = 0$, and $\psi_1 = \hbar k\pi A_4 \cos(k\pi x/L)/2imcL$, and a similar independent solution is obtained if ψ_4 is chosen to be zero and $\psi_3 = A_3 \sin(k\pi x/L)$. The two independent solutions for the same quantum number k,

$$[\Psi'_k(x)]_\downarrow = A_4 \begin{pmatrix} \dfrac{i(c\hbar\, k\pi)/L}{W + mc^2} \cos \dfrac{k\pi x}{L} \\[2ex] 0 \\[1ex] 0 \\[1ex] \sin \dfrac{k\pi x}{L} \end{pmatrix} e^{-i\frac{W}{\hbar}t};$$

$$[\Psi'_k(x)]_\uparrow = A_3 \begin{pmatrix} 0 \\[2ex] \dfrac{i(c\hbar\, k\pi)/L}{W + mc^2} \cos \dfrac{k\pi x}{L} \\[2ex] \sin \dfrac{k\pi x}{L} \\[2ex] 0 \end{pmatrix} e^{-i\frac{W}{\hbar}t} \qquad \begin{array}{l}[11\text{--}38 \text{ and} \\ [11\text{--}39a^{25}\end{array}$$

exist, however, *only if*

$$W = + \sqrt{\left(\frac{c\hbar\, k\pi}{L}\right)^2 + m^2 c^4} \qquad k = 1,\, 2,\, 3,\, \cdots \qquad [11\text{--}40$$

$$\cong mc^2 + \frac{1}{2}\frac{\hbar^2 k^2 \pi^2}{mL^2} \;\; \text{(when } c\hbar\, k\pi/L \ll mc^2\text{)} \qquad [11\text{--}41$$

A_4 and A_3 are obtained from the normalization requirement.

Appendix XI shows that, for the *positive* energy potential walls assumed above, bound states can exist only for certain discrete *positive* values of W. For $-W$ there are no bound states. There is, however, a continuum of negative-energy *unbound* states (that is, states for which the wave function outside the well does not tend rapidly to zero, as $|x| \to \infty$ but rather has the periodic form characteristic of a free particle).

A single particle can be represented simultaneously by both "spin states," given above in [11–38] and [11–39a], even if the two states have different quantum numbers, since the Dirac equation is linear. Any superposition of these eigenfunctions is also an acceptable solution to the wave equation.

When ψ_3 (and necessarily ψ_2) are excited (and $\psi_4 = \psi_1 = 0$), one speaks of the particle as being in the pure spin state, "spin up." When ψ_4 (and neces-

---

[25] Equations [11–43] and [11–44] give the nonrelativistic approximations to these expressions.

sarily ψ_1) are excited (and $\psi_3 = \psi_2 = 0$), the particle is said to be in the other spin state, "spin down." These two pure states are orthogonal, since $\psi_\uparrow^* \cdot \psi_\downarrow$ is identically zero, see [11–34c].

(3) Two Identical Particles in the One-Dimensional Well

In the same manner as in the nonrelativistic case, we separate the *two-particle* wave equation [11–48] for noninteracting low-velocity particles into three equations, using the assumption,

$$\Psi = u(x_1)\, v(x_2)\, \phi(t) \qquad\qquad [11–49$$

u and v are each four-component column symbols (see [11–50]). One column symbol is a function of x_1 and the other is a function of x_2. The two space-dependent equations are identical to [11–25].

If the walls, located at $x = 0$ and $x = L$, are infinitely high positive-energy barriers due to electrostatic forces, then u and v may have the functional form of either one of the two *single-particle* eigenfunctions given above in [11–38] and [11–39a]. For a given n and k ($n \neq k$), there are eight well-behaved solutions for the two-particle wave equation, each possessing an integrable square. Using the notation of [11–38] and [11–39a] above, a typical one of the eight possible solutions is

$$\Psi(x_1,\, x_2,\, t) = [\Psi_k(x_1)]_\downarrow\ [\Psi_n(x_2)]_\downarrow \qquad \begin{matrix} [11–52 \\ [11–53 \\ [11–54 \end{matrix}$$

Since the two particles are assumed to have the same mass and electric charge, and are in every other respect identical, the eight solutions all belong to the *same* energy level,

$$W \cong 2\, mc^2 + (\hbar^2\, \pi^2/2\, mL^2)(k^2 + n^2) \qquad\qquad [11–61$$

(for low-velocity, noninteracting particles).

Any *one* of the eight functions that are possible when $n \neq k$ has, in itself, neither symmetry nor antisymmetry with respect to the interchange of the two coordinates x_1 and x_2. There are, however, four linear combinations of the degenerate, two-particle eigenfunctions that *are* antisymmetric to interchange of x_1 and x_2 and can, therefore, by the Pauli exclusion principle, represent electrons. The four superpositions are written out in [11–57] through [11–60]. It is clear from the form of the four functions that one must regard the two particles as *sharing* both the two (spatial) quantum numbers and the two "spin states." There are, then, only four antisymmetric states available to the two particles. These states will all have the same energy, [11–61], if the particles have no mutual interaction and are bound by a pure electrostatic potential well. The effects of mutual interaction can readily be calculated using first-order perturbation theory.

If $n = k$, however, three of the antisymmetric wavefunctions, [11–57], [11–58], and [11–59], automatically vanish. These three states, called the triplet states, are further associated by the fact that, when they exist, that is, when $n \neq k$, they have the *same* probability distribution [11–62], which differs markedly from the probability distribution for the remaining state, [11–63], called the singlet state. For the three triplet states, the particles tend to be found as far apart in physical space as they can get, considering the constraining walls (see Fig. 11.6). For the singlet state, however, as Figure 11.6 also shows, the particles tend to clump together in physical space. When the two particles have mutual repulsive forces as do electrons, the singlet state will lie at a higher energy level than the three triplet states (for a given n and k). The effect is experimentally observed, for example, in the helium spectrum (Fig. 11.8).

PROBLEMS

Problem 11.1. Show that the matter waves of Figure 11.1a are propagating to the right with a velocity $v_{(wave)} = c^2/v_{(particle)}$. Starting from [11–28], the complete expression for the matter wave, show that the above relation is true. Suggestion: as a function of x, sketch the real (or the imaginary) part of [11–28] at $t = 0$. At a slightly later time t, again sketch the wave as a function of x. The shift in its position will give its velocity. Thus the matter waves for low-velocity particles propagate much faster than the velocity of light. If these waves are superposed to form a packet, so as to "localize the particle," the packet can be made to move at the *particle* velocity even though the wavelets of the superposition continuously "run through" the region of the packet. The spreading ring of wavelets from a stone dropped in still water shows the same behavior. The individual wavelets, if followed by the eye, are clearly going much faster than the principal disturbance, or packet.

Problem 11.2. In Section 11.4 it was shown that $\beta^2 = 1$, and also that $a_x a_y = - a_y a_x$. Show for all other combinations that the requirements [11–9] and [11–11] are met.

Problem 11.3

(a) Calculate the scalar product, $\psi^*_{\Sigma=+1} \psi_{\Sigma=+1}$ [11–57], and show that it gives [11–62].
(b) Show that $\psi^*_{\Sigma=-1} \psi_{\Sigma=-1}$ also gives [11–62].
(c) Show that $\psi^*_{S=0} \psi_{S=0}$ gives [11–63].
(d) Show that $\psi^*_{\Sigma=0} \psi_{\Sigma=0}$ gives [11–62].

Problem 11.4

(a) Calculate the scalar product $\psi^*_{\Sigma=+1} \psi_{\Sigma=-1}$.
(b) Calculate the scalar product $\psi^*_{\Sigma=+1} \psi_{S=0}$.

Problem 11.5. Assume that the electrons in Figure 11.6 are in a one-dimensional box for which $L = 10^{-8}$ cm. With the aid of the figure, *estimate* the increase in system energy of the triplet states when the mutual repulsion of the electrons is allowed for. (Hint: Assume that the two electrons have an average spacing of the distance between the two "hills" in the lower figure.)

Problem 11.6. For the same conditions as in Problem 11.5, *estimate* the increase in system energy caused by the electrostatic repulsion of the two electrons in the singlet state. (Hint: Pick a reasonable distance for the average electron spatial separation. Defend your choice.) Note: Both Problem 11.5 and Problem 11.6 can be solved using the basic perturbation theory used in Chapter 9 for two spinless particles. The only difficulty arises from the complexity of calculating the matrix element when H' is equal to $e^2/|x_1 - x_2|$. In atoms, the exact calculation using this H' gives an excellent prediction of the energy difference between the singlet and the three triplet states.

Problem 11.7. For the singlet state [11–55b], where the two electrons share the same spatial quantum number k, calculate the probability density and plot in the manner of Figure 11.6. A qualitative sketch is adequate.

(a) Let $k = 1$.
(b) Let $k = 2$.

Problem 11.8. Let an electron in a one-dimensional box have, for its initial state, the "spin up" wave function $\Psi_\uparrow$ [11–44], where $k = 1$. Now apply a periodic electric field, $E_x^0 \sin \omega_0 t$, which causes a perturbation energy term $H' = e\, x\, E_x^0 \sin \omega_0 t$, and let $\omega_0 = \omega_n - \omega_k$ where n is the spatial quantum number of a higher energy state. Let $n = 2$.

(a) Will this perturbation cause a growth in the amplitude of the $n = 2$ state [11–43], which is the "spin down" state?
(b) Will this perturbation cause a growth in the amplitude of the state [11–44] (quantum number = 2), which is a "spin up" state? Consider the small components of the wave function amplitudes as being negligibly small (although this is not essential to the results). The operator x is the matrix,

$$\begin{pmatrix} x & 0 & 0 & 0 \\ 0 & x & 0 & 0 \\ 0 & 0 & x & 0 \\ 0 & 0 & 0 & x \end{pmatrix}$$

and after performing the matrix operations [(row symbol for final state) (operator) (column symbol for initial state)], the ordinary spatial integration can be carried out in the normal manner. For further discussion, see Appendix XII.

Problem 11.9.   Apply the same time-varying electric field of the previous problem to a two-electron system, again in a one-dimensional box. (The electrons are assumed to have negligible mutual interaction.) Now, the perturbation term is

$$H' = e(x_1 + x_2) E_x^0 \sin \omega_0 t$$

since *each* electron, individually, has a potential energy in the external electric field.

(a)   Let the system wave function have, as its initial amplitude, the $\psi_{s=0}$ function of [11–60]—a singlet state. Let $n = k = 1$ (which simply reduces [11–60] to [11–55b]). Let the final state *also* be of the singlet type [11–60], for which we let $n = 1$ and $k = 2$ ("one electron excited"—or rather, two electrons *share* the spatial quantum numbers, 1 and 2). Will H' cause the higher energy state to grow in intensity? Assume that ω_0 equals [W(higher state) $- W$(lower state)]/$\hbar$, that is, assume resonance.

(b)   Now, let the upper state only be the triplet state—ψ of [11–57]. Can the perturbation excite this state?

(c)   Finally, let the upper state be the $\Sigma = 0$ triplet state [11–59]. Will the perturbation excite this state, starting as before from the same singlet ground state? The operator $(x_1 + x_2)$ is the sum of two matrices, each of the form given in Problem 11.8. The x_1 operator affects only the x_1-dependent factor in the symbolic product, and the x_2 operator affects only the x_2-dependent factor. For example, the operation

$$\left[\begin{pmatrix} x_1 & 0 & 0 & 0 \\ 0 & x_1 & 0 & 0 \\ 0 & 0 & x_1 & 0 \\ 0 & 0 & 0 & x_1 \end{pmatrix} + \begin{pmatrix} x_2 & 0 & 0 & 0 \\ 0 & x_2 & 0 & 0 \\ 0 & 0 & x_2 & 0 \\ 0 & 0 & 0 & x_2 \end{pmatrix} \right]$$

$$\begin{pmatrix} 0 \\ 0 \\ f(x_1) \\ 0 \end{pmatrix} \begin{pmatrix} 0 \\ 0 \\ 0 \\ g(x_2) \end{pmatrix}$$

yields the sum of two symbolic products,

$$\begin{pmatrix} 0 \\ 0 \\ x_1 f(x_1) \\ 0 \end{pmatrix} \begin{pmatrix} 0 \\ 0 \\ 0 \\ g(x_2) \end{pmatrix} + \begin{pmatrix} 0 \\ 0 \\ f(x_1) \\ 0 \end{pmatrix} \begin{pmatrix} 0 \\ 0 \\ 0 \\ x_2 g(x_2) \end{pmatrix}$$

Compare:

$$[(\partial/\partial x) + (\partial/\partial y)][f(x)\, g(y)] = \frac{\partial f(x)}{\partial x}\, g(y) + f(x)\, \frac{\partial g(y)}{\partial y}$$

After the matrix operation of the type just described, the row symbols can be brought in from the left. As described in the footnote relating to equation [11–62], a typical operation of this sort yields

$$[0, 0, F(x_1), 0][0, 0, 0, G(x_2)] \begin{pmatrix} 0 \\ 0 \\ x_1 f(x_1) \\ 0 \end{pmatrix} \begin{pmatrix} 0 \\ 0 \\ 0 \\ x_2 g(x_2) \end{pmatrix}$$
$$= [F(x_1)\, x_1 f(x_1)][G(x_2)\, x_2 g(x_2)]$$

and the final result is subject to ordinary integration with respect to its two independent variables, x_1 and x_2.

This problem illustrates the type of calculations which, for atomic systems, result in the selection rule: "Singlet-triplet transitions are forbidden in electric dipole transitions, in low-Z atoms." In the energy-level diagram for helium, for example, the singlet and triplet levels form independent systems. The operator used here for the time-varying electric field is correct only for low-velocity electrons.

APPENDIXES

THE SOLUTION OF THE AMPLITUDE EQUATION FOR THE HARMONIC OSCILLATOR

The amplitude equation [3-7]

$$\frac{d^2\psi}{dx^2} + \frac{2m}{\hbar^2}\{W - \tfrac{1}{2}kx^2\}\,\psi = 0 \qquad\qquad [3\text{-}7$$

may be written as

$$\frac{d^2\psi}{dx^2} + (\lambda - a^2 x^2)\,\psi = 0 \qquad\qquad [1$$

where

$$\lambda = \frac{2\,mW}{\hbar^2}; \quad a = \frac{2\,\pi\nu_0\,m}{\hbar}; \quad 2\,\pi\nu_0 = \sqrt{\frac{k}{m}}$$

We find the solution to the equation for very large values of $|x|$ and then find what modifications are needed to make the solution suitable for all values of $|x|$.

When x is large enough, so that $\lambda \ll a^2 x^2$, we can neglect λ, and [1] becomes

$$\frac{d^2\psi}{dx^2} = a^2 x^2\,\psi \qquad\qquad [2$$

which is called the "asymptotic form" of [1]. This is satisfied (*only* for large values of x) by

$$\psi = e^{\pm(a/2)x^2}$$

[3

This can be seen by calculating the derivatives of [3]

$$\frac{d\psi}{dx} = \pm\, a\, x\, e^{\pm ax^2/2}; \frac{d^2\psi}{dx^2} = a^2\, x^2\, e^{\pm ax^2/2} \pm a\, e^{\pm ax^2/2}$$

The second term, in $d^2\psi/dx^2$, is negligible, if $a^2\, x^2 \gg a$. This requirement can always be met by taking $|x|$ to be large enough. Thus, either

$$\psi = e^{+(a/2)x^2} \text{ or } \psi = e^{-(a/2)x^2}$$

[4

is an "asymptotic solution" to the "asymptotic equation." Only the latter, however, will approach zero as $x \to \pm \infty$, and is therefore a possible form for a wave function to have at large x.

Whatever the shape of the wave function for small x, it must, at large enough x, become indistinguishable from $e^{-(a/2)x^2}$.

We now assume that

$$\psi = e^{-(a/2)x^2} f(x)$$

[5

and then find the form of $f(x)$ which causes [5] to satisfy the basic equation [1]. To do this, we substitute [5] into the original equation [1]. Since

$$\frac{d\psi}{dx} = e^{-(a/2)x^2} \left(- \, axf + \frac{df}{dx} \right)$$

and

$$\frac{d^2\psi}{dx^2} = e^{-(a/2)x^2} \left(a^2\, x^2\, f - af - 2\, ax\, \frac{df}{dx} + \frac{d^2f}{dx^2} \right)$$

[1] becomes

$$\frac{d^2f}{dx^2} - 2\, ax\, \frac{df}{dx} + (\lambda - a) f = 0$$

[6

To put this equation into a standard form, it is necessary to define a new variable,

$$\xi = \sqrt{a}\, x$$

[7

Let us change the notation, by replacing $f(x)$ with $H(\xi)$. Thus

$$\frac{d}{dx}\, f(x) = \frac{d}{dx}\, H(\xi), \quad \frac{d}{dx}\, H(\xi) = \frac{d}{d\xi}\, H(\xi)\, \frac{d\xi}{dx}$$

thus

$$\frac{d}{dx}\, f(x) = \frac{d}{d\xi}\, H(\xi)\, \sqrt{a}$$

and, similarly,

$$\frac{d^2}{dx^2} f(x) = a \frac{d^2 H(\xi)}{d\xi^2}$$

Thus [6] becomes

$$\frac{d^2 H}{d\xi^2} - 2\xi \frac{dH}{d\xi} + \left(\frac{\lambda}{a} - 1\right) H = 0 \qquad [8$$

This equation can be solved by the power series method. We let

$$H(\xi) = a_0 + a_1 \xi + a_2 \xi^2 + a_3 \xi^3 + a_4 \xi^4 + \cdots$$

$$\frac{dH}{d\xi} = 0 + a_1 + 2 a_2 \xi + 3 a_3 \xi^2 + 4 a_4 \xi^3 + \cdots \qquad [8a$$

$$\frac{d^2 H}{d\xi^2} = 0 + 0 + 1 \cdot 2 a_2 + 2 \cdot 3 a_3 \xi + 3 \cdot 4 a_4 \xi^2 + \cdots$$

and [8] becomes

$$1 \cdot 2 a_2 + 2 \cdot 3 a_3 \xi \qquad + 3 \cdot 4 a_4 \xi^2 \qquad + 4 \cdot 5 a_5 \xi^3 \qquad + \cdots$$
$$- 2 a_1 \xi \qquad - 2 \cdot 2 a_2 \xi^2 \qquad - 2 \cdot 3 a_3 \xi^3 \qquad - \cdots$$
$$\left(\frac{\lambda}{a} - 1\right) a_0 + \left(\frac{\lambda}{a} - 1\right) a_1 \xi + \left(\frac{\lambda}{a} - 1\right) a_2 \xi^2 + \left(\frac{\lambda}{a} - 1\right) a_3 \xi^3 + \cdots = 0$$

If $H(\xi)$ is a solution of [8] for *all* values of the independent variable ξ, then the sum of the coefficients of *each* power of ξ must be zero. Thus,

$$1 \cdot 2 a_2 + \left(\frac{\lambda}{a} - 1\right) a_0 = 0$$

$$2 \cdot 3 a_3 + \left(\frac{\lambda}{a} - 1 - 2\right) a_1 = 0$$

$$3 \cdot 4 a_4 + \left(\frac{\lambda}{a} - 1 - 2 \cdot 2\right) a_2 = 0$$

$$4 \cdot 5 a_5 + \left(\frac{\lambda}{a} - 1 - 2 \cdot 3\right) a_3 = 0$$

etc.

In general, for the coefficient of ξ^ν,

$$(\nu + 1)(\nu + 2) a_{\nu+2} + \left(\frac{\lambda}{a} - 1 - 2\nu\right) a_\nu = 0, \qquad \nu = 0, 1, 2, 3, \cdots$$

or

$$a_{\nu+2} = - \frac{\left(\frac{\lambda}{a} - 2\nu - 1\right)}{(\nu + 1)(\nu + 2)} a_\nu \qquad [9$$

which relates, in this case, coefficients separated by $\Delta \nu = 2$. Thus, if a_0 is known, the coefficients of all even powers are determined by [9]. If a_1 is known, all odd powers are determined. These two arbitrary constants are the ones that are always present in any second-order differential equation. Equation [9] is called a "recursion formula."

If, for some value of ν, the numerator equals zero,

$$\frac{\lambda}{a} - 2\nu - 1 = 0 \tag{10}$$

then all of the a's with higher indexes $a_{\nu+2}$, $a_{\nu+4}$, $a_{\nu+6}$, etc., will be zero. This series termination may be accomplished by selecting some value of λ—that is, by picking some definite system energy, W. If [10] is true for ν even, then we set $a_1 = 0$ to eliminate *all* odd powers of ξ in [8a]. For certain discrete values of λ, then, $H(\xi)$ will *not* be an infinite series, but will stop at ξ^ν where ν is an even integer. For example, suppose λ has such a value that [10] is true when $\nu = 6$. Then we set $a_1 = 0$, and [8a] becomes

$$H(\xi) = a_0 + a_2 \xi^2 + a_4 \xi^4 + a_6 \xi^6$$

where a_2, a_4, and a_6 can be found, from [9], in terms of a_0.

If λ has such a value that [10] is satisfied for ν odd, then we set $a_0 = 0$ and $H(\xi) =$ polynomial of *odd* powers of ξ. We must, in any case, prevent $H(\xi)$ from being an infinite series.

To see the necessity of this cutting-off process, we now show that, if H is an infinite series, then the wave function $\psi(x)$, which is

$$(\text{constant}) \, e^{-\xi^2/2} \, H(\xi)$$

will approach infinity at large ξ (i.e., at large x), in spite of the factor $e^{-\xi^2/2}$.

Compare the series for e^{ξ^2}

$$e^{\xi^2} = 1 + \xi^2 + \frac{\xi^4}{2!} + \frac{\xi^6}{3!} + \cdots + \frac{\xi^\nu}{\left(\dfrac{\nu}{2}\right)!} + \frac{\xi^{\nu+2}}{\left(\dfrac{\nu+2}{2}\right)!} + \cdots$$

with the (unterminated) series for $H(\xi)$

$$H(\xi) = a_0 + a_1 \xi + a_2 \xi^2 + \cdots + a_\nu \xi^\nu + a_{\nu+1} \xi^{\nu+1} + a_{\nu+2} \xi^{\nu+2} + \cdots$$

We will show that for large ν, $H(\xi)$ will behave like e^{ξ^2}, making the product $e^{-\xi^2/2} H(\xi)$ behave like $e^{+\xi^2/2}$, which is unsatisfactory. For the series e^{ξ^2}, the ratio r_1 of the coefficient of $\xi^{\nu+2}$ to the coefficient of ξ^ν is

$$r_1 = \frac{\left(\dfrac{\nu}{2}\right)!}{\left(\dfrac{\nu}{2}+1\right)!} = \frac{\left(\dfrac{\nu}{2}\right)\left(\dfrac{\nu}{2}-1\right)\left(\dfrac{\nu}{2}-2\right)\cdots}{\left(\dfrac{\nu}{2}+1\right)\left(\dfrac{\nu}{2}\right)\left(\dfrac{\nu}{2}-1\right)\left(\dfrac{\nu}{2}-2\right)\cdots} = \frac{1}{\dfrac{\nu}{2}+1}$$

or, for $\nu \gg 2$ (which are the only important terms as $\xi \to \infty$),

$$r_1 \cong \frac{2}{\nu}$$

On the other hand, for large ν the recursion formula [9] gives the ratio r_2, for the coefficient of the $(\nu + 2)$-term to the ν-term of $H(\xi)$,

$$r_2 \cong \frac{2\nu}{\nu^2} = \frac{2}{\nu} \left(\text{when } 2\nu \gg \frac{\lambda}{a} - 1, \text{ and } \nu \gg 2 \right)$$

We see then that (for large ν) for *both* series, when ν changes from ν to $\nu + 2$, the coefficients are changed by the *same* factor, $\nu/2$. Thus, whatever ratio c the νth coefficient of e^{ξ^2} bears to the νth coefficient of $H(\xi)$, this ratio will be preserved for *all* larger values of ν. Thus, no matter how large ν becomes, the corresponding coefficients of the two series differ only by the constant factor, c. As $\xi \to \infty$, $H(\xi) \to$ (constant) e^{ξ^2}, so the product $e^{-\xi^2/2} H(\xi)$ becomes (constant) $e^{\xi^2/2}$, an ill-behaved function. Therefore, the series for $H(\xi)$ *must be terminated*. This can be done only by setting

$$\lambda = (2\nu + 1) a \qquad\qquad [11]$$

in equation [9], *and* by setting either a_0 or a_1 equal to 0.

For example, if $a_1 = 0$, there are no odd powers of ξ (no odd powers of x) in the wave function, and we obtain $\psi_0, \psi_2, \psi_4, \cdots$, which are all symmetrical about $\xi = 0$ $(x = 0)$. If $\nu = 0$ then $\lambda = a$, $a_2 = 0$, $a_4 = 0$, $\cdots$, and

$$\psi_0 = e^{-\xi^2/2} a_0$$

If we pick $\nu = 2$ then $\lambda = (2 \cdot 2 + 1) a$, $a_4 = 0$, $a_6 = 0$, $\cdots$, but, by [9], $a^5 = -2 a_0$ so that, by [8a],

$$\psi_2 = e^{-\xi^2/2} [a_0 - 2 a_0 \xi^2]$$

The value of a_0 is determined for each of these two cases by the requirement that

$$\int\limits_{-\infty}^{+\infty} \psi^* \psi \, dx = 1$$

On the other hand, if $a_0 = 0$, and if $\lambda = (2 \cdot 1 + 1) a$, then $a_3 = 0$, $a_5 = 0$, $\cdots$, and

$$\psi_1 = e^{-\xi^2/2} [a_1 \xi]$$

If $\lambda = (2 \cdot 3 + 1) a$, then $a_5 = 0$, $a_7 = 0$, etc., and by [9], $a_3 = -\frac{2}{3} a_1$

$$\psi_3 = e^{-\xi^2/2} [a_1 \xi - \frac{2}{3} a_1 \xi^3]$$

In each case a_1 is determined by the normalization requirement.

If, in [11], we substitute $\lambda = 2 mW/\hbar^2$, and $a = 2 \pi \nu_0 m/\hbar$ from equation

[1], we have (writing $n = \nu$),

$$W_n = (2n + 1) \tfrac{1}{2} h\nu_0$$

which are the characteristic energy values for the harmonic oscillator.

The polynomials $H(\xi)$ obtained here are known as the Hermite polynomials. They can be defined in other ways, and various relationships between their derivatives can be established. Many textbooks[1] have extensive discussions of these functions, which, incidentally, were well known to mathematicians before their application to quantum mechanics.

This method of finding eigenvalues and eigenfunctions is widely used, and the case of the harmonic oscillator is a typical example of its application. A recursion formula such as [9] can usually be found, but not so simply as here, due to the presence of singular points. Once found, the series must be terminated by the proper selection of the parameter whose eigenvalue is being determined. In every case one must show that the unterminated series will produce an ill-behaved function, and that the terminated series is a satisfactory function.

The normalized amplitude eigenfunctions for the harmonic oscillator are

$$\psi_n(x) = N_n \, e^{-\xi^2/2} \, H_n(\xi)$$

where

$$\xi = \sqrt{a}\, x, \quad a = 2\,\pi\nu_0\, m/\hbar, \quad \nu_0 = \frac{1}{2\pi}\sqrt{\frac{k}{m}}$$

$$N_n = \left(\sqrt{\frac{a}{\pi}} \cdot \frac{1}{2^n\, n!} \right)^{\frac{1}{2}}$$

The first few Hermite polynomials are

$$H_0(\xi) = 1$$
$$H_1(\xi) = 2\,\xi$$
$$H_2(\xi) = 4\,\xi^2 - 2$$
$$H_3(\xi) = 8\,\xi^3 - 12\,\xi$$
$$H_4(\xi) = 16\,\xi^4 - 48\,\xi^2 + 12$$
$$H_5(\xi) = 32\,\xi^5 - 160\,\xi^3 + 120\,\xi$$

---

[1] L. Pauling and E. B. Wilson, *Introduction to Quantum Mechanics* (1935, McGraw-Hill Book Co., Inc., New York); and V. Rojansky, *Introductory Quantum Mechanics* (1942, Prentice-Hall, Inc., New York).

ORTHOGONALITY OF WAVE FUNCTIONS CORRESPONDING TO DIFFERENT ENERGY LEVELS

Consider the one-dimensional amplitude equation [3–4] when $W = W_n$, one of the eigenvalues. Then ψ must be an eigenfunction, ψ_n, belonging to W_n.

$$\frac{d^2 \psi_n}{dx^2} + \frac{2m}{\hbar^2} [W_n - V(x)] \psi_n = 0 \qquad [1$$

The complex conjugate equation is

$$\frac{d^2 \psi_k^*}{dx^2} + \frac{2m}{\hbar^2} [W_k - V(x)] \psi_k^* = 0 \qquad [2$$

for a different eigenvalue, W_k.

We will show that if $W_n \neq W_k$, then

$$\int_{-\infty}^{+\infty} \psi_k^* \psi_n \, dx = 0 \qquad [3$$

Multiply [1] by ψ_k^*, and [2] by ψ_n and subtract.

$$\psi_k^* \frac{d^2 \psi_n}{dx^2} - \psi_n \frac{d^2 \psi_k^*}{dx^2} + \frac{2m}{\hbar^2} (W_n - W_k) \psi_k^* \psi_n = 0 \qquad [4$$

We now integrate [4] over all values of x,

$$\frac{2\,m}{\hbar^2}\,(W_n - W_k)\int_{-\infty}^{+\infty} \psi_k^* \, \psi_n \, dx = -\int_{-\infty}^{+\infty}\left(\psi_k^* \frac{d^2\,\psi_n}{dx^2} - \psi_n \frac{d^2\,\psi_k^*}{dx^2}\right) dx \qquad [5$$

Using the identity

$$\frac{d}{dx}\left(\psi_k^* \frac{d\psi_n}{dx} - \psi_n \frac{d\psi_k^*}{dx}\right) = \psi_k^* \frac{d^2\,\psi_n}{dx^2} - \psi_n \frac{d^2\,\psi_k^*}{dx^2} \qquad [6$$

we have

$$\int_{-\infty}^{+\infty}\left(\psi_k^* \frac{d^2\,\psi_n}{dx^2} - \psi_n \frac{d^2\,\psi_k^*}{dx^2}\right) dx = \left[\psi_k^* \frac{d\psi_n}{dx} - \psi_n \frac{d\psi_k^*}{dx}\right]_{-\infty}^{+\infty} \qquad [7$$

From Postulate III, the slope $d\psi/dx$ is required to be everywhere finite. When $x \to \infty$, $\int \psi^* \, \psi \, dx \to \infty$, unless $|\psi| \to 0$ as $x \to \infty$. Postulates III and IV require, therefore, that both ψ_k^* and ψ_n are zero for very large x, and, since the slope must be finite as $x \to \infty$,

$$\frac{2\,m}{\hbar^2}\,(W_n - W_k)\int_{-\infty}^{+\infty} \psi_k^* \, \psi_n \, dx = 0 \qquad [8$$

Since it has been required that $W_n \neq W_k$, the integral is 0.

In the case of the infinite-wall potential well between $x = 0$ and $x = L$, $\psi = 0$ at each end point and, since the slope is finite, the orthogonality condition is again fulfilled. The basic requirement for the existance of orthogonality, [8], is met whenever [7] equals zero, the limits of integration being any boundaries of the wave function—not necessarily $x = \pm \infty$ as we have used above.

We see, then, that the orthogonality of the eigenfunctions which correspond to different energy levels is a *basic* characteristic. It is a necessary consequence of the wave equation itself and of the boundary conditions, as required by the postulates.

What happens when $W_n = W_k$, but the wave functions ψ_n and ψ_k are different functions of x? It is now possible that $\int \psi_k^* \, \psi_n \, dx$ is non-zero that is, that ψ_k and ψ_n are not orthogonal. We construct two linear combinations of ψ_n and ψ_k, using four constants, a, b, c, and d,

$$f = a \, \psi_k + b \, \psi_n \qquad [9$$

and

$$g = c \, \psi_k + d \, \psi_n \qquad [10$$

and require that *they* be orthogonal, i.e.,

$$\int_{-\infty}^{+\infty} f^* g \, dx = 0 \qquad [11$$

The four constants must meet the requirement

$$a^* c \int \psi_k^* \psi_k \, dx + a^* d \int \psi_k^* \psi_n \, dx + b^* c \int \psi_n^* \psi_k \, dx + b^* d \int \psi_n^* \psi_n \, dx = 0 \qquad [12$$

The integrals are all uniquely determined by the eigenfunctions, which are assumed to be known.

When f and g are each normalized to unity, a, b, c, and d must meet two requirements in addition to [12]. That is, $\int f^* f \, dx = 1$ and $\int g^* g \, dx = 1$. We have therefore four constants with only three conditions placed upon them, so that there is an infinite number of ways to select these constants.

Thus, even though it should happen that $W_n = W_k$, we can still construct two orthogonal, normalized functions (such as f and g) belonging to this particular energy. A single energy level with two different eigenfunctions, ψ_n and ψ_k, is called a twofold degenerate level.

The great importance of being able to construct orthogonal functions, even for degenerate levels, is seen in the application of perturbation theory in Chapter 8.

Although the analysis here has been performed only for one dimension, it is relatively simple to extend it to three or more dimensions.

The right-hand side of [7] is also 0 if $\psi(x)$ obeys "periodic boundary conditions" at $x = -L/2$ and $x = L/2$ which we now take to be the limits of integration (and also the domain of definition of the wave function). "Periodic boundary conditions" means that $\psi(-L/2) = \psi(L/2)$ and

$$(d\psi/dx)_{x=-L/2} = (d\psi/dx)_{x=L/2}.$$

and similarly for ψ^* and $d\psi^*/dx$. These together cause the right-hand side of [7] to vanish when the limits of integration are $-L/2$ and $L/2$; therefore the eigenfunctions [3] are orthogonal in the interval. This type of boundary condition is used in Section 5.6 in the analysis of wave packets.

COMPLEX NUMBERS

A complex number differs from an ordinary real number much as a vector differs from a scalar. The symbol, such as ψ, stands for a *pair* of real numbers which are subject to special rules for the basic operations of addition, multiplication, etc. (The symbol **A**, for a vector, stands for an ordered triplet of three numbers, which are also processed by a special set of rules.)

Let ψ_1 be represented by the ordered pair

$$\psi_1 = (a, b)$$

where a and b are real numbers, and let ψ_2 be represented by the ordered pair [1]

$$\psi_2 = (c, d)$$

The complex conjugate of the number $\psi_1 = (a, b)$ is designated by ψ_1^* and is defined to be $(a, -b)$. Similarly, $\psi_2^* = (c, -d)$.

By definition: the sum is,

$$\psi_1 + \psi_2 = (a + c, \ b + d) \tag{1}$$

the difference is,

$$\psi_1 - \psi_2 = (a - c, \ b - d) \tag{2}$$

the product is,

$$\psi_1 \psi_2 = (ac - bd, \ ad + bc) \tag{3}$$

---

[1] Note: the pair $(a, 0)$ is called the real number, a, and the pair $(0, b)$ is called the "imaginary number, b."

344

and the quotient is,

$$\frac{\psi_1}{\psi_2} = \left(\frac{ac + bd}{c^2 + d^2}, \frac{bc - da}{c^2 + d^2}\right)$$

[4

Also,

$$\frac{d\psi}{dx} = \left(\frac{da}{dx}, \frac{db}{dx}\right)$$

[5

and,

$$\int \psi \, dx = \left(\int a \, dx, \int b \, dx\right)$$

[6

Thus the basic mathematical operations using ordered pairs result, by definite rules, in ordered pairs. It is easy to verify that if

$$\psi_1 = a + ib \text{ and } \psi_2 = c + id$$

[7

where $i^2 = -1$, the above results are all duplicated. Thus the use of the symbol i, as in [7], is a convenient, though not essential, means of remembering these rules for the algebra of ordered pairs.

To change any number ψ into its complex conjugate one need only to change the sign of i.

The identity operation,

$$\psi_1 = \psi_2$$

[8

means that $a = c$ and $b = d$. (This is similar to the case of the identity of two vectors, in which the equation $\mathbf{A} = \mathbf{B}$ symbolizes *three* equalities, between corresponding components. Vectors, however, have rules for multiplication that are different from those for complex numbers.)

In quantum mechanics, complex numbers are usually written in terms of the complex exponential function. Figure 1 shows

$$\psi_1 = (x_1, y_1)$$

where x_1 has been plotted as the abscissa and y_1 as the ordinate. From trigono-

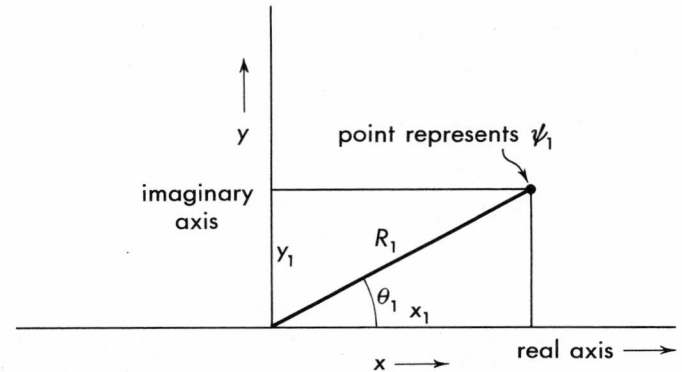

App. III, Fig. I. The graphical representation of a complex number.

metry, and by [3],

$$\psi_1 = (R_1 \cos \theta_1, \; R_1 \sin \theta_1) = \underbrace{(R_1, \; 0)}\underbrace{(\cos \theta_1, \; \sin \theta_1)}$$

the real number, R_1 (called the *amplitude* of ψ_1)   complex number (ordered pair)

If we write the ordered pair

$$(\cos \theta_1, \; \sin \theta_1)$$

as

$$\cos \theta_1 + i \sin \theta_1$$

which, as we have seen above, produces the correct rules for the basic operations, and if we use the identity

$$e^{i\theta_1} = \cos \theta_1 + i \sin \theta_1 \qquad\qquad [9$$

then

$$\psi_1 = R_1 \, e^{i\theta_1} \qquad\qquad [10$$

which is the form in which the ψ-functions usually appear.

The identity [9] is most easily demonstrated by noting that the series expansions of both sides are identical, term by term.

The complex conjugate of ψ_1 is

$$\psi_1^* = R_1 \, e^{-i\theta_1}$$

which also can be written

$$\psi_1^* = R_1(\cos \theta_1 - i \sin \theta_1)$$

Again, observe that to form the complex conjugate of any expression, one needs only to change the sign of the *second* term in the ordered pair, or to change the sign of the exponent, *i.e.*, to change the sign of i.

Often the wave function has the form

$$\psi = (a, \; 0)$$

i.e., the second term of the ordered pair of numbers is 0. For this case, $\psi = \psi^*$.

The expression, $\psi_1^* \psi_1 = a^2$ is always "real," i.e., the second term of the ordered pair $(a^2, 0)$ is 0.

As was demonstrated in Chapter 2, the use of complex notation in the Schrödinger wave equation is merely a convenience. With the use of complex numbers (i.e., ordered pairs), a single equation is equivalent to two coupled, differential equations involving real numbers.

The fact that complex numbers are involved in the ψ-wave functions does not imply that ψ-waves are any more unusual than other types of waves. It merely means that ψ-waves, at any point, can only be described in terms of a *pair* of related numbers. (The electromagnetic field, for example, can only be described in terms of four related quantities, four of the six components of **E** and **B**, or **A** and ϕ.)

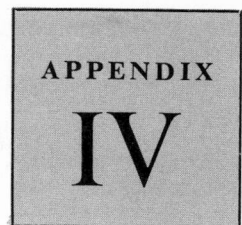

THE SEPARATION OF THE
WAVE EQUATION FOR THE
HYDROGEN ATOM

In Section 4.3 the wave equation is solved for a particle in a central field, about a fixed origin, 0. We show here how the translational and rotational motions of the hydrogen atom are separated, and how one of the resulting equations is identical to that of a particle in a fixed, central field.

The hydrogen atom consists of two particles of charge $+e$ and $-e$, and of mass m_1 and m_2, respectively. At any instant, the two particles might be located as in Figure 1. m_1 has the Cartesian coordinates x_1, y_1, and z_1, and m_2 has the coordinates x_2, y_2, and z_2. The particles are separated by a distance

$$r = \sqrt{(x_2 - x_1)^2 + (y_2 - y_1)^2 + (z_2 - z_1)^2} \qquad [1$$

and their mutual potential energy is $V = - e^2/r$ ergs (if e is expressed in esu and r in cm). The kinetic energy of m_1 is

$$\frac{1}{2\,m_1}\,p_1^2$$

the kinetic energy of m_2 is

$$\frac{1}{2\,m_2}\,p_2^2$$

Thus, the wave equation is

$$-\frac{\hbar^2}{2\,m_1}\left(\frac{\partial^2\,\Psi}{\partial\,x_1^2}+\frac{\partial^2\,\Psi}{\partial\,y_1^2}+\frac{\partial^2\,\Psi}{\partial\,z_1^2}\right)$$

$$-\frac{\hbar^2}{2\,m_2}\left(\frac{\partial^2\,\Psi}{\partial\,x_2^2}+\frac{\partial^2\,\Psi}{\partial\,y_2^2}+\frac{\partial^2\,\Psi}{\partial\,z_2^2}\right)+V(x_1,y_1,z_1,x_2,y_2,z_2)\Psi=-\frac{\hbar}{i}\frac{\partial}{\partial t}\Psi \quad [2$$

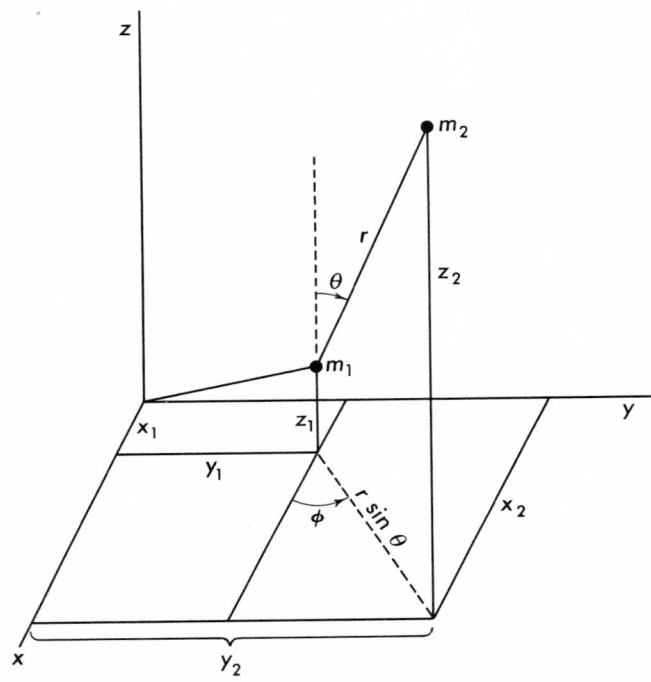

App. IV, Fig. I. Two particles, separated by a distance r.

$$r=\sqrt{(x_2-x_1)^2+(y_2-y_1)^2+(z_2-z_1)^2}$$

where we extend Postulate I to say that $\Psi = \Psi(x_1,\ y_1,\ z_1,\ x_2,\ y_2,\ z_2,\ t)$. We shall assume that $V = V(r)$, where r, the separation distance of the two particles, is given by [1]. $V = 0$ when $r \to \infty$. If the two electric charges have opposite sign, V will have negative values.

Since V is independent of time, the substitution of

$$\Psi = \psi_T(x_1,\ y_1,\ z_1,\ x_2,\ y_2,\ z_2)\ \phi(t) \qquad [3$$

into [2] results in two separated equations, connected by the constant W_T, the total energy (K.E. + P.E.) of the system. The time-dependent equation (identical to [3–3]) has the solution

$$\phi(t) = e^{-i(W_T/\hbar)t}$$

The space-dependent equation is

$$\frac{1}{m_1}\left(\frac{\partial^2\,\psi_T}{\partial\,x_1^2} + \frac{\partial^2\,\psi_T}{\partial\,y_1^2} + \frac{\partial^2\,\psi_T}{\partial\,z_1^2}\right)$$

$$+ \frac{1}{m_2}\left(\frac{\partial^2\,\psi_T}{\partial\,x_2^2} + \frac{\partial^2\,\psi_T}{\partial\,y_2^2} + \frac{\partial^2\,\psi_T}{\partial\,z_2^2}\right) + \frac{2}{\hbar^2}\{W_T - V(r)\}\,\psi_T = 0 \qquad [4$$

In order to separate this equation into two, involving three variables each, it is necessary first to introduce new coordinates—those of the center of mass (x, y, and z), and those of relative location (r, θ, φ) of the two masses.

The new coordinates are related to the Cartesian coordinates of the two particles by the equations

location of
center of mass
$$\begin{cases} x = \dfrac{m_1\,x_1 + m_2\,x_2}{m_1 + m_2} \\[2mm] y = \dfrac{m_1\,y_1 + m_2\,y_2}{m_1 + m_2} \\[2mm] z = \dfrac{m_1\,z_1 + m_2\,z_2}{m_1 + m_2} \end{cases}$$

relative location
of m_1 and m_2
$$\begin{cases} r = \sqrt{(x_2 - x_1)^2 + (y_2 - y_1)^2 + (z_2 - z_1)^2} \\[2mm] \theta = \cos^{-1}\left[\dfrac{z_2 - z_1}{\sqrt{(x_2 - x_1)^2 + (y_2 - y_1)^2 + (z_2 - z_1)^2}}\right] \\[2mm] \phi = \cos^{-1}\left[\dfrac{x_2 - x_1}{\sqrt{(x_2 - x_1)^2 + (y_2 - y_1)^2}}\right] \end{cases} \qquad [5$$

The last three equations may be obtained, by geometry, directly from Figure 1.

If ψ_T is considered a function of the new independent variables (x, y, z, r, θ, φ), using [5] and the rules for partial differentiation, [4] becomes

$$\frac{1}{m_1 + m_2}\left[\frac{\partial^2\,\psi_T}{\partial\,x^2} + \frac{\partial^2\,\psi_T}{\partial\,y^2} + \frac{\partial^2\,\psi_T}{\partial\,z^2}\right]$$

$$+ \frac{m_1 + m_2}{m_1\,m_2}\left[r^2\frac{\partial}{\partial r}\left(\frac{r^2\,\partial\,\psi_T}{\partial r}\right)\right.$$

$$\left. + \frac{1}{r^2\sin\theta}\frac{\partial}{\partial\theta}\left(\sin\theta\frac{\partial\,\psi_T}{\partial\theta}\right) + \frac{1}{r^2\sin^2\theta}\frac{\partial^2\,\psi_T}{\partial\,\phi^2}\right]$$

$$+ \frac{2}{\hbar^2}\left[W_T - V(r)\right]\psi_T = 0 \qquad [6$$

Rather than show this step, we will outline the reverse process—that is, to show how [6] reduces to [4].

In Appendix V, the method is outlined by which the middle term in [6] is shown to be equal to

$$\frac{m_1 + m_2}{m_1 m_2} \left[\frac{\partial^2 \psi_T}{\partial u^2} + \frac{\partial^2 \psi_T}{\partial v^2} + \frac{\partial^2 \psi_T}{\partial w^2} \right] \qquad [7$$

where

$$u = r \sin \theta \cos \phi$$
$$v = r \sin \theta \sin \phi \qquad [8$$
$$w = r \cos \theta$$

But, from Figure 1,

$$u = x_2 - x_1; \quad v = y_2 - y_1; \quad w = z_2 - z_1 \qquad [9$$

Using [5] and [9], we obtain $x_1, y_1, z_1, x_2, y_2, z_2$ in terms of x, y, z, u, v, w:

$$x_1 = - \frac{m_2}{m_1 + m_2} u + x$$

$$x_2 = + \frac{m_1}{m_1 + m_2} u + x$$

$$y_1 = - \frac{m_2}{m_1 + m_2} v + y$$

$$y_2 = + \frac{m_1}{m_1 + m_2} v + y \qquad [10$$

$$z_1 = - \frac{m_2}{m_1 + m_2} w + z$$

$$z_2 = + \frac{m_1}{m_1 + m_2} w + z$$

Using these coordinate transformation equations and the rules for partial differentiation (see Appendix V), the expression

$$\frac{1}{m_1 + m_2} \left[\frac{\partial^2 \psi_T}{\partial x^2} + \frac{\partial^2 \psi_T}{\partial y^2} + \frac{\partial^2 \psi_T}{\partial z^2} \right] + \frac{m_1 + m_2}{m_1 m_2} \left[\frac{\partial^2 \psi_T}{\partial u^2} + \frac{\partial^2 \psi_T}{\partial v^2} + \frac{\partial^2 \psi_T}{\partial w^2} \right]$$

becomes, quite simply,

$$\frac{1}{m_1} \left[\frac{\partial^2 \psi_T}{\partial x_1^2} + \frac{\partial^2 \psi_T}{\partial y_1^2} + \frac{\partial^2 \psi_T}{\partial z_1^2} \right] + \frac{1}{m_2} \left[\frac{\partial^2 \psi_T}{\partial x_2^2} + \frac{\partial^2 \psi_T}{\partial y_2^2} + \frac{\partial^2 \psi_T}{\partial z_2^2} \right]$$

which demonstrates that the wave equation [6] is equivalent to the wave equation [4].

It is also possible, though more laborious, to use the coordinate transformation [5] and derive [6] from [4].

In [6] the wave function is dependent not on the individual coordinates of the particles, but upon the coordinates of the center of mass, and upon the relative coordinates r, θ, and ϕ.

Let

$$M = m_1 + m_2 \text{ (the total mass)} \qquad [11$$

$$\mu = \frac{m_1 m_2}{m_1 + m_2} \text{ (the reduced mass)} \qquad [12$$

If we assume that

$$\psi_T(x, y, z, r, \theta, \phi) = F(x, y, z)\, \psi(r, \theta, \phi)$$

and

$$V = V(r, \theta, \phi) + V_{tr}(x, y, z) \qquad [13$$

and if we substitute these expressions into [6], the wave equation, [6] separates into two parts. One is dependent only on x, y, and z, and the other only on r, θ, and ϕ. Each part must equal a constant. Let the x, y, z equation equal W_{tr}, and the r, θ, ϕ equation equal W. The two separated equations are

$$\frac{\partial^2 F}{\partial x^2} + \frac{\partial^2 F}{\partial y^2} + \frac{\partial^2 F}{\partial z^2} + \frac{2M}{\hbar^2}\{W_{tr} - V_{tr}(x, y, z)\}\, F = 0 \qquad [14$$

and

$$\frac{1}{r^2}\frac{\partial}{\partial r}\left(r^2 \frac{\partial \psi}{\partial r}\right) + \frac{1}{r^2 \sin \theta}\frac{\partial}{\partial \theta}\left(\sin \theta \frac{\partial \psi}{\partial \theta}\right) + \frac{1}{r^2 \sin^2 \theta}\frac{\partial^2 \psi}{\partial \phi^2}$$

$$+ \frac{2\mu}{\hbar^2}\{W - V(r, \theta, \phi)\}\, \psi = 0 \qquad [15$$

where

$$W_{tr} + W = W_T \qquad [16$$

$F(x, y, z)$ is the wave function of a particle of mass $M = m_1 + m_2$ moving in a potential field $V_{tr}(x, y, z)$, dependent only upon the center of mass of the atom. Thus, if the walls of a box effectively act upon the atom as a whole, independent of its orientation, we have the particle in the box whose wave function F has been discussed in Section 4.2. It is the F-wave function which causes neutral molecules or atoms to show interference effects when they are scattered from crystal faces, as described in Chapter 1. ($\lambda = h/Mv$, where v is the velocity of the center of mass of the atom.)

The equation for $\psi(r, \theta, \phi)$ is that for a particle of mass

$$\mu = \frac{m_1 m_2}{m_1 + m_2}$$

in a central, fixed, potential field. It is further analyzed in Section 4.3. The solution ψ, found in Section 4.3, is thus only one factor in ψ_T, the complete wave function.

Suppose the hydrogen atom is in a box, then $F(x, y, z)$ will be an eigenfunction, $F_{k_x k_y k_z}(x, y, z)$, dependent upon the size and shape of the box and the "height" of the walls, where the k's are integers (see Section 4.2). As shown in Section 4.3, the ψ-functions are ψ_{nlm} where n, l, and m are integers. Thus the complete wave function is

$$\Psi = (\text{constant}) \cdot F_{k_x k_y k_z}(x, y, z)\, \psi_{nlm}(r, \theta, \phi)\, e^{-i(W_T/\hbar)t} \qquad [17$$

where

$$W_T = W_{tr} + W \qquad [18$$

THE OPERATOR ∇² IN SPHERICAL COORDINATES

The operator arising from the kinetic energy term in the expression for the total energy of a system,

$$\frac{\partial^2}{\partial x^2} + \frac{\partial^2}{\partial y^2} + \frac{\partial^2}{\partial z^2}$$

[1

is denoted by ∇^2.

We indicate the method by which one can show that the operator

$$\frac{1}{r^2} \frac{\partial}{\partial r}\left(r^2 \frac{\partial}{\partial r}\right) + \frac{1}{r^2 \sin\theta} \frac{\partial}{\partial\theta}\left(\sin\theta \frac{\partial}{\partial\theta}\right) + \frac{1}{r^2 \sin^2\theta} \frac{\partial^2}{\partial\phi^2}$$

[2

is identical to the operator [1] when x, y, and z are related to r, θ, and ϕ by the equations

$$x = r \sin\theta \cos\phi$$
$$y = r \sin\theta \sin\phi$$
$$z = r \cos\theta$$

[3

We expand [2] and operate on $\psi(x, y, z)$:

$$\nabla^2 \psi = \left(\frac{\partial^2}{\partial r^2} + \frac{2}{r} \frac{\partial}{\partial r} + \frac{1}{r^2} \frac{\partial^2}{\partial\theta^2} + \frac{\cos\theta}{r^2 \sin\theta} \frac{\partial}{\partial\theta} + \frac{1}{r^2 \sin^2\theta} \frac{\partial^2}{\partial\phi^2}\right) \psi(x, y, z)$$

[4

It is necessary to find

$$\frac{\partial}{\partial r}\,\psi(x,\,y,\,z),\quad \frac{\partial^2}{\partial r^2}\,\psi(x,\,y,\,z)$$

and the corresponding derivatives with respect to θ and ϕ. Using the rules for partial differentiation,

$$\frac{\partial\psi}{\partial r} = \psi_x\,\frac{\partial x}{\partial r} + \psi_y\,\frac{\partial y}{\partial r} + \psi_z\,\frac{\partial z}{\partial r}$$

where $\psi_x = \dfrac{\partial\psi}{\partial x},\ \psi_y = \dfrac{\partial\psi}{\partial y},\ \psi_z = \dfrac{\partial\psi}{\partial z}$ [5

$$\frac{\partial\psi}{\partial\theta} = \text{same, except } \theta \text{ replaces } r$$

$$\frac{\partial\psi}{\partial\phi} = \text{same, except } \phi \text{ replaces } r$$

Using [5]

$$\frac{\partial^2\psi}{\partial r^2} = \frac{\partial}{\partial r}\left(\psi_x\,\frac{\partial x}{\partial r}\right) + \frac{\partial}{\partial r}\left(\psi_y\,\frac{\partial y}{\partial r}\right) + \frac{\partial}{\partial r}\left(\psi_z\,\frac{\partial z}{\partial r}\right)$$ [6

$$= \frac{\partial\psi_x}{\partial r}\,\frac{\partial x}{\partial r} + \psi_x\,\frac{\partial^2 x}{\partial r^2} + \frac{\partial\psi_y}{\partial r}\,\frac{\partial y}{\partial r} + \psi_y\,\frac{\partial^2 y}{\partial r^2} + \frac{\partial\psi_z}{\partial r}\,\frac{\partial z}{\partial r} + \psi_z\,\frac{\partial^2 z}{\partial r^2}$$

But ψ_x, ψ_y, and ψ_z are each functions of x, y, and z, so that, for example,

$$\frac{\partial\psi_x}{\partial r} = \frac{\partial\psi_x}{\partial x}\,\frac{\partial x}{\partial r} + \frac{\partial\psi_x}{\partial y}\,\frac{\partial y}{\partial r} + \frac{\partial\psi_x}{\partial z}\,\frac{\partial z}{\partial r}$$

and there are similar expressions for

$$\frac{\partial\psi_y}{\partial r}\quad \text{and for}\quad \frac{\partial\psi_z}{\partial r}$$

so [6] becomes

$$\frac{\partial^2\psi}{\partial r^2} = \left(\frac{\partial\psi_x}{\partial x}\,\frac{\partial x}{\partial r} + \frac{\partial\psi_x}{\partial y}\,\frac{\partial y}{\partial r} + \frac{\partial\psi_x}{\partial z}\,\frac{\partial z}{\partial r}\right)\left(\frac{\partial x}{\partial r}\right) + \psi_x\,\frac{\partial^2 x}{\partial r^2}$$

$$+ \left(\frac{\partial\psi_y}{\partial x}\,\frac{\partial x}{\partial r} + \frac{\partial\psi_y}{\partial y}\,\frac{\partial y}{\partial r} + \frac{\partial\psi_y}{\partial z}\,\frac{\partial z}{\partial r}\right)\left(\frac{\partial y}{\partial r}\right) + \psi_y\,\frac{\partial^2 y}{\partial r^2}$$ [7

$$+ \left(\frac{\partial\psi_z}{\partial x}\,\frac{\partial x}{\partial r} + \frac{\partial\psi_z}{\partial y}\,\frac{\partial y}{\partial r} + \frac{\partial\psi_z}{\partial z}\,\frac{\partial z}{\partial r}\right)\left(\frac{\partial z}{\partial r}\right) + \psi_z\,\frac{\partial^2 z}{\partial r^2}$$

$\dfrac{\partial^2\psi}{\partial\theta^2}$ and $\dfrac{\partial^2\psi}{\partial\phi^2}$ have the same form as [7], except θ and ϕ, respectively, everywhere replace r.

If one now uses [3] to calculate the derivatives of x, y, and z with respect to r, θ, and ϕ which are required in [5] and [7], and then uses [5] and [7] in [4], the operator ∇^2, originally in the form [2], reduces to the simple Cartesian expression [1]. Trigonometric identities, and many term cancellations, are responsible for the great simplification.

It is a somewhat more elaborate calculation, but no different in principle, to start with $\partial^2/\partial x^2 + \partial^2/\partial y^2 + \partial^2/\partial z^2$, and, using the reverse of the transformation [3], obtain the operator [2].

THE HYDROGEN-LIKE WAVE FUNCTIONS

Hydrogen, singly ionized helium, doubly ionized lithium, etc., have the potential function

$$V(r) = -\frac{Ze^2}{r}$$

[1

where Ze is the electric charge of the nucleus.

The energy levels are dependent upon only one quantum number, n,

$$W_n = -\frac{\mu Z^2 e^4}{2\hbar^2 n^2}$$

[2

where

$$\mu = \frac{m_e m_N}{m_e + m_N}$$

[3

is the "reduced mass." Here, m_e = mass of the electron and m_N = mass of the nucleus, in grams.[1]

---

[1] $m_e = 9.11 \times 10^{-28}$ gm
  $H^1 = 1.008$ amu (atom)
proton $= 1.00759$ amu   Where 1 amu (atomic mass unit) $= 1.6598 \times 10^{-24}$ gm
  $H^2 = 2.014$ amu
  $He^4 = 4.003$ amu
  $Li^7 = 7.018$ amu

We designate

$$a_0 = \frac{\hbar^2}{\mu\,e^2} \text{ (for hydrogen, } 0.528 \times 10^{-8} \text{ cm)}$$ [4

e = electron charge $(4.80 \times 10^{-10}$ esu). a_0 and r are in cm, and

$$\hbar = \frac{h}{2\pi} = 1.054 \times 10^{-27} \text{ erg sec.}$$

Note that a_0, defined in [4], is slightly different for each different nuclear mass.

The amplitude wave functions, $\psi_{n,l,m}$, are most naturally classified by the value of n, the "principal" quantum number.

K Shell (n = 1)

$$\psi_{1,\,0,\,0} = \frac{1}{\sqrt{\pi}} \left(\frac{Z}{a_0}\right)^{3/2} e^{-\sigma}, \qquad \sigma = \frac{Zr}{a_0}$$

L Shell (n = 2)

$$\psi_{2,0,0} = \left(\frac{1}{4\sqrt{2\pi}} \left(\frac{Z}{a_0}\right)^{3/2} e^{-\sigma/2}\right)(2 - \sigma)$$

$$\psi_{2,1,0} = \left(\quad '' \quad \right) \sigma \cos\theta$$

$$\psi_{2,1,1} = \left(\quad '' \quad \right) \sigma \sin\theta\, e^{i\phi} \cdot \left(\frac{1}{\sqrt{2}}\right)$$

$$\psi_{2,1,-1} = \left(\quad '' \quad \right) \sigma \sin\theta\, e^{-i\phi} \cdot \left(\frac{1}{\sqrt{2}}\right)$$

M Shell (n = 3)

$$\psi_{3,0,0} = \left(\frac{1}{81\sqrt{\pi}} \left(\frac{Z}{a_0}\right)^{3/2} e^{-\sigma/3} \right) \frac{1}{\sqrt{3}} (27 - 18\,\sigma + 2\,\sigma^2)$$

$$\psi_{3,1,0} = \left(\qquad '' \qquad \right) \sqrt{2}\,(6\,\sigma - \sigma^2)\cos\theta$$

$$\psi_{3,1,1} = \left(\qquad '' \qquad \right) \sqrt{2}\,(6\,\sigma - \sigma^2)\sin\theta\,e^{i\phi}$$

$$\psi_{3,1,-1} = \left(\qquad '' \qquad \right) \sqrt{2}\,(6\,\sigma - \sigma^2)\sin\theta\,e^{-i\phi}$$

$$\psi_{3,2,0} = \left(\qquad '' \qquad \right) \frac{1}{\sqrt{6}}\,\sigma^2\,(3\cos^2\theta - 1)$$

$$\psi_{3,2,1} = \left(\qquad '' \qquad \right) \sqrt{2}\,\sigma^2\sin\theta\cos\theta\,e^{i\phi}$$

$$\psi_{3,2,-1} = \left(\qquad '' \qquad \right) \sqrt{2}\,\sigma^2\sin\theta\cos\theta\,e^{-i\phi}$$

$$\psi_{3,2,2} = \left(\qquad '' \qquad \right) \frac{1}{\sqrt{2}}\,\sigma^2\sin^2\theta\,e^{+i2\phi}$$

$$\psi_{3,2,-2} = \left(\qquad '' \qquad \right) \frac{1}{\sqrt{2}}\,\sigma^2\sin^2\theta\,e^{-i2\phi}$$

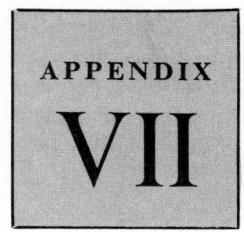
THE ANGULAR MOMENTUM OPERATORS IN SPHERICAL COORDINATES

In Section 6.1 the operators corresponding to the angular momentum components along the x-, y-, and z-axes were shown to be [6–6],

$$M_x \to (\hbar/i)(y\,\partial/\partial z - z\,\partial/\partial y)$$
$$M_y \to (\hbar/i)(z\,\partial/\partial x - x\,\partial/\partial z) \qquad [1$$
$$M_z \to (\hbar/i)(x\,\partial/\partial y - y\,\partial/\partial x)$$

The transformation equations relating Cartesian and spherical coordinates are

$$
\begin{aligned}
x &= r\sin\theta\cos\phi & \qquad r &= \sqrt{x^2 + y^2 + z^2} \\
y &= r\sin\theta\sin\phi & \quad\text{or}\quad \cos\theta &= z/\sqrt{x^2 + y^2 + z^2} \qquad [2 \\
z &= r\cos\theta & \qquad \tan\phi &= y/x
\end{aligned}
$$

If the wave function upon which $\partial/\partial z$ is to operate is expressed in terms of r, θ, and ϕ, then

$$(\partial/\partial z)\,\psi(r, \theta, \phi) = (\partial r/\partial z)(\partial\psi/\partial r) + (\partial\theta/\partial z)(\partial\psi/\partial\theta) + (\partial\phi/\partial z)(\partial\psi/\partial\phi) \qquad [3$$

There are similar expressions for the operation by $\partial/\partial y$ and $\partial/\partial x$, in which z is everywhere replaced by y, or by x, respectively.

To express the operators [1] in terms of r, θ, and ϕ, we will need the following partial derivatives, which can be obtained directly from the transformation equations [2]:

$$\partial r/\partial z = \cos\theta \qquad\qquad \partial r/\partial y = \sin\theta\sin\phi$$
$$\partial\theta/\partial z = -\sin\theta/r \qquad\qquad \partial\theta/\partial y = \cos\theta\sin\phi/r \qquad\qquad [4$$
$$\partial\phi/\partial z = 0 \qquad\qquad \partial\phi/\partial y = (\cos\phi)/(r\sin\theta)$$

$$\frac{\partial r}{\partial x} = \sin\theta\cos\phi$$

$$\frac{\partial\theta}{\partial x} = (\cos\theta\cos\phi)/r$$

$$\frac{\partial\phi}{\partial x} = -(\sin\phi)/(r\sin\theta)$$

Thus, for example,

$$M_x \rightarrow (\hbar/i)(y\partial/\partial z - z\partial/\partial y)$$

$$= (\hbar/i)\left[\underbrace{r\sin\theta\sin\phi}_{=\,y}\;\underbrace{\left(\frac{\partial r}{\partial z}\frac{\partial}{\partial r} + \frac{\partial\theta}{\partial z}\frac{\partial}{\partial\theta} + \frac{\partial\phi}{\partial z}\frac{\partial}{\partial\phi}\right)}_{=\,\partial/\partial z}\right.$$

$$\left. -\underbrace{r\cos\theta}_{=\,z}\;\underbrace{\left(\frac{\partial r}{\partial y}\frac{\partial}{\partial r} + \frac{\partial\theta}{\partial y}\frac{\partial}{\partial\theta} + \frac{\partial\phi}{\partial y}\frac{\partial}{\partial\phi}\right)}_{=\,\partial/\partial y}\right] \qquad [5$$

which, using [4], simplifies to

$$M_x \rightarrow (\hbar/i)[-\sin\phi\,\partial/\partial\theta - \cot\theta\cos\phi\,\partial/\partial\phi]$$

Similarly,

$$M_y \rightarrow (\hbar/i)[\cos\phi\,\partial/\partial\theta - \cot\theta\sin\phi\,\partial/\partial\phi] \qquad [6$$
$$M_z \rightarrow (\hbar/i)[\partial/\partial\phi]$$

which are the operators used in [6–8].

The operator for M^2 is derived from the classical expression,

$$M^2 = M_x M_x + M_y M_y + M_z M_z \qquad [7$$

The first term on the right becomes the operator

$$(-\hbar^2)(y\partial/\partial z - z\partial/\partial y)(y\partial/\partial z - z\partial/\partial y)$$

This expression consists of four terms. When operating upon $\psi(r, \theta, \phi)$, a typical term is

$$[y\partial/\partial z][y\partial\psi(r, \theta, \phi)/\partial z] = y^2(\partial/\partial z)(\partial\psi/\partial z)$$

where $\partial\psi/\partial z$ is given by [3] and must be regarded as a function of r, θ, and ϕ when being operated upon by $\partial/\partial z$. This results in a greatly expanded expression, but with the aid of the transformation equations [4] it can be expressed in terms of r, θ, ϕ and the partial derivatives involving these three variables.

If one calculates, in the above manner, each of the four terms arising from $M_x M_x$, the four terms from $M_y M_y$, and the four terms arising from $M_z M_z$, collects terms, and then simplifies, using some trigonometric identities, the final result is

$$M^2 \to (-\hbar^2)\left[\frac{1}{\sin\theta}\frac{\partial}{\partial\theta}\left(\sin\theta\frac{\partial}{\partial\theta}\right) + \frac{1}{\sin^2\theta}\frac{\partial^2}{\partial\phi^2}\right] \qquad [8$$

which is the operator belonging to the square of the angular momentum.

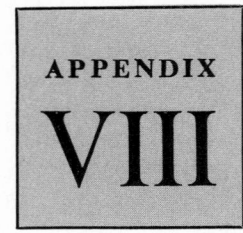

THE CLASSICAL WAVE EQUATION AND THE SCHRÖDINGER WAVE EQUATION

The classical wave equation, in one dimension, is

$$\frac{\partial^2 u}{\partial x^2} = \frac{1}{v^2} \frac{\partial^2 u}{\partial t^2}$$ [1

This applies, for example, to the wave traveling with velocity v along a rope. Assume a solution of the form

$$u = u_0(x)\, e^{-i\omega t}$$ [2

and substitute it into the wave equation [1], thus obtaining

$$\frac{d^2 u_o}{d x^2} + \frac{\omega^2}{v^2} u_0 = 0$$ [3

but $f\lambda = v$ and $2\pi f = \omega$, so [3] becomes

$$\frac{d^2 u_0}{d x^2} + \frac{4\pi^2}{\lambda^2} u_0 = 0$$ [4

We now use the de Broglie expression for the wavelength of matter waves,

$$\lambda = h/p \text{ where } p^2 = 2m(E - V) \qquad [5$$

Here E is the total energy of the particle and V is its potential energy, so that $(E - V)$ is its kinetic energy.

Using the de Broglie wavelength, [4] becomes

$$\frac{d^2 u_0}{dx^2} + \frac{4\pi^2}{h^2} 2m(E - V) u_0 = 0 \qquad [6$$

which is the Schrödinger amplitude equation (See Chapter 3) for a particle of total energy E. This analysis is a heuristic argument, not a derivation, but it does suggest the association $p_x \rightarrow (\hbar/i) \, \partial/\partial x$.

THE TOTAL ENERGY OF A PARTICLE IN SPECIAL RELATIVITY

One of the important consequences of the theory of relativity is the relationship

$$M = \frac{m}{\sqrt{1 - v^2/c^2}}$$

[1

where m is the rest mass of the particle and M is the inertial mass, which the particle appears to have when traveling in the laboratory with a velocity v. This relationship can be experimentally verified by measuring the curvature (in a magnetic field) of electrons traveling with measured velocity v.

We define the kinetic energy T of the particle as the work necessary to accelerate it from rest to the final velocity v. Consider the acceleration to occur in the positive x-direction and define the force by Newton's Law

$$F_x = (d/dt)(Mv_x)$$

[2

Then, with the understanding that v stands for v_x,

$$T = \int_{v=0}^{v=v} F \, dx = \int_{v=0}^{v=v} \frac{d}{dt} (Mv) \frac{dx}{dt} \, dt = \int_{v=0}^{v=v} v \frac{d}{dt} (Mv) \, dt = \int_{v=0}^{v=v} v \, d(Mv)$$

Using [1]

$$T = \int_0^v v d\left(\frac{mv}{\sqrt{1 - v^2/c^2}}\right) = m \int_0^v v\left(\frac{1}{(1 - v^2/c^2)^{1/2}} + \frac{v^2/c^2}{(1 - v^2/c^2)^{3/2}}\right) dv$$

$$= m \int_0^v \frac{v dv}{(1 - v^2/c^2)^{3/2}} = mc^2 \frac{1}{(1 - v^2/c^2)^{1/2}}\bigg|_0^v$$

Thus defined, the kinetic energy of a particle of rest mass m and velocity v is

$$T = mc^2\left(\frac{1}{\sqrt{1 - v^2/c^2}} - 1\right) \tag{3}$$

If we expand the radical in powers of v then

$$T = (1/2) m v^2 + (3/8) m v^4/c^4 + \cdots$$

so that, at low velocities when the second term can be neglected, the particle will have the Newtonian value for the kinetic energy.

Combining [1] and [3], the kinetic energy of a particle is

$$T = (M - m) c^2 \tag{4}$$

This equation suggests that we should regard the total energy W of the particle as consisting of Mc^2,

$$W = Mc^2 \tag{5}$$

and, when the particle is at rest, its total energy reduces to mc^2, the "rest energy." Since the momentum is defined to be the inertial mass times the velocity—that is, $p_x = Mv_x$—and since from [5] $M = W/c^2$, then

$$v_x = p_x c^2/W \tag{6}$$

Using [1], [5] becomes

$$W = \frac{mc^2}{\sqrt{1 - v_x^2/c^2}} \tag{7}$$

Eliminating v_x between [6] and [7],

$$W^2 = m^2 c^4 + p_x^2 c^2 \tag{8}$$

where we have picked the x-axis for the direction of the momentum. If $\mathbf{p}$ were not along the x-axis, we would obtain the result

$$W^2/c^2 = p_x^2 + p_y^2 + p_z^2 + m^2 c^2 \tag{9}$$

which is the relativistic Hamiltonian for the free particle, [11–1], and is used as the basis of the Dirac wave equation.

THE FORCE ON A CURRENT LOOP IN AN INHOMOGENEOUS MAGNETIC FIELD

Figure 6.2b outlines the arrangement of the Stern-Gerlach experiment in which neutral atoms, possessing a magnetic moment μ, are deflected in an inhomogeneous magnetic field. We show here how a loop of current can, under these circumstances, experience a net translational force. The atoms pass in a thin beam, in the y-direction, between two magnet pole faces, as shown in Figure 1a. The same pole faces are shown, in cross section, in Figure 1b. Although the magnetic field B is generally in the z-direction, the pole faces are shaped so that B increases in intensity as z increases. The dotted circle in Figure 1b indicates the region occupied by the beam as it travels in the y-direction. Figure 1c shows this region greatly magnified.

Assume that a small rectangular loop of current, i coulomb/sec, flowing in the sense indicated, is located in the region of the beam, as shown in Figure 1c. The loop has a dimension of b meters perpendicular to the plane of the diagram and a dimension of d meters in the x-direction so that its area is db(meters)^2 and its magnetic moment μ is defined to have the magnitude

$$\mu = db\,i$$

[1

with direction along the $+z$-axis, as indicated. If B_0 is the average magnitude of the magnetic field in the plane of the loop, then the total flux Φ traversing the loop is

$$\Phi = B_0\, db \qquad\qquad [2$$

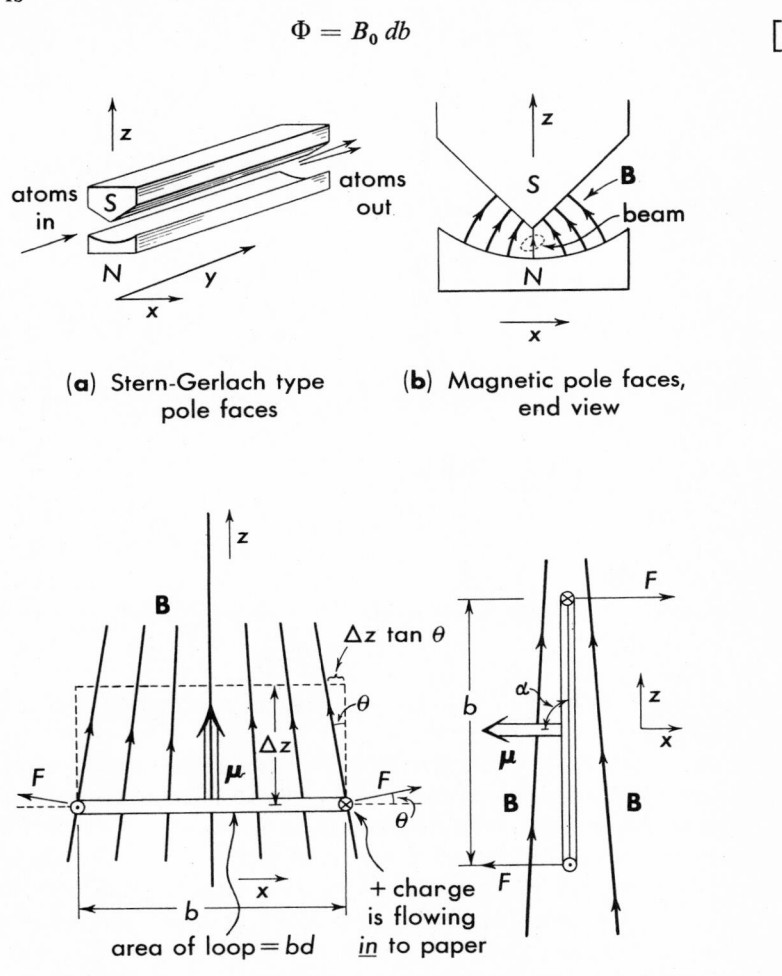

(a) Stern-Gerlach type pole faces

(b) Magnetic pole faces, end view

(c) Net force, in z-direction

(d) No net force on loop

App. X, Fig. 1. The calculation of the translational force on a current loop in an inhomogeneous magnetic field.

At a distance Δz in the $+z$-direction, the same lines of B go through a smaller cross-sectional area, $(d - 2\,\Delta z \tan\theta)\,b$. (The shrinkage is in only one dimension, since $\mathbf{B}$ is everywhere parallel to the x–z plane.) Thus, at a distance Δz

above the plane of the loop, the magnitude of **B** is

$$B_1 = \Phi/(d - 2\,\Delta z \tan\theta)\,b \qquad\qquad\qquad [3$$

$$= (B_0\,db)/(d - 2\,\Delta z \tan\theta)\,b$$

$$\cong B_0\left(1 + \frac{2\,\Delta z \tan\theta}{d}\right), \qquad \Delta z \tan\theta \ll d$$

Let $B_1 - B_0 = \Delta B$, and for small θ, $\tan\theta \cong \sin\theta$, so [3] becomes

$$\Delta B/\Delta z \cong B_0\,2\sin\theta/d \qquad\qquad\qquad [4$$

The force $F = B_0 ib$ acts in the direction shown in Figure 1c, on each of the sides b, producing a net force F_z, in the z-direction, of

$$F_z = 2\,B_0 ib \sin\theta \qquad\qquad\qquad [5$$

Using [4],

$$F_z = db\ i(\Delta B/\Delta z)$$

$$F_z = \mathbf{\mu}\,(\partial B/\partial z) \qquad\qquad\qquad [6$$

where $\mathbf{\mu}$ is pointing in the z-direction.

If the loop is rotated 90 degrees to the position shown in Figure 1d, the forces on the sides, b, no longer have any z-component, and there is no net translational force acting on the loop. It can be shown that

$$F_z = \mu_z(\partial B/\partial z) \qquad\qquad\qquad [7$$

where μ_z is the component of the magnetic moment in the z-direction. (Figures 1c and 1d are two special cases of [7].)

F_z is in newtons, if μ is (coulomb m²) or [joules/(nt sec/coulomb m)] B is (nt sec/coulomb m) or "webers per m^2," and z = meters (MKS).

F_z is in dynes, if μ is ergs/gauss and z = cm.

In Problem 6.8 we calculate, classically, the magnetic moment of an electron which is moving in a circle with an angular momentum $\hbar$ about an axis through the center of the circle. This magnetic moment is called the Bohr magneton, and has the value 0.927×10^{-23} joule/(nt sec/coulomb m), or 0.926×10^{-20} erg/gauss (1 nt sec/coulomb m, or webers/m², $= 10^4$ gauss, and 1 joule $= 10^7$ ergs).

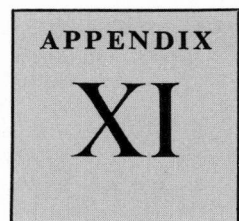

THE DIRAC PARTICLE IN A ONE-DIMENSIONAL BOX WITH FINITE WALLS

Consider a box with walls at $x = -L/2$ and $x = +L/2$ and of height V_0, as shown in Figure 1a. We assume that inside the box one of the components of the fourth Dirac wave equation has the form

$$\psi_4 = A_4 \cos ax \qquad [1$$

The state drawn in Figure 1b has the smallest value of a—slightly smaller than (π/L). (For ∞ walls, the smallest $a = \pi/L$.)

The Dirac equation [11–37] applies to this system, providing that in the regions where $|x| > L/2$, the quantity $(W - V_0)$ is substituted for W. (V_0 = electrostatic potential energy.)

Inside the well, with ψ_4 given by [1], the first equation of [11–37] gives

$$\psi_1 = \frac{\dfrac{c\hbar a}{i} A_4 \sin ax}{W + mc^2}$$

and the fourth equation gives

$$\psi_1 = -\frac{i}{c\hbar a}(W - mc^2) A_4 \sin ax + \text{constant}$$

which can both be true only if the constant $= 0$ and

$$W = \pm \sqrt{(c\hbar a)^2 + m^2 c^4} \cong \pm [mc^2 + (1/2)\, c\hbar a] \qquad [2$$

Outside the well, for $x > L/2$, we assume that

$$\psi_4 = B_4\, e^{-bx} \qquad [3$$

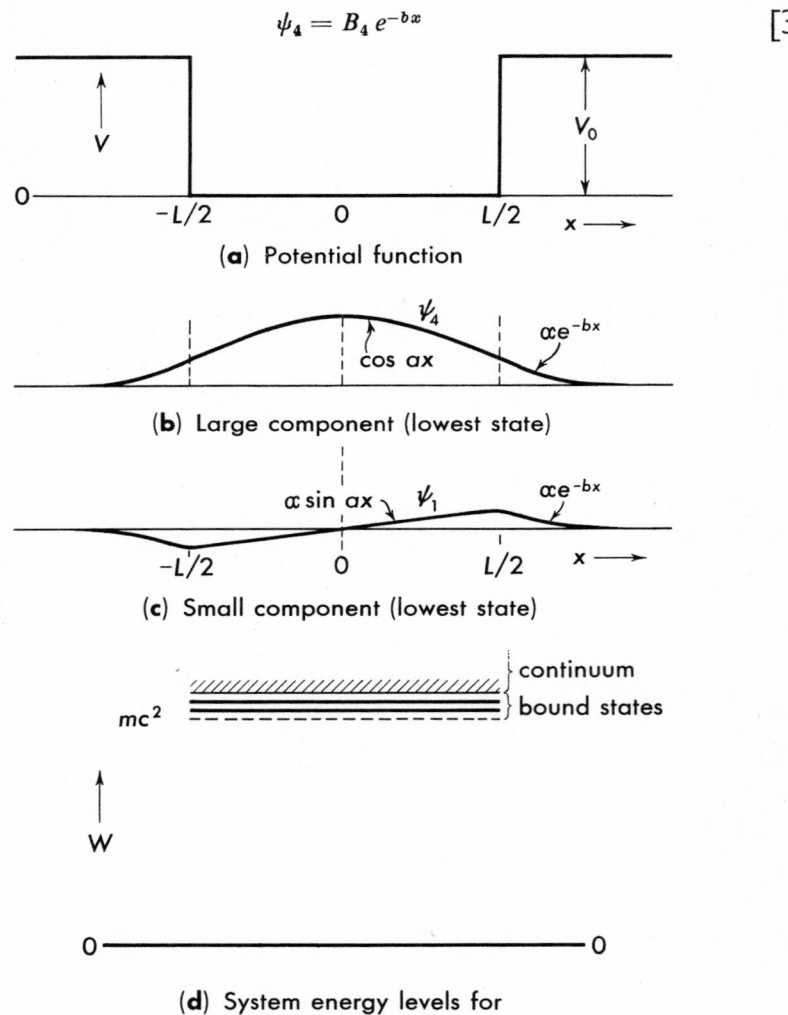

(a) Potential function

(b) Large component (lowest state)

(c) Small component (lowest state)

(d) System energy levels for
positive energy particles

App. XI, Fig. I.   The Dirac particle (positive energy) in a one-dimensional, finite-potential well.   *Note:* If the zero for the potential energy in (a) is assigned at the top of the barrier, the energy scale in (d) is shifted the same amount, then the positive energy bound states occur just below mc^2 and the continuum begins at mc^2.

which will permit a well-behaved ψ_4 with an integrable square. Using [3], the first equation of [11–37] gives, outside the well,

$$\psi_1 = \frac{\dfrac{c\hbar b}{i} B_4 e^{-bx}}{W - V_0 + mc^2}$$
[3a

and the fourth equation of [11–37] gives,

$$\psi_1 = \frac{i}{c\hbar b} (W - V_0 - mc^2) B_4 e^{-bx} + \text{constant}$$
[3b

If we require that the large component ψ_4 is continuous in both magnitude and slope at $x = \pm L/2$, we find that the magnitude of the small component ψ_1 is continuous, but that the slope $d\psi_1/dx$ is discontinuous. ψ_1 is sketched in Figure 1c.

The two expressions [3a] and [3b] for ψ_1 outside the barrier can both be true if the constant is 0, and if

$$W - V_0 = \pm \sqrt{-(c\hbar b)^2 + m^2 c^4} \cong \pm [mc^2 - (1/2) c\hbar b]$$
[4

Taking the positive sign in both [2] and [4] (that is, assuming the particle has positive total energy), we find

$$V_0 \cong (1/2) c\hbar(a + b)$$
[5

which is the ordinary nonrelativistic result for particles bound by positive potential barriers. Both a and b are positive numbers.

If, on the other hand, we take the negative sign in both [2] and [4], we have

$$V_0 \cong -(1/2) c\hbar(a + b)$$
[6

That is, bound negative energy states can exist only if V_0 is negative. Thus, for the positive energy potential barriers of Figure 1 (corresponding, for example, to the potential well formed for the electron by the proton), bound states exist *only* for positive energy particles.

As in the nonrelativistic case, a continuum of unbound states exists for positive energy particles whose total energy exceeds the barrier, that is, for values of W greater than $mc^2 + V_0$, as shown in Figure 1d. The *unbound* states are distinguished by their periodic wave function (sin bx or cos bx) *outside* the potential well. Using the same method of analysis as above, for V_0 positive and for a periodic wave function both inside and outside, we have, for the positive energy states, the requirement $V_0 = (1/2) c\hbar(a - b)$. Thus, for positive energy states, a must be larger than b—that is, the curvature of the wave function is sharper (the wavelength is shorter) inside the potential well, as in non-relativistic theory. Taking the negative sign in the equations corresponding to [2] and [4], however, we obtain the condition that the continuum of negative energy states exists if $V_0 = - c\hbar(a - b)$. Since we assume V_0 to be positive, these states exist only when a is smaller than b—that is, if the waves have *longer* wavelength inside the potential well. Thus the particles in the negative energy states act as if they are repelled by the same well that attracts particles in the positive energy states. The continuum of negative energy states actually begins at $- mc^2 + V_0$, and extends to $- \infty$. From $- mc^2 + V_0$ down to $- mc^2$, however, the wave functions "leak" into the potential well with the exponential attenuation characteristic of barrier penetration. For energy values below $- mc^2$, the wave function is everywhere periodic. It has a long wavelength and periodic form inside the well, and a shorter wavelength and periodic form outside.

It should be noted that an antiparticle such as the positron is not an electron in a negative energy state, but rather is interpreted as being a vacancy or hole in an otherwise filled sea of negative energy states. Surrounding a proton, there are no *bound* negative energy electron states, and therefore there is no possibility of "bound vacancies." Near a negative meson, however, there *are* bound, negative energy electron states, and localized vacancies—that is, localized positrons—are possible.

SOME SAMPLE CALCULATIONS
USING DIRAC WAVE FUNCTIONS

To illustrate the method of calculating quantities such as expectation values, using the four component Dirac wave functions, we will employ the eigenfunctions of the particle in the infinite-wall box, [11–43] and [11–44].

Suppose that the system is in a pure state having only the eigenfunction [11–43], which is correct for $W_k \ll mc^2$. The probability density is

[let $d = (\hbar k \pi / 2\, mcL)$]

$$\Psi_{\downarrow}^* \Psi_{\downarrow} = A_4^* A_4 \left(-i\, d \cos \frac{k\pi x}{L}, 0, 0, \sin \frac{k\pi x}{L} \right) \begin{pmatrix} id \cos \dfrac{k\pi x}{L} \\ \\ 0 \\ \\ 0 \\ \\ \sin \dfrac{k\pi x}{L} \end{pmatrix}$$

$$= A_4^* A_4 \left[d^2 \cos^2 \frac{k\pi x}{L} + \sin^2 \frac{k\pi x}{L} \right]$$

[1

an ordinary number.

Normalizing,

$$\int_0^L \Psi_\downarrow^* \Psi_\downarrow \, dx = 1$$

thus,

$$1 = A_4^* A_4 \frac{L}{2} [d^2 + 1]$$

thus,

$$A_4^* A_4 = \frac{2}{L} \frac{1}{d^2 + 1} \qquad [2$$

Next, we calculate $\bar{x}$

$$\bar{x} = A_4^* A_4 \int_0^L \left(-i\, d \cos \frac{k\pi x}{L}, 0, 0, \sin \frac{k\pi x}{L} \right) \begin{pmatrix} x & 0 & 0 & 0 \\ 0 & x & 0 & 0 \\ 0 & 0 & x & 0 \\ 0 & 0 & 0 & x \end{pmatrix}$$

$$\begin{pmatrix} ib \cos \dfrac{k\pi x}{L} \\ 0 \\ 0 \\ \sin \dfrac{k\pi x}{L} \end{pmatrix} dx \qquad [3$$

The operator x is written in the form of a diagonal four-by-four matrix, since it must operate upon the four-component column symbol. This operation produces a new column symbol which differs from the original in that each term is multiplied by x. Performing the row-symbol–column-symbol "dot" product, we have

$$\bar{x} = A_4^* A_4 \left[\int_0^L x\, d^2 \cos^2 \frac{k\pi x}{L}\, dx + \int_0^L x \sin^2 \frac{k\pi x}{L}\, dx \right]$$

$$= A_4^* A_4 \frac{L^2}{4} (d^2 + 1) = \frac{L}{2} \qquad [4$$

We next calculate the expectation value of the momentum:

$$\bar{p} = A_4^* A_4 \int_0^L \left(-id \cos \frac{k\pi x}{L},\, 0,\, 0,\, \sin \frac{k\pi x}{L} \right)$$

$$\begin{pmatrix} \dfrac{\hbar}{i} \dfrac{\partial}{\partial x} & 0 & 0 & 0 \\[2mm] 0 & \dfrac{\hbar}{i} \dfrac{\partial}{\partial x} & 0 & 0 \\[2mm] 0 & 0 & \dfrac{\hbar}{i} \dfrac{\partial}{\partial x} & 0 \\[2mm] 0 & 0 & 0 & \dfrac{\hbar}{i} \dfrac{\partial}{\partial x} \end{pmatrix} \begin{pmatrix} id \cos \dfrac{k\pi x}{L} \\[2mm] 0 \\[2mm] 0 \\[2mm] \sin \dfrac{k\pi x}{L} \end{pmatrix} dx \qquad [5$$

$$= A_4^* A_4 \int_0^L \left(-id^2 \frac{\hbar k\pi}{L} \cos \frac{k\pi x}{L} \sin \frac{k\pi x}{L} + \frac{\hbar k\pi}{L} \sin \frac{k\pi x}{L} \cos \frac{k\pi x}{L} \right) dx = 0$$

To calculate $\bar{p^2}$, the operator is applied twice, with the result:

$$\bar{p^2} = A^* A \frac{L}{2} \left(\frac{\hbar k\pi}{L} \right)^2 (d^2 + 1) = \left(\frac{\hbar k\pi}{L} \right)^2 \qquad [6$$

All of the above results happen to be the same as in the nonrelativistic theory. There is, however, a relativistic effect in the system energy.

The expectation value of W is

$$\bar{W} = A^* A \int_0^L (\cdots) e^{i(W_k/\hbar)t} \left(-\frac{\hbar}{i} \frac{\partial}{\partial t} \right) \begin{pmatrix} \cdot \\ \cdot \\ \cdot \\ \cdot \end{pmatrix} e^{-i(W_k/\hbar)t} \, dx \qquad [7$$

where the operator affects only the time-dependent factor at the right. For simplicity, the space-dependent terms in the wave functions are not written down. Due to the normalization of the Ψ's, [7] gives

$$\bar{W} = W_k, \text{ so that } \overline{W^2} = W_k^2, \text{ etc.} \qquad [8$$

The exact value of W_k is

$$W_k = + mc^2 \sqrt{1 + \left(\frac{\hbar k\pi}{mcL} \right)^2} \qquad [9$$

Using $\sqrt{1+x} = 1 + x/2 - x^2/8 + \cdots$, we have

$$W_k = mc^2 \left[1 + \frac{1}{2}\left(\frac{\hbar k\pi}{mcL}\right)^2 - \frac{1}{8}\left(\frac{\hbar k\pi}{mcL}\right)^4 + \cdots \right]$$

[10

Since only *differences* in system energy levels are observed (that is, one observes $W_n - W_k$ as in a radiative transition), it appears, to first order, that the energy levels are governed by the second term in [10]. Accurate measurements, however, will reveal that the third term in [10] is present since the levels with different quantum number k are not all shifted the same amount by the presence of the third term. In the hydrogen spectrum, for example, the relativistic shift is observable.

Thus far, we have considered the system to be in the pure (spin-down) state [11–43], with a given value of k. An electron, however, can exist in any combination of states which has an acceptable wave function. As an example, let the electron be represented by waves which have equal intensity in the spin-down state for $k = 1$, and in the spin-up state, for $k = 2$. We assume the small component to be negligible ($W_k \ll mc^2$),

$$\Psi = \frac{1}{\sqrt{2}}\left[\sqrt{\frac{2}{L}}\begin{pmatrix} 0 \\ 0 \\ 0 \\ \sin\dfrac{\pi x}{L} \end{pmatrix} e^{-i(mc^2 + W_1)t/\hbar} \right.$$

$$\left. + \sqrt{\frac{2}{L}}\begin{pmatrix} 0 \\ 0 \\ \sin\dfrac{2\pi x}{L} \\ 0 \end{pmatrix} e^{-i(mc^2 + W_2)t/\hbar} \right]$$

[11

where $W_k = (\hbar^2 k^2 \pi^2/2\, mL^2)$. (Note that this definition of W_k differs from that used in [7], [8], [9], and [10].)

For the wave function above, the probability density is

$$\Psi^*\Psi = (1/L)(\sin^2 \pi x/L + \sin^2 2\pi x/L)$$

[12

the two cross terms disappearing because of the orthogonal wave functions. The probability density is, therefore, constant in time.

If, however, the first column symbol is changed to $\sin \pi x/L$ in the third position and zero in the fourth, that is, if both terms are "spin-up" states, the probability density becomes,

$$\Psi^* \Psi = (1/L)[\sin^2 \pi x/L + \sin^2 2 \pi x/L$$
$$+ 2 \sin (\pi x/L) \sin (2 \pi x/L) \cos (W_2 - W_1) t/\hbar] \qquad [13$$

which has a time-dependent term.

We see from [12] and [13] that if an electron shares states of opposite spin, the system is in a stationary state even though one state is excited, but if an electron shares states of the *same* spin, one of which is excited, the probability density fluctuates periodically.

If we use [11] to calculate $\bar{x}$, we obtain $\bar{x} = L/2$. If, on the other hand, both terms in the superposition have either the third component or the fourth component excited—that is, if both the ground state and the excited state have the *same* spin—then

$$\bar{x} = L/2 + \frac{2}{L}\left[\int_0^L x \sin \pi x/L \sin 2 \pi x/L \, dx\right] \cos (W_2 - W_1) t/\hbar \qquad [14$$

The integral in [14] is not zero. It is the same as that involved in the matrix element for dipole transitions. Thus, we expect dipole radiation and absorption to occur between two states with the same spin, but not between two states with opposite spin. The result that a time-varying electric field will not "flip the spin" in the process of stimulated emission is true for low-velocity particles. The operator for the electric field is not a simple diagonal matrix if the particle has high velocity, and for this case dipole transitions are possible between states of opposite spin.

SOME IMPORTANT PHYSICAL CONSTANTS AND CONVERSION FACTORS

$c = 2.997 \times 10^{10}$ cm/sec.   Velocity of light (vacuum) $= 2.997 \times 10^{8}$ m/sec

$e = 4.803 \times 10^{-10}$ esu.   Chg. of electron $= 1.60 \times 10^{-19}$ coulomb

$m = 9.11 \times 10^{-28}$ gm.   Mass of electron $= 9.11 \times 10^{-31}$ kg

$h = 6.63 \times 10^{-27}$ erg sec.   Planck's constant $= 6.63 \times 10^{-34}$ joule sec

$\hbar = h/2\pi = 1.05 \times 10^{-27}$ erg sec.   Planck's constant $= 1.05 \times 10^{-34}$ joule sec

$k = 1.38 \times 10^{-16}$ erg/deg K (Boltzmann's constant)

$a_o = \hbar^2/me^2 = 0.529 \times 10^{-8}$ cm (Bohr radius)

$(1/a) = \hbar c/e^2 = 137.04$ (a = fine structure constant)

$R_\infty = 109{,}737.31$ cm^{-1}. The Rydberg (wave number ,cm^{-1}, is the number of wavelengths per cm)

$\mu_0 = 0.9273 \times 10^{-20}$ erg/gauss (the Bohr magneton, unit of magnetic moment)
$= 0.9273 \times 10^{-23}$ joules/(webers/m^2)

H^1 = 1.008142 amu (proton = 1.00759 amu)

H^2 = 2.014 amu m (electron) $= 0.5109 \times 10^{6}$ e.v.

He^4 = 4.003 amu M (proton) $= 938.23 \times 10^{6}$ e.v.

Li^7 = 7.018 amu

neutron = 1.00898 amu

1 e.v. $= 1.602 \times 10^{-12}$ erg $= 1.602 \times 10^{-19}$ joule

1 amu $= 1.6598 \times 10^{-24}$ gm

1 volt $= 1/299.8$ esu of potential difference, or "stat-volt."

1 weber/m^2 or (nt sec./coulomb m) $= 10^4$ gauss

1 joule $= 10^7$ ergs

1 cm^{-1} (wave number) $= 1.99 \times 10^{-16}$ erg (energy, ergs $=$ energy, cm^{-1} $\times hc$)

1 gm $= 9 \times 10^{20}$ ergs ($E = mc^2$)

INDEX